# principles of SCIENCE Book Two

## Author

**Charles H. Heimler** is a Professor of Science Education and Director of Teacher Education at California State University, Northridge, CA. He received his B.S. degree from Cornell University and his M.A. and Ed.D. degrees from Columbia University and New York University. He has 32 years of teaching experience at the junior high, high school, and university levels. Dr. Heimler is a member of the American Association for the Advancement of Science, National Science Teachers Association, and the National Association of Biology Teachers. He is currently a consultant in science education to several California school districts. Dr. Heimler is author of the Merrill *Focus on Life Science* program and co-author of the *Focus on Physical Science* program.

## Consultant

**Charles D. Neal** is Professor Emeritus of Education at Southern Illinois University, Carbondale, IL. Dr. Neal has taught at the junior high school level and has lectured extensively on the teaching of science in the elementary and junior high school. He received his B.S. degree from Indiana University, his M.A. degree from the University of Illinois, and his M.S. and Ed.D. degrees from Indiana University. He is a member of various professional organizations and is the author of numerous science books for children and adults.

### Content Consultants

*Earth Science:* Dr. Jeanne Bishop, Parkside Junior High School, Westlake, OH
*Life Science:* Lucy Daniel, Rutherfordton-Spindale High School, Rutherfordton, NC
*Physical Science:* Dr. Richard H. Moyer, University of Michigan-Dearborn

### Reading Skills Consultant

Dr. David L. Shepherd, Hofstra University

**Charles E. Merrill Publishing Co.**
Columbus, Ohio

# A Merrill Science Program

**Principles of Science, Book Two Program**

**Principles of Science, Book Two** and Teacher's Annotated Edition

**Principles of Science, Book Two,** Teacher Resource Book

**Principles of Science, Book Two,** Activity-Centered Program, Teacher's Guide

**Principles of Science, Book Two,** Evaluation Program, Spirit Duplicating Masters

**Principles of Science, Book One Program**

(This program contains components similar to those in the Book Two Program.)

**Reviewers**

Cynthia Y. Addison, Academic Specialist-Science: Kalamazoo Public Schools, Kalamazoo, MI
Betty T. Cox, Science Curriculum Coordinator: Monroe County School District, Key West, FL
Kay M. Doughty, Principal: Hillel School of Tampa, Tampa, FL
Oliver D. Hansen, Science Department Chairperson: Bayview Middle School, Pasadena, MD
John D. Johnson, Science Teacher: Williams Middle School, Williams, AZ
Dr. Iraj M. Nuban, Science Department Chairperson: C. K. McClatchy High School, Sacramento, CA
John C. O'Gorman, Vice Principal/Science Teacher: Clissold School, Chicago, IL
Annette M. Saturnelli, formerly Science Coordinator: Marlboro School District, Marlboro, NY
John E. Tyler, Science Teacher: Hardyston Township School, Franklin, NJ

**Special Features Consultant**

Douglas E. Wynn, Science Teacher: Westerville North High School, Westerville, OH

**Cover Photograph:** Earth is the environment for all living creatures. Rugged mountains are home to Dall sheep, grazing animals that are able to climb near-vertical slopes. In winter months the sheep move down to lower elevations in search of food. The changes that occur in a mountain environment are both physical and chemical. In *Principles of Science, Book Two,* you will study about changes in matter and energy, as well as changes in your body.

Photograph by *Bill McRae*

*Series Editor:* Terry B. Flohr; *Project Editor:* Joyce T. Spangler; *Editors:* Jane L. Parker, Peter R. Apostoluk; *Book Design:* Patricia Cohan; *Project Artist:* Shirley Beltz; *Illustrators:* Bill Robison, Jim Shough, Dick Smith; *Photo Editor:* Lindsay Gerard; *Production Editor:* Joy E. Dickerson

ISBN 0-675-07092-9

*Published by*
**Charles E. Merrill Publishing Company**
**Columbus, Ohio**

# Preface

**Principles of Science, Book Two** is a modern general science program. The interrelationships among the life, earth, and physical sciences are emphasized. Basic science principles of matter and energy and their interaction in understanding natural phenomena are stressed. Interesting everyday examples using science concepts and their practical applications are presented throughout the text to stimulate student interest and motivation. Science activities are included where appropriate to teach the methods of scientific inquiry through direct student involvement. Science is presented as an ever expanding body of knowledge that is useful in everyday life and in science-related careers.

**Principles of Science, Book Two** is organized to provide the maximum flexibility and adaptation to middle, junior high, or high school programs. Emphasis is given to the organization of the material for improved teachability and maximum student learning. The six units provide comprehensive coverage of important topics in the life, earth, and physical sciences. Unit 1 begins with a chapter on science and technology, and then presents the major human body systems. Unit 2 discusses several aspects of human health. Units 3 and 4 present topics on chemistry and energy. Unit 5 discusses astronomy and space exploration. Unit 6 ends the text with a discussion of human ecology. Science content has been carefully selected to provide a unified, basic general science program that furnishes a proper background for the student's future study of science. Concrete examples of abstract concepts are provided. Relevant topics such as cancer, solar energy, nuclear energy, pollution, and conservation are included.

Chapters are subdivided into numbered sections that form logical teaching blocks. The chapter organization provides students with a basic outline for the chapter. Reading level is carefully controlled by monitoring sentence length and the introduction of new terms. Margin notes, most in the form of questions, are printed in the margins of each chapter. These notes serve as guides for learning and reviewing important concepts, thereby increasing student comprehension.

Each chapter contains attractive, scientifically accurate diagrams, photographs, and tables that are related to the text material both in content and placement. Important new terms are emphasized by boldfaced type and are defined where they first appear. Many new terms are spelled phonetically to assist the student in learning the correct pronunciations. Science activities that provide for student participation are included in all chapters. These activities are especially designed to increase student motivation and strengthen skills in problem-solving methods. *Making Sure* questions at the end of some sections provide for immediate review and reinforcement.

Chapter-end material contains study aids designed to enhance student achievement. The *Main Ideas* section summarizes the content of the chapter. Important new terms introduced in the chapter are listed in *Vocabulary*. The *Study Questions* section provides for a thorough review of the chapter. This section provides four types of questions including both recall and application questions. The *Challenges* section contains ideas for projects and special assignments. Selected reading references are listed under *Interesting Reading*.

Many chapters contain magazinelike pages entitled *Perspectives*. These pages contain articles and photographs describing interesting careers, current developments in research and technology, and skills. The pages discussing skills are designed to assist students in developing reading and other communication skills important to the study of general science. *Side Roads* are special feature pages that present interesting additional information related to the unit. There is one *Side Roads* in each unit of **Principles of Science, Book Two.** The goals of **Principles of Science, Book Two** are to develop the student's understanding of the environment and the interrelationships of science and technology. The textbook will be valuable in preparing each student for future studies in science and in developing knowledge necessary for making decisions regarding the choice of a science-related career.

# To the Student

Science is interesting and exciting. Why? Science helps you understand the world in which you live. For example, science explains how airplanes fly and how birds find their way when they travel long distances. In addition, people use science to make discoveries that have practical value. One of these discoveries is the use of light to carry telephone messages through a glass wire. Another is the lengthening of human life through the use of heart pacemakers and other mechanical devices.

In your future, there will be an endless number of new scientific discoveries. These discoveries will affect your career and your daily life. Television, computers, and Space Shuttles are part of today's world. Who can imagine what new, yet to be discovered developments lie ahead? In the future, scientists may discover how to predict earthquakes and how to produce an endless supply of energy. Someday you may live and work in a space station in orbit around the earth. Scientists will continue to make discoveries that will change the world in which you live.

A science class provides a great opportunity to increase your understanding of the world around you, to study your environment, and to learn about ways in which you can play an active role in the future that is science. You may find you like science so much that you may plan to become a scientist. There are many interesting careers related to science such as nursing, engineering, and electronics.

This textbook contains many study aids to help you achieve your goals. For example, pictures and diagrams are included to increase your understanding. Margin questions are designed to help you get more out of your reading. Questions at the end of many sections as well as the chapter review questions will help you review and sum up what you have learned. Many interesting hands-on activities allow you to experience some of the methods scientists use.

As with any opportunity, much depends on you. Your success in the study of science will be related to the time and effort you give. Learning science is not any more difficult than learning other subjects. However, it does take time and practice, just like sports or anything else worth doing. Success in the study of science will be richly rewarding. It will give you knowledge and skills you will use throughout your life.

# Textbook Inventory

A student's textbook is his/her primary learning tool. Therefore, an inventory is an excellent way to introduce a new textbook. An inventory introduces the general structure of the book. It also points out the various features of the textbook as well as highlighting the different kinds of study aids.

Use your textbook to answer the following questions.

**A. Introduction**

1. What is the name of your textbook?
2. Who is the author?
3. Read To the Student on page v. Why should science be important to you?
4. Look at the Table of Contents. How many chapters are in this book? In which section in Chapter 9 would you learn about genetic diseases?

**B. Graphic Aids**

5. Where does Unit 1 begin? How is the photograph at the beginning of Unit 1 used to introduce the unit?
6. Look at the beginning of Chapter 5. Why was the photograph chosen to begin Chapter 5?
7. What is the title of Table 10–2 on page 186? What are the three main types of information given in the table?
8. How could the information in Figure 13–2b on page 249 be shown in a table?
   In what ways is the picture better than a table?

**C. Study Aids**

9. What should be your goal as you read Chapter 7?
10. In Chapter 7, what is discussed in Section 7:2?
11. How can you use the blue margin notes on page 134 to help you study?
12. What is the purpose of the example problems on page 230? How are example problems helpful?

13. Why are Making Sure questions included at the end of many sections?
14. List the important terms you should know when you read Section 19:1 on page 381.

**D. Activities**

15. How is the Activity on page 254 different from the activity on page 258?
16. What is the purpose of the activity on page 254?
17. What types of fabrics are used in the activity on page 254?
18. What is the purpose of the chlorine bleach in the activity on page 254?
19. What may happen if you touch the bleach in the activity on page 254?
20. In the activity on page 172, what is to be done with the data once it has been collected and organized in table form?

**E. Chapter Review**

21. Look at the end of Chapter 6 that begins on page 119. What section would you review if you did not understand how a vitamin deficiency disease is caused?
22. How many new terms were introduced in Chapter 6?
23. How many kinds of study questions are included in the Chapter Review?
24. Where can you find activity ideas to extend your knowledge of the chapter subjects?
25. Where can you find sources of additional information about the subjects of the chapter?

**F. Other Features**

26. What is the purpose of the Perspectives and Side Roads pages?
27. What six learning skills are covered in the Perspectives features?
28. What information is provided in the Appendix? How can this information be useful?
29. In what section are all vocabulary terms defined?
30. On what page is the term pulsar discussed?

# Table of Contents

*The opening parade of the Montreal Olympics illustrates that the world is inhabited by many people. Despite differences, people are alike in many ways. One way is that all people have certain body systems that must be functioning properly to keep them healthy. What are these systems? How can you keep your systems healthy?*

P. Beck/FPG

# Human Life

# unit I

*Science and technology are important in your everyday life. You act like a scientist whenever you work on a problem. Science is a method of solving problems. Here, a medical team is aiding an injured man. How does science aid the team in caring for the injured man? What is technology? How is technology used in the medical professions and other science related fields?*

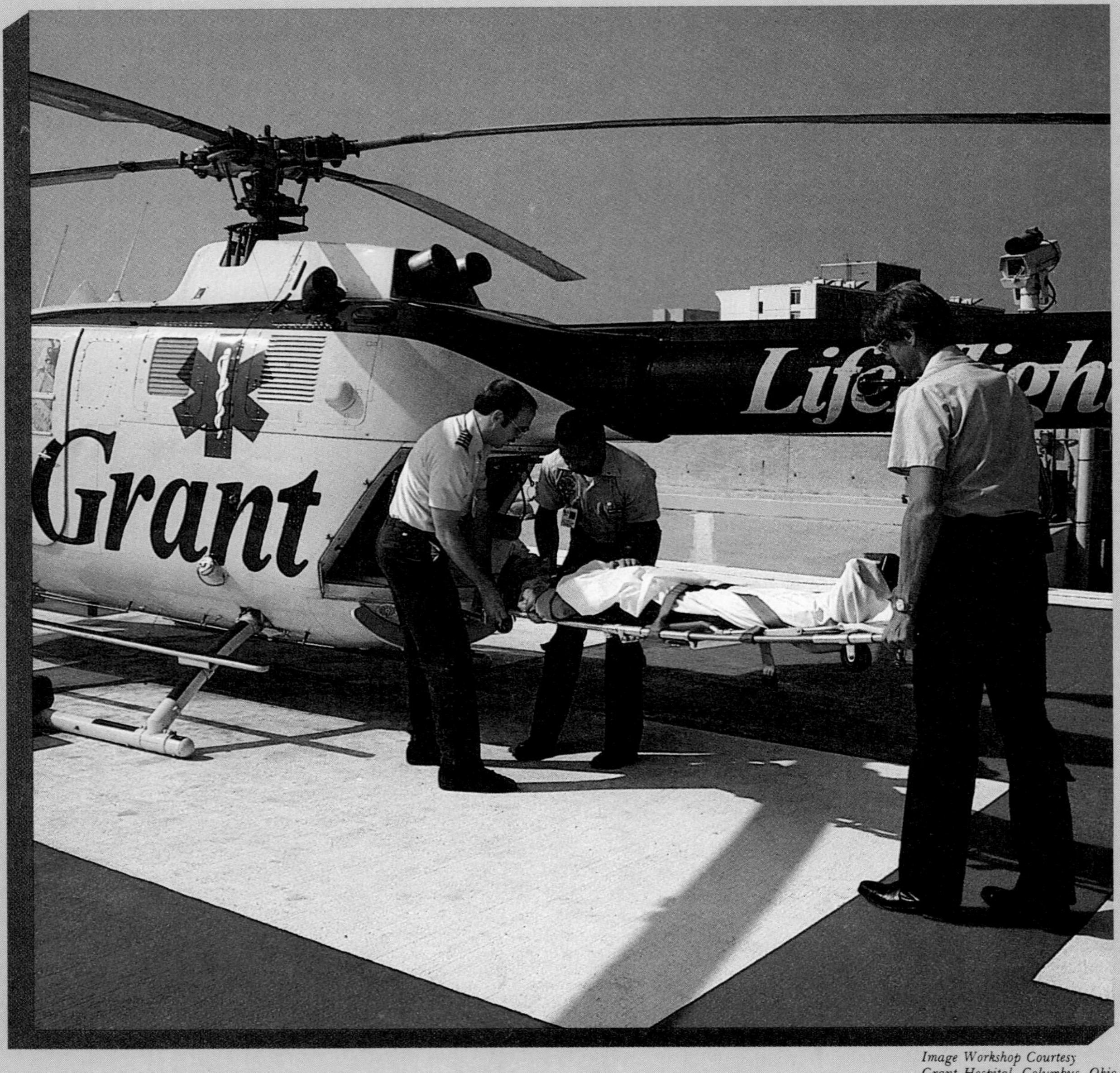


*Image Workshop Courtesy*
*Grant Hospital, Columbus, Ohio*

# Science and Technology

# chapter 1

## 1:1 Scientists and Science

GOAL: You will learn what science is, how observations and measurements are used in science, and how science and technology are related.

Scientists are people who gain knowledge through study and investigation. Some scientists try to find out how human cancer cells are produced. Others study the effects of drugs on people. Some scientists investigate athletic training to see how it changes the body. The effects of weightlessness and radiation on astronauts are of interest to scientists also.

Scientists test facts and ideas to discover new information. In this process, scientists make observations and measurements. They also perform experiments. Knowledge in science is always being tested. It can be corrected if new evidence shows that it should be. Most important, a scientist must think to find answers to questions and solutions to problems. The imagination of a scientist is vital to the development of new ideas.

Latent Image

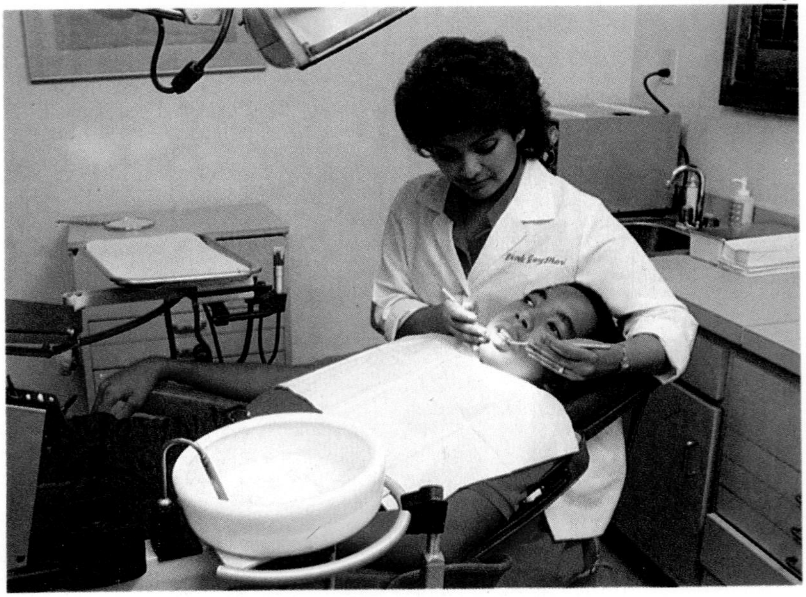

FIGURE 1–1. During her training, this dental hygenist studied human biology.

What is science?

**Science** refers to facts collected and ideas developed by scientists as well as methods used in obtaining information. Science includes facts about the human body and how it works. It also includes what scientists have discovered about substances—how they can be taken apart and put together.

Name three branches of science. What is studied in each branch?

Biology, chemistry, and physics are three main branches of science. Biology is the study of organisms. It includes botany, (BAHT nee), the study of plants, and zoology, (zoh AHL uh jee), the study of animals. Human biology includes the study of human diseases, reproduction, and how the human body works. Chemistry is the study of what matter is and how it changes. The study of substances and their physical and chemical properties is part of chemistry. Physics deals with the way matter and energy are related. Light, heat, and electricity are some areas of study in physics. Table 1-1 lists some other fields of scientific study.

Science is applied in many fields such as medicine, engineering, dentistry, nutrition, and agriculture. People who have a background in science work in these areas.

**Table 1–1.**
Some Sciences

| Science | Topics of Study |
|---|---|
| Astronomy | Stars, planets, galaxies, origin of the universe |
| Agronomy | Soils, fertilizers, soil management |
| Entomology | Insects and their structure, habitat, and relationship to people |
| Genetics | Heredity, selective breeding, genetic diseases |
| Geology | Rocks, minerals, structure of earth |
| Meteorology | Weather, clouds, storms, climate |

### making sure

1. In which field of science is a person most likely to do each of the following?
   (a) produce a new plastic
   (b) observe a star through a telescope
   (c) study a rock with a magnifying glass
   (d) measure the energy used by a light bulb

## 1:2 Observations

A scientist is a kind of detective who must ask questions, follow clues, solve problems, and write logical answers and reports. Observation is one of the scientist's most important tools. An **observation** is noting or recognizing something that has occurred. For example, you have probably noticed that you breathe faster when you run. You have made an observation. You can make observations by using your senses. You also can use instruments to aid in making observations. A microscope can be used to observe the cells of the body. A telescope can be used to observe the stars and planets.

Recorded observations are called **data.** Quantitative (KWAN tuh tayt ihv) data include numbers. A person's age, height, weight, pulse rate, and blood pressure are examples of quantitative data.

FIGURE 1–2. This nurse is making an observation that includes numbers.

*Latent Image*

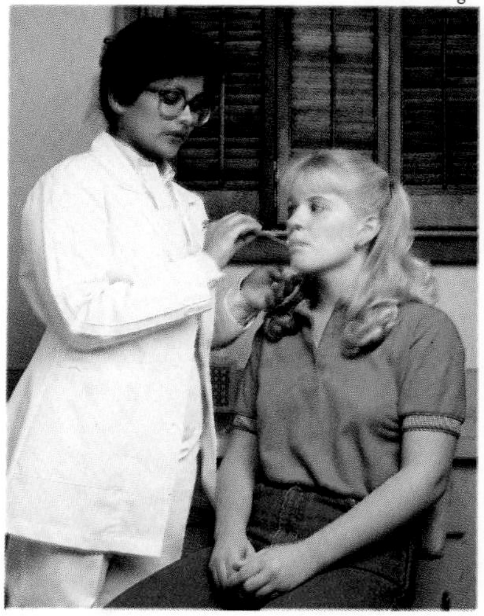

## activity
### MAKING OBSERVATIONS

(1) Look at the photograph on pages 2-3 of your textbook. Make a list of 10 observations of the photograph. (2) Place a check beside each observation that is quantitative. (3) Compare your observations with those of your classmates. How many made the same observations you did? Do you have some different observations? What might be a reason for the differences in observations?

### making sure

2. List five observations you can make about your classroom. Do you need a measuring instrument for any of the observations? Which instruments?
3. What senses would you use in observing a rotten egg?

## 1:3 Measurement

What is a unit?

**Measurement** is the dimension, capacity, or amount of something. For example, your height and weight tell how much of you there is. All measurements include a unit of measure and a number identifying how much or how many of the units are present. One unit is the second (s), a unit of time. Hold your breath for 10 s. The unit is the second. You held your breath for 10 of that unit.

A paper clip could be used as a unit of length. To measure the length of a book, you would lay paper clips end to end the full length of the book. A certain book might be 7 paper clips long. The length of the book is 7 times the length of 1 paper clip.

There are problems with using the paper clip as a unit of length. Not all paper clips are the same length. Also, to be a unit, everyone who measures would have to agree to use it. Some units have been standardized for measuring length. What units do you know that are used for measuring length?

## making sure

4. How could you use a penny as a unit of length?
5. How could you use a water glass as a unit of volume?
6. Why are a penny and a water glass not good units for measuring?

## 1:4 Units of Measurement

Today, with the exception of a few nations, the world is using a decimal system for measuring. In 1960, an international conference was held in which this system was revised and simplified. The name Le Système International d'Unités (International System of Units), with the abbreviation SI, was adopted.

Scientists use SI units in measuring. **SI** is a decimal measurement system based on 10 and multiples of 10. Table 1–2 lists some frequently used units of measurement. Other units are listed in Appendix A.

Why do we say that SI is a decimal system?

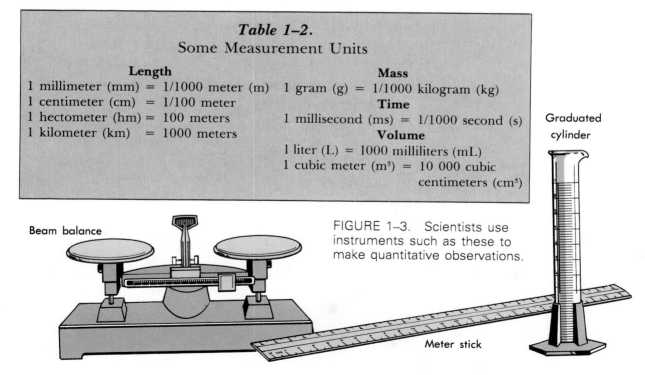

***Table 1–2.***
Some Measurement Units

| **Length** | | **Mass** |
|---|---|---|
| 1 millimeter (mm) | = 1/1000 meter (m) | 1 gram (g) = 1/1000 kilogram (kg) |
| 1 centimeter (cm) | = 1/100 meter | **Time** |
| 1 hectometer (hm) | = 100 meters | 1 millisecond (ms) = 1/1000 second (s) |
| 1 kilometer (km) | = 1000 meters | **Volume** |
| | | 1 liter (L) = 1000 milliliters (mL) |
| | | 1 cubic meter ($m^3$) = 10 000 cubic centimeters ($cm^3$) |

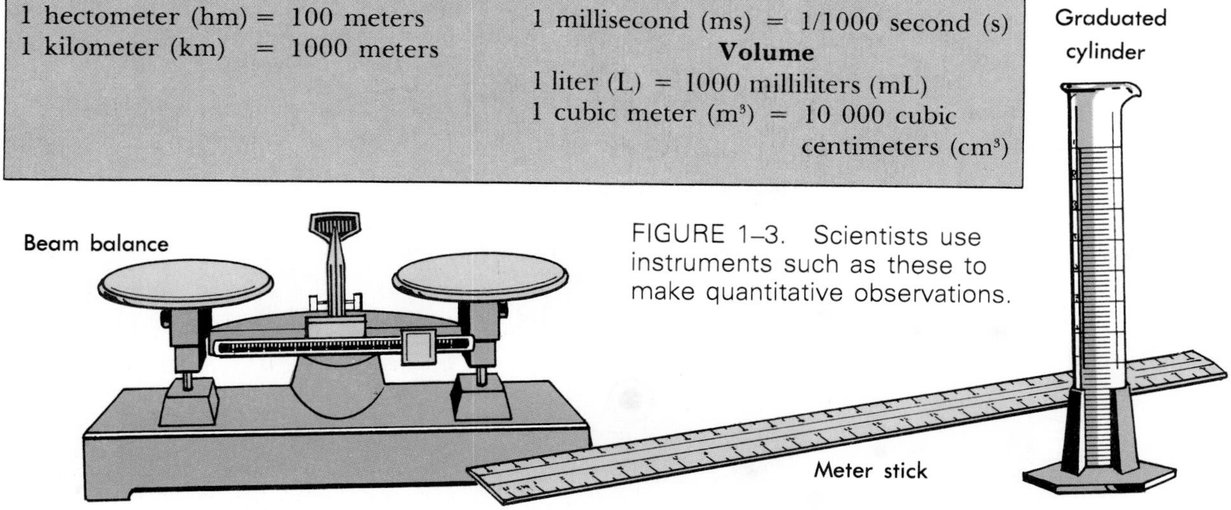


FIGURE 1–3. Scientists use instruments such as these to make quantitative observations.

What are the SI units of length, volume, and mass?

The **meter (m)** is the basic unit of length in SI. A meter is about half the height of a door, or the width of a twin bed. A meter is divided into 100 equal units called centimeters (cm). To measure the length of shorter objects, each centimeter is divided into 10 equal units called millimeters (mm). There are 1000 mm in 1 m.

The **cubic meter ($m^3$)** is the basic unit of volume in SI. The cubic meter is a very large unit. Most volume measurements are made using smaller units like the liter (L). For even smaller volumes, the milliliter (mL) or cubic centimeter ($cm^3$) are used. One liter contains 1000 mL or 1000 $cm^3$.

The **kilogram** (**kg**) is the basic unit of mass in SI. **Mass** is the amount of matter in an object. A kilogram is divided into 1000 equal units. Each of these units is called a gram (g). You will use grams in your measurements in this course.

In what unit is temperature measured in science?

Temperature is measured in degrees **Celsius** (**C**). The Celsius (SEL see us) temperature scale has 100 degrees between the freezing and boiling points of water. Water freezes at 0°C and boils at 100°C at sea level. Your body temperature is about 37°C. A healthful room temperature is about 21°C.

*Image Workshop*

FIGURE 1–4. Precise measurements are important in some everyday activities.

## activity

### MEASURING

**Objective:** To gain experience in measuring

**Materials**

baby food jar
balance
beaker, 250 mL
Celsius thermometer
graduated cylinder, 100 mL
ice cube
metric ruler
milk carton, empty
nail
paper clip
pencil
stirring rod
water

**Procedure**

1. Copy the data table into your notebook.
2. Measure the length of the nail, paper clip, and pencil in millimeters. Record the results in your data table.
3. Measure the length of the three objects in Step 2 in centimeters and record your results.
4. Use the balance to measure the mass of the three objects in Step 2. Record your results.
5. Use the graduated cylinder and measure the volume of the baby food jar and the milk carton. Record these volumes.
6. Determine and record the mass of the empty graduated cylinder.
7. Determine and record the mass of the graduate containing 10 mL of water. Record your results.
8. Pour 100 mL of water into the beaker and record the water temperature.
9. Place an ice cube in the water and stir until the ice is gone. Record the temperature of the water again.

**Observations and Data**

| Object | Length | | Mass |
|---|---|---|---|
| | mm | cm | g |
| Nail | | | |
| Paper Clip | | | |
| Pencil | | | |
| Graduate | | | |
| Graduate and water | | | |

| Object | Volume |
|---|---|
| Baby food jar | |
| Milk carton | |

| Substance | Temperature |
|---|---|
| Water | |
| Water and melted ice | |

**Questions and Conclusions**

1. How much longer than the paper clip was the pencil?
2. Which had the greater mass, the nail or the paper clip?
3. What was the volume of the baby food jar? The milk carton?
4. Calculate the mass of 1 mL of water.
5. What effect did the ice cube have on the temperature of the water?

## making sure

7. Which is larger, a meter or a centimeter?
8. How many mL are in 1 L?
9. How many g equal 1 kg?

## 1:5 Technology

What is technology?

People apply the facts and ideas of science to the solutions of everyday problems. Science is used to design and build things such as rockets, cameras, microscopes, and artificial body parts. **Technology** is the application of science for practical purposes. The fields of engineering and electronics are two examples of technology. People who work in these fields need a background in science to do their jobs.

Science and technology depend upon each other. Science is used to invent and improve technical devices. New inventions are used by scientists when they study nature. For example, high-speed photography can be used to learn how a bird flaps its wings. Electron microscopes enable scientists to take pictures of disease-causing viruses. Computers are used to store, retrieve, and analyze large amounts of data. A computer can perform a complex mathematical operation in a small fraction of the time it would take a person to do it.

FIGURE 1–5. High-speed cameras help scientists study how birds fly (a). New metals are used to make replacement joints such as this hip joint (b).

a

*Rosemary Scott/Taurus Photos*

b

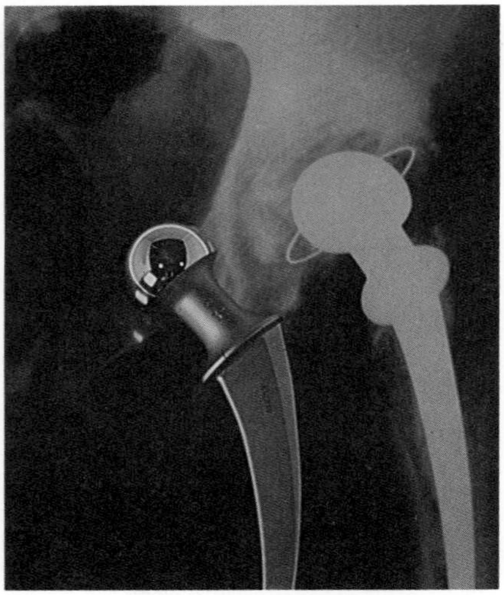

*National Bureau of Standards*

Improving the environment requires the use of science and technology. Why? Solutions to pollution and other environmental problems often depend on new discoveries and inventions. Scientists work to discover new ways to prevent air and water pollution. Engineers use principles of physics to design quieter jet engines. Biologists test food preservatives to find out which ones are safe and will not harm the human body. New technology has reduced the pollution from some power plants, made cars safer, and improved medical care.

Science and technology can aid in the development and careful use of natural resources. Biologists find ways to control harmful insects without using chemicals that harm the environment in other ways. Scientific management of forests can increase the yield of lumber. Development and use of improved fertilizers increases soil fertility, thereby helping farmers grow more food.

Finding new sources of energy helps conserve the world's supply of fuels. One new energy source is geothermal (jee oh THUR mul) energy. Geothermal energy refers to heat deep within the earth's rocks. This heat is removed by pumping water in and out of the rocks. Other energy sources include nuclear energy, solar energy, wind power, and natural gas obtained from garbage. Someday these energy sources may become our major energy supplies. Science and technology are needed to make this happen.

Courtesy of Apple Computer, Inc.

FIGURE 1–6. Computers are used in science, business, medicine, and the home.

How are science and technology helping to improve the environment?

## activity

### SCIENCE AND TECHNOLOGY ON TELEVISION

This activity is to be done at home. Make a list of examples of science and technology you observe while watching television. Keep a record of the programs in which you make your observations. Bring your list to class and compare it with your classmates' data.

# PERSPECTIVES

skills

## Chapter Preview

All athletes "warm up" before they play a game. Have you ever considered what a warm-up does and why an athlete does it? A warm-up usually consists of exercises to get the muscles working well. During a warm-up, an athlete may also review certain plays and the proper ways of handling the ball or other playing equipment. A warm-up enables the athlete to play at the highest peak of performance.

Just as a warm-up aids in preparing the body to play a game, a preview aids in preparing the mind to study. Previewing material you are about to read is an important study technique. The preview aids you in knowing what you will be reading, what types of information are included, and how the ideas are related and organized. Through previewing, you can also identify new words and some of the main ideas that will be discussed. Previewing is a way to prepare for concentrating on and understanding new material. Previewing is a kind of warm-up that aids you in making sense of the many facts and ideas presented in the reading material.

You may preview Chapter 1 by answering the following questions:

1. What is the title of Chapter 1?
2. What do you think the chapter is about?
3. From reading the title, do you think science and technology are related? Why or why not?
4. Read the section titles. What subjects are discussed?
5. What information would you expect to find in Section 1:1?
6. Look at each section title and change it to a question. Use words such as what, where, when, why, how, and who to begin your questions.
7. How many tables are in the chapter and what kinds of information can be found in them?
8. How can you use the *Making Sure* questions?
9. Look at the activities in Chapter 1. How are they similar? Different?
10. Read the margin questions as you preview the chapter. How will they aid your study?
11. Notice the boldface words. How many words do you already know? List the words you do not know and write the definitions as you read the chapter.
12. Read the *Main Ideas* on page 15. How do these statements give you an overview of the important information in the chapter? How do you know which section in the chapter discusses each main idea?
13. Look at the *Vocabulary* list on page 15. Can you put each vocabulary word with the appropriate main idea?
14. How are the vocabulary words and the boldface words in the chapter related?
15. Look at the pictures in the chapter. Why do you think these pictures were included in the chapter?

Previewing a chapter before you read it may seem to take more time when you study. However, the results of previewing are well worth the time spent. Remember, no athlete would want to play a game without first warming up. You will be rewarded with better concentration and understanding if you also "warm-up" by previewing your chapters.

## main ideas

# Chapter Review

1. Scientists gain knowledge through study and investigation. 1:1
2. Science is facts and ideas developed by scientists and methods used by scientists to gain information. 1:1
3. Observation is an important tool of scientists. 1:2
4. Measurement is dimensions, capacity, or the amount of something. 1:3
5. A unit is a fixed amount or quantity used by everyone when measuring. 1:3
6. SI is a decimal system based on 10 and multiples of 10. 1:4
7. The basic units of SI are the meter (m), the cubic meter ($m^3$), and the kilogram (kg). 1:4
8. Temperature is measured in degrees Celsius (°C). 1:4
9. Technology is the application of science for practical purposes. 1:5
10. Science and technology depend upon each other. 1:5

## vocabulary

*Define each of the following words or terms.*

| | | |
|---|---|---|
| Celsius (C) | mass | science |
| cubic meter ($m^3$) | measurement | SI |
| data | meter (m) | technology |
| kilogram (kg) | observation | |

## study questions

**DO NOT WRITE IN THIS BOOK.**

**A. True or False**

*Determine whether each of the following sentences is true or false. If the sentence is false, rewrite it to make it true.*

1. Science includes methods for discovering new facts and ideas.
2. Technology and science are the same thing.
3. All observations that include numbers are data.
4. Your height is a quantitative observation.
5. Volume is measured in square centimeters.
6. Your height can be measured in liters.
7. Length may be measured in millimeters.

8. A centimeter is equal to 1/1000 of a liter.
9. There are 100 degrees between the freezing and boiling points of water on the Celsius temperature scale.
10. A graduated cylinder is used to measure volume.

## B. Multiple Choice

*Choose one word or phrase that completes correctly each of the following sentences.*

1. A (*paper clip, penny, meter*) is a standard unit.
2. The color of this paper is a(n) (*observation, quantitative observation, measurement*).
3. (*Kilogram, Centimeter, Meter, Liter*) is a unit of mass in the metric system.
4. The freezing point of water is (*0°, 21°, 100°*) Celsius at sea level.
5. The practical uses of science are called (*experiment, conservation, technology*).
6. (*Biology, Chemistry, Physics*) is the study of what matter is and how it changes.
7. (*Astronomy, Genetics, Geology*) is the study of rocks, minerals, and the structure of Earth.
8. SI refers to (*units of measure, a unit of size, a branch of science*).
9. One mL is equal to one ($m^3$, $cm^3$, $mm^3$).
10. The way matter and energy is related is likely to be investigated by scientists in (*biology, chemistry, physics*).

## C. Completion

*Complete each of the following sentences with a word or phrase that will make the sentence correct.*

1. Technology refers to the practical uses of ______.
2. The main branches of science are biology, ______, and ______.
3. A biologist studies ______.
4. The use of laws of physics and chemistry to design a new battery is an example of ______.
5. A telescope is a tool used by scientists in ______.
6. A ______ observation includes a number.
7. Most measurements include a ______ and a ______.

8. A(n) ______ is noting or recognizing that something has occurred.
9. The ______ is the basic unit of mass in SI.
10. A liter is a unit of ______.

**D. How and Why**

1. List three reasons it is important to study science.
2. Why are observations important in science?
3. What instrument is used to measure length, mass, and volume?
4. Name three careers that are related to science.
5. Why are units important in science?

## challenges

1. Choose a science field in which you are interested. Obtain information from a library on careers in this field. Learn what education is needed for each career.
2. Write a report tracing the development of the International System of Units.
3. SI units and Celsius temperatures are being used more often in daily life. Keep a log of the times you see or hear an SI unit or a Celsius temperature. For example, watch for them on packages and listen for them on radio or television weather reports.
4. Obtain a biography of a famous scientist such as Ander Celsius, Albert Einstein, Sir Isaac Newton, or Enrico Fermi. Read the book and write a short book report.
5. Research and prepare a report on some of the practical benefits of the United States space program.

## interesting reading

Cobb, Vicki and Kathy Darling, *Bet You Can't! Science Impossibilities to Fool You.* New York: Lothrop, 1980.

National Geographic Society. *On the Brink of Tomorrow: Frontiers of Science.* Washington, DC: National Geographic Society, 1982.

Weiss, Harvey, *How To Be An Inventor.* New York: Harper and Row, 1980.

*The human body is a unique machine. The body's basic support system is made of bones and muscles. Because bones and muscles work together, you can walk, sit, write, and even read. What do bones do? How do muscles work? Are all muscles the same?*

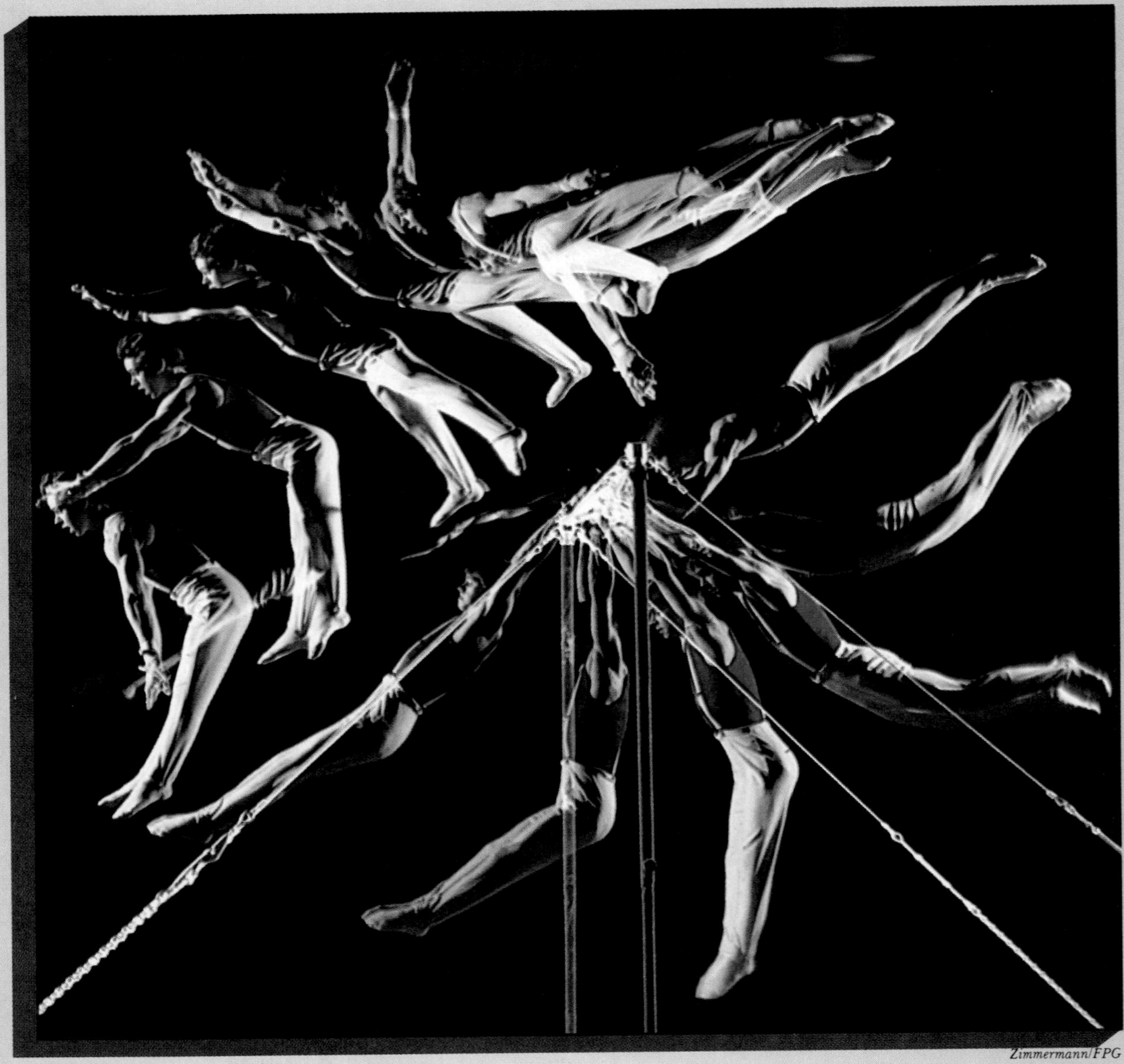

Zimmermann/FPG

# The Human Body

# chapter 2

## 2:1 Human Beings

GOAL: You will learn the main parts of the body and how they function.

Scientists classify human beings in the Animal Kingdom, one of the five major groups of living organisms. The body parts and life activities of people are like those of other groups of living organisms. We eat, breathe, excrete wastes, and reproduce. We also run, climb, swim, and obtain food.

How are mammals different from other animals?

In the Animal Kingdom, humans are members of the Mammalia group. Mammals are animals that have hair on their bodies and nurse their young. Mammals also have an internal skeleton of bones and a spinal cord connected to a brain. The spinal column is the part of the skeleton that protects the spinal cord. Another part of the skeleton, the skull, protects the brain.

Mammals are classified into smaller groups or orders. One of these orders is primates. Humans, chimpanzees, and gorillas are examples of primates. Some characteristics of primates are hands that can grasp and a large brain.

The scientific name for humans is *Homo sapiens* (HOH moh • SAY pee unz). All people in the world belong to one species. A species is a group of closely related organisms that can produce fertile offspring. How are *Homo sapiens* different from other animals?

National Bureau of Standards

FIGURE 2–1. People are the only animals that can read, write, and use numbers.

What sets humans apart from other animals?

People have larger, more complex brains than most other animals. They use these brains to do many things other animals cannot do. Right now as you read these words, you are doing something known only to *Homo sapiens*. People are the only animals that make symbols such as letters and numerals. These symbols are used to communicate ideas through writing and reading. What is the main idea in this paragraph? How do you know?

What features enable you to tell people apart?

Most human beings have legs, arms, a torso, and a head. These parts, which are seen when you look at another human being, are the external body features. Study the external features of the people around you. Each person is different. This is how you can tell one person from another. Even identical twins differ—usually enough so that their parents and close friends can tell them apart. Besides external features, everyone has internal body features. These are parts, such as the heart and lungs, that are inside the body. The internal features of human beings are not exactly alike either. For example, the appendix is not always on the lower right side of the body. In some people, it is located on the left side or in the center of the body. In most people the kneecap is one bone. Some people have a kneecap made of two or three bones.

activity

## LUNG CAPACITIES

**Objective:** To compare lung capacities

### Materials

beaker, 250 mL
dishpan
graduated cylinder, 100 mL
marking pencil
jar/lid, 4–6 L
rubber tubing, 50 cm
water
3 wood blocks, same size

FIGURE 2–2.

### Procedure

1. Fill the dishpan half full of water. Place the wood blocks on the bottom.
2. Completely fill the jar with water and tighten the lid.
3. Hold the jar over the dishpan, turn it upside down and set it in the dishpan.
4. Keeping the mouth of the jar underwater, remove the lid. Place the jar on the wood blocks (Figure 2–2). Be careful not to lift the mouth of the jar above water.
5. Slide one end of the rubber tubing into the jar. Be careful to keep the other end of the tubing higher than the dishpan at all times.
6. *Inhale* deeply, taking as much air into your lungs as you can. Then *exhale* all the air in your lungs through the rubber tubing.
7. Mark the level of water with the marking pencil after you have exhaled into the jar. Label the mark with your initials.
8. Repeat Steps 6 and 7 for several of your classmates. Mark each water level and label it with each student's initials.
9. Remove the jar from the dishpan and empty the water.
10. Use the graduate to fill the jar to the first mark with water. Record the volume. Without emptying the jar, add water to the next mark using the graduate. Record this amount. Continue adding water and recording until all volumes have been recorded. Recorded volumes are a measure of each person's lung capacity.

### Observations and Data

1. Use your data to draw a bar graph showing the lung capacities and the number of students with each capacity.
2. Draw a second bar graph that compares the lung capacities of males and females.

### Questions and Conclusions

1. What was your lung capacity?
2. Did everyone have the same capacity?
3. What was the largest lung capacity? The smallest? The average?
4. From your data, what can you conclude about the lung capacities of males versus females in your class?

## 2:2 Cells, Tissues, and Organs

Every person's body is made of cells. The **cell** is the basic unit of structure and function in all living organisms. Cells are the blocks from which all larger body parts are made. The human body is made of trillions of cells. Within each cell, changes occur that keep the body alive.

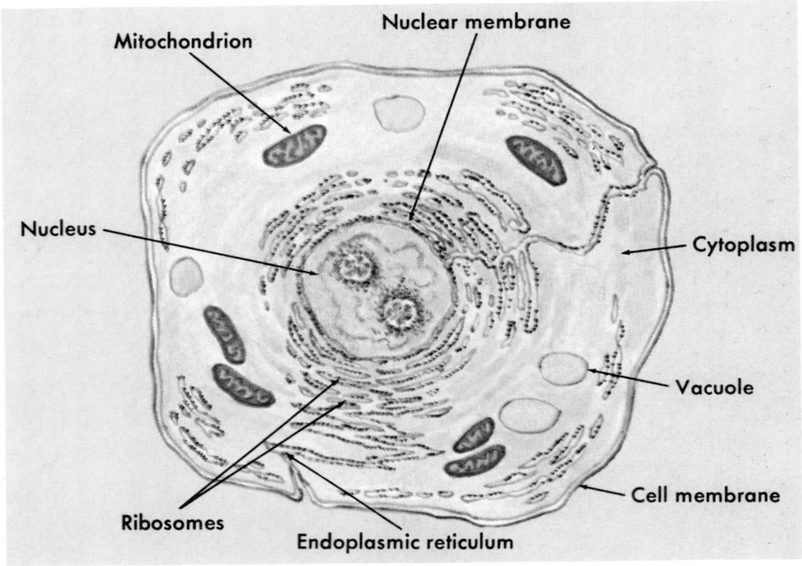


Figure 2–3. A typical animal cell is composed of many smaller parts.

Name the three parts of a human body cell and describe each.

The cell **nucleus** is a dense, ball-shaped mass usually found near the center of the cell (Figure 2–3). A membrane surrounds the nucleus and separates it from the cytoplasm. The nucleus controls the activities of a cell and its reproduction. Also, the nucleus carries information for traits, such as hair color, body size, and facial features.

A human cell contains **cytoplasm** (SITE uh plaz um), a jellylike material with a unique property—it is alive. Cytoplasm is a mixture of water, salts, and other materials. A thin, living cell membrane surrounds the cell. It is visible only with the aid of an electron microscope. The cell membrane is flexible and is a living, functioning part of the cell. The cell membrane controls the movement of materials into and out of the cell. The cell membrane is selective. Only certain dissolved materials can pass through. In

Figure 2–4. Gases diffuse from areas of higher concentration to areas of lower concentration, filling the space evenly.

general, very large particles cannot pass through a cell membrane.

Dissolved materials move through a cell membrane by a process called diffusion. **Diffusion** is the movement of particles of a material from regions of higher concentration to regions of lower concentration of that material (Figure 2–4). Food and oxygen diffuse from the blood through the cell membrane into the cytoplasm of the cell. Waste materials diffuse in the opposite direction, from the cell into the blood through the cell membrane.

Explain how osmosis and diffusion are related.

A special kind of diffusion, called osmosis, also occurs through a cell membrane. **Osmosis** is the diffusion of water through a membrane. Water moves into and out of a cell by osmosis.

Life functions occur in each body cell. The combined functions of many cells keep you alive. Your body has different kinds of cells that do different jobs. There are muscle cells, blood cells, nerve cells, and other kinds of cells. Some cells contain structures that perform special jobs. For example, cells that line your throat have tiny, hairlike cilia (SIHL ee uh). Cilia filter out dust from the air you breathe.

FIGURE 2–5. Human cells have many shapes and sizes.

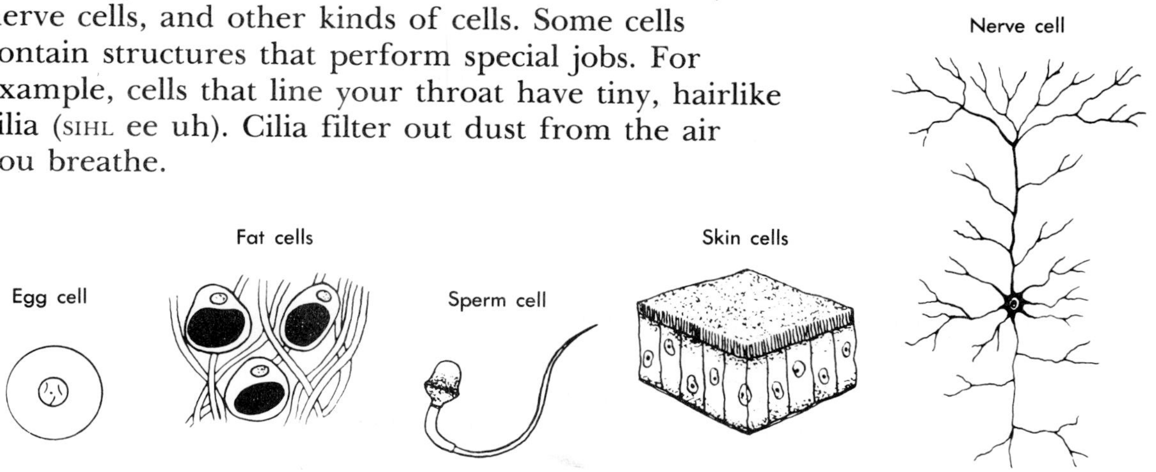

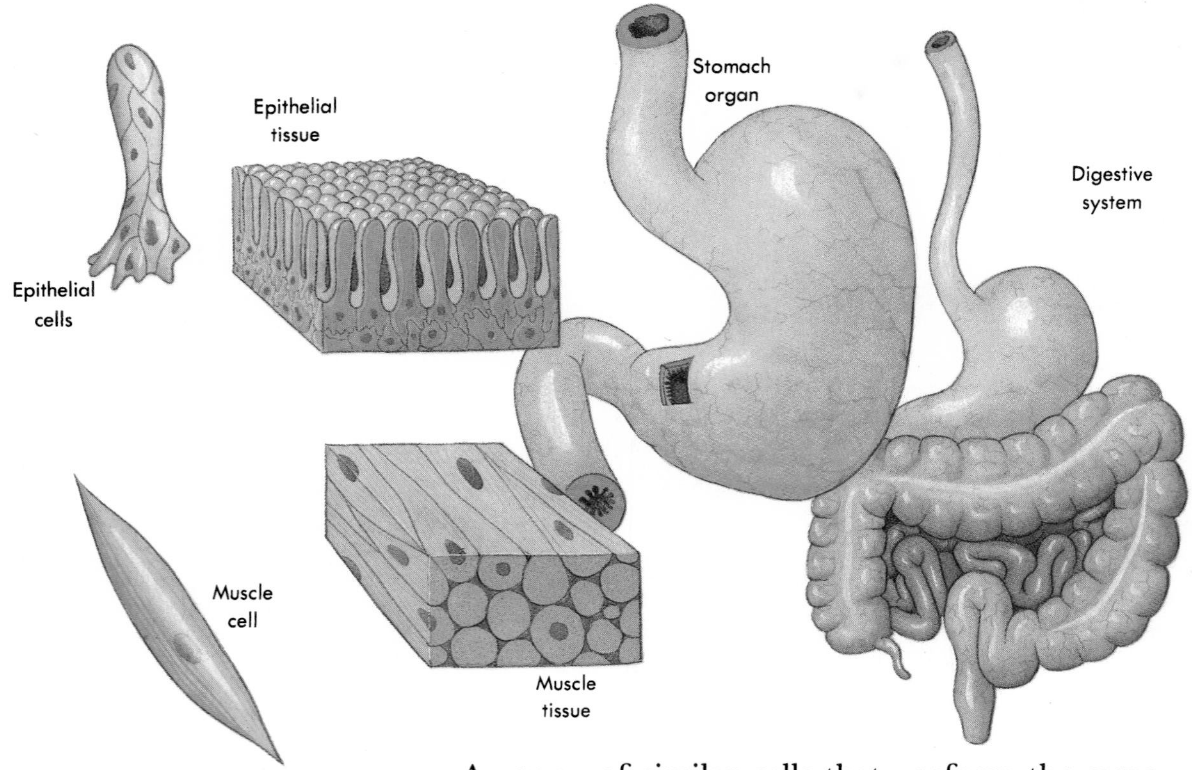


Figure 2–6. The digestive system is composed of organs. The organs are composed of tissues. Tissues are composed of cells.

Define tissue. Name two kinds of tissue.

A group of similar cells that perform the same function is called a **tissue.** Muscle is a tissue because it is composed of many similar muscle cells. Muscle cells work together to produce motion by contraction and relaxation. Other kinds of tissues include bone tissue, blood tissue, nerve tissue, and epithelial (ep uh THEE lee ul) tissue. The skin that covers the surface of your body is epithelial tissue. It also lines the nose, throat, windpipe, and digestive tract. Epithelial tissue provides protection.

Several different tissues working together to perform a function are called an **organ**. Your heart is an example of an organ. It is mostly muscle tissue. The heart also contains blood, nerve, and epithelial tissues. Some other organs are the lungs, stomach, and intestines.

Organs that work together to perform one main function make up a **system**. An example is the circulatory system. The heart and blood vessels work together to circulate blood. Some other systems are the digestive system and the skeletal system.

## activity

### HUMAN CELLS

**Objective:** To observe human cheek cells using a microscope

**Materials**

dropper
microscope slide/coverslip
iodine solution
microscope
toothpick
water

**Procedure**

1. Place a drop of water in the center of the slide.
2. Gently scrape the inside lining of your cheek with one end of the toothpick. Stir that end of the toothpick in the drop of water. Put the toothpick into a trash container.
3. Use the dropper to add a drop of iodine solution to the water.
4. Place the coverslip on the slide. Place the slide on the stage of the microscope. Focus first using low power and then switch to high power.
5. Observe the cheek cells and sketch a diagram of one as observed under high power.
6. When you have completed your observations, remove the slide, and wash and dry it.

FIGURE 2–7.

**Observations and Data**

1. Label the following cell parts on your diagram: cell membrane, cytoplasm, nucleus.

**Questions and Conclusions**

1. Why did you mix the cheek cells with water?
2. How did the iodine solution affect the cheek cells?
3. Describe the cytoplasm.
4. Describe the nucleus.
5. How is a cell different from a tissue?

## making sure

1. Examples of different human body cells are shown in Figure 2–5. Draw a sketch of each cell in your notebook. Identify in each cell the cytoplasm, cell membrane, nucleus, and any other features that make the particular cell unique.

## 2:3 Skeletal System

What is the function of the skeleton?

Humans have an internal skeleton that protects most of the organs of the body. Its 206 separate bones support the body and serve as a framework for the attachment of muscles (Figure 2–8). The skeleton is about 18 percent of your body's weight.

Figure 2–8. The human skeleton contains bones and joints that aid body movement.

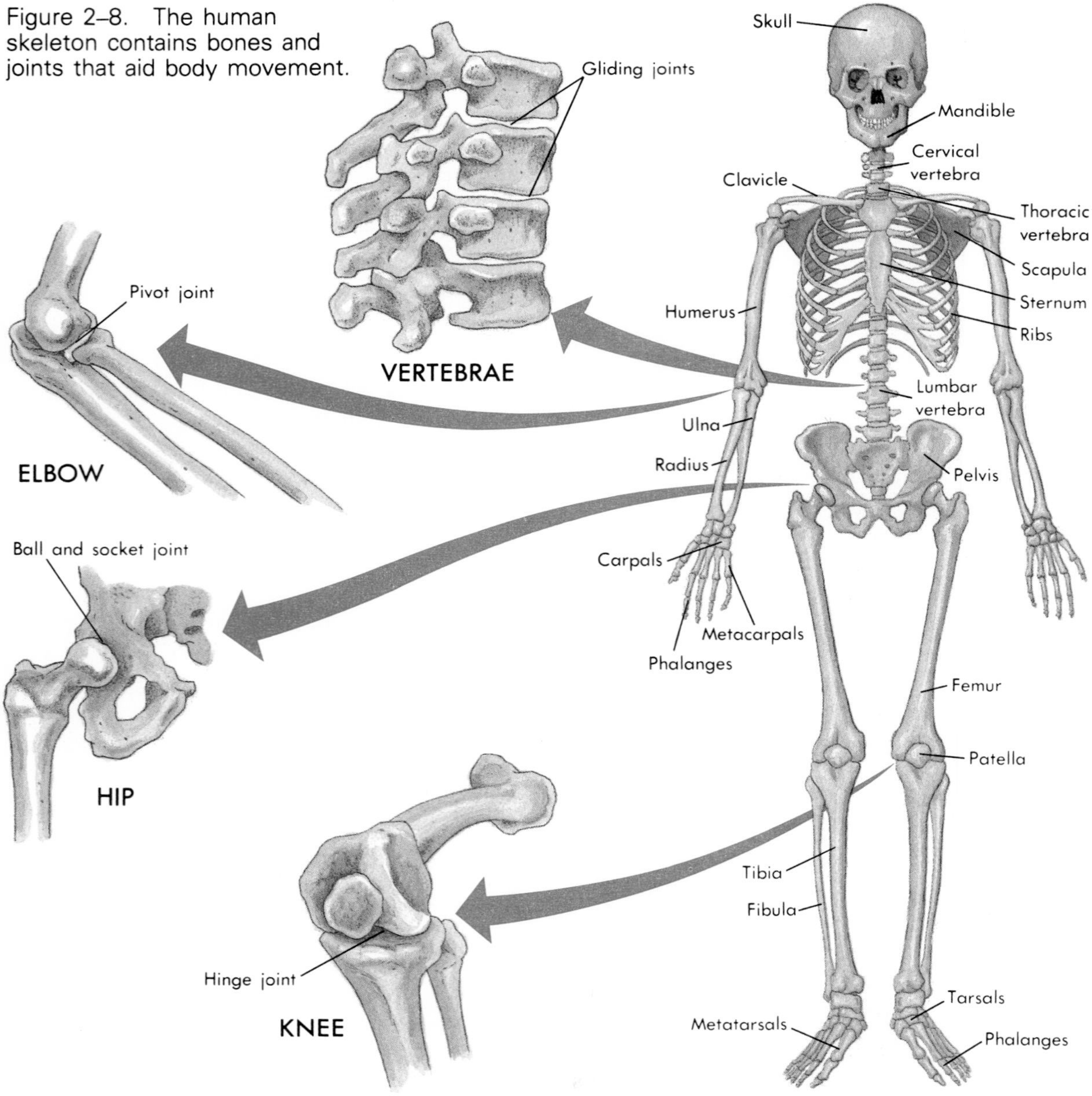

Bones in the skeleton are held together by strands of tough tissue called **ligaments.** Ligaments stretch to allow bones to move. The point at which two bones move against one another is called a joint. Some bone joints are shown in Figure 2–8. Shoulder and hip joints are examples of ball-and-socket joints. Hinge joints are those found in the knees, elbows, and toes. Gliding joints are found in the wrists and between vertebrae. A pivot joint is present in the neck and allows the head to turn.

**Cartilage** (KART ul ihj) is a bluish-white, rubbery tissue present in most joints. Here it serves as a cushion between the bones of the joints. You can pinch the end of your nose or ear and feel the cartilage inside. Cartilage is tough and supportive. Many injuries occuring in contact sports, such as football, result in torn cartilage. Often surgery is required to repair the cartilage.

### making sure

2. Using the skeleton in Figure 2–8, locate each of the following bones: femur, patella, humerus, sternum, mandible, and phalanges.
3. Where are joints found in the body? Give an example of a ball-and-socket joint, a gliding joint, a hinge joint, and a pivot joint.

## 2:4 Bone Tissue

Bone is a tissue made of minerals and living matter. Each bone must have a supply of blood to nourish living cells. A bone contains several parts that can be observed when it is cut lengthwise (Figure 2–8). The outer covering of a bone is called the **periosteum** (per ee AHS tee um). It is a tough covering of living tissue that carries food to the bone. Also, it aids in repairing injuries to the bone and provides a surface to which muscles can attach.

Bone material beneath the periosteum varies from very hard to spongy. In long bones, such as

Figure 2–9. A cross section of a human long bone reveals several important parts.

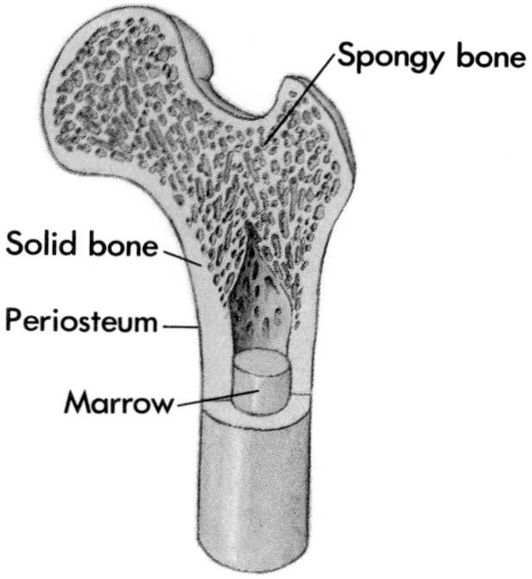

FIGURE 2–10. Channels are visible in a cross section of a bone.

J. Gennaro for Photo Researchers

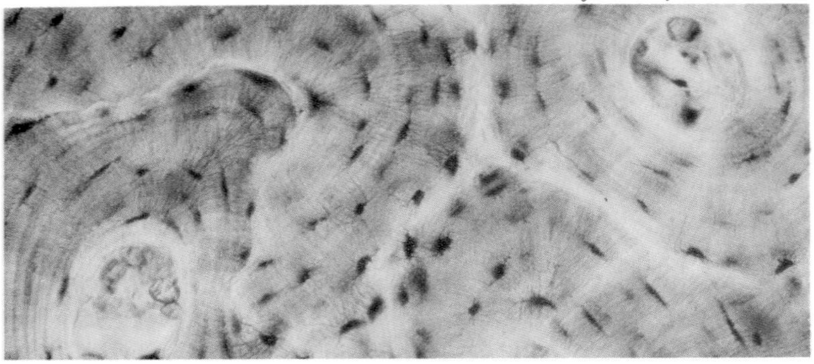

the bones of the arms and legs, the bony material is hard in the inner portion and spongy at both ends. The hardness of bone is related to the amount of mineral matter in it. The hardest part of a bone has the most mineral matter. Most mineral matter in bones is calcium and phosphorus.

What mineral elements are plentiful in bone?

A break in a bone is called a **fracture.** Fractures heal as the broken bone grows back together again. To heal properly, the broken bone must be set and kept from moving out of position. Usually a cast is used to keep the broken ends of the bone from separating.

Numerous channels are found throughout bone. They form a network through which blood vessels connect the interior of the bone with the external periosteum. Blood vessels in the channels transport digested food and oxygen to the bone cells and remove wastes.

a

b

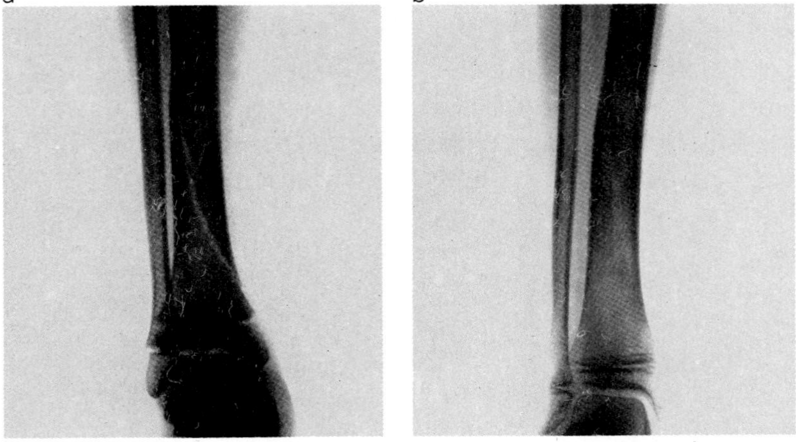

Drs. Pappas and Freeman, Inc.

FIGURE 2–11. X rays show a fractured bone (a) and the same bone after healing (b).

**Marrow** is a soft tissue in the center of many bones. It has many nerves and blood vessels. Red marrow is found in flat bones and in the ends of long bones. Red bone marrow produces blood cells. Yellow marrow, found in the center of long bones, is primarily fat tissue. Yellow bone marrow may produce red blood cells when there is a great loss of blood or when a person is suffering from certain blood diseases.

The skeleton of a human changes. The skeleton of a human before birth is soft and flexible. It is composed largely of cartilage. As a baby develops, cartilage is replaced by bone. The replacement of cartilage by bone is the result of the addition of minerals to the material between the bone cells. These minerals include calcium compounds. Bones develop rapidly throughout childhood and at a reduced rate throughout adulthood. As people grow older, their bones may become brittle and break more easily.

a

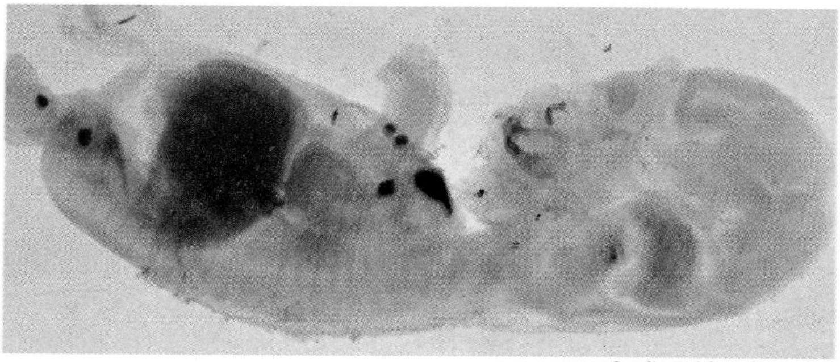

*Carolina Biological Supply Co.*

b

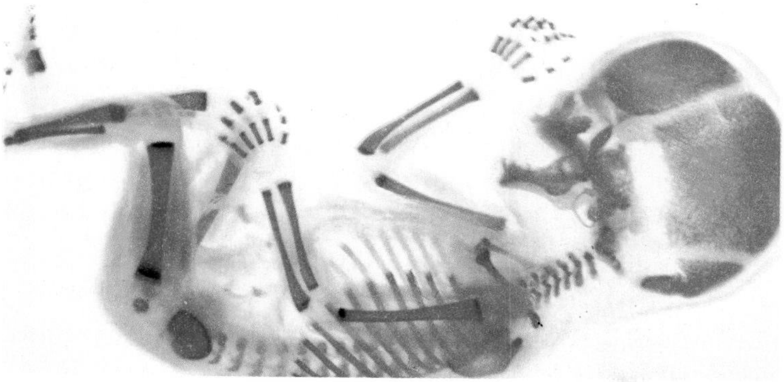

*Carolina Biological Supply Co.*

FIGURE 2–12. A fetal skeleton begins as cartilage (a). Cartilage gradually turns into bone (b). Cartilage is white and bone is red in these photographs.

## activity

MATTER IN BONE

**(1)** Obtain a fresh beef bone. **(2)** Measure and record the mass of the bone. Describe the bone's appearance—hard, spongy, and so on. **(3)** Heat the bone in an oven at 65°C for 3 h. Allow the bone to cool. **(4)** Measure and record the bone's mass again. What happened to the mass of the bone? What material was lost from the bone? What bone material was left? What percentage of the bone's mass was mineral matter?

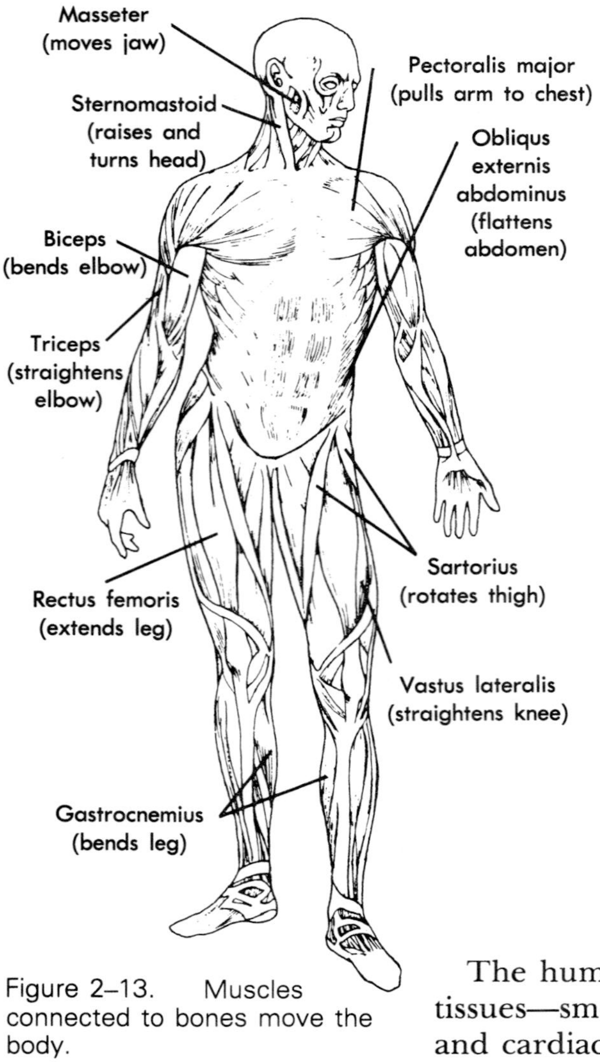


Figure 2–13. Muscles connected to bones move the body.

## 2:5 Muscles

All body movement from blinking an eyelid to kicking a ball requires the use of muscles. Digestion, circulation of blood, and excretion of wastes also depend on the action of muscles. **Muscle** is a tissue that moves the parts of your body. The nearly 650 muscles of the body are about 33 percent of a person's body weight.

There are two types of muscles—voluntary and involuntary. Voluntary muscles are those muscles you consciously control. The muscles you use to move your arms and legs are voluntary muscles. Voluntary muscles respond quickly and tire quickly. Involuntary muscles are muscles that you cannot control consciously. The muscles in your stomach and intestines are involuntary muscles. Involuntary muscles respond slowly and tire slowly. Some muscles, such as those that move your lungs and eyelids, are both voluntary and involuntary.

The human body contains three kinds of muscle tissues—smooth muscle, striated (STRI ayt ud) muscle, and cardiac (KARD ee ak) muscle. Smooth muscle is

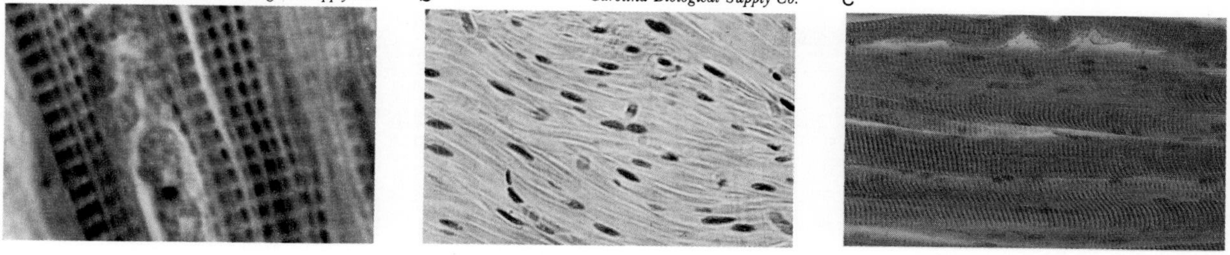


FIGURE 2–14. Microscopic views of cardiac muscle (a), smooth muscle (b), and striated muscle (c) show some of the differences among the three types.

present in the walls of many internal organs. For example, the walls of the stomach, intestines, and blood vessels contain smooth muscle. Smooth muscle is involuntary muscle. You cannot directly control its movement.

Where are smooth, striated, and cardiac muscles found?

Striated muscle has bands called striations. These bands are visible when muscle is viewed with a microscope. Striated muscles in your body are under voluntary control. When you walk, talk, jump, and run, you use striated muscles. These muscles are attached to the bones of the skeleton. Thus, striated muscles are also called skeletal muscles. Striated muscles are connected to bones by tough bands of connective tissue called **tendons**. Your bones and limbs are moved by contraction and extension of striated muscles.

Opposing pairs of muscles are found in several places in the body. Observe the biceps and triceps muscles in Figure 2–13. When the forearm is raised, the biceps contracts and the triceps extends. When the forearm is lowered, the muscles reverse. The triceps contracts and the biceps extends. Locate other opposing muscles in your body.

Cardiac muscle or heart muscle is present in your heart. Heart muscle is similar to striated muscle because it also contains striations. However, unlike striated muscle, cardiac muscle is involuntary. Cardiac muscle combines the quick responses of striated muscle with the endurance of smooth muscle.

## making sure

**4.** What is the difference between voluntary and involuntary muscles?

# PERSPECTIVES

## skills

# How Words Are Formed

As new ideas and discoveries are made in science, the need for new words becomes necessary. New words come from many sources. Many times they are formed from Latin and Greek words. Latin was the language of the ancient Romans. Tracing a word to its original source or language is the study of etymology.

Forming new words can be compared to building with blocks. You may begin with the root or the main block and then add other blocks to make a complete word. Blocks added before the root word are called prefixes. Blocks added after the root are called suffixes. Look at the word reproduction and note its parts.

reproduction:

| | | |
|---|---|---|
| *re* | (prefix) | means again |
| *pro* | (prefix) | means forward |
| *duc* | (root) | means to lead |
| *tion* | (suffix) | means capable of |

By putting all of these meanings together, you arrive at a complete meaning: "capable of leading forward again." It refers to living organisms producing other living organisms.

When you begin to take words apart, you find that the same root may be part of many different words. This is also true of prefixes and suffixes. For example, note other words that contain the Latin root *ducere* (to lead):

| | |
|---|---|
| conduct | deduce |
| conduction | deduction |
| conducive | |
| produce | |
| production | |
| productive | |
| reduce | |
| reduction | |

Below is a list of science words. A list of word parts with meanings is also given. Can you define each word by knowing the meaning of its parts?

| **Word** | **Word Parts** | **Meaning** |
|---|---|---|
| chlorophyll | *protos* | to change |
| chloroplast | *spirare* | to blow, breathe |
| cytoplasm | *chloros* | greenish yellow |
| endospore | *flagellare* | to whip, wave |
| flagella | *zo* | animals |
| neuron | *cyto* | cell |
| protist | *plasserin* | to mold |
| respiration | *phyllon* | leaf |
| spore | *sporo* | seed |
| zoology | *endo* | within |
| | *neuro* | nerve |
| anthropology | *logy* | study of |
| gymnosperms | *anthropo* | humans |
| hypothermia | *hypo* | beneath, under |
| arthropods | *pod* | foot |
| cytology | *derm* | skin |
| echinoderm | *echin* | spiny |
| pseudopods | *gymno* | naked |
| microbiology | *sperm* | seed |
| epiglottis | *epi* | on, above |
| multicellular | *glottis* | mouth of windpipe |
| | *macro* | large |
| | *micro* | small |
| | *coel* | hollow |
| | *chrom* | color |
| | *hetero* | different |
| | *therm* | heat |
| | *odont* | tooth |

The list of word parts and meanings given above is a very small sample of those used to form English words. Science vocabulary study is greatly aided by knowing the meaning of many prefixes, suffixes, and roots.

## main ideas

1. Humans belong to the Animal Kingdom, the Mammalia group, and are called *Homo sapiens.* 2:1
2. The cell is the basic unit of the human body. The functions of all cells keep a human alive. 2:2
3. The human body is composed of cells that are organized into tissues, organs, and systems. 2:2
4. The major parts of a cell are a cell membrane, cytoplasm, and a nucleus. 2:2
5. Dissolved materials move into and out of a cell across the cell membrane by the processes of diffusion and osmosis. 2:2
6. The skeletal system, which supports and protects body organs, is composed of living tissue called bone. 2:3–2:4
7. Bones and muscles move body parts. 2:5
8. The body contains three types of muscle tissue—smooth, striated, and cardiac. 2:5
9. Muscles are either voluntary or involuntary. Voluntary muscles can be controlled consciously; involuntary muscles cannot. 2:5

## vocabulary

*Define each of the following words or terms.*

cartilage
cell
cytoplasm
diffusion
fracture
ligaments
marrow
muscle
nucleus
organ
osmosis
periosteum
system
tendons
tissue

## study questions

**DO NOT WRITE IN THIS BOOK.**

### A. True or False

*Determine whether each of the following sentences is true or false. If the sentence is false, rewrite it to make it true.*

1. Every person has the same size lungs.
2. A tissue contains several different kinds of cells.
3. Bones contain minerals.

4. The skeleton protects internal organs.
5. The knee is a hinge joint.
6. Vertebrae are muscles.
7. Tendons connect bones to other bones.
8. The periosteum nourishes bone tissue.
9. Muscles are attached to bones with ligaments.
10. A living bone contains blood vessels.

**B. Multiple Choice**

*Choose the word or phrase that completes correctly each of the following sentences.*

1. Cytoplasm is a(n) (*element, compound, mixture*).
2. The (*molecule, cell, nucleus*) is the basic unit of structure in organisms.
3. Osmosis is the diffusion of water (*inside, outside, into or out of*) a cell.
4. Blood cells are produced in a bone's (*periosteum, channels, marrow*).
5. (*Ligaments, Tendons, Cartilage*) connect bone to bone.
6. (*Ligaments, Tendons, Cartilage*) connect muscles to bones.
7. (*Cardiac, Smooth, Striated*) muscles are under conscious control.
8. (*Cardiac, Striated, Smooth*) muscle is also called heart muscle.
9. A body system is (*tissues, cells, organs*) that work together to perform one main function.
10. Muscle is a (*cell, tissue, system*).

**C. Completion**

*Complete each of the following sentences with a word or phrase that will make the sentence correct.*

1. Food and oxygen move into a cell by ______.
2. The ______ of a cell regulates the cell's activities.
3. In the process of osmosis, water moves through the ______.
4. A dissolved material moves throughout a liquid by the process of ______.
5. The muscles that move your fingers are called ______ muscles.
6. The soft tissue in the center of a long bone is called ______.
7. Your shoulder joint is a ______ joint.

8. Body parts that are composed of different tissues are called ______.
9. Bone channels contain many ______.
10. Skin is a body system composed of ______ tissue.

**D. How and Why**

1. What is the relationship between cartilage and bone?
2. Compare the structures and functions of the three types of muscles.
3. Name two pairs of opposing muscles and explain how they work.
4. Draw a sketch of an epithelial cell and label its parts.
5. Explain how the functions of muscles and bones are related.

## challenges

1. Obtain and study a book on the anatomy of a cat. Compare a cat skeleton with a human skeleton.
2. Obtain photographs showing broken bones and bones that have healed. Use the photographs to illustrate a report on how bones heal.
3. Obtain prepared slides of human tissues from a medical laboratory. Study these slides with a microscope to identify tissues and cells. Make drawings of your observations.

## interesting reading

Bruun, Ruth Dowling and Bertel Bruun, *The Human Body.* New York: Random House, 1982.

Daly, Kathleen N., *Body Words: A Dictionary of the Human Body, How It Works, and Some of the Things That Can Affect Its Health.* Garden City, NY: Doubleday and Co., 1980.

Nourse, Alan E., *Your Immune System.* New York: Franklin Watts, Inc., 1982.

Ward, Brian R., *The Skeleton and Movement.* New York: Franklin Watts, Inc., 1981.

*Blood is a vital fluid in the human body. Blood contains many parts including red blood cells. Red blood cells travel in single file through this capillary in muscle tissue. The capillary is less than $\frac{1}{10}$ the thickness of a hair. Why are red blood cells important? What other substances are in the blood? Is all blood alike?*

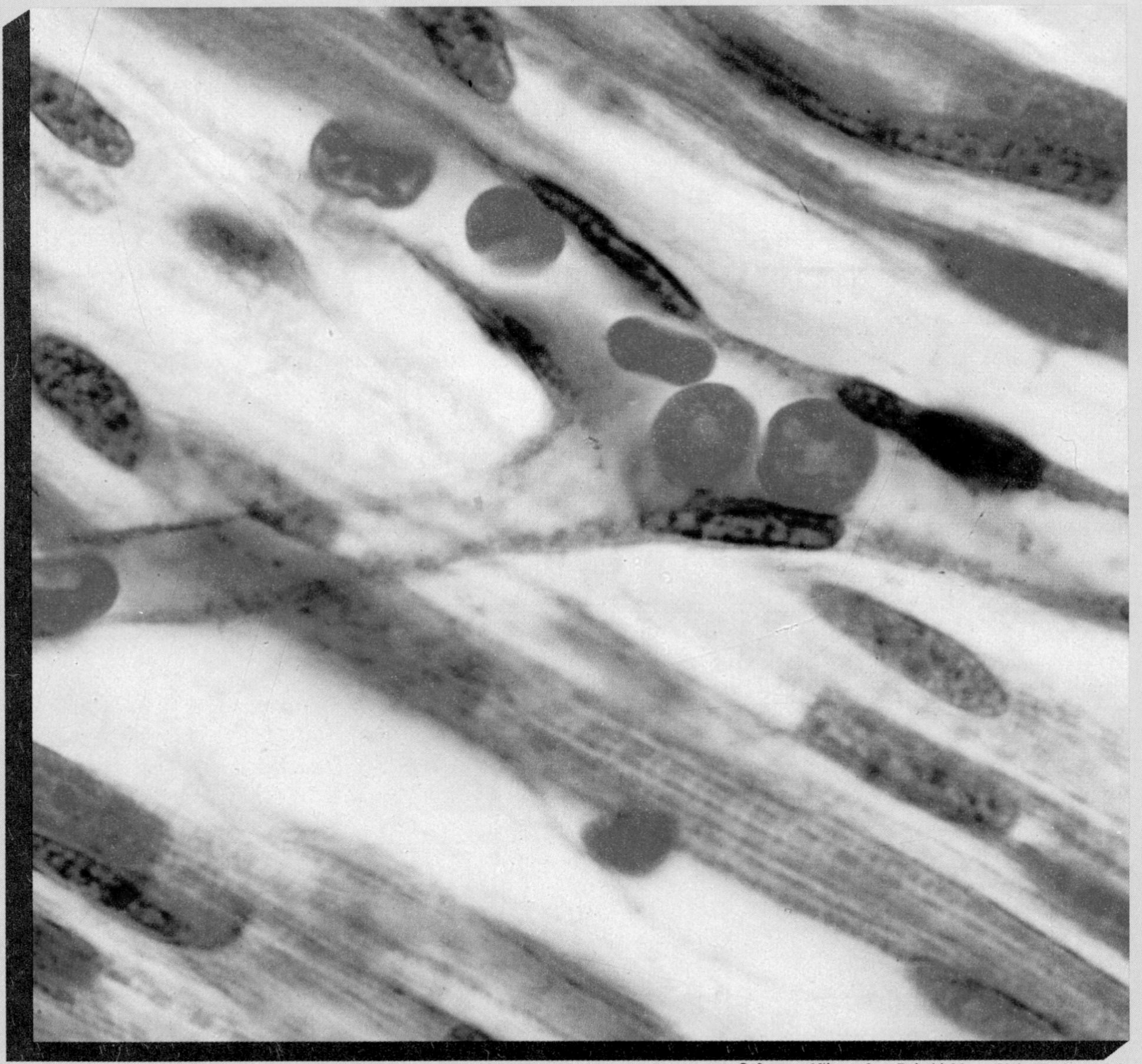

# Circulatory Systems

# chapter 3

## 3:1 Blood

GOAL: You will learn the main features of blood, how it circulates, and some diseases of the circulatory system.

How much blood can a person lose and still be alive? About 1.5–2 L of a person's blood may be lost without resulting in death. However, the loss of 3 L will probably be fatal.

The body of an average adult has 5 to 6 L of blood. Blood serves many functions. It transports food and oxygen to the cells. It carries waste products and excess water to the kidneys, and carbon dioxide to the lungs. Blood also helps maintain body temperature, fights disease, and carries chemicals produced by the body.

List the functions of the blood.

Blood is a complex substance. It is more dense than water, having a density of 1.06 $g/cm^3$. Blood contains a fluid called plasma, red and white blood cells, and platelets (PLAYT luts). A platelet is a cell-like structure. In addition, dissolved gases, salts, blood proteins, food, and dissolved chemicals are found in blood. Blood is about 55 percent plasma. Plasma is about 90 percent water. In addition to water, plasma contains dissolved salts, digested food, and some of the body's waste products. Elements dissolved in plasma include calcium, sodium, magnesium, and potassium. Without calcium, your blood would not clot in a wound. Blood is about 44 percent red blood cells. About 1 percent of blood is white cells and platelets.

Name four elements present in blood.

Kessel/Shih, © 1976 Springer-Verlag

FIGURE 3–1. Red blood cells are flat in the middle. Mature red blood cells do not have nuclei.

## 3:2 Blood Cells

Describe red blood cells.

**Red blood cells** are the most numerous blood cells. There are from 4 600 000 to 6 200 000 red blood cells in 1 $mm^3$ of blood. The large number of red blood cells indicates that they are very small. Red blood cells are disc shaped (Figure 3–1). They are thinner in the middle than around the edges. This shape is related to the main function of the red blood cells. The main function is to carry gases to and from the body's cells. The red blood cell's shape provides a larger surface to carry gases.

What substance in the blood carries oxygen?

A red blood cell is about ⅓ hemoglobin (HEE muh gloh bun) by volume. **Hemoglobin** is a protein that contains iron. As oxygen dissolves in the blood, it reacts with the iron to form oxyhemoglobin. Oxyhemoglobin is bright red. The blood carries oxygen to the body cells where oxygen leaves the hemoglobin and moves into the cells. When oxygen leaves the hemoglobin, the color of the hemoglobin changes to dark red.

The number of air particles per cubic centimeter decreases at higher altitudes. Therefore, the amount of oxygen also is decreased and the body may not get enough oxygen. This lack of oxygen can cause rapid breathing, nausea, headache, and other unpleasant symptoms. People who live at higher altitudes do not suffer these symptoms. After a period of time their bodies adjust to the lowered levels of oxygen. Mountain climbers carry oxygen supplies with them to avoid the symptoms. Airplanes flying at high altitudes have pressurized cabins to keep the amount of oxygen at a comfortable level for breathing.

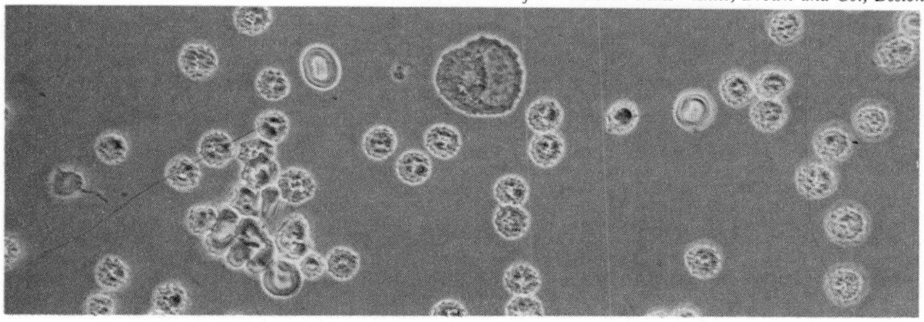

FIGURE 3–2. White blood cells have nuclei.

Red blood cells carry carbon dioxide, a waste, from body tissues to the lungs. Carbon dioxide attaches to the protein part of hemoglobin in the red cells. However, most of the carbon dioxide is carried to the lungs by the plasma. Carbon dioxide leaves your body when you exhale.

Red blood cells are formed in the bone marrow. Young red blood cells have a nucleus. Mature red blood cells do not have a nucleus. The space normally occupied by a nucleus holds hemoglobin. Red blood cells have a life span of about 120 days. Dead red blood cells are removed from the blood by the liver and spleen. Doctors estimate that $\frac{1}{5}$ of the mature red blood cells in the body are replaced daily.

**White blood cells** are produced in bone marrow and in the spleen. There are from 5 000 to 10 000 white blood cells in 1 $mm^3$ of blood. White cells live from a few hours to several days. Each white blood cell has a nucleus. Some white blood cells fight disease. Pus in an infected wound is composed largely of decomposed white blood cells. Other white

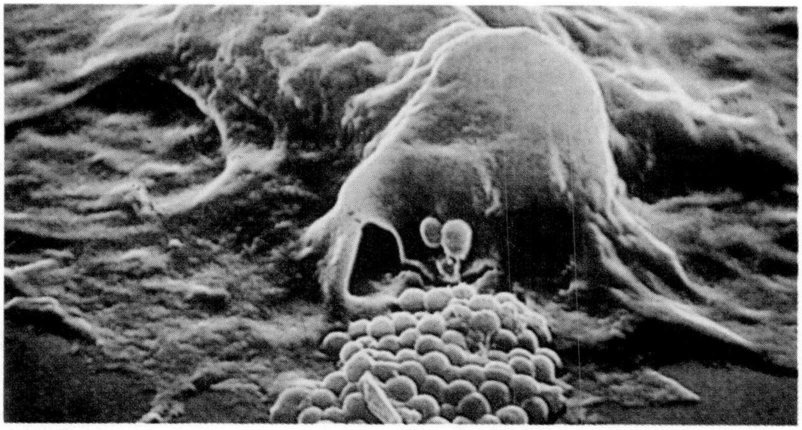



FIGURE 3–3. In the body, white blood cells attack and destroy bacteria (the green cells).

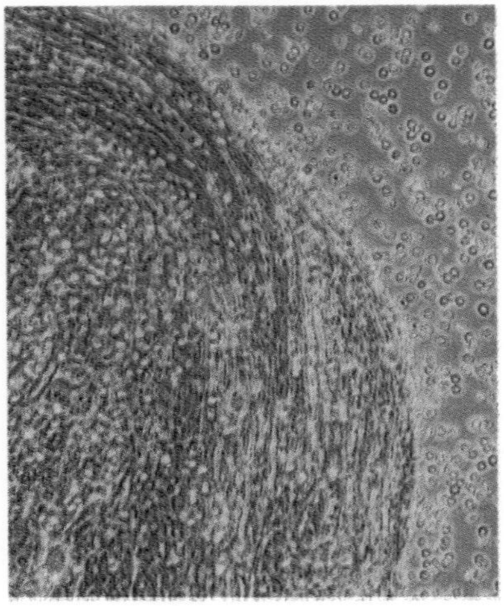

FIGURE 3–4. Long fibers of a protein form a network in a wound that prevents blood from escaping.

State the function of antibodies.

How is a blood clot formed?

blood cells produce substances called antibodies. These antibodies fight disease germs by dissolving them and neutralizing their poisons. Measuring the number of white cells in a person's blood is one test used to detect disease.

**Platelets** are small cell-like structures that live only a few days. They are about ¼ the size of a red blood cell. Like red blood cells, platelets are produced in the bone marrow. Platelets produce blood clots when there is bleeding. Bleeding occurs when the skin or a blood vessel is punctured, letting blood escape. You know that a clot forms in a wound, and the bleeding stops. It is vital that blood forms a clot, or a very small wound could cause death.

Platelets release chemicals that start a series of chemical reactions in the blood to form a clot. Calcium and other blood parts are needed for these reactions to occur. When bleeding occurs, a protein called fibrinogen (fi BRIHN uh jun) is produced. Fibrinogen fibers form a net that traps blood cells and other platelets forming a blood clot (Figure 3–4). A blood clot prevents further blood loss and dries to form a scab. A black and blue mark results from a blood clot that forms under the skin.

Scientists have discovered several chemical compounds that prevent blood clotting. These chemicals have practical uses. Added to blood stored in blood banks, they prevent clotting. They are prescribed for people who have had heart attacks to prevent blood clots from forming inside the heart. A chemical that prevents blood clotting is used in some rat poisons.

FIGURE 3–5.

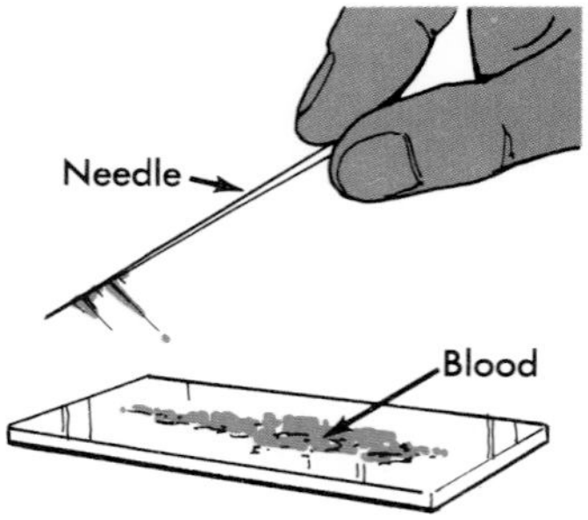


## activity BLOOD CLOTTING

Place a drop of blood on a microscope slide. Draw a needle through the blood every half minute. When solid material begins to cling to the needle, clotting has begun. How long does it take for clotting to begin?

## making sure

1. How long do red blood cells live?
2. How is oxygen carried to cells by red blood cells?
3. How may white blood cells fight a disease?
4. How do platelets help form blood clots when you cut your finger?
5. What does fibrinogen do?

## 3:3 Blood Vessels

Arteries, veins, and capillaries are the main kinds of blood vessels. **Arteries** carry blood away from the heart. **Veins** carry blood to the heart. **Capillaries** connect arteries to veins. An artery has a thicker wall and smaller pathway than a vein. The walls of veins are thin and contain less muscle tissue than those of arteries.

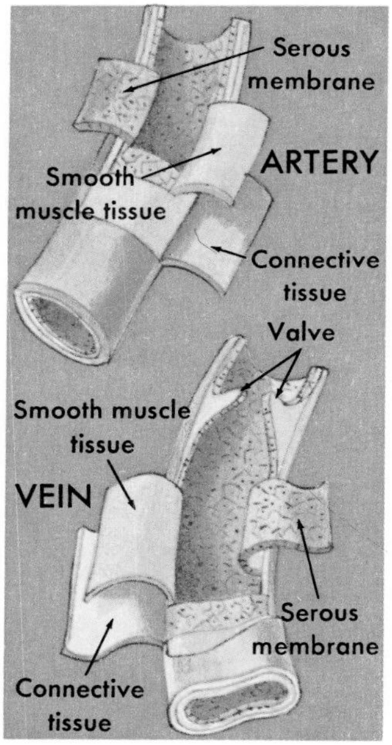


FIGURE 3–6. Arteries have more muscle tissue than veins.

Each beat of the heart causes a surge of blood in the arteries. Arteries are elastic. When the blood is forced into the arteries, they expand. The artery in your wrist expands as it fills with blood. You can feel the movement in your wrist as the artery contracts and expands. This movement of the artery wall is called a pulse. Your heartbeat rate and your pulse rate are the same.

The expansion and contraction of large arteries in your body help to move the blood. When arteries contract, they exert a pumping force. In effect, they pump the blood along.

How is an artery different from a vein?

How do arteries regulate the flow of blood in capillaries?

Veins have cuplike valves that keep the blood flowing toward the heart. All veins except those from the lungs carry dark-red blood that is low in oxygen. Your veins do not appear dark red, they appear blue. This is because the vein wall and your skin color change the vein's appearance. Where on your body can you locate veins?

Capillaries are tiny blood vessels invisible to the unaided eye. They are the smallest and most numerous blood vessels in the body. Red blood cells pass through the smallest capillaries in single file.

Several exchanges occur between capillaries and the tissues through which they pass. Food and oxygen diffuse from the blood in the capillaries to the tissues. White cells leave the bloodstream through the capillary walls and enter the tissues. Wastes from the tissues enter the capillaries and are removed by the blood.

How does the face of a person doing hard exercises change? The person's skin turns red because of the presence of more blood than usual. The redness shows that a large amount of blood is being supplied to capillaries in the skin. The flow of blood through the capillaries is controlled by tiny muscles. These muscles are in the walls of the arteries that lead to the capillaries.

When the weather is hot, the amount of blood flowing through the capillaries of your skin increases. As a result the capillaries give off heat from your body. When the air temperature is low, the rate of blood flow to the capillaries of the skin is reduced. In this way, body heat is conserved.

## making sure

6. Explain what happens when a person blushes.
7. When you engage in sports and other exercises, the flow of blood to the digestive system decreases. Why is it unwise to engage in strenuous exercise right after a meal?

*Bill King* *J. Baker/Alpha*

FIGURE 3–7. During hard exercise, such as running or bicycling, a large amount of blood is supplied to the skin.

# 3:4 The Heart

The human heart is a muscular organ about the size of a large fist. It is located in the center of the chest. In the heart are four chambers. The two upper chambers are called the left atrium and the right atrium. The two lower chambers are the left and right ventricles (Figure 3–8). A wall separates the chambers on the left side from the chambers on the right side of the heart. Right and left refer to the body's right and left sides. On each side of the heart, a valve separates the atrium from the ventricle below it.

Name the four chambers of the human heart.

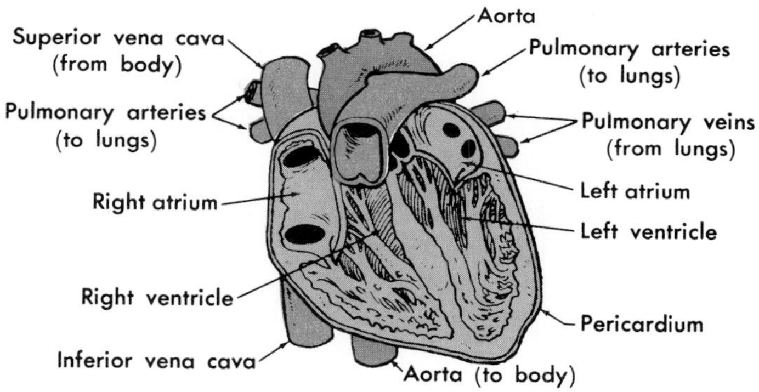


FIGURE 3-8. The human heart has four chambers that receive and pump blood to all parts of the body.

The tip of the heart points toward the left side of the body. In the tip, the heartbeat is strongest. This is why you feel the heart's presence in the left side of your chest.

For you to remain alive, your heart must pump constantly. Pumping is produced by alternate contraction and relaxation of the atria and ventricles. The pumping moves blood throughout the body.

A human heart contracts more than three billion times during a normal lifetime. The heartbeat of a human at rest is usually between 60 and 80 beats per minute. Age, sex, and physical condition affect the heartbeat rate. Infants have a heartbeat rate of about 130 beats per minute. The rates of women are usually slightly higher than those of men. The rate of a person in good physical condition is often lower than the average rate.

With each beat of the heart, 80 to 100 mL of blood are pumped. In one minute about 8 L of blood are moved in the body. The work done by the heart each day is about equal to lifting a 69-kg mass 30 m off the ground.

Contraction of the heart causes pressure in the arteries. This blood pressure is the force of the blood against the walls of the arteries. During contraction, normal blood pressure ranges from about 100 to 140 mm of mercury. Millimeters of mercury are the units used to measure blood pressure. During relaxation, the pressure is 70 to 90 mm of mercury. Blood pressure is given as two numbers, the contraction pressure over the relaxation pressure. For example, 110/80 indicates a contraction pressure of 110 mm and a relaxation pressure of 80 mm. Blood pressure is one indicator of a person's health (Figure 3–9). Both high and low blood pressure can be harmful.

Explain the meaning of a blood pressure reading of 110/80.

## activity HEARTBEAT RATE: THE PULSE RATE

**(1)** Place the tips of your index and middle fingers gently on one side of your neck. Place the fingers below the jawbone and halfway between the main neck muscles and the windpipe. Locate a throbbing inside your neck. **(2)** Count the number of throbs you feel in 10 seconds. Record this number. **(3)** Multiply the number by 6 and record it. This is your pulse rate—the number of throbs or beats in one minute. **(4)** Repeat Steps 1–3 two more times. **(5)** Determine your average pulse rate by adding the three pulse rates and dividing the sum by 3. **(6)** Record the average pulse rate for each member of your class. What is the highest rate in your class? The lowest rate? What is the average pulse rate for your class? How do you think your pulse rate would be affected by exercise? Devise an activity to test your hypothesis.

American Red Cross

American Red Cross

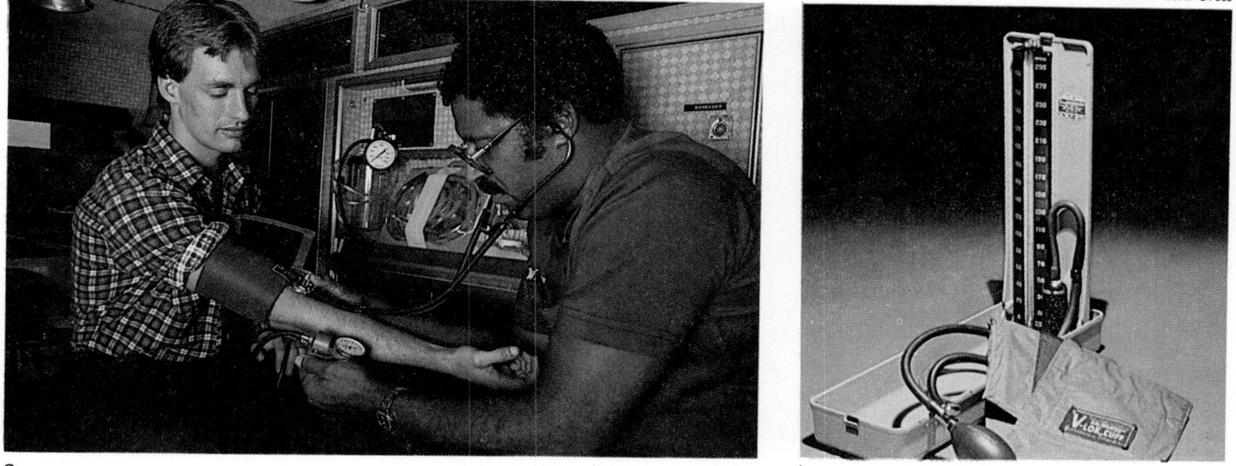

a

b

FIGURE 3–9. Blood pressure in a person's arteries (a) is measured with a blood pressure gauge (b).

## 3:5 Pulmonary and Coronary Circulation

Several pathways make up the circulatory system through which blood travels to all parts of the body. The pathway of blood from the heart to the lungs and back to the heart is called **pulmonary circulation.** In pulmonary circulation, oxygen is added to the blood. Carbon dioxide and water vapor are removed. When the right ventricle contracts, blood is forced from the heart into the pulmonary

Describe pulmonary circulation.

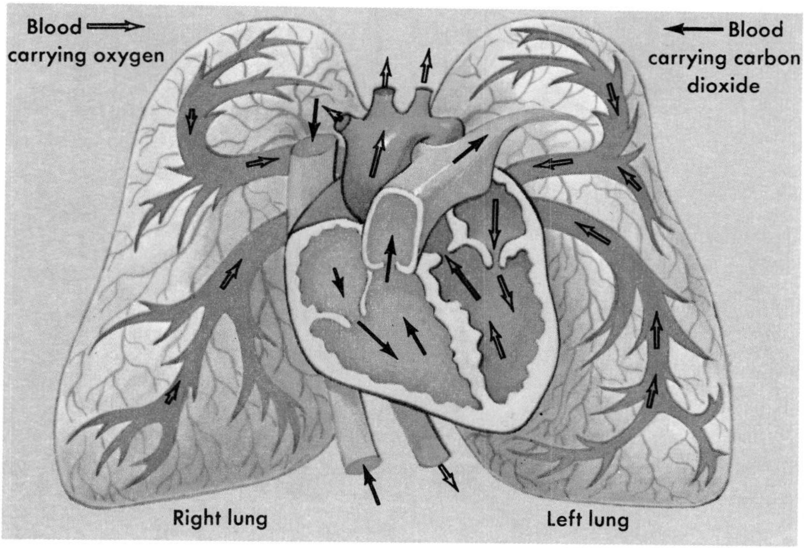


FIGURE 3–10. In pulmonary circulation, blood low in oxygen is pumped to the lungs. Oxygen-rich blood is returned to the heart.

artery. Blood travels through the pulmonary artery to the lungs. Oxygen diffuses into the blood as it flows through the capillaries of the lungs. The oxygen-rich blood then travels from the lungs through the pulmonary vein to the left atrium of the heart.

Blood is pumped from the left atrium into the left ventricle. Oxygen-rich blood is pumped out of the left ventricle into the aorta (ay ORT uh). The **aorta** is the largest artery in the body. It connects to smaller arteries that connect to capillaries.

As the left ventricle contracts, it exerts more force than any other heart chamber. When you listen to a heartbeat with a stethoscope, you hear two sounds. The "lub" sound is produced by the contraction of the ventricles and the closing of the heart valves. The "dub" sound is produced when the ventricles relax. This sound is produced by the closing of the valves at the entrance to the aorta.

Describe coronary circulation.

Every cell in the heart needs food and oxygen. This food and oxygen is brought to the heart cells by the blood. Movement of the blood through the tissues of the heart is called **coronary circulation.** Two main coronary arteries leave the aorta and curve downward on each side of the heart. From these arteries, smaller arteries branch off and enter the heart muscle. These arteries lead to the

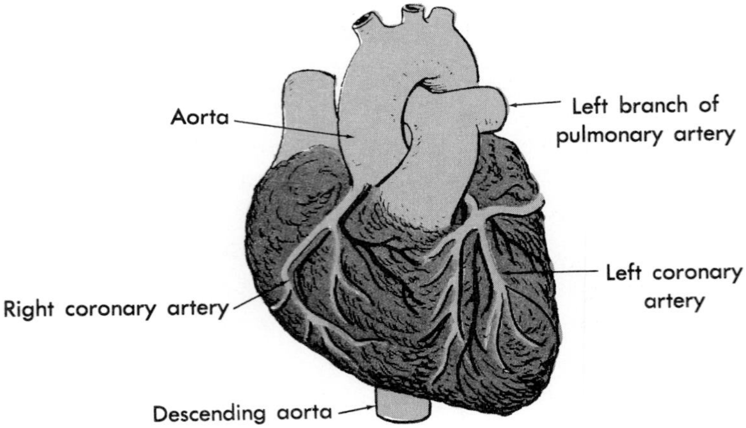


FIGURE 3–11. Coronary circulation furnishes heart cells with food and oxygen and removes wastes.

capillaries that carry the blood into the tissues of the heart. Coronary capillaries join to form coronary veins. The veins empty the blood into the right atrium of the heart.

Coronary circulation is short but vital. The constant pumping of the heart depends on a constant, swift flow of blood through this organ. If the tissues of the heart do not receive food and oxygen they may be damaged.

**activity** THE HEARTBEAT

Listen to a person's heartbeat with a stethoscope. What sounds do you hear repeated over and over again in perfect rhythm? Listen to the heartbeats of several people of different ages. How are the sounds similar and different?

**making sure**

8. What is the function of pulmonary circulation?
9. Which chambers of the heart contain blood rich in oxygen?
10. What is the function of coronary circulation?
11. What causes the "lub" sound of the heart? What causes the "dub" sound?

## 3:6 Systemic Circulation

A major pathway through which blood flows each time the heart pumps is called the systemic circulation. **Systemic circulation** supplies body tissues with digested food and oxygen. It also removes wastes from body tissues.

In systemic circulation, blood is pumped from the left ventricle into the aorta. The aorta carries blood from the heart to the organs and tissues. Materials diffuse back and forth between the capillaries and the cells in the tissues. Blood returns from the body tissues through the veins and enters the right atrium of the heart.

FIGURE 3–12. Systemic circulation furnishes each body cell with food and oxygen and removes wastes.

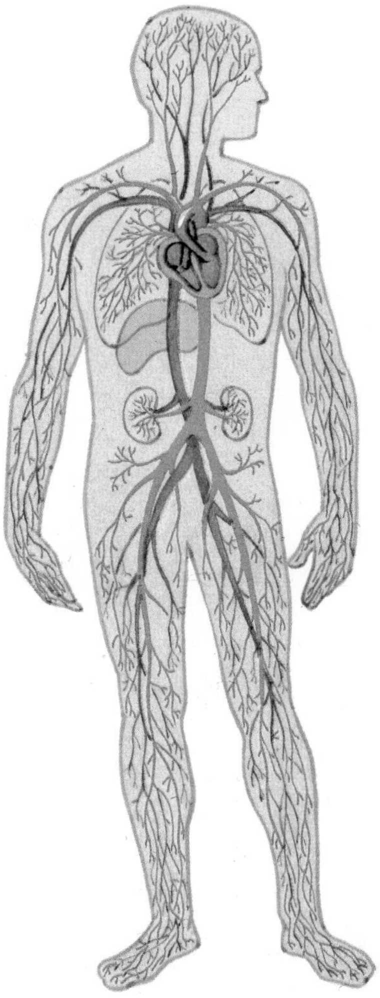

FIGURE 3–13. Wastes are removed as blood circulates through the kidneys.

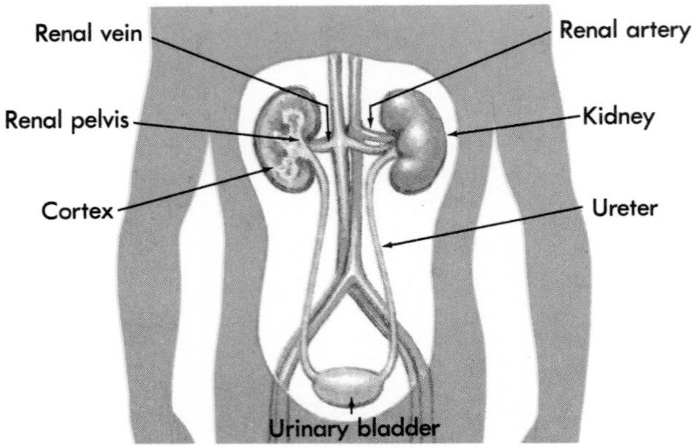


Renal (REEN ul) circulation is part of systemic circulation. Renal circulation includes the blood vessels that pass through the kidneys. Kidneys are organs that remove wastes and excess water from blood. A separate artery connects to each kidney. From these arteries, blood travels through the kidneys in capillaries. These capillaries join to form veins that return the blood to the heart.

What is the function of the kidneys?

Portal circulation is also part of systemic circulation. Food enters the blood in portal circulation. Blood carries food away from the small intestine, an organ that digests food. Small veins join to form a single, large portal vein. The portal vein passes through the liver. Part of the food sugar may be removed from the blood and stored in the liver as a starch. This is available if the body has a sudden need for energy.

What is the function of portal circulation?

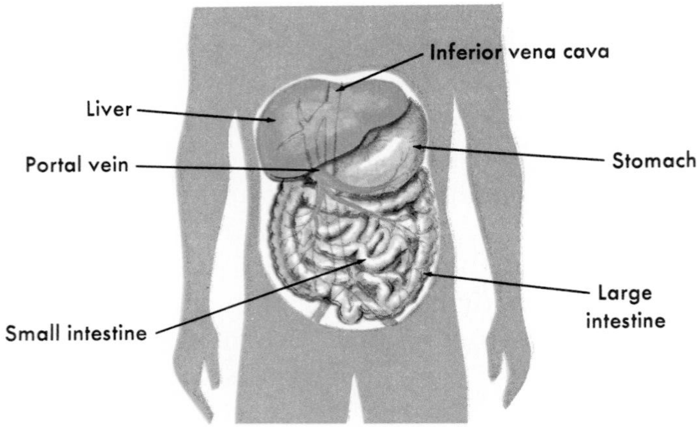


FIGURE 3–14. Nutrients enter the blood in portal circulation.

### making sure

12. Name two parts of systemic circulation.
13. Where are wastes removed from the blood?
14. Where does oxygen enter the blood?
15. Where does food enter the blood?

## 3:7 Blood Types

Not all human blood is exactly alike. Each person has a particular combination of materials in his or her blood. These substances can react with each other when blood from two different people is mixed. If the wrong blood is given to a person, clumping of cells and death may occur. Safe transfusions of blood depend upon the careful matching of the blood of the people involved.

There are many substances in blood, but only a few cause serious problems during transfusions. They are called A, B, and O. A person whose blood has only substance A has type A blood. A person with only substance B has type B blood; one with both A and B has type AB blood; and one with neither A nor B has type O blood. All humans have one of these four blood types.

Name the four major blood types.

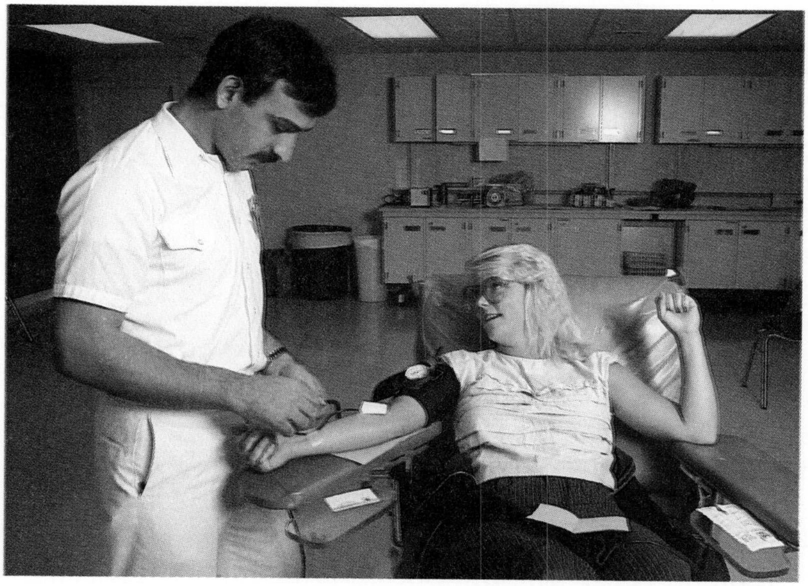

Image Workshop

FIGURE 3–15. A person may donate 450 mL of blood every two months.

A person who has type A blood also carries an anti-B substance in the blood. Since the B and anti-B substances react, a person with type A blood cannot receive a transfusion of type B blood. Table 3–1 shows the blood types and the permitted transfusions for each blood type.

*Table 3–1.*
Blood Types and Safe Transfusions

| Blood type | Blood substances | Best transfusion | Emergency transfusion |
|---|---|---|---|
| A | A, anti-B | A | O |
| B | B, anti-A | B | O |
| AB | A, B | AB | A, B, O |
| O | Anti-A, anti-B | O | None |

The substances in a person's blood are present at birth and cannot be changed by a normal transfusion. Most Americans have type O or type A blood. Type B and type AB occur in less than 15 percent of the people. The actual percentages of people with each blood type vary among racial groups.

FIGURE 3–16. Blood transfusions save many lives.

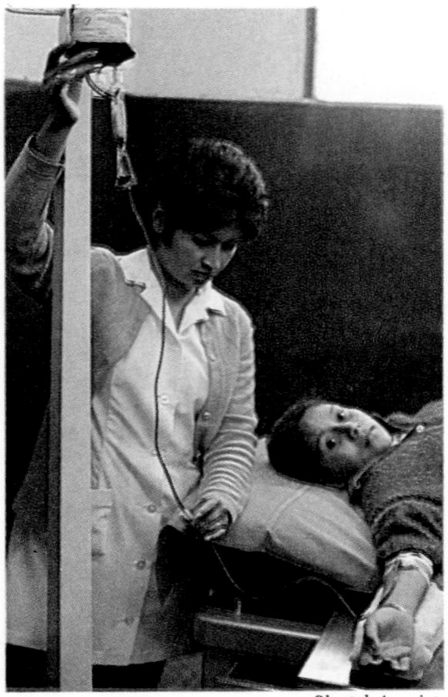

Shostal Associates

## 3:8 Rh Factor

About 85 percent of the people of the United States have a substance called the Rh factor in their red blood cells. Their blood is called Rh positive (Rh+). The other 15 percent do not have this substance. Their blood is Rh negative (Rh−).

The Rh factor may have a harmful effect on a newborn child. About one out of every 400 babies in the United States is born to a mother with Rh− blood and a father with Rh+ blood. The baby may have Rh+ blood, inheriting the Rh+ from its father. Rh+ blood cells from the baby's body may enter the Rh− mother's bloodstream. Her blood will then begin to produce antibodies to destroy these Rh+ red blood cells. The antibodies attack the Rh+ cells that enter the body as if they were harmful to the mother's body. If the Rh+ antibodies enter the baby's bloodstream, they will destroy the baby's Rh+ red blood cells. If too many red blood cells are destroyed, the unborn baby could die. An Rh− mother can now receive an injection after the birth of each baby. This injection prevents the buildup of antibodies that could endanger her future children.

What is the Rh factor? How does it affect childbirth?

However, if a baby has a severe blood problem at birth, its life may be saved by a blood transfusion right after birth. In making the transfusion, most of the baby's blood is withdrawn and replaced with blood having the same Rh factor. Blood transfusions may also be given to an unborn baby.

## 3:9 Diseases of the Circulatory System

Diseases affecting the circulatory system can be divided into two main groups. One group includes those diseases that affect the heart and blood vessels. The second group includes diseases of the blood.

Diseases affecting the heart and blood vessels can be inherited, caused by infection, or can result from

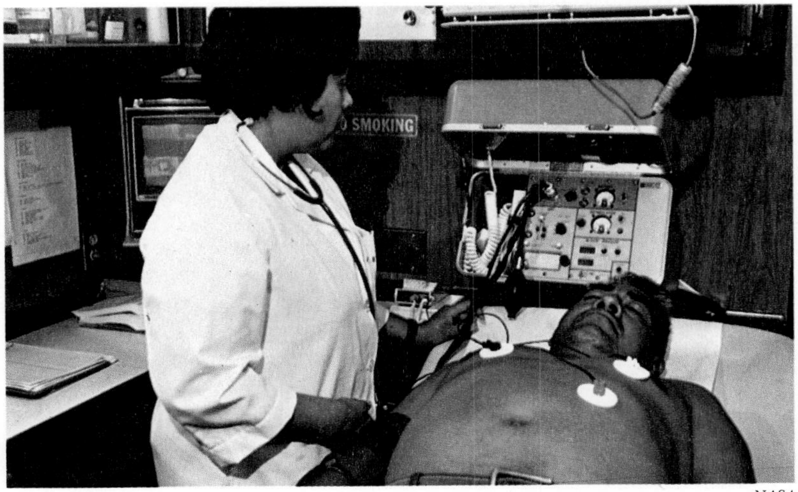

NASA

FIGURE 3–17. A doctor will study the recording from an electrocardiograph to find out if the patient's heart is working properly.

living habits. Recent figures from the American Heart Association show that nearly one million deaths a year are caused by heart diseases. Some of the major heart diseases are high blood pressure, heart attack, stroke, arteriosclerosis (ar tihr ee oh skluh ROH sus), and rheumatic fever.

What two conditions can high blood pressure cause?

High blood pressure is a leading cause of death in the United States. One in every four adults has some elevation of blood pressure. Some studies have found high blood pressure in children as young as four years old. High blood pressure can result in strokes or heart attacks. A stroke is caused by a blood clot in the brain that blocks an artery or by a ruptured vessel in the brain. The affected area of the brain does not receive oxygen. Blood clots in an artery of the heart are the cause of many heart attacks. High blood pressure can be detected by a simple blood pressure test. Effective treatment is available once the disease is found.

What is arteriosclerosis?

Arteriosclerosis is a slowly progressive disease that may contribute to a stroke or heart attack. This disease may begin early in life. As it progresses, the linings of the arteries become thick and rough with deposits of fat and calcium. These deposits cause the arteries to lose their ability to contract and expand, making it easier for a clot to block the artery. Scientists are studying the effects of diet and exercise on arteriosclerosis.

Rheumatic fever most often strikes children between the ages of five and fifteen. It is preceded

a

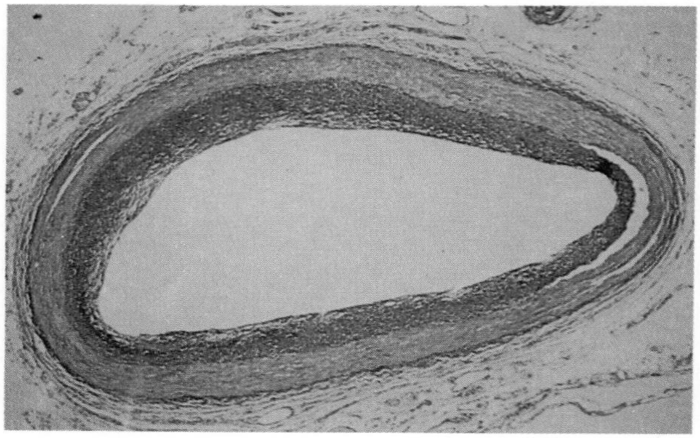

b

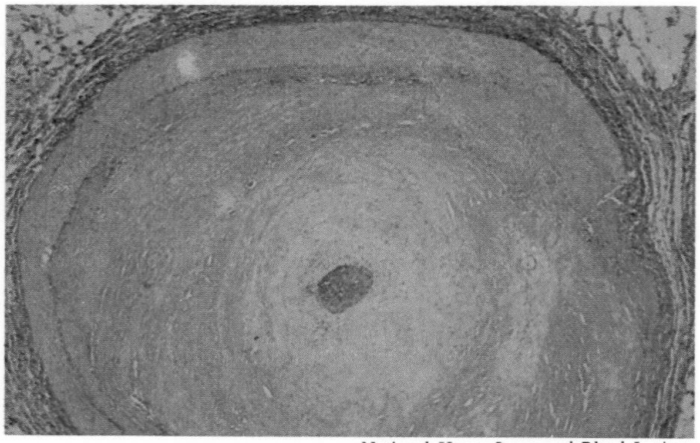

National Heart, Lung and Blood Institute

FIGURE 3-18. An artery is usually open (a). Fat deposits can block the flow of blood in an artery (b).

by an infection caused by bacteria. Rheumatic fever is inflammation of the joints and heart valves. The heart valves can become scarred and deformed.

How can heart valves be affected by rheumatic fever?

Diseases of the blood include anemia, sickle-cell anemia, and leukemia. Anemia is a disease in which the oxygen supply to the tissues is decreased. It is caused by a deficiency in red blood cells, in hemoglobin, or in total blood volume.

What is anemia? What causes anemia?

There are several different kinds of anemia. Thus, treatments for the disease vary. Blood transfusions, iron supplements, vitamin $B_{12}$, and other drugs are used to treat the various kinds of anemia. In sickle-cell anemia, the hemoglobin is abnormal. The red blood cells become sickle-shaped (Figure 3–19). Sickle-cell anemia results in a lack of oxygen to body tissues. Symptoms of the disease include pain, fever, and damaged tissue. Sickle-cell anemia occurs mostly in black people.

What is sickle-cell anemia?

*Harrington Pix/Peter Arnold, Inc.*

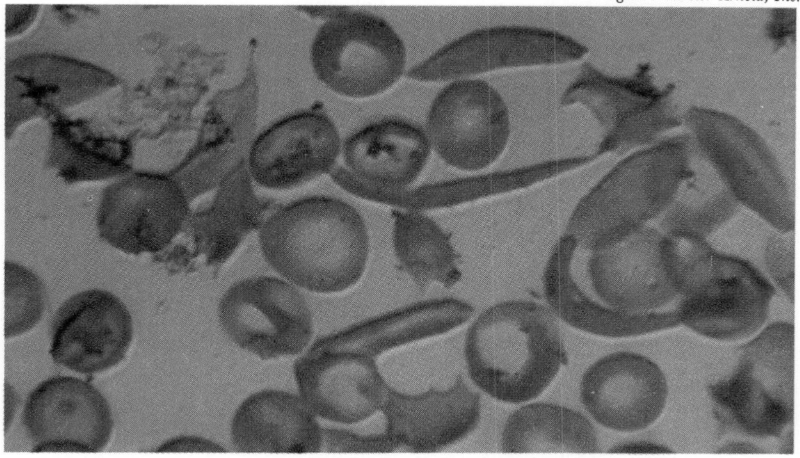

FIGURE 3–19. Sickled red blood cells cannot carry enough oxygen to body cells.

In leukemia, the bone marrow or lymph glands produce white cells in large numbers. Overproduction of white cells results in an underproduction of red cells. The lack of red cells produces anemia. Transfusions are not a cure for leukemia because white blood cells are still produced in large numbers. Scientists have found treatments that can control some types of leukemia. Because of these treatments, many people with leukemia live normal lives.

What is leukemia?

## 3:10 Lymphatic System

What is lymph and what is its function?

As blood passes through the capillaries, some of the liquid part leaves the capillaries and enters the tissues. This colorless liquid is called lymph. **Lymph** carries food into the cells and carries wastes out of the cells. Lymph moves through the tissues and around the cells.

Some of the lymph reenters the capillaries. The rest of the lymph is collected in a network of tiny tubes. This network is called the lymphatic system (Figure 3–20). Lymph is returned to the blood from the lymphatic system through a large tube called the thoracic duct. The thoracic duct empties lymph into a large vein in the left shoulder.

Where are most lymph nodes located?

Lymph vessels pass through clumps of tissue called lymph nodes. Most lymph nodes are located in the neck, armpit, elbow, or groin. The tonsils and adenoids are lymph nodes. Lymph nodes produce white blood cells and clean the lymph.

Lymph vessels are important parts of the body's defense system. Lymph carries bacteria and harmful foreign matter to the lymph nodes. Here the infectious material is destroyed by white blood cells. An infection may cause the lymph nodes to swell. Swelling is produced by the increased production of white blood cells needed to fight the infection.

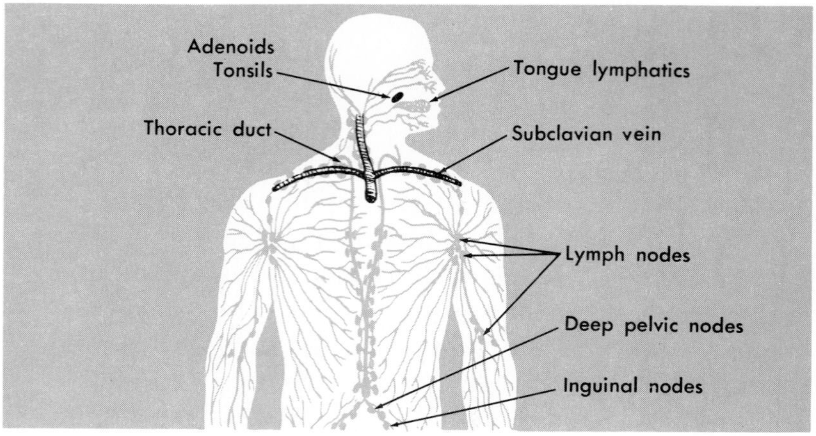


FIGURE 3–20. The lymphatic system transports lymph from tissues to a large vein in the shoulder.

## main ideas

1. Blood carries food, wastes, gases, and other materials. 3:1
2. Red blood cells carry oxygen to all body cells. White blood cells fight infections. Platelets are involved in blood clotting. 3:2
3. Blood travels away from the heart in arteries and returns to the heart in veins. 3:3
4. Materials are exchanged between tissues and the blood in the capillaries. 3:3
5. The heart is a muscular organ that pumps blood through the body. 3:4
6. The three pathways of blood circulation are the pulmonary, coronary, and systemic. 3:5; 3:6
7. All humans have either A, B, AB, or O type blood. 3:7
8. Most people have the Rh factor in their red blood cells. 3:8
9. High blood pressure, anemia, arteriosclerosis, sickle cell anemia, and leukemia are diseases of the circulatory system. 3:9
10. Lymph is the fluid from the blood that carries food to cells and wastes away from cells. The lymphatic system is made up of lymph nodes and a network of tubes that carries lymph. 3:10

## vocabulary

*Define each of the following words or terms.*

aorta
arteries
capillaries
coronary circulation
hemoglobin
lymph
platelets
pulmonary circulation
red blood cells
systemic circulation
veins
white blood cells

## study questions

**DO NOT WRITE IN THIS BOOK.**

**A. True or False**

*Determine whether each of the following sentences is true or false. If the sentence is false, rewrite it to make it true.*

1. The heart is made of muscle tissue.

2. Blood is pumped directly from the ventricles to the atria.
3. The aorta is the largest artery in the body.
4. Pulmonary vein carries blood from the heart to the lungs.
5. A blood clot in a coronary artery can cause a heart attack.
6. Platelets are involved in the formation of a blood clot.
7. Arteries carry blood away from the heart.
8. Your heartbeat rate and your pulse rate are the same.
9. Coronary circulation supplies heart tissue with food and oxygen.
10. Every person has the same blood type.

**B. Multiple Choice**

*Choose the word or phrase that completes correctly each of the following sentences.*

1. (*Arteries, Veins, Capillaries*) are the smallest blood vessels.
2. Blood returns to the heart in the (*veins, arteries, lymph vessels*).
3. When you are overheated, the blood supply to your skin (*increases, decreases, remains the same*).
4. Excess water is removed from the blood by the (*heart, kidneys, liver, pancreas*).
5. The (*aorta, pulmonary vein, renal vein*) contains blood low in wastes.
6. The (*aorta, pulmonary vein, portal vein*) carries blood rich in digested food.
7. Blood from the lungs first enters the (*left atrium, right atrium, left ventricle, right ventricle*) of the heart.
8. The density of blood is (*greater than, less than, the same as*) water.
9. A stroke is caused by a blood clot in an artery in the (*heart, brain, lungs*).
10. Rheumatic fever is preceded by an infection caused by a (*virus, bacterium, lack of sleep*).

**C. Completion**

*Complete each of the following sentences with a word or phrase that will make the sentence correct.*

1. Red blood cells are produced in the ______ of bones.
2. Oxygen is carried by ______ in red blood cells.
3. The ______ returns lymph to the blood system.

4. ______ are examples of lymph nodes.
5. ______ is a blood protein involved in the formation of a blood clot.
6. The ______ remove wastes from the blood.
7. A person with type A blood can receive type ______ and type ______ blood in a transfusion.
8. Anti-A serum will cause red blood cell clumping when added to type ______ blood.
9. About 85 percent of the people in the United States have Rh ______ blood.
10. ______ is a blood disorder in which too many white cells are produced.

**D. How and Why**

1. What are the main parts of the human circulatory system?
2. How are wastes removed from the blood?
3. How does blood fight infection?
4. What is lymph? How does it aid the circulation of materials in the body?
5. Name the materials that form a blood clot and describe the chemical changes by which the clot is produced.

## challenges

1. Send for literature from the American Heart Association to learn more about diseases of the circulatory system. Use the literature to make a bulletin board with information on taking care of your heart.
2. Write to the American Cancer Society for information about the harmful effects of smoking.
3. Obtain information on advances in treating heart attack victims. Prepare a report on such procedures and devices as pacemakers, artery bypass surgery, and valve replacements.

## interesting reading

The American Heart Association, *Heart Book.* New York: E. P. Dutton, 1980.

James, Daniel E., *What About Blood Pressure?* Burlington, NC: Carolina Biological Supply Co., 1981.

*Activities are constantly occurring inside your body. When you sit, eat, exercise, even sleep, internal processes are occurring. These activities keep you alive and growing. What are some of these activities? What body processes are occurring in the racers? What must be done to keep these activities occurring?*

J. Webber/Tom Stack & Associates

# Internal Body Processes

# chapter 4

## 4:1 Metabolism

GOAL: You will learn how body processes keep a person alive and healthy.

The sum of all the activities inside your body that keep you alive is called **metabolism.** Metabolism includes respiration, digestion, building and repairing tissues, and excretion of wastes. The speed at which metabolism occurs in the body is called the metabolic rate.

Define metabolism.

The metabolic rate is lowest when physical activity is at a minimum. When you are sleeping or resting, the metabolic rate is low. This lowest rate is called the basal (BAY sul) metabolic rate. The basal metabolic rate is determined by measuring the amount of oxygen the body consumes during a certain period of time. Oxygen is consumed as the body produces energy from food. As a person becomes more active, the amount of energy needed increases. The person's metabolic rate increases to produce the energy. Since oxygen is used to produce energy, the amount used also increases. Thus, oxygen use can be used to measure metabolic rates. A person's metabolic rate can be a clue to aid doctors in detecting certain diseases.

How is basal metabolism measured?

## 4:2 Respiration

How does respiration help keep an organism alive?

Respiration is part of metabolism. **Respiration** is the process through which cells receive oxygen, obtain energy, and release carbon dioxide. Blood carries oxygen to the cells and carbon dioxide away from the cells. Breathing is the method by which oxygen is brought into the lungs.

## 4:3 Respiratory System

How do your diaphragm and ribs make it possible for you to breathe?

Your respiratory system includes your lungs and the tubes by which air reaches your lungs (Figure 4–1). By moving your ribs and diaphragm you force air into and out of your lungs. The **diaphragm** (DI uh fram) is a sheet of muscle stretched across the bottom of the chest cavity. In its relaxed position, the diaphragm is dome-shaped and extends up into the chest cavity. As the diaphragm contracts, it flattens slightly and increases the size of the chest cavity. The size of the chest cavity is increased further by an upward-outward movement of the ribs.

Increasing the volume of the chest cavity causes decreasing air pressure in the lungs. The greater air pressure outside the body forces air into the lungs. Air moves from areas of high pressure to areas of

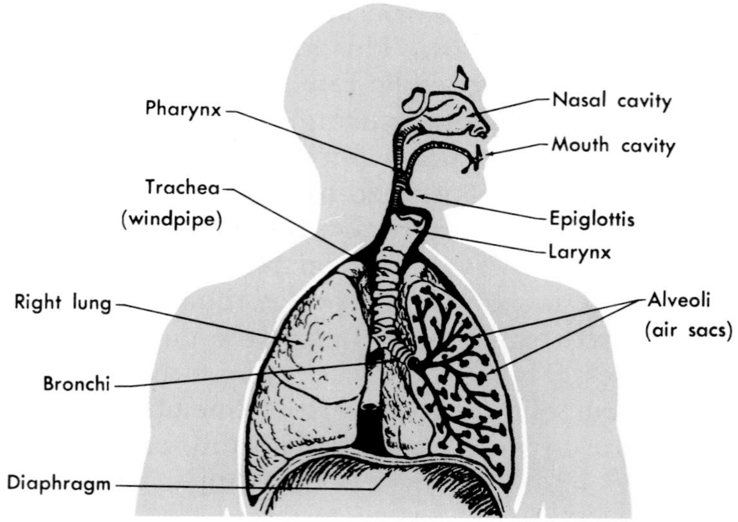


FIGURE 4–1. The human respiratory system includes the lungs and the tubes leading to the lungs.

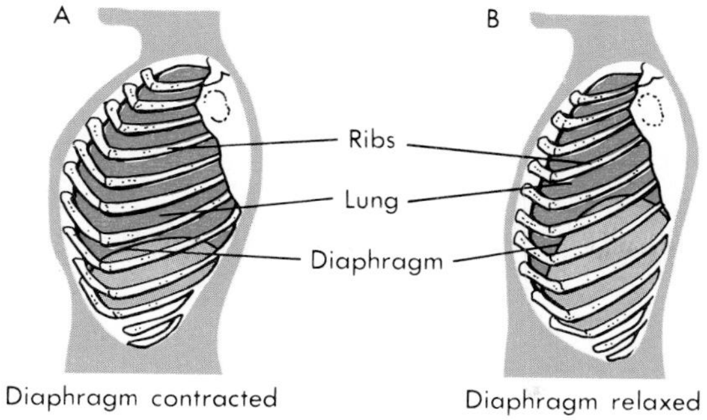


FIGURE 4–2. When you inhale, the diaphragm contracts and the ribs expand (a). When you exhale, the diaphragm and ribs relax (b).

low pressure. Taking air into the lungs is called inhaling (Figure 4–2a).

When you exhale, air is forced out of your body. Your diaphragm relaxes and your ribs move inward. Decreasing the volume of the chest cavity causes increasing air pressure in your lungs (Figure 4–2b).

Air enters the body through the nose. As air passes through the nose, it is warmed. Dust particles are removed by fine hairs. Also, tissues in the nose add moisture to the air. The air passes from the back of the nose and mouth into the **trachea** (TRAY kee uh). The trachea is a tube leading into the chest cavity. It divides to form the **bronchial** (BRAHN kee ul) **tubes** that go to the lungs.

Inside each lung, the bronchial tube divides into many smaller tubes. These tubes connect to tiny sacs called alveoli (al VEE uh li) (Figure 4–3). **Alveoli** are spongy, air-filled sacs lined with moist membranes. Through these membranes, carbon dioxide and oxygen are exchanged. The exchange occurs between air in the lungs and blood in the capillaries around the air sacs. Carbon dioxide leaves the blood and oxygen enters the blood.

A flap of cartilage called the **epiglottis** (ep uh GLAHT us) protects the upper end of the trachea. The epiglottis prevents food from entering the respiratory tract. However, it allows air to pass in and out. Have you ever choked on a piece of food? Choking is caused when food moves past the epiglottis into the trachea. When you choke, your immediate reaction is to cough. Coughing causes the food to be blown out of your trachea.

FIGURE 4–3. Oxygen is absorbed into the blood and carbon dioxide is released from the blood in the alveoli of the lungs.

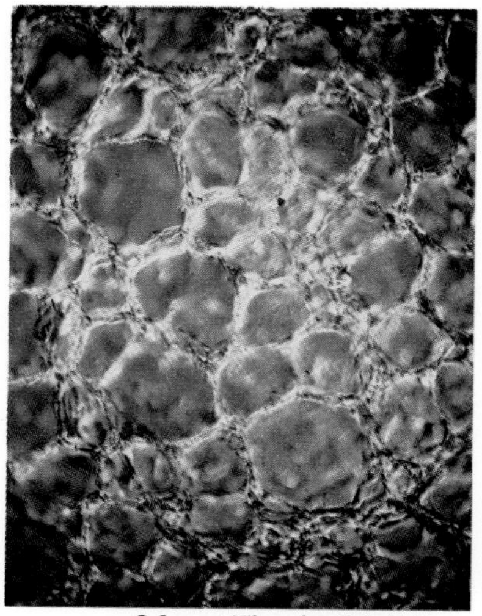



What gases are exchanged in the lungs?

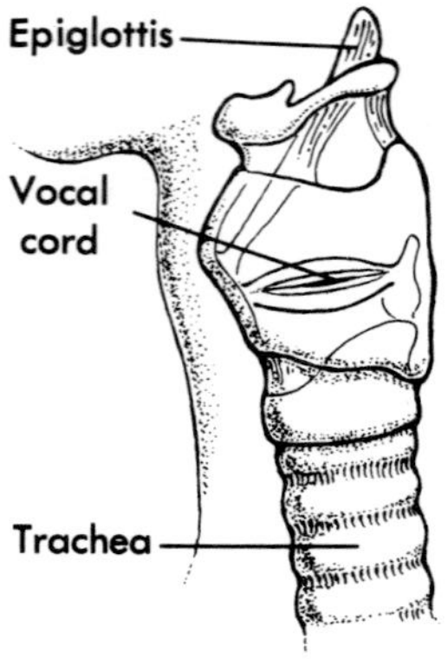


FIGURE 4–4. Vibrations of the vocal cords produce sounds. The sounds are modified and connected to form patterns called speech.

The enlarged upper end of the trachea is called the larynx (LER ingks), or Adam's apple. The larynx is a boxlike structure made of cartilage. The **larynx** contains flexible vocal cords (Figure 4–4). Air passes through these cords and causes them to vibrate. The vibrating air shaped by the mouth and tongue are the sounds of speech. Another name for the larynx is the voice box.

**activity** RATE OF BREATHING

**(1)** Sit quietly and count the number of breaths you take in 1 min. Use a watch with a second hand. **(2)** Repeat Step 1 two more times. **(3)** Calculate the average number of breaths you take per minute. Compare your rate of breathing with the rates of your classmates. **(4)** Run in place for 2 min. **(5)** Immediately determine your breathing rate as you did in Step 1. **(6)** Repeat Steps 4 and 5 two more times and calculate an average. How did your breathing rate change when you exercised? How would your breathing rate after swimming 10 min compare to the rate after walking 10 min? Explain your answer.

**making sure**

1. Name the tubes that connect the lungs to the trachea.
2. Explain how air is pumped into and out of the lungs.
3. What is the function of the epiglottis?
4. Where is the larynx located? How is it used to produce speech?
5. How are alveoli used in respiration?
6. What does coughing do?

## 4:4 Digestion

What is digestion?

**Digestion** is a chemical and physical process in which foods are changed to a form that can be taken into the cells. Digestion takes place largely through the action of enzymes. An **enzyme** is a substance that can speed a chemical reaction in the body. In the chemical reaction, the enzyme is not used up or changed in any way. Without enzymes, the chemical reactions in the body would occur very slowly. All living cells contain enzymes. Table 4–1 lists some enzymes found in the body.

***Table 4–1.***
Enzymes in the Digestive Tract

| **Enzyme** | **Digestive juice** | **Acts on** | **Changes them to** |
|---|---|---|---|
| Amylase | Pancreatic | Starches | Complex sugars |
| Lactase | Intestinal | Milk sugars | Glucose |
| Lipase | Pancreatic | Fats | Fatty acids |
| Pepsin | Gastric | Proteins | Simpler proteins |
| Ptyalin | Saliva | Starches | Complex sugars |
| Rennin | Gastric | Milk proteins | Simpler proteins |
| Trypsin | Pancreatic | Proteins | Simpler proteins |

Digestion also requires water. When a large food particle is digested, it is broken into smaller particles by water and enzymes. Simple sugars, amino acids, fatty acids, and glycerol are end products of digestion. Simple sugars come from the digestion of carbohydrates. Amino acids are formed in the digestion of proteins. Fatty acids and glycerol come from the breakdown of fats.

FIGURE 4–5. During digestion, large particles are split into small particles by enzymes and water.

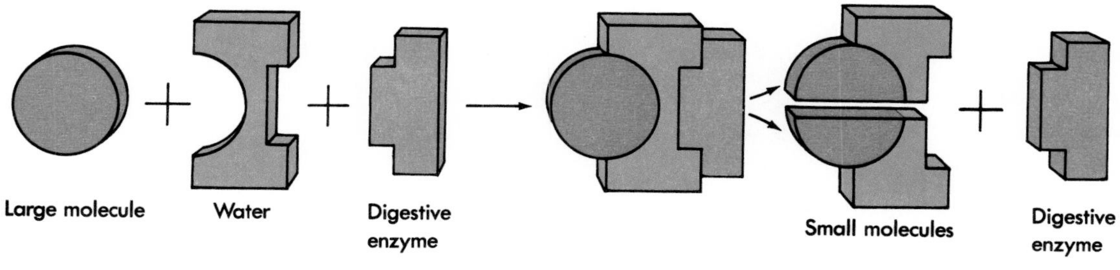

activity

# A PLANT ENZYME

**Objective:** To observe the effects of an enzyme

## Materials

barley seed–water mixture, 50 mL
burner
2 beakers, 100 mL
filter paper
funnel
graduate, 10 mL
iodine solution
marking pencil
spoon
starch solution
6 test tubes/stoppers
test tube clamp
test tube rack

## Procedure

### Part A

1. Filter a barley seed–water mixture by pouring it through a funnel lined with filter paper. Save the milky liquid. It contains the enzyme diastase. Dispose of the crushed seeds in a trash container.
2. Label 5 test tubes *A, B, C, D,* and *E.* Place them in the test tube rack.
3. Add 1 mL of the milky solution to each test tube. Save the rest of the milky solution for Part B.
4. Add 1 mL of starch solution to each test tube. Put a stopper in each tube and mix by inverting several times.
5. Add 3 drops of iodine solution to tube *A.* Mix by inverting. Record the color in your data table. If starch is present, the iodine will change color to blue-black.
6. Wait 5 min, then add 3 drops of iodine solution to tube *B.* Mix, observe, and record any color change.
7. Continue to add iodine to the remaining test tubes at 5 min intervals. Mix, observe, and record any color changes.
8. Empty and rinse the test tubes.

### Part B

1. Pour the remaining diastase liquid into a test tube. Boil the liquid gently for 2 min. **CAUTION:** do not overheat or the liquid will boil out of the test tube.
2. Relabel the five test tubes *F, G, H, I,* and *J.* Place them in the test tube rack.
3. Add 1 mL of the boiled liquid and 1 mL of starch solution to each test tube. Add stoppers and mix each test tube.
4. Repeat Steps 6–8 of Part A. Record any color changes.

## Observations and Data

| Test tube | Materials added | Results | Starch present | |
|---|---|---|---|---|
| | | | yes | no |
| *A* | | | | |
| | | | | |

## Questions and Conclusions

1. What happened when you added the iodine solution to test tube *A?*
2. Was starch present in tube *A?* How do you know?
3. Did all of the test tubes that contained starch have the same amount of starch? Explain.
4. What happened when you added the iodine solution to test tube *F*?
5. What is the function of the enzyme diastase?
6. How did boiling affect the action of diastase?

**making sure**

7. What is an enzyme?
8. Why are enzymes important in digestion?
9. What could happen if your body did not produce a particular enzyme?

## 4:5 The Digestive System

Name the organs of the digestive system.

The digestive system is composed of the digestive tract and the organs that aid digestion (Figure 4–6). The digestive tract contains the following organs: mouth, esophagus (ih SAHF uh gus), stomach, small intestine, and large intestine. Two other organs, the liver and pancreas, aid digestion although they are not part of the digestive tract.

Swallowing forces food from the mouth into the esophagus, a tube about 30 cm in length. The lower end of the esophagus is connected to the stomach. Food moves through the esophagus and the other parts of the digestive tract mostly by a series of rhythmic movements. Muscles of the digestive tract

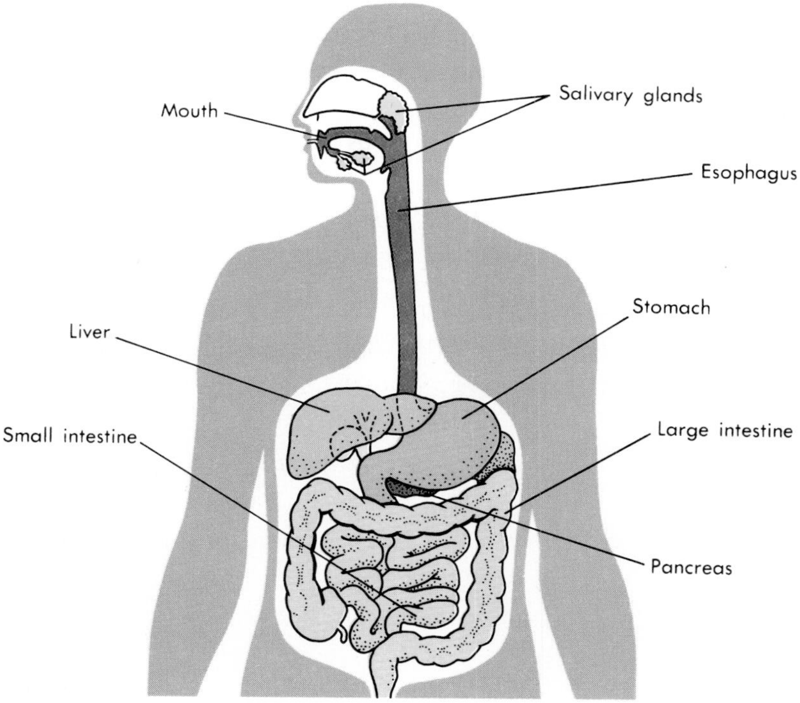


FIGURE 4–6. The digestive system includes the mouth, esophagus, stomach, small intestine, and large intestine.

a

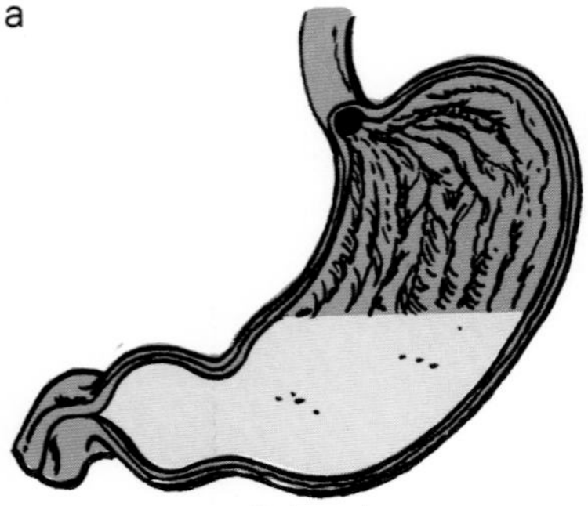


b

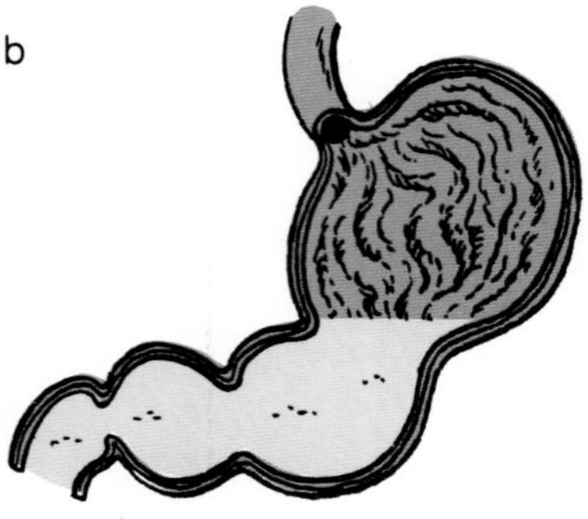


FIGURE 4–7. When food moves into the stomach (a), it is mixed by contraction of the stomach muscles (b).

How does gastric juice digest protein?

How does dilute HCl aid digestion? When is it harmful?

in front of a food mass relax, causing the tract to widen. Behind the food mass, the muscles contract causing the wall of the digestive tract to squeeze the food. As the wall squeezes the food, it pushes it forward. The series of relaxations and contractions pushes the food from one end to the other.

The stomach is an organ of the digestive system. It is a muscular organ with a thick, wrinkled lining. Gastric glands in the stomach lining secrete a liquid called gastric juice. Gastric juice contains dilute hydrochloric acid (HCl) and an enzyme called pepsin. Pepsin digests protein. The dilute HCl aids the action of pepsin by maintaining an acid condition. Too much acid sometimes causes an open sore, called an ulcer, to form inside the stomach.

Gastric juice and the crushing contractions of the stomach wall reduce food to a souplike mixture that leaves the stomach and enters the small intestine. It passes into the small intestine in small squirts.

The **small intestine** is a coiled tube about 7 m long and 2.5 cm in diameter. Most of the digestive process occurs in this organ. Three digestive juices—intestinal juice, pancreatic (pan kree AT ihk) juice, and bile—are present.

A watery mass of undigested food remains after digestion. This material leaves the small intestine and enters the large intestine. The large intestine extracts water from the undigested food mass. It also secretes a fluid that smoothes the passage of undigested wastes out of the body.

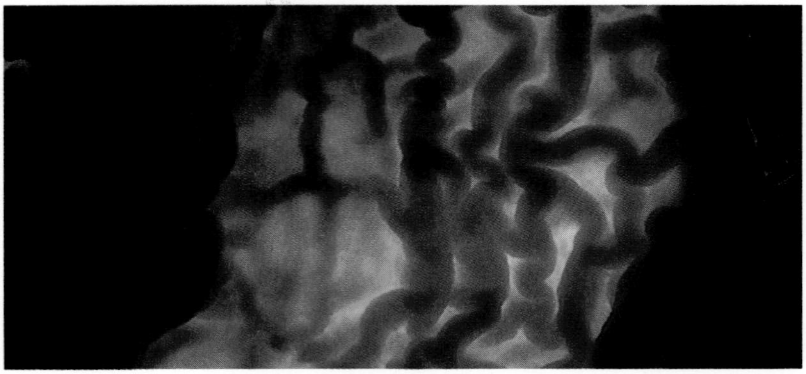

FIGURE 4–8. The stomach walls contain strong muscles that mix and churn food.

## activity PROTEIN DIGESTION

**(1)** Separate the white from a hard-boiled egg. Dispose of the rest of the egg. **(2)** Cut 4, 1-cm cubes from the egg white. **(3)** Label four test tubes *A, B, C,* and *D.* Add one cube of egg white to each tube. **(4)** Add the following to the test tubes as indicated.

*A*—10 mL water
*B*—10 mL pepsin solution
*C*—10 mL hydrochloric acid
*D*—10 mL pepsin solution and 2 drops dilute hydrochloric acid

**(5)** Place the test tubes in a very warm place and leave overnight. **(6)** Observe the test tubes. Why were the test tubes left in a warm place? In which test tubes did digestion occur? How do you know? What chemicals were present in the test tubes in which protein was digested?

### making sure

**10.** List the organs of the digestive system.
**11.** Where is most of the food a person eats digested?
**12.** How does food move through the esophagus?
**13.** What causes ulcers inside the stomach?
**14.** What is the function of the large intestine?

FIGURE 4–9. The salivary glands are located near the ears, near the jaw, and under the tongue.

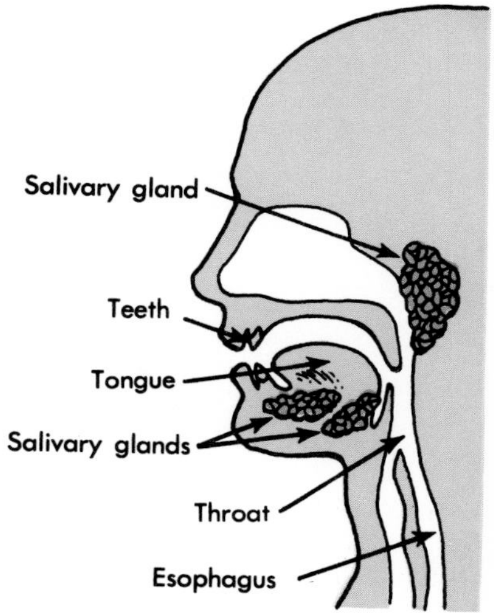


## 4:6 Digestion in the Digestive Tract

The digestion of food can be traced as it passes through the digestive tract. Digestion begins inside the mouth. The teeth grind solid chunks of food into tiny pieces. With the aid of the tongue, the teeth mix the food with saliva. Saliva is a liquid secreted into the mouth by the salivary (SAL uh ver ee) glands. The glands are connected to the mouth by tiny ducts. These ducts enter the mouth at points under the tongue, behind the jaw, and in front of the ear. Saliva adds water and mucus to the food. Mucus acts as a lubricant to ease the passage of food through the esophagus.

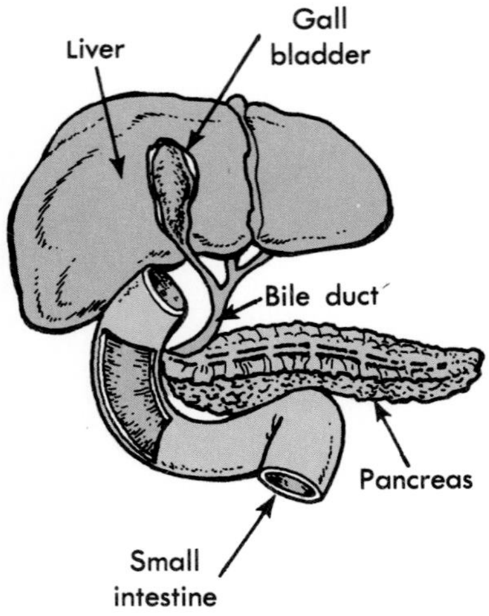


FIGURE 4–10. Ducts from the liver, pancreas, and gall bladder enter the small intestine.

In what part of the digestive tract does most digestion occur?

Saliva contains a starch-digesting enzyme called ptyalin (TI uh lun). Ptyalin begins to change starch to sugar. The change from starch to sugar involves many chemical reactions. Digestion continues in the stomach where proteins are changed to a simpler form. Gastric juice in the stomach contains dilute hydrochloric acid and two enzymes that begin the digestion of protein. Protein digestion occurs more rapidly in a dilute acid than in a neutral solution.

Most digestion occurs in the small intestine. Intestinal juice, formed in the walls of the small intestine, completes the digestion of carbohydrates and proteins. Pancreatic juice, formed by the pancreas, digests fats, carbohydrates, and proteins. Bile aids the digestion of fats. Bile is produced in the liver and stored in the gall bladder. The gall bladder is a greenish-colored sac attached to the liver. Bile is carried to the small intestine by the bile duct. Bile does not contain enzymes. However, it does perform a vital function. Bile breaks fat into tiny pieces, speeding its digestion by fat-digesting enzymes.

## activity STARCH DIGESTION

**(1)** Label 3 test tubes *A, B,* and *C.* Crumble a soda cracker and put ¼ of it in test tube *A.* **(2)** Add 3 mL of water. Mix by rotating the test tube between the palms of your hands. **(3)** Add 3 or 4 drops of iodine solution. Did the cracker contain starch? How do you know? **(4)** Put ¼ of the cracker into test tube *B.* **(5)** Add 5 mL of Benedict's solution to the test tube. **(6)** Place the test tube in a beaker half full of water. **(7)** Chew a cracker for 1 min. **(8)** Place the chewed cracker in test tube *C.* Add 5 mL of Benedict's solution. **(9)** Place the test tube in the beaker with test tube B. Heat the water in the beaker for 5 min. If sugar is present, the color will change from green to orange. Did the unchewed cracker contain sugar? Did the chewed cracker? How did you tell? What happened to the starch in the chewed cracker?

## activity FAT DIGESTION

(1) Label 3 test tubes *A, B,* and *C.* Add 10 mL water to each test tube. **(2)** Add 3 drops vegetable oil to each test tube. **(3)** Add a small amount of baking soda (the amount that stays on the wide end of a flat toothpick) to test tube *B.* **(4)** Add 5 drops bile solution to test tube *C.* **(5)** Stopper each test tube and mix the oil and water by inverting and shaking each tube several times. **(6)** Allow the test tubes to stand for 10 min. In which test tubes did the oil and water separate? How did the baking soda affect the rate of separation? How does bile affect the mixing of oil and water? Does bile cause a chemical change in fats? (Hint: See page 68.)

### making sure

**15.** State two functions of saliva.
**16.** Where does the digestion of food begin?
**17.** What is the function of bile?

## 4:7 Absorption of Food

Most substances produced during digestion are absorbed into the bloodstream through the wall of the small intestine. The lining of the small intestine is covered with thousands of small, fingerlike projections called **villi** (VIHL i). Villi increase the surface area of the small intestine. They are so numerous they give a velvety appearance to the intestinal lining. Each villus (singular of villi) contains a rich supply of capillaries and lymph vessels (Figure 4–11).



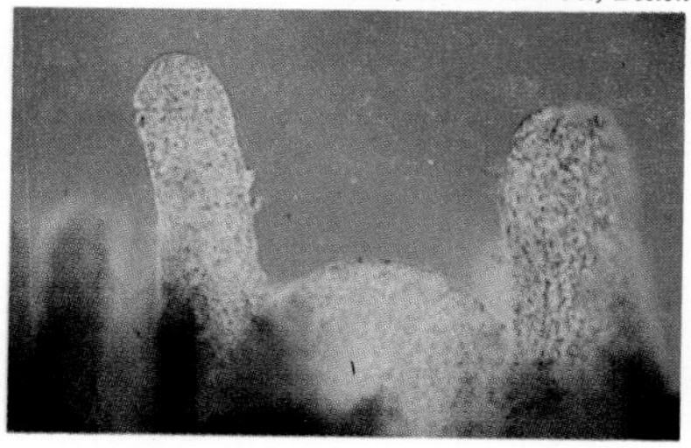

FIGURE 4–11. Food in the small intestine is absorbed by blood in the villi.

How do digested food nutrients enter the blood and the lymph?

Blood in the capillaries and lymph in the lymph vessels absorb digested food. Small food particles enter the blood and lymph by diffusion. Amino acids, simple sugars, mineral salts, and some vitamins are absorbed by blood. Fatty acids, glycerin, and some vitamins are absorbed by lymph. Together, blood and lymph carry the food molecules to all parts of the body.

FIGURE 4–12. Villi increase the food absorption area of the small intestine.

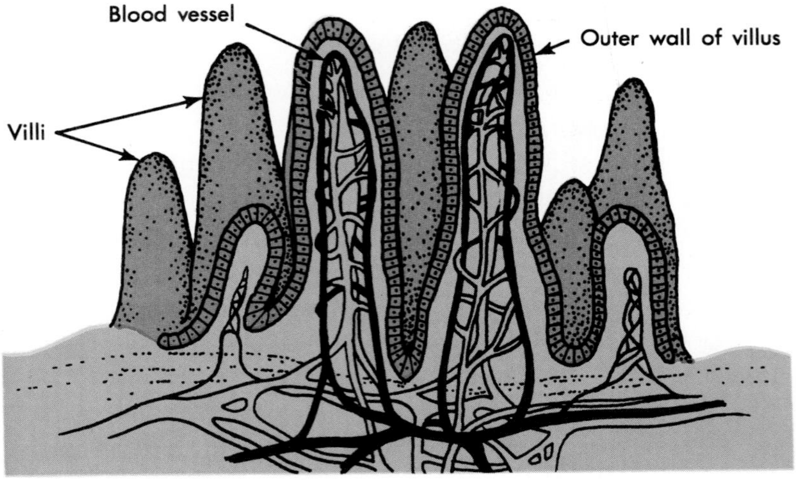


## activity DIFFUSION AND ABSORPTION

(1) Fill 2 large, empty mayonnaise jars with iodine solution. (2) Cut two lengths of dialysis tubing. Cut one length 20 cm and the other length 60 cm. (3) Tie one end of each piece of tubing shut with pieces of string. (4) Pour 20 mL of starch solution into each piece of dialysis tubing. Tie the remaining ends of the tubing closed. (5) Rinse the outside of each piece of dialysis tubing with water. (6) Put one piece of tubing containing the starch solution into each jar of iodine. Be sure the ends of the tubing are above the solution level. (7) Let the jars stand for 10 min. Observe and record the color of the starch solution in each jar. What happened to the color of the starch? What caused this change? Was there a difference in the color of the starch in the two jars? How do you account for this difference? How is this activity similar to food absorption in the body? How would food absorption be affected if there were no villi in the small intestine?

## making sure

**18.** How is food carried to the body's cells?

**19.** What are villi? How do they aid in food absorption?

# 4:8 Excretion and Excretory System

**Excretion** is the removal of wastes from the body. The lungs, kidneys, skin, and large intestine are excretory organs. Waste products are collected and removed from the body in these organs. If the excretory organs are damaged by disease or injury, serious health problems arise. Body tissues fill with waste products and swelling can occur. As a result the tissues cannot function properly. Poisoning, fever, and death may result.

The **kidneys** are two bean-shaped organs about 10 cm long in an adult. They are found on either side of the spine in the "small" of the back. Kidneys remove wastes from the blood that are then excreted from the body. They aid in maintaining the correct balance of chemicals in the blood and other body tissues. Except for carbon dioxide, nearly all wastes are filtered from the blood by the kidneys. These wastes include excess water, minerals, and urea (yoo REE uh). Urea is a waste formed from the breakdown of proteins. Most urea is made by liver cells. Urea and other wastes combine in the kidneys to form a liquid called urine (YOOR un).

What wastes are removed from the blood by the kidneys?

Urine collected in the kidneys is carried by two long tubes, called ureters (YOOR ut urz), to the urinary (YOOR uh ner ee) bladder. Urine is excreted by muscular contractions of the bladder.

a

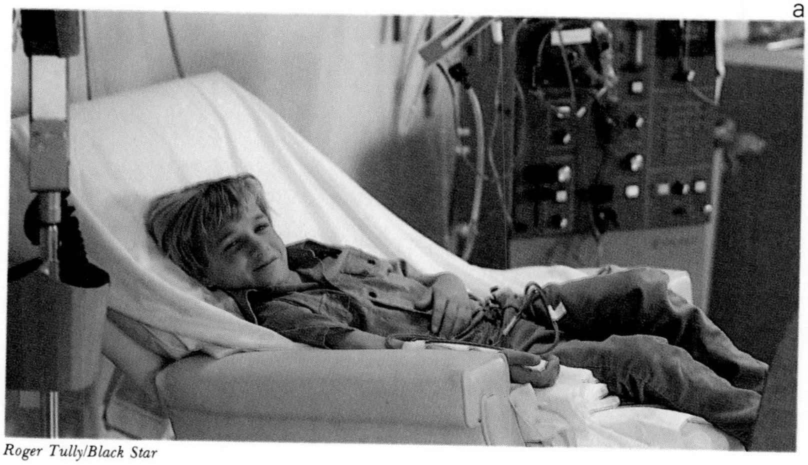

*Roger Tully/Black Star*

FIGURE 4–13. A kidney machine (a) performs the same functions as the kidneys do in maintaining the chemical balance of the blood (b).

b

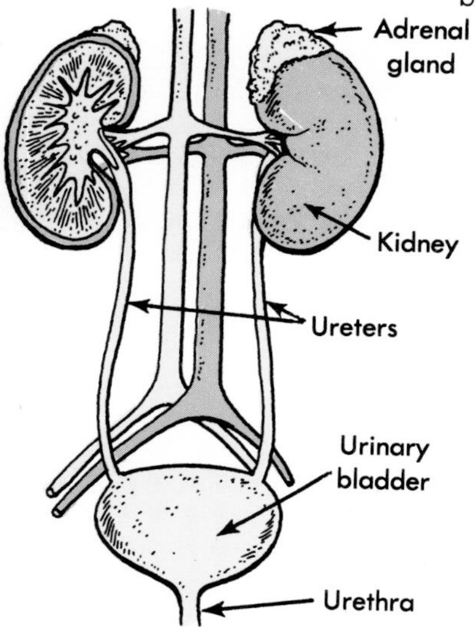

Water, salts, and a small amount of urea are excreted through the skin as sweat. Sweat is drawn from capillaries within the skin's sweat glands. It is released at the body surface through pores. The evaporation of this fluid aids in maintaining the body's temperature.

What is the function of the large intestine?

Excretion also occurs from the large intestine. The large intestine absorbs water from the undigested food mass within it. A solid waste called feces is expelled from the body at periodic intervals. When too much water is removed, constipation (kahn stuh PAY shun) results. When not enough water is removed, diarrhea (di uh REE uh) results. Diarrhea can be a serious problem if the body loses too much water over a short period of time.

a

Latent Image

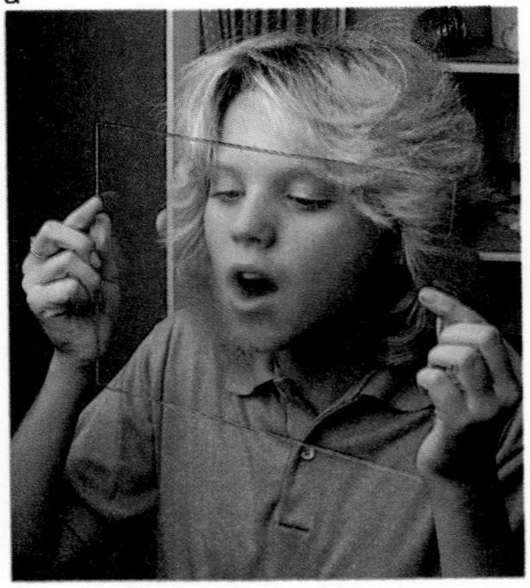

b

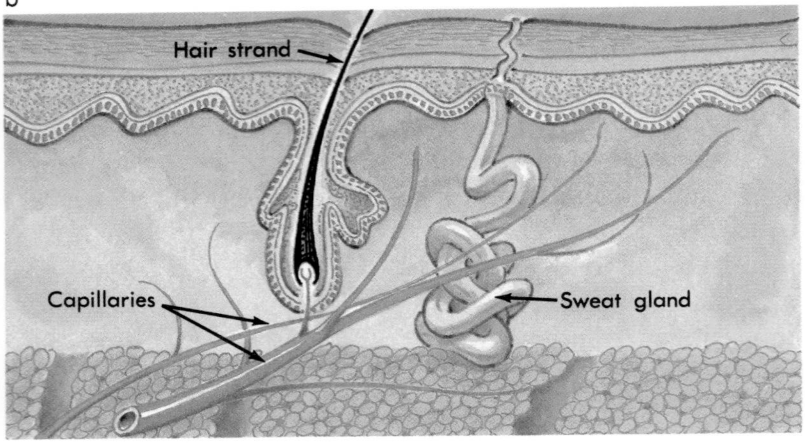


FIGURE 4–14. Water vapor is excreted when a person exhales (a). Water and salts are excreted from the sweat glands in the skin (b).

## making sure

20. What is excretion? Name four excretory organs.
21. What can occur if the excretory organs are damaged by injury or disease?
22. What is the function of the kidneys?
23. What waste product is not removed from the blood by the kidneys?
24. Why is evaporation important to the body?
25. What wastes are excreted through the skin?
26. How does the large intestine function in excretion?
27. Why is excretion vital to the health of a person?

# main ideas — Chapter Review

1. Metabolism is the sum of all body processes needed to maintain life. These processes include respiration, digestion, growth and repair of tissues, and excretion. 4:1
2. Basal metabolism is a person's lowest metabolic rate. 4:1
3. An exchange of carbon dioxide and oxygen occurs in the lungs. 4:2
4. Movements of the diaphragm and the ribs during breathing cause air pressure changes inside the lungs. 4:3
5. Digestion is the changing of food particles to smaller substances that can be used by cells. 4:4
6. Digestive juices contain enzymes that aid food digestion. 4:4
7. Most food is digested in the small intestine. 4:5
8. Digestion and absorption of food are the functions of the digestive system. 4:6, 4:7
9. Wastes are removed from the body by the lungs, kidneys, skin, and large intestine. 4:8

# vocabulary

*Define each of the following words or terms.*

| | | |
|---|---|---|
| alveoli | epiglottis | metabolism |
| bronchial tubes | excretion | respiration |
| diaphragm | kidneys | small intestine |
| digestion | larynx | villi |
| enzyme | | |

# study questions

**DO NOT WRITE IN THIS BOOK.**

**A. True or False**

*Determine whether each of the following sentences is true or false. If the sentence is false, rewrite it to make it true.*

1. Your rate of breathing remains the same throughout the day.
2. The diaphragm pumps air into and out of your lungs.
3. The diaphragm is a muscle.
4. The air pressure inside your lungs never changes.

5. Carbon dioxide enters the blood in the lungs.
6. Metabolism is higher when a person is resting than when working.
7. The epiglottis produces speech sounds.
8. Vocal cords vibrate when a person talks.
9. The lungs, kidneys, and skin are organs of excretion.
10. Urea is a waste compound.

### B. Multiple Choice

*Choose the word or phrase that completes correctly each of the following sentences.*

1. The (*liver, pancreas, bladder, small intestine*) is part of the digestive tract.
2. (*Ptyalin, Starch, Bile, Hydrochloric acid*) is an enzyme.
3. (*Pancreatic juice, Bile, Pepsin*) digests carbohydrates.
4. Chewing food causes (*an increase, a decrease, no change*) in the food's surface area.
5. Saliva contains (*bile, ptyalin, starch*).
6. Digestion begins in the (*mouth, esophagus, stomach*).
7. (*Pepsin, Ptyalin, Bile*) breaks fat into tiny particles.
8. Pepsin is produced in the (*stomach, pancreas, liver*).
9. Blood in the (*capillaries, veins, arteries*) absorbs digested food.
10. Most of the digestion of food takes place in the (*stomach, small intestine, large intestine, pancreas*).

### C. Competion

*Complete each of the following sentences with a word or phrase that will make the sentence correct.*

1. ______ is produced when carbohydrates are digested.
2. In the lungs are spongy air-filled sacs called ______.
3. ______ are formed when proteins are digested.
4. Enzymes plus ______ cause the breakdown of food into small molecules.
5. ______ increase the surface area of the small intestine.
6. Wastes are filtered from the blood in the ______.
7. ______, digestion, building and repair of tissues, and excretion are all part of metabolism.

8. As the rate of metabolism increases, the consumption of oxygen ______.
9. The basal metabolic rate is found by measuring the amount of ______ consumed during a certain period of time.
10. ______ is a waste made in the liver from the breakdown of proteins.

**D. How and Why**

1. How do your chest muscles and diaphragm help you breathe?
2. How are wastes excreted from the body?
3. Where is each of the following digested—carbohydrate, protein, fat?
4. How are digested foods absorbed into the blood?
5. Explain the nature of diarrhea and constipation.

## challenges

1. Diabetes is a disease in which sugar appears in the urine. Find out how diabetes is detected and treated.
2. Prepare a library report on kidney transplants and dialysis treatments for kidney patients.
3. Ulcers can form in the stomach and intestine. Find out what causes ulcers and how they can be treated.

## interesting reading

"Asthma: The Giant Hand." *Current Health*, March 1980, pp. 22-23.

Beeshad, Carol and Deborah Berniek, *Bodyworks: The Kid's Guide to Food and Physical Fitness.* New York: Random House, 1980.

Comroe, Julius H., "Doctor, You Have Six Minutes." *Science 84,* Jan/Feb 1984, pp. 62-68.

Foster, Lee, "Life Without Kidneys." *Reader's Digest,* Sept. 1980, pp. 99-103.

*Your brain is within your skull. Your brain controls your every activity. It is working when you are awake and when you are asleep. How a person reacts to something is controlled by the nervous and endocrine systems. How does the brain communicate with the rest of the body? How is your nervous system related to behavior? What do hormones have to do with communication?*

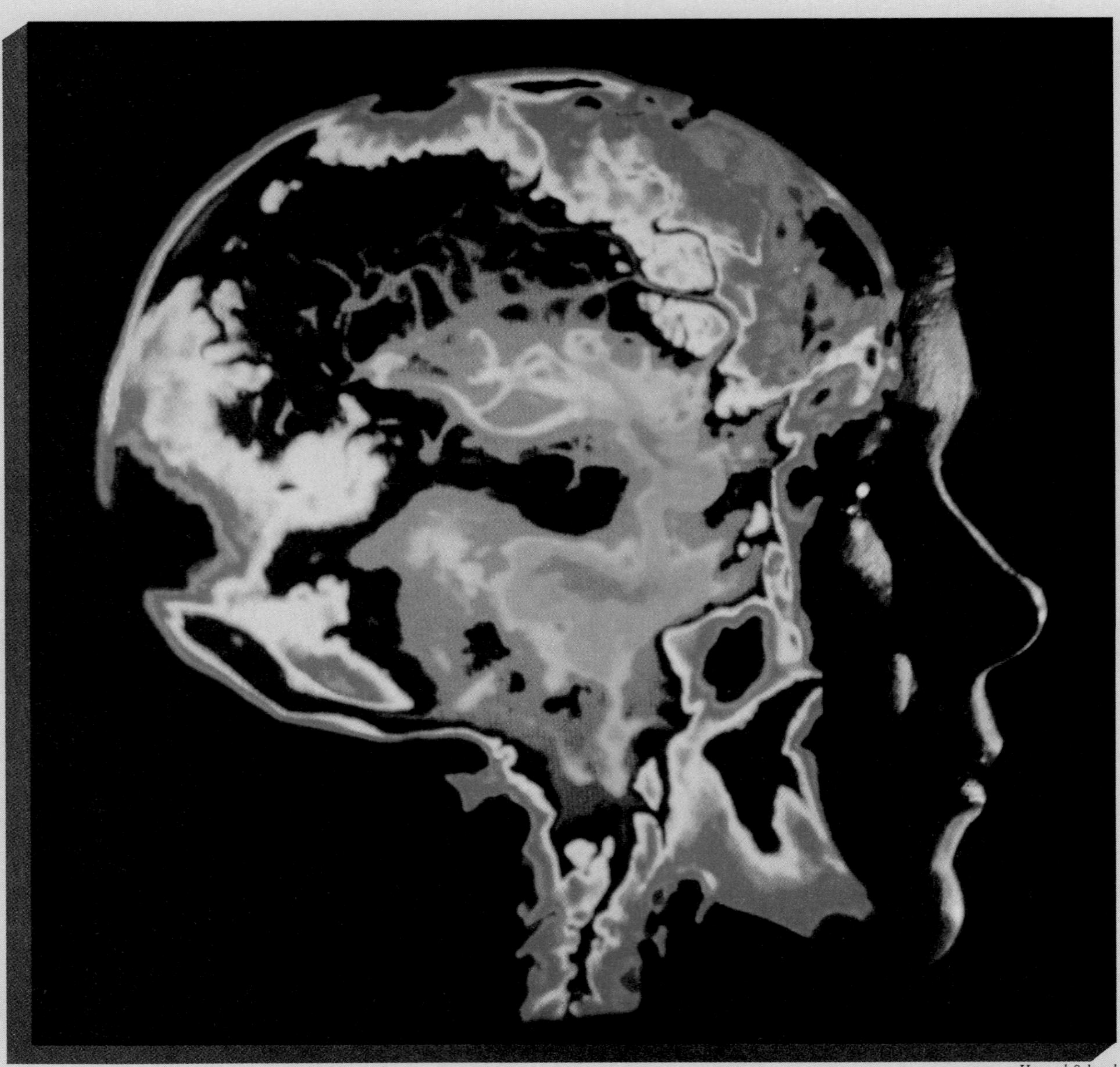

Howard Schurek

# Nervous and Endocrine Systems

chapter 5

## 5:1 Behavior and Its Regulation

GOAL: You will learn how the body is controlled and regulated by the nervous and endocrine systems.

Everything a person does is called behavior. Eating, playing, studying, walking, and talking are all examples of behavior. You eat when you are hungry. You run when you are in danger. You sleep when you are tired. **Behavior** is the ability of an organism to react to its internal and external environments. Anything that causes behavior is a **stimulus.** How an organism reacts to a stimulus is a **response.**

Many responses and activities are controlled by the endocrine (EN duh krun) system through chemicals released into the blood. These chemicals are produced by endocrine glands. However, chemical control is a slow process compared to the action of the nervous system. What type of response is needed when a bicycle rider sees a fast-approaching car? Quick responses to this kind of stimulus are controlled by the nervous system. Nerves carry messages from the brain to all parts of the body.

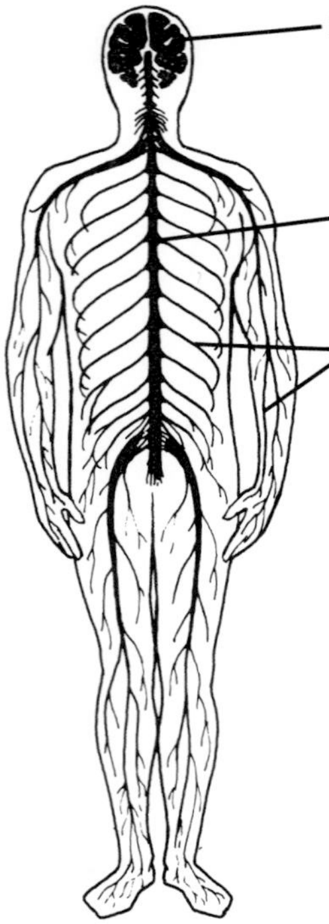


FIGURE 5–1. The brain, spinal cord, and peripheral nerves make up the nervous system.

What is the function of the central nervous system?

## 5:2 The Central Nervous System

The control center of your nervous system is called the central nervous system. It is made of your brain and spinal cord. The central nervous system is enclosed and protected by bone and bathed in fluid.

Your brain is about 1/40 of your mass, yet it is the major control center of your body. The brain is a complex organ containing over ten billion nerve cells. The brain has three major parts—cerebrum (suh REE brum), cerebellum (ser uh BEL um), and medulla (muh DUL uh).

The **cerebrum** is the largest part of the human brain. Human intelligence is due largely to a highly developed cerebrum. The cerebrum controls thought, memory, learning, and some voluntary movements. It also controls the senses of sight, hearing, touch, taste, and smell. Brain operations on humans have revealed the location of control centers within the cerebrum (Figure 5–2b). If any one of these centers is damaged or destroyed, the activity or sense that it controls is lost.

The **cerebellum** is smaller and lies below and behind the cerebrum. The cerebellum's major function is to coordinate muscular activities such as walking and running. It also maintains the body's

FIGURE 5–2. The cerebrum of the brain has two halves (a). Certain areas of the brain are associated with certain senses and activities (b).

a

Dr. Baba, Ohio State University

b

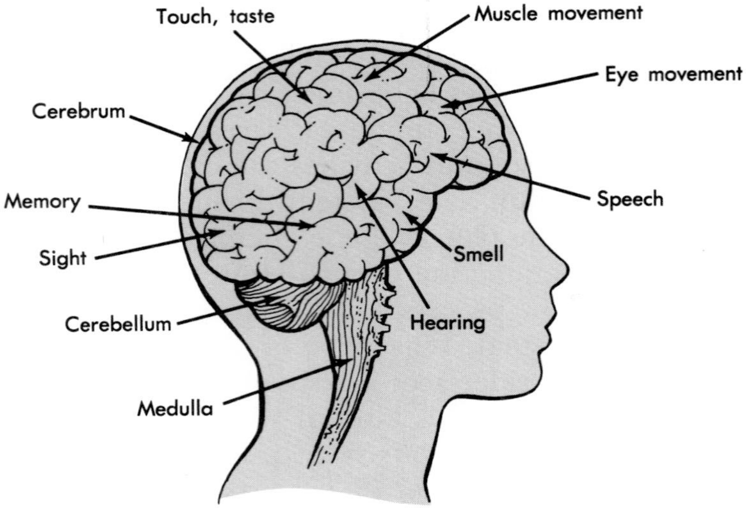

sense of balance. Suppose you pick up a ball and throw it. The motion of your fingers, hand, and arm are controlled by the cerebellum. However, the decision to throw the ball, the choice of target, and the aiming are controlled by the cerebrum.

List the parts of the brain and the function of each.

The **medulla** is the smallest part of the brain. It is located at the base of the skull, just below the cerebellum. The medulla is the enlarged upper end of the spinal cord. It controls breathing, heartbeat, muscular action of the digestive tract, and secretion by some glands.

Reach around to the center of your back and feel the bones in your spine. Your spine is made of vertebrae, a series of bones. The spinal canal is in the center of these vertebrae. Extending from the medulla down through the spinal canal is a thick cord of nerves. These nerves compose the **spinal cord.** The spinal cord extends almost the entire length of your spine. It is the connection center between the brain and the nerves that extend throughout your body. Spinal fluid bathes the spinal cord.

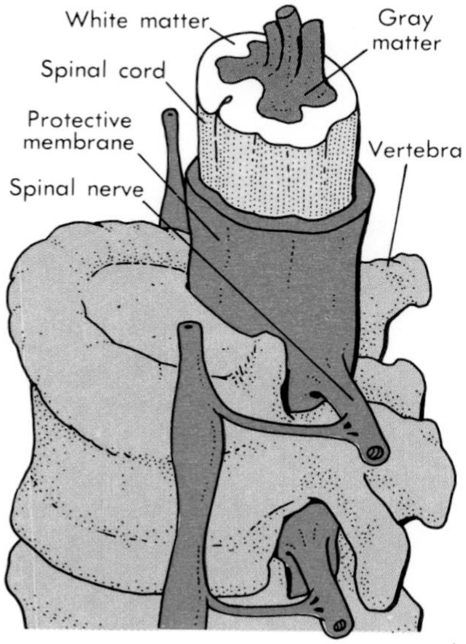


FIGURE 5–3. The spinal column protects the delicate tissues of the spinal cord.

All the nerves outside the brain and spinal cord compose the peripheral nervous system. These nerves carry messages between the central nervous system and the rest of the body. Thirty-one pairs of nerves branch from the spinal cord. One nerve in each pair carries messages to the spinal cord. The other nerve in each pair carries messages away from the spinal cord. If the spinal cord were cut, all parts of the body controlled by nerves below the cut would become paralyzed. They would no longer receive messages from the brain.

## making sure

**1.** How might the body be affected by damage to each of these parts of the brain?
(a) cerebrum
(b) cerebellum
(c) medulla
(d) spinal cord

**2.** Why are the nerves that branch from the spinal cord paired?

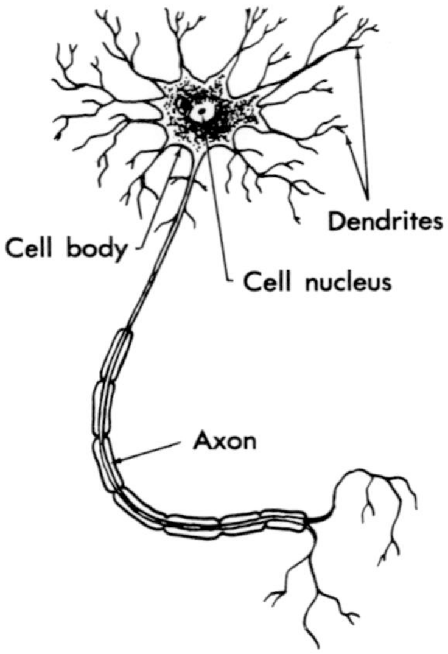


FIGURE 5–4. A neuron is composed of a cell body, dendrites, and an axon.

Philip Harris Biological Limited

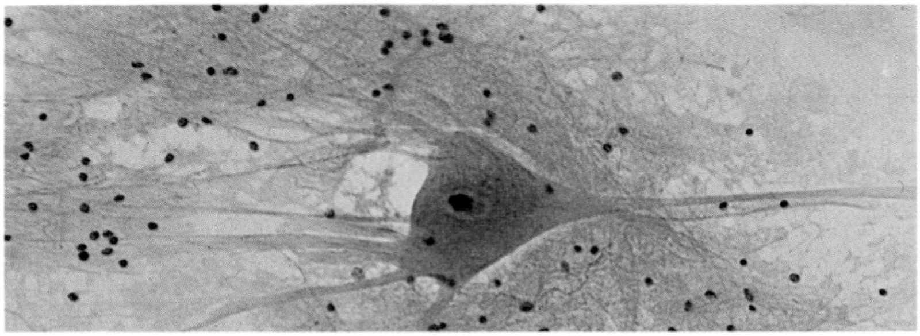

## 5:3 Neurons

Define nerve impulse.

**Neurons** (NOO rahnz) are the cells that make up the nervous system. These cells carry nerve impulses. A nerve **impulse** is a "message" that moves rapidly from one end of a neuron to the other. Nerve impulses in the human body travel at speeds from 0.5 m/s to 100 m/s. A neuron is composed of many nerve fibers attached to a cell body. These fibers include one long fiber, the axon, and one or more shorter fibers, the dendrites. Dendrites carry messages into the cell body. The axon carries messages away from the cell body. Some neurons are very long, such as those that extend from the toes to the spinal cord. Others extend from the fingertips to the spinal cord.

List three types of neurons and the function of each.

There are three types of neurons in the human body—sensory, motor, and association. Sensory neurons carry impulses from receptors to the central nervous system. **Receptors** are specialized structures that detect changes in the environment, or stimuli. The eyes, ears, nose, and skin contain receptors that detect stimuli.

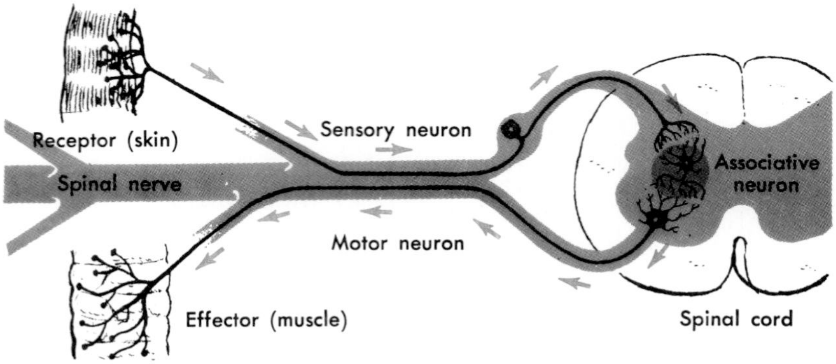


FIGURE 5–5. Neurons carry impulses from receptors to the nervous system and then to the effectors.

Motor neurons carry impulses away from the central nervous system to the effectors. **Effectors** are structures that respond when nerve impulses are received. Muscles are effectors that contract when they receive nerve impulses.

Association neurons connect sensory neurons and motor neurons. These neurons are present in the brain and spinal cord. Association neurons transfer impulses from sensory neurons to motor neurons.

## 5:4 Sense Organs

Nerve receptors are located all over your body. Without receptors you would be unaware of the world around you. Many receptors are in the sense organs. Sense organs are special organs for receiving stimuli. The sense organs are eyes, ears, nose, taste buds, and skin. The stimuli they receive include light, sound, odors, tastes, pressure, temperature, and pain.

List your five sense organs and the "messages" they receive.

In the human eye, the retina contains receptors that connect with the optic nerve (Figure 5–6). The optic nerve goes from the eye to the brain. Receptors in the retina are stimulated by light. Light enters the eye through the pupil. When light strikes the retina, impulses are sent to the brain through the optic nerve. The brain interprets the impulses it receives as images.

How do your retinas enable you to see?

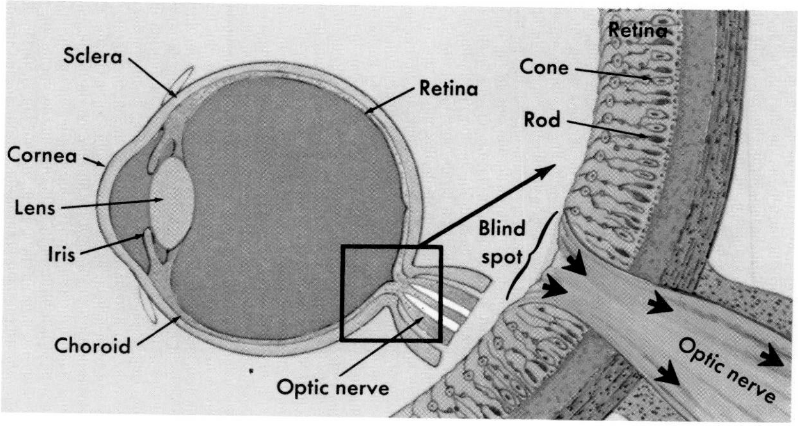


FIGURE 5–6. Receptors in the rods and cones of the retina receive light stimuli and transmit impulses to the brain.

There are two types of receptors in the retina—cones and rods. Cones are sensitive to bright light and to color. Rods are not sensitive to color. Thus, they are responsible for black and white vision. Rods respond to dim light and aid night vision.

More than 500 000 neurons lead from the retina to the optic nerve. There are no rods or cones at the point where the retina joins the optic nerve. This point is called the blind spot because there is no vision there.

How do your ears enable you to hear?

Sound is detected by the ears. The outer ear gathers sound waves. Sound waves pass through the canal of the ear to the eardrum, which vibrates. The vibrations pass through three small bones—hammer, anvil, and stirrup—to a liquid inside the cochlea (KAHK lee uh). The cochlea is a coiled tube containing nerve receptors. Vibrations in the liquid produce nerve impulses in the auditory nerve. The auditory nerve connects the ear with the brain. In the brain, impulses from the ears are interpreted as sound.

A taste bud is a receptor in the tongue that is sensitive to taste. There are four types of taste buds. Each type is located in a different area of the tongue. These areas detect different tastes—sour (acid), sweet, salty, and bitter.

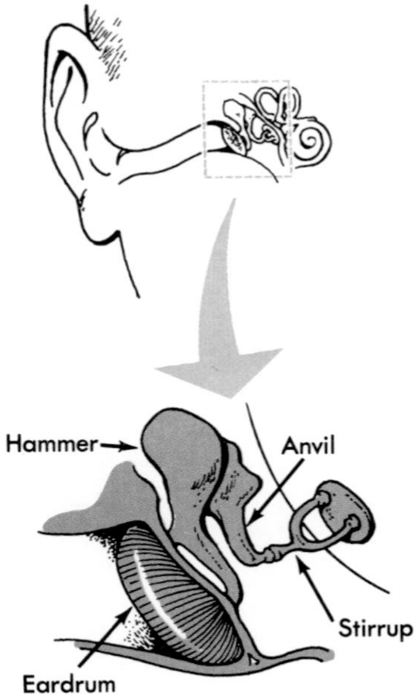


FIGURE 5–7. Sound waves are transferred by the hammer, anvil, and stirrup to receptors in the cochlea.

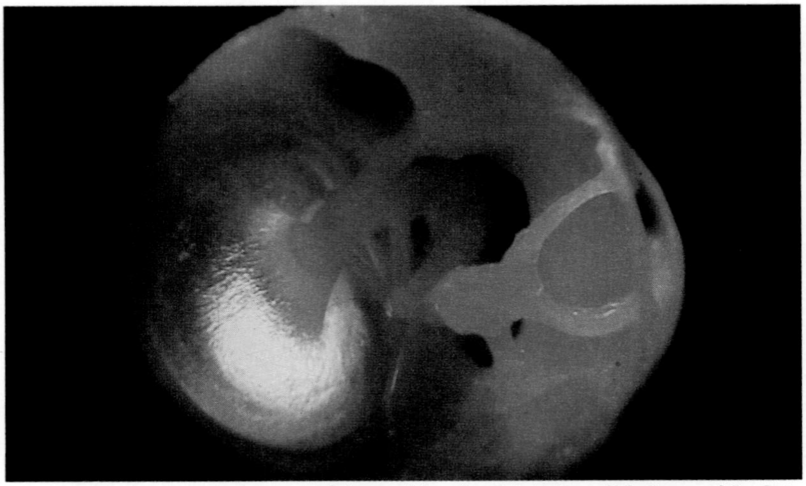

© *Lennart Nilsson from* Behold Man—*Little, Brown and Co., Boston*

Image Workshop

FIGURE 5–8. The smell of food enhances its taste.

Much of what you believe to be "taste" is really smell. Vapors from foods enter your nose as you eat. You connect the smell with the taste of food. Apples have a different "taste" if you eat them when you have a head cold and your nose is blocked.

Odors are detected through receptors in the nose. These receptors are cells with long hairlike cilia attached. The cilia are bathed in a mucous layer. For an odor to be noticed, vapor molecules must enter the mucus. This action stimulates the cilia and causes nerve impulses to be sent to the brain. In the brain, the impulses are interpreted as different odors. It is estimated that only eight vapor molecules are needed to trigger an impulse in a nerve ending. About forty nerve endings must be triggered before an odor can be detected.

Skin contains many receptors. There are separate kinds of receptors for touch, pressure, cold, warmth, and pain. Certain areas of the body surface have more receptors than others. For example, hands have more receptors per square centimeter than arms or legs.

Your sense organs detect only a small portion of the events in your environment. For example, they cannot detect some kinds of light and sound. People have built instruments that record events not detected by sense organs. These instruments aid awareness of a larger part of the world.

FIGURE 5–9. The skin contains many different receptors.

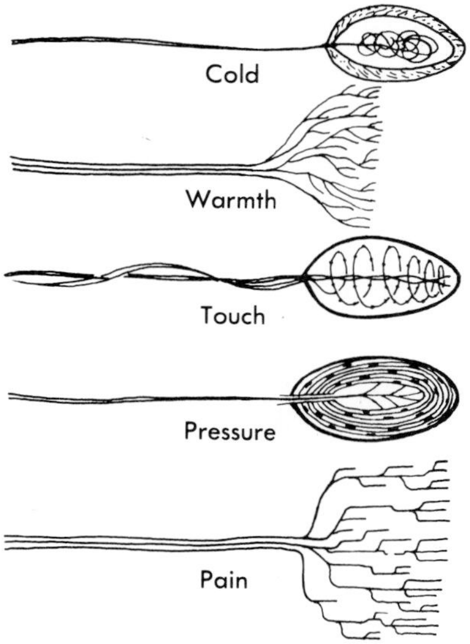

## activity

### THE SENSE OF TOUCH

**Objective:** To investigate the sense of touch in different areas of the body

**Materials**

large index card
metric ruler
2 round toothpicks

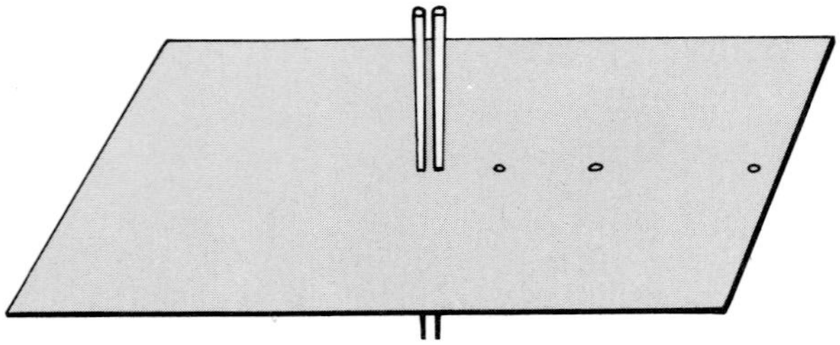

FIGURE 5–10.

FIGURE 5–11.

**Procedure**

1. Use a toothpick to punch a small hole in the center of the index card.
2. Use the ruler and toothpick to measure and punch holes 1 mm, 3 mm, 5mm, and 10 mm from the first hole.
3. Insert the two toothpicks into the holes that are 1 mm apart. The ends of the toothpicks should be even.
4. Work with a partner. Have the person close his or her eyes. Gently touch the tips of the toothpicks to the skin surface of the fingertips, palm, back of the neck, and above the elbow. Have your partner tell you how many toothpick tips are touching the skin in each area. Record a 1 or a 2.
5. Repeat Step 4 with the toothpicks placed at 3 mm, 5 mm, and 10 mm. Record the results.

**Observations and Data**

| Distance | Number of toothpicks felt | | | |
|---|---|---|---|---|
| | finger-tips | palm | back of neck | above the elbow |
| 1 mm | | | | |
| 3 mm | | | | |
| 5 mm | | | | |
| 10 mm | | | | |

**Questions and Conclusions**

1. Which skin area was most sensitive?
2. Why are some areas of the body more sensitive to touch than other areas?
3. In what ways is touch important in preventing injury?

## activity TASTE

**(1)** Working with a partner, prepare 4 solutions. Place 400 mL of water in each of 4 beakers. To the first beaker add 1 spoonful of sugar; to the second beaker add 1 spoonful of baking soda; to the third beaker add 1 spoonful of salt; and to the fourth beaker add 1 spoonful of vinegar. **(2)** Have your partner label the beakers and then move them around so you do not know which solution is in each beaker. Using a sterile cotton swab, dip into the first solution and run the swab over your tongue. Record the taste of the solution. **(3)** Discard the swab and rinse your mouth with water. **(4)** Using a new swab each time, repeat Steps 2 and 3 for the other solutions. Record your results. What taste sensations did you identify? Did you have to taste any solution a second time in order to identify it? If so, which solution? Hold your nose and try the taste tests again. Did you have any difficulty identifying the solutions this time? Why or why not?

### making sure

**2.** Have you ever noticed that in dim light you see only in shades of black and not in color? How can this observation be explained?

**3.** Why is it impossible to see anything in total darkness?

## 5:5 Reflex

A **reflex** is the simplest type of reaction. In a reflex, a response to a stimulus occurs without the person being aware of it. It often occurs without the impulse going to the brain. A reflex is automatic. You do it without thinking. Reflexes are present at birth. They are not learned. A loud noise may cause a person to jump. The jump is the response to the stimulus of a loud noise.

A **reflex arc** is the path in a reflex. The impulse moves from a receptor through a sensory neuron, an association neuron, and a motor neuron, to an effector. Suppose you prick your finger with a pin. The stimulus causes nerve impulses to travel along a

What is a reflex arc?

FIGURE 5–12. A reflex arc is the simple nerve impulse pathway in an involuntary act.

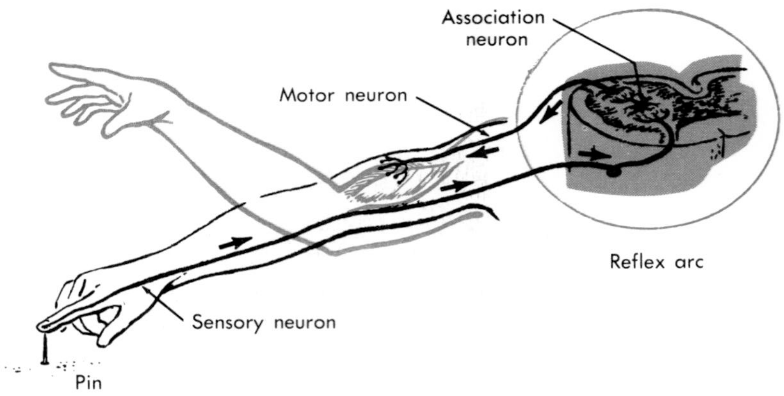


reflex arc. Impulses go from the sensory neurons of the finger to the spinal cord. Here the impulses are transferred by association neurons to a motor neuron. Nerve impulses travel through the motor neuron to muscles in your arm and cause the muscles to contract. As a result, you pull your finger away. Pulling your finger away from the pin is the response. In this reflex, you pull your finger away automatically—your brain does not send an impulse to the muscles in your hand and arm.

Change in the size of the pupil in the eye is another example of a reflex. The size of the pupils

FIGURE 5–13. The size of the pupil changes in response to changes in light intensity. This change is a reflex.

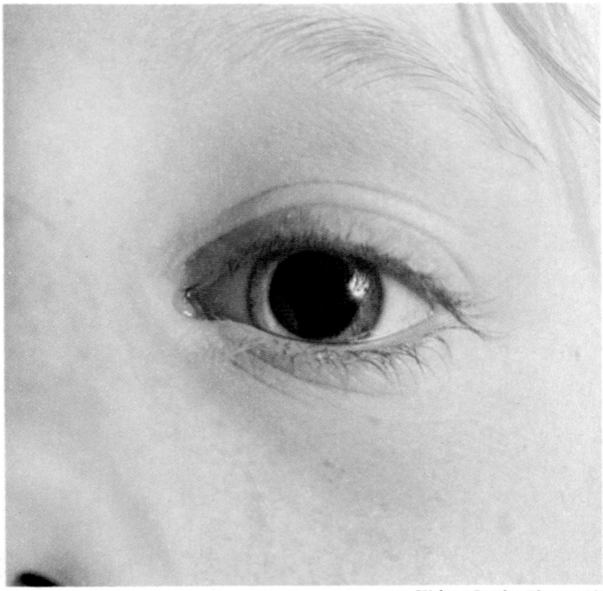

*Hickson-Bender Photography*

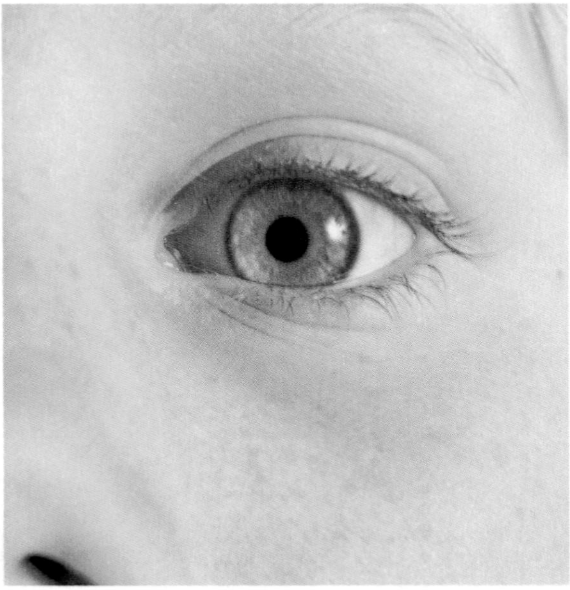

*Hickson-Bender Photography*

in your eyes is controlled by eye muscles. When you go outside on a bright sunny day, your pupils become smaller in size. This action reduces the amount of light that enters your eyes. Light is a stimulus. A decrease in the size of the pupils is the response. As in all reflex actions, the response results from nerve impulses traveling through a reflex arc.

***Table 5–1.***
Reflexes

| Stimulus | Examples of Responses |
|---|---|
| Cold | Shivering |
| Heat | Perspiring |
| Pinprick | Jerk finger away |
| Pinch | Withdrawal from pinch |
| Sound | Jerk at loud noise |
| Light | Contraction of pupil of eye |
| Fear | Release of adrenaline |
| Candy | Salivating, swallowing |
| Pollen in air | Sneezing, coughing |

## activity REFLEX ACTIONS

Stand in front of the class with a sheet of clear plastic in front of your face. Have another student throw small cotton balls or crumpled paper at the plastic. What was your reaction? What was the stimulus? Was this a learned behavior? Explain.

## activity KNEE JERK

Sit down on a chair and cross your legs. Allow one leg to swing freely and relaxed. Then use the side of your hand to tap the area of your free leg just below the kneecap. What happens? What is the stimulus? What is the response? Is this a reflex act? Describe the path of the impulse.

## 5:6 Conditioned Reflex

What is a conditioned reflex?

Reflexes can be changed or conditioned. A **conditioned reflex** is one in which a new stimulus takes the place of the original stimulus. For instance, in an experiment, a scientist rang a bell and reduced the light where a person was sitting. The decrease in light caused the pupils in the person's eye to enlarge. This procedure was repeated over and over again. After a time, the pupils of the person's eyes enlarged when only the bell was rung. No decrease in light was needed. The ringing of the bell replaced the original stimulus, the dimming of the light.

### activity

**CHANGING A STIMULUS**

Stand behind a friend seated at a desk. Ask the friend to respond by drawing a line on a piece of paper each time you say "write." Every time you say "write" tap the chair or desk with a ruler. Do this about twenty times. Now, tap the ruler but do not use the stimulus "write." Have you produced a conditioned reflex in your friend? How does a behavior become a conditioned reflex?

FIGURE 5–14.

### making sure

4. Give an example of a reflex action. Give an example of a conditioned reflex. How are they different?
5. Look at the word "pizza." Does it make you secrete saliva? If so, explain why this action is a conditioned reflex.
6. When people play "Simon says", what mistakes do they make? Why do they make these mistakes?

## 5:7 The Autonomic Nervous System

What are the functions of the autonomic nervous system?

The **autonomic nervous system** does its work without your thinking about it. The system is involuntary and automatic. For example, you do not think about the beating of your heart. Your heart just beats. The regulation of your heartbeat, the supply of blood to the arteries, and the movement of muscles in the digestive tract are controlled by the autonomic nervous system.

Two nerve cords on each side of the spinal cord are part of the autonomic nervous system (Figure 5–15). Each cord contains clumps of nerve tissue. A clump of nerve tissue is called a ganglion (GANG glee un). Each ganglion is a relay station that is connected to the spinal cord by a nerve. Another nerve connects the ganglion to an organ. Through this network of nerves and ganglia, the body organs are controlled and regulated.

What is the function of a ganglion?

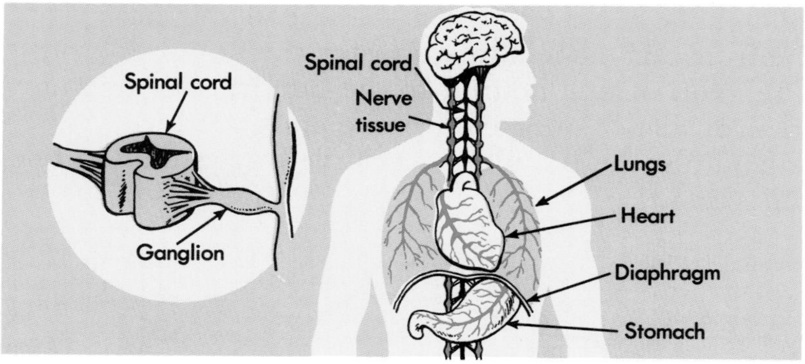


FIGURE 5–15. The autonomic nervous system regulates involuntary body functions.

## 5:8 Loewi's Experiment

How do nerves regulate the human body? An experiment performed by Otto Loewi (AHT oh·LOH ee) in 1921 has helped answer this question. In Loewi's experiment, two live, beating, frog hearts were used. One heart, with its vagus (VAY gus) nerve attached, was placed in a special salt solution. The solution was designed to keep the heart alive for several days. The second heart, without its vagus nerve, was placed in the same kind of salt solution.

Describe Loewi's experiment with living frog hearts.

The vagus nerve of the first heart was stimulated with a weak electric current. As expected, the heartbeat slowed. This reaction usually occurs when the vagus nerve is stimulated. Loewi took some of the solution from the dish containing the first heart. He added it to the solution in the dish containing the second heart. The heart rate of the second heart was slowed.

Loewi concluded that stimulation of the vagus nerve of the first heart released a chemical. The chemical slowed the heartbeat. Some of the chemical entered the salt solution and was transferred to the dish containing the second heart. The chemical then slowed the heartbeat of the second heart.

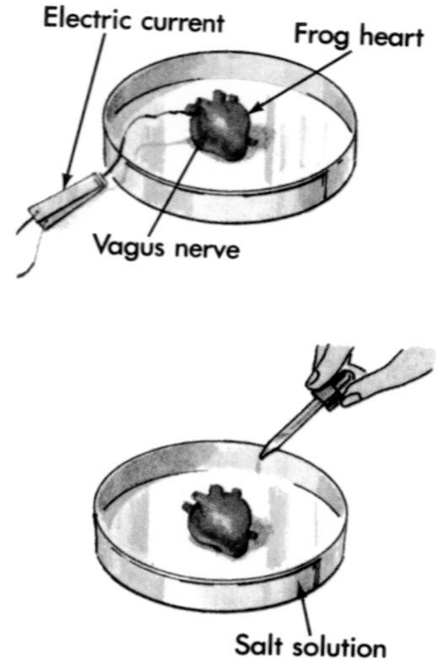


FIGURE 5–16. In Loewi's experiment, some solution surrounding a stimulated heart was transferred to the solution surrounding a second heart.

How are nerve impulses transferred between neurons?

Loewi's experiment led to an understanding of how nerve impulses are carried between neurons. There are spaces between neurons called **synapses** (suh NAP seez). Contact is made across these spaces by chemicals that are formed at the ends of the neurons. The chemicals transfer the impulses from the axon of one neuron to the dendrites of another neuron. Since only axon nerve ends produce chemicals, the impulse in a nerve travels only in one direction.

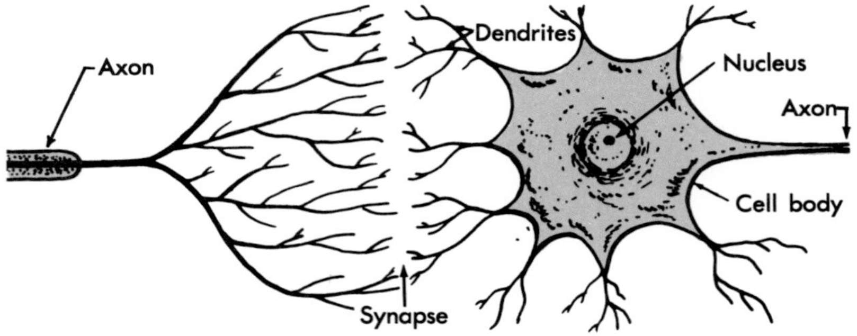


FIGURE 5–17. Nerve impulses travel from the axon of a neuron to the dendrites of another neuron across a synapse.

The ends of nerves can also release a chemical that causes heart muscles to contract. This chemical increases the heartbeat. Nerves regulate the heart rate through chemicals they release into the muscle cells of the heart.

### *MAKING SURE*

**7.** Describe Loewi's experiment. What did it show about nerve impulses?

**8.** What are the spaces between neurons called?

## 5:9 The Endocrine System

Together, the nervous system and the endocrine system control all body functions. The **endocrine system** is made of ductless glands that produce hormones. A **hormone** is a chemical that controls certain body functions. Table 5–2 lists some hormones. Hormones produced by ductless glands are not carried away by ducts or tubes. The hormones produced are released directly into the blood where they are circulated through the body.

The adrenal glands are located on the kidneys. One is found on the upper part of each kidney. Adrenal glands illustrate the action of endocrine glands. A hormone called adrenaline is secreted from the central part of the adrenals. When a person is angry, frightened, or excited, this hormone is released. It travels to all parts of the body in the blood. It may help a person perform great feats by causing the body to release large amounts of energy. Adrenaline also increases the flow of blood to the brain and heart.

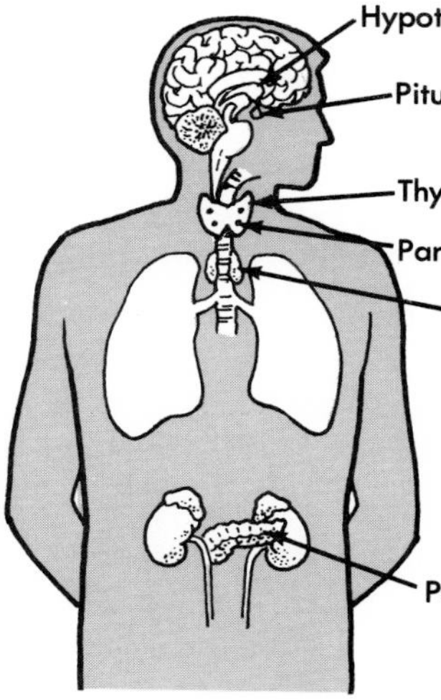


FIGURE 5–18. Endocrine glands are located in several places in the body. They produce chemicals that control certain body functions.

What makes up the endocrine system?

How does adrenaline cause the release of energy? Much of the body's reserve supply of energy is stored in the liver in a form called glycogen (GLI kuh jun). Among other things, adrenaline acts on the liver cells causing them to rapidly change stored glycogen to sugar. Sugar is quickly carried by the blood to the body cells such as muscles. There, it is used at once. As the sugar is broken down, energy is quickly released. Glycogen is known as "animal starch." Can you explain why?

What is glycogen? What is its purpose?

### making sure

**9.** Describe a situation in which the action of adrenaline may have helped you perform better than normal.

**10.** In an emergency, a person may experience the "fight or flight" feeling. The person may stay and try to solve the problem or run away to escape possible harm. How is adrenaline involved in the person's behavior?

**Table 5–2.**
Some Major Endocrine Glands

| Gland | Hormone produced | Tissue affected | Function |
|---|---|---|---|
| Adrenal | Adrenaline | Heart | Increases heartbeat, blood pressure, and blood sugar level |
| | Aldosterone | Kidneys | Regulates mineral metabolism |
| | Cortisol | Body cells, liver | Influences metabolism, antibody production, and tissue repair |
| Pancreas | Glucagon | Liver | Regulates blood sugar level |
| | Insulin | Liver | Regulates blood sugar level and promotes synthesis of proteins and fats |
| Parathyroids | Parathormone | Bones, intestines, kidneys | Regulates calcium and phosphorous metabolism |
| Pituitary | GH or somatotropin | Body cells | Regulates bones and muscle growth |
| | Corticotropin | Adrenal gland | Stimulates adrenal cortex |
| | Prolactin | Mammary glands | Stimulates the production of milk |
| | ADH or Vasopressin | Kidneys | Regulates the water concentration in body fluids |
| | Gonadotrophins | Testes, ovaries | Stimulates sex organs |
| | Oxytocin | Uterus | Influences birth process |
| | Parathyrotrophin | Parathyroid | Stimulates the parathyroid gland |
| Thyroid | Thyroxin | Body cells | Regulates metabolism and growth |
| | Triiodothyronine | Body cells | Same as above |
| | Calcitonin | Bones | Maintains calcium and phosphorus levels in the blood |

## 5:10 Behavior and Habit

Behavior is the response of an organism to the things around it. A simple, natural kind of behavior is called a reflex. Behavior also includes conditioned reflexes. Conditioned reflexes are examples of learned behavior. Behavior is controlled by the nervous and endocrine systems.

Human behavior is complex and difficult to study. Human behavior is influenced by heredity and environment. Most human behavior is more complex than reflexes. Most human behavior involves learning.

A **habit** is a learned pattern of behavior. It is done without thinking about how to do it. Buttoning your coat, reading, writing, and riding a bicycle are examples of habits. At first, each one of these behaviors must be learned. A behavior becomes a habit when it becomes automatic as a result of constant repetition.

Habits can be time and thought savers. Many of the things you do are habits. If you had to think through each act you perform each day, you might not have enough time to do anything else. Not all habits are good ones. Do you have any bad habits? How could you break these habits?

Behavior that brings satisfaction or pleasure to the learner may become a habit. For example, as a young child you may have enjoyed writing your name. Through practice and resulting satisfaction, this act became a habit. Behavior that avoids something unpleasant may also become a habit.

Psychology is the scientific study of behavior. It holds great promise for future discoveries. One of the major contributions of psychology is the discovery of the importance of early childhood. Research has shown that a person's attitudes, beliefs, and judgments are largely influenced by early home environment. Thus, the first few years of a person's life have a great influence on future behavior.

Edward Shay

*Jan Lukas/Photo Researchers, Inc.*

FIGURE 5–19. Reading, writing, and playing basketball are examples of learned behaviors.

Define behavior.

How is a habit different from a reflex?

What science deals with the study of behavior?

### making sure

**11.** How does a child learn to walk? What are the rewards involved?

# PERSPECTIVES

## frontiers

# New Ways to Treat Pain

Everyone is familiar with some type of pain. The pain of a headache or a pulled muscle is called acute pain. Acute pain does not last very long. Pain that lasts three months or more is called chronic pain. People who suffer from chronic pain may suffer for years.

Scientists are learning more about pain and its treatment. Often, doctors rely on drugs to treat pain. However, other treatments are also being used to aid pain sufferers.

Acupuncture is an ancient Chinese method of pain treatment in which needles are placed under the skin at specific body sites. Some doctors believe that acupuncture causes the body to release natural pain killers.

Some types of chronic pain such as pain caused by tension can be relieved by teaching the patient to relax. In some cases a sound producing machine is used to indicate the degree of muscle tension. This machine enables the patient to monitor his or her condition and work at controlling it. This method of pain relief is called biofeedback.

Years ago people used electric eels to provide a shock to alleviate pain. Two modern methods of pain treatment also involve the use of shock. Brain stimulation involves placing electrodes in the brain. A small battery-powered generator provides electricity for the electrodes. When pain occurs, the patient presses a small control button, activating the generator, and causing the electrodes to produce a mild shock. Electrodes may also be implanted at or taped near the site of pain. The intensity of the shock provided by the electrodes can be controlled by the patient. This method of treatment has an eighty percent success rate for acute pain sufferers, and a somewhat lower success rate for chronic pain sufferers.

Nerve blocks or surgery may be used in extreme cases where no other methods have worked. Chemicals can be injected into nerves, permanently or temporarily blocking impulses to the brain. If pain is severe, it may be necessary to cut the nerves that carry the pain impulses. Because cutting the nerve usually affects other body functions, it is only used where no other treatment has worked.

Even though many treatments are currently in use, doctors continue to search for better ways to kill pain. Scientists are learning more about nerve functions, how pain signals are transmitted, and the body's natural pain killers. It is hoped that this information will someday lead to life without pain.

*Image Workshop*

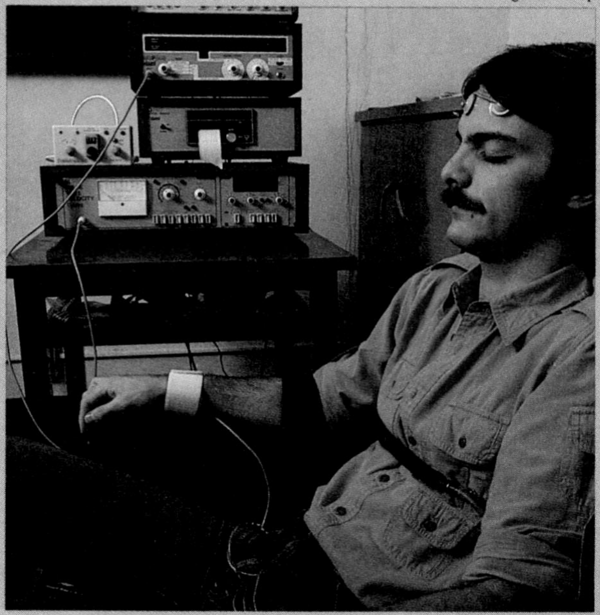

# main ideas — Chapter Review

1. All body functions and behavior are controlled and regulated by the nervous system and endocrine system. 5:1
2. The brain and spinal cord (central nervous system) are the major nerve centers. 5:1, 5:2
3. Messages, called impulses, travel through neurons from receptors to effectors. 5:3, 5:4
4. A reflex act is an unlearned, involuntary response to a stimulus. 5:5
5. A reflex act may be conditioned or modified by substituting a new stimulus for the original one. 5:6
6. Ganglia are nerve centers in the autonomic nervous system that regulate involuntary actions such as heartbeat. 5:7
7. Impulses are transferred across synapses by chemicals. 5:8
8. Hormones are secreted into the blood by endocrine glands. 5:9
9. Human behavior is influenced by both heredity and environment. 5:10
10. A habit is an unconscious, learned behavior pattern resulting from repetition. 5:10

# vocabulary

*Define each of the following words or terms.*

autonomic nervous system
behavior
cerebellum
cerebrum
conditioned reflex
effectors
endocrine system
habit
hormone
impulse
medulla
neurons
receptors
reflex
reflex arc
response
spinal cord
stimulus
synapses

# study questions

**DO NOT WRITE IN THIS BOOK.**

**A. True or False**

*Determine whether each of the following sentences is true or false. If the sentence is false, rewrite it to make it true.*

1. The ganglia are major nerve centers in the spinal cord.
2. The brain and spinal cord are parts of the central nervous system.

3. Thinking is regulated by the cerebellum.
4. Seeing is controlled by the cerebrum.
5. The medulla regulates body balance and muscular coordination.
6. The spinal cord is bathed in spinal fluid.
7. Paralysis results if the spinal cord is severed.
8. Nerve impulses travel from receptors to effectors.
9. A reflex arc bypasses the spinal cord.
10. A reflex is an example of conscious behavior.

## B. Multiple Choice

*Choose the word or phrase that completes correctly each of the following sentences.*

1. The retina is located in the (*ear, eye, nose, tongue*).
2. (*Effectors, Rods, Cones, Association neurons*) are sensitive to different colors of bright light.
3. The blind spot is a point on the retina in which (*rods, cones, rods and cones*) are absent.
4. The receptors in the human nervous system are unaffected by (*sound, red light, heat, infrared light*).
5. *(Psychology, Physiology, Philosophy)* is the study of human behavior.
6. The endocrine system is a network of (*duct glands, ductless glands, nerves, ganglia*).
7. Endocrine glands secrete (*enzymes, hormones, saliva*).
8. When a person is excited, the adrenaline content of the blood (*increases, decreases, remains the same*).
9. A sudden flash of light into your eyes is a(n) (*response, effector, receptor, stimulus*).
10. A dog secreting saliva at the sound of a bell is an example of a(n) (*habit, conscious act, conditioned reflex*).

## C. Completion

*Complete each of the following sentences with a word or phrase that will make the sentence correct.*

1. A(n) ______ is a learned, complex pattern of behavior.
2. ______ and spinal cord make up the central nervous system.
3. ______ is an example of a habit.

4. In a reflex arc, an impulse travels from a receptor through a(n) ______ to the spinal cord.
5. A(n) ______ connects the spinal cord with an effector.
6. ______ is an example of a receptor.
7. ______ is an example of an effector.
8. ______ is the scientific study of behavior.
9. The autonomic ______ system is involuntary.
10. ______ are chemicals produced by endocrine glands.

**D. How and Why**

1. Describe the parts of a reflex arc and explain how they may cause a reflex act when stimulated.
2. Compare the functions of the central nervous system with the functions of the autonomic nervous system.
3. How do hormones regulate the human body?
4. How would you use the principles of habit formation to break a "bad habit"?
5. Explain how you would attempt to produce a conditioned reflex in a friend.

## challenges

1. Devise an experiment to change a simple reflex in an animal to a conditioned reflex.
2. The human brain is a frontier in scientific study. Prepare a report on recent research in one area of study related to the human brain.
3. Prepare a report on biofeedback. What is it? Does it help?
4. Rules for the Olympic Games forbid the use of steroids by athletes before they compete. Find out the effects of steroids on the body and why there are rules against their use.

## interesting reading

Cobb, Vicki, *How to Really Fool Yourself: Illusions For All Your Senses.* New York: J. B. Lippincott, 1981.

Simon, Hilda, *Sight and Seeing: A World of Light and Color.* New York: Philomel, 1983.

# SIDE ROADS

## Taming Snake Venom

Doug Wynn

*All of the body systems described in this unit work in a closely coordinated manner, enabling a human to survive. When one system fails, the others are quickly affected. Many substances are known to interfere with the proper functioning of these systems.*

*In 1957, Dr. Karl Schmid, one of the foremost authorities on snakes, was bitten by an African boomslang. During the following 24 hours, Dr. Schmidt kept detailed notes on how his body reacted to the venom. His symptoms included nausea, chills, and bleeding of the mucous membranes in the nose and mouth. At noon on the day following the bite, he began to have trouble breathing. He was taken to the hospital where he was pronounced dead at 3:00 P.M. An autopsy revealed extensive bleeding, as the blood vessels surrounding the brain, intestinal wall, heart wall, and kidneys had hemorrhaged.*

*Since 1957, scientists have learned much about snake venoms. Some of the most common substances found in snake venoms, called neurotoxins, prevent nerve cells from functioning. Others, called hemotoxins, affect the circulatory system by damaging blood vessels, bursting blood cells, or preventing blood clotting. The composition and effects of a venom vary with snake species. Cobras and coral snakes have venoms that primarily affect the nervous system. Rattlesnake, copperhead, and water moccasin venoms affect the circulatory system.*

*Dr. Anthony Tu, a biochemist at Colorado State University, has been studying snake venoms since 1964. Currently he is studying neurotoxins in Southeast Asian and Central American sea snake venoms and hemotoxins in rattlesnake venoms. Dr. Tu collects venom from the snakes either by removing the venom gland or by inserting a thin tube into the fang and squeezing venom through the tube into a container. The venom is then purified and separated into its different components. The components are identified and tested as to their effects on human tissue or laboratory animals.*

*The results from these tests provide many answers as to how venoms affect body systems. For example, normally nerve cells release a chemical that flows to muscle cells, causing them to contract. The neurotoxins in cobra venom bind to the muscle cells and prevent the chemical from reaching them. Thus, contraction of the muscle is inhibited. Because these neurotoxins usually affect the nerves that control breathing, an individual bitten by a cobra may undergo respiratory failure.*

*Doug Wynn*

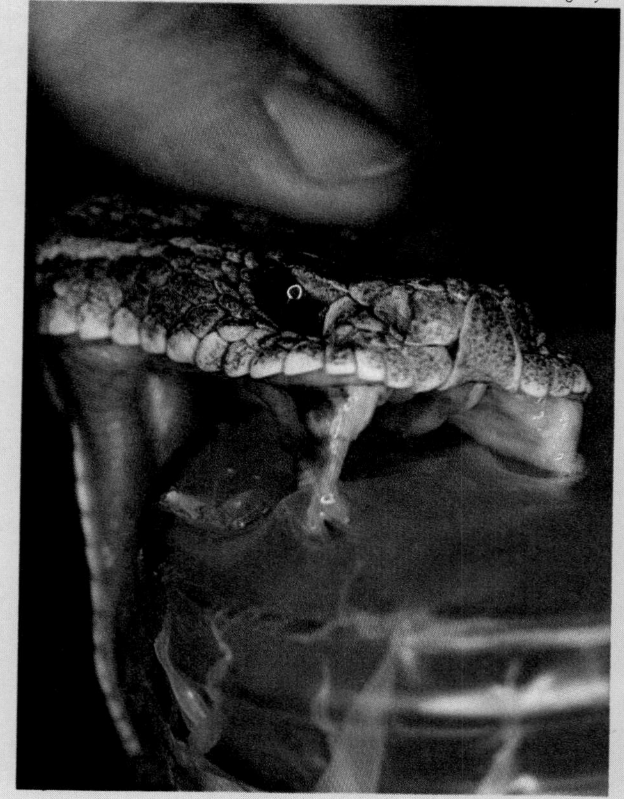

*Doug Wynn*

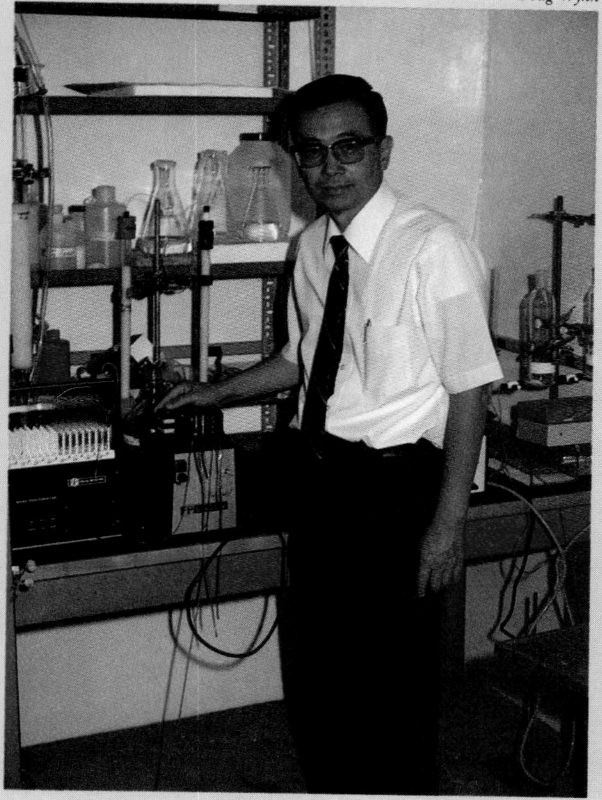

*Tests such as those conducted by Dr. Tu may result in the use of venoms to fight disease. In Europe, venoms are used to prevent blood clotting in people with heart diseases. Venom is also being used to study how substances enter and leave cells. Although unsubstantiated, some people believe that snake venoms can be used to treat arthritis and multiple sclerosis. In the future, a substance that was only used to aid a snake in obtaining food and protecting itself may aid humans in their efforts to prevent and cure disease.*

*Many people today are concerned about health and fitness. Some people show this concern by controlling their diet or taking vitamins. Others exercise regularly. How do these activities help keep people healthy? What activities can harm your health? What safeguards help prevent disease?*

Rick Kocks

# Human Health

## unit 2

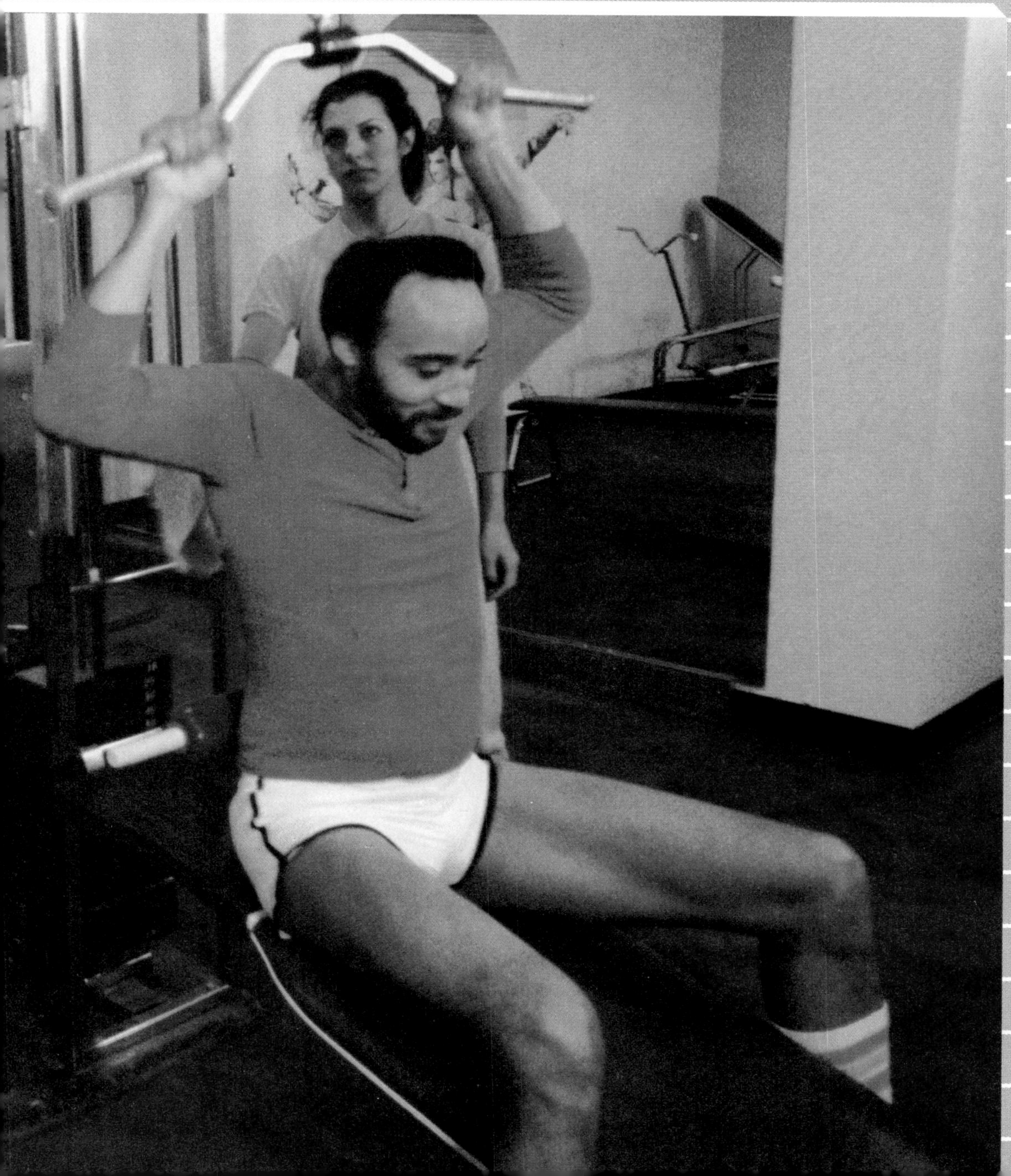

*You need to eat a variety of foods for good nutrition. With many foods from which to choose, it is not always easy to choose the best foods for your health. Are some foods more nutritional than others? How can you find out what is in the foods that you eat? How can you be sure you are getting enough of the proper foods?*

Roland and Sabrina Michaud/Woodfin Camp and Assoc.

# Nutrition

## chapter 6

### 6:1 Food and Health

GOAL: You will learn how nutrients are used in the growth and repair of body tissues.

Your body needs energy to carry on its life processes. Energy is needed to build and repair body tissues. Energy is needed to work muscles so you can walk and run. Any substance that provides this energy for the body is called a **food.** Foods contain a variety of nutrients that are used by the body to carry on life processes. A **nutrient** is a material required by cells. There are six main types of nutrients—water, minerals, carbohydrates, fats, proteins, and vitamins. The study of nutrients and their use by the body is called **nutrition.**

Define the terms food and nutrition.

Good nutrition requires that you eat foods that provide the correct amounts and kinds of nutrients each day. A balanced diet provides the proper amounts of nutrients. It is not hard to eat a balanced diet. Choosing wisely from the four food groups provides a balanced diet. Fruits and vegetables are a good source of nutrients. They also contain fibers that stimulate the muscles of the digestive organs. Figure 6–1 shows the four food groups.

How can you have a balanced diet?

FIGURE 6–1. The four food groups are the milk group (a), the meat group (b), the vegetable-fruit group (c), and the bread-cereal group (d).

## activity

### DO YOU EAT A BALANCED DIET?

List the foods you eat each day for a week. Did you eat a food from each of the four food groups? If not, what was missing? Save this list of foods to use later.

## making sure

**1.** Why is a diet containing fiber important?

## 6:2 Water

Have you ever been without water for a long period of time? How did you feel? Water is vital to your health. About 65 percent of your body is water. A water loss of 10 percent results in serious illness. A 20 percent loss usually results in death.

Water is needed to digest food and remove wastes. Blood plasma, which carries food to your cells, is about 90 percent water. Urine and other body wastes also contain water. All food contains some water. Vegetables and fruits have a high water content. You also obtain water by drinking it and by drinking milk and juices. You should drink six to eight glasses of liquid each day to be sure you are getting enough water.

Hickson/Bender Photography

FIGURE 6–2. Fruits such as grapes contain a lot of water (a). Raisins are formed when most of the water is removed (b).

## 6:3 Minerals

**Minerals** are chemical substances needed by the body. Calcium and phosphorus are needed for the formation of strong bones and teeth. Iron is needed for the formation of red blood cells. Chlorine is needed by the glands in the stomach to make hydrochloric acid. Human hair contains 4 to 6 percent sulfur. Other minerals are needed for the formation of hormones, enzymes, and other body substances. Foods from the four food groups are good sources of minerals.

State the function of water in your body.

Name a use for calcium, iron, phosphorus, and chlorine in the body.

The absence of minerals can harm the body. A lack of iodine in the diet can cause a goiter, an enlargement of the thyroid gland. Iodine compounds are added to table salt so that the body gets enough of the mineral to prevent thyroid enlargement.

Minerals used by the body must be in the form of compounds. In a compound, the minerals are combined with other elements. Many minerals needed by the body are poisonous in their element form. The elements sodium and chlorine are poisonous. Table salt, a chemical compound of sodium and chlorine, is a necessary nutrient. Sodium is necessary to maintain proper blood pressure.

In what form are minerals used by the body?

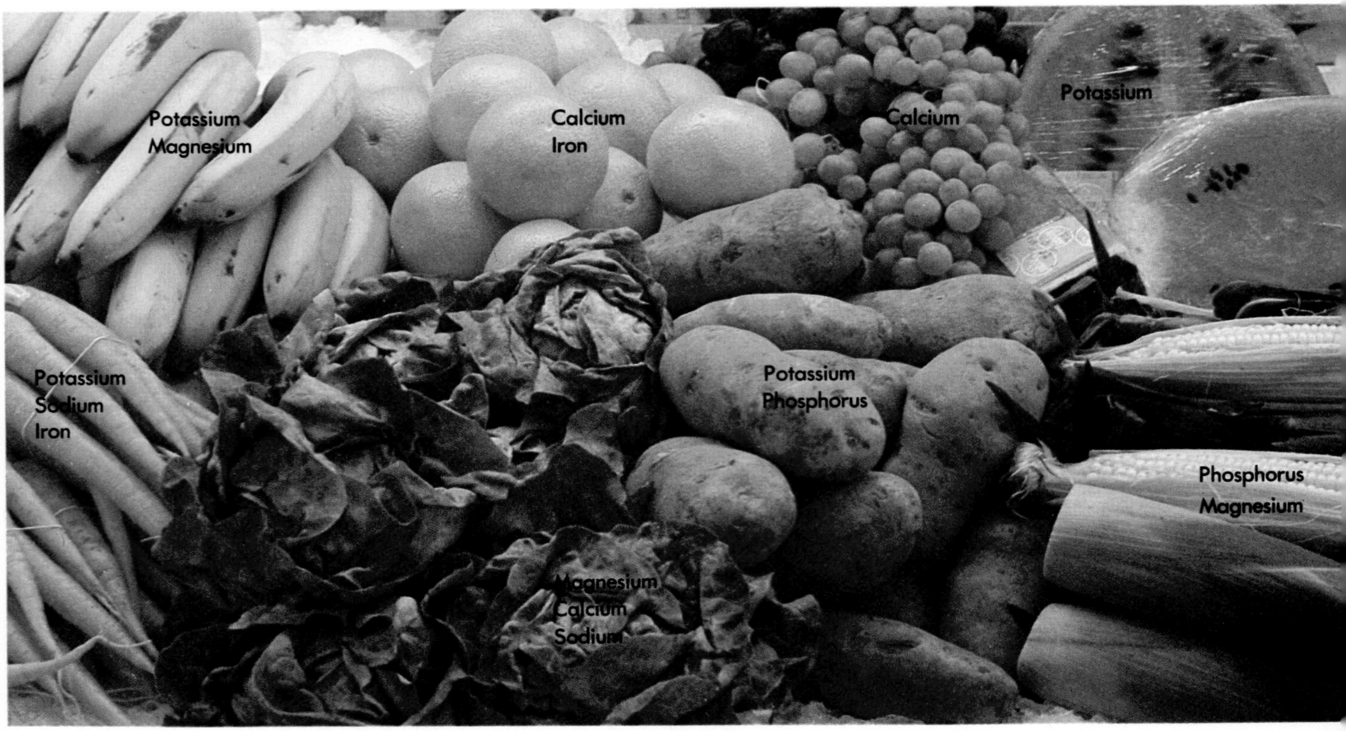


FIGURE 6–3. Fruits and vegetables are good sources of the minerals needed by the body.

Chlorine is an essential part of digestive fluids and helps the blood carry carbon dioxide.

Can minerals be harmful to the body? Explain.

As with most nutrients, you can get too much of a good thing. If used in large amounts, minerals can be harmful to your health. For example, a high table salt intake has been linked to high blood pressure in some people.

a b

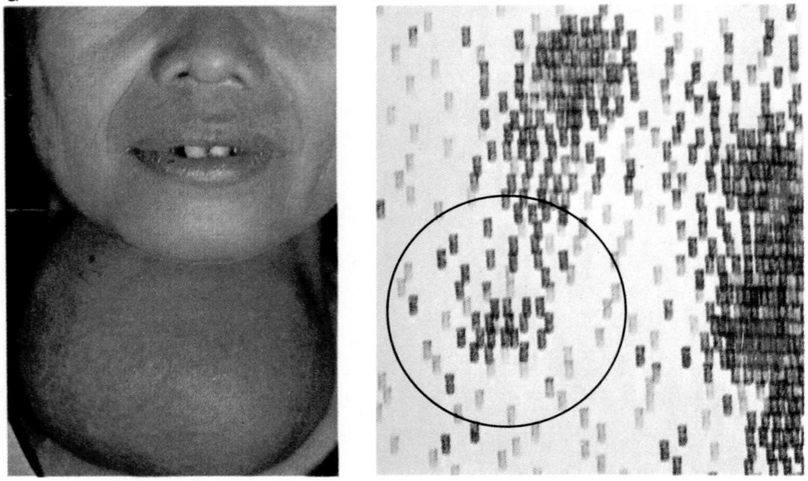

Centers for Disease Control, Atlanta, GA. Camera M.D. Studios, Inc.

FIGURE 6–4. A goiter (a) is an enlarged thyroid gland. Radioactive iodine is used to detect goiter. Goiter shows up as clear areas (circle) where little or no iodine was absorbed (b).

*Table 6–1.*
Some Minerals Needed by the Human Body

| Mineral | Suggested daily amount (mg) | Body function |
|---|---|---|
| Calcium | 800 | Blood clotting, development of bones and teeth |
| Chlorine | 1700–5100 | Essential to food digestion, helps blood carry carbon dioxide to lungs |
| Chromium | 0.05–0.2 | Helps regulate insulin |
| Copper | 2–3 | Helps produce hemoglobin |
| Fluorine | 1.5–4 | Formation of bones and tooth enamel |
| Iodine | 0.15 | Thyroid function |
| Iron | 10 | Essential part of hemoglobin |
| Magnesium | 350 | Regulates body temperature |
| Manganese | 2.5–5 | Conversion of food into proteins and energy |
| Phosphorus | 800 | Formation of bones and teeth |
| Potassium | 1875–5625 | Fluid levels in cells |
| Selenium | 0.05–0.2 | Blood functions |
| Sodium | 1100–3300 | Regulates amount of fluids in body, essential to nerve impulse movement |
| Zinc | 15 | Growth of tissues, helps heal wounds |

## 6:4 Carbohydrates

**Carbohydrates** contain the elements carbon, hydrogen, and oxygen. Sugar and starch are two carbohydrates. Bread, rice, potatoes, beans, and cereals are good sources of starch. Green and yellow vegetables and fruits contain natural sugars that are easily digested.

What is a carbohydrate? Name two.

Carbohydrates are changed to a sugar called glucose when they are digested. Glucose is used by body cells to produce energy for life activities. More than half of your diet is probably made of carbohydrates. Yet there are few carbohydrates stored in your body. Carbohydrates stored in your body are changed from glucose to glycogen. Glycogen is stored in the liver and muscles. It can be changed to glucose when it is needed to provide energy. Scientists estimate that an adult requires 100 g of carbohydrates daily to maintain good health.

How is glycogen related to glucose?

# activity

## STARCH OR SUGAR

**Objective:** To test various food samples for starch and sugar

### Materials

beaker, 600 mL
Benedict's solution
burner
2 droppers
glass dinner plate
graduated cylinder, 10 mL
iodine solution
knife
marking pencil
matches
ring stand/ring
6 test tubes
test tube holder
test tube rack
water
wire screen
food samples:
  apple juice
  bread
  candy
  carrot
  cornstarch
  corn syrup
  egg white, hard boiled
  milk
  potato
  rice

### Procedure

1. Put a small amount of potato, egg white, rice, bread, cereal, candy, carrot, and cornstarch on the glass plate.
2. Add a drop of iodine solution to each food sample. Observe and record any color changes.
3. Label the test tubes, *A, B, C, D, E,* and *F.* Add 5 mL of Benedict's solution to each test tube.
4. Add the following to the test tubes as indicated.
   *A*—4 drops corn syrup
   *B*—small piece of candy
   *C*—small piece of bread
   *D*—5 mL apple juice
   *E*—small piece of egg white
   *F*—2 mL milk
5. Fill the beaker half full of water and bring the water to a boil using the burner. Place the test tubes in the hot water. Let them stand for 5 minutes.
6. Remove the test tubes from the hot water with the test tube holder. Observe and record any color changes.

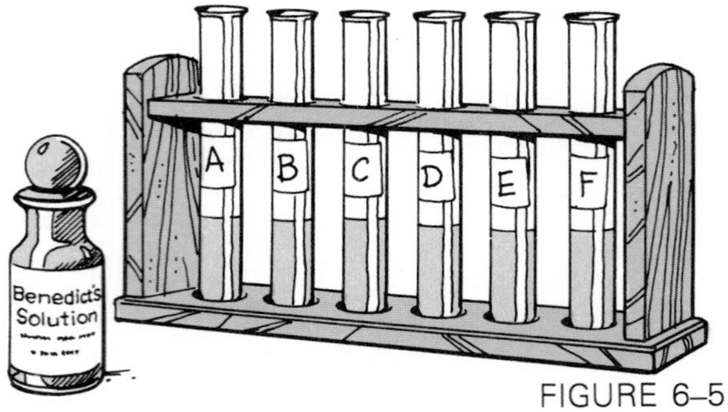


FIGURE 6–5.

### Observations and Data

| Food sample/ test tube | Color change |
|---|---|
| *A* | |
| | |

### Questions and Conclusions

1. If starch is present, the brown-red color of iodine changes to a deep blue-black. Which foods contained starch?
2. To what basic food group does each food sample that contained starch belong?
3. What foods contained sugar? How do you know? (HINT: What happened to the Benedict's solution?)
4. What is the test for starch? For glucose?

Gerard Photography

FIGURE 6–6. Cooking oil, butter, and cheese are some foods rich in fats and oils.

## 6:5 Fats and Oils

What elements are present in fats and oils?

**Fats** and **oils** are compounds rich in energy. They contain the elements carbon, hydrogen, and oxygen. Fats and oils have more energy per gram than carbohydrates. Cheese, milk, butter, margarine, and nuts are foods rich in fats and oils. Fats are solids at room temperature. Oils are liquids at room temperature.

What is the function of fat in the body?

When a person eats more food than the body can use, the excess is stored as body fat. This body fat serves as a reserve supply of energy. It also helps to protect the internal organs from injury. Fat deposits can also build up inside blood vessels. This build up reduces the flow of blood and can lead to a heart attack or stroke. As a result, many doctors recommend a diet low in animal fat. Such a diet limits the amount of meat, eggs, cheese, and other foods high in animal fat. The minimum fat requirement in the human diet is not known. Scientists believe that a balanced diet provides an adequate amount of fats and oils.

### activity
### WHICH FOODS ARE RICH IN FATS?

Obtain a piece of unglazed paper, such as brown wrapping paper. Hold the paper up to a light. Does any light come through the paper? Now rub some fat or oil on the paper. Again, hold the paper up to a light. What change has occurred? This smear test is the test for fats. Test samples of margarine, butter, peanut butter, cheese, bacon, banana, and salad dressing to see if these foods contain fats or oils. Which foods contained fats or oils?

*Latent Image*

FIGURE 6–7. Meats, dairy products, and nuts are good sources of protein.

How are proteins used in the body?

## 6:6 Proteins

A **protein** is a compound made of amino acids. More than 20 amino acids have been discovered. At least 10 amino acids are vital to the repair and growth of body tissue. All **amino acids** contain carbon, hydrogen, oxygen, and nitrogen. Some also contain sulfur and phosphorus. Amino acids are used by cells to make hormones, enzymes, and antibodies. Amino acids are good energy sources.

Lean meat, eggs, milk, fish, peas, beans, cheese, and soybeans are good sources of protein. Soybean meal is sometimes added to foods to increase the protein content. Soybeans are low in one amino acid needed by the body. Therefore, they cannot completely replace animal protein in a diet.

## 6:7 Vitamins

A **vitamin** is a complex compound that aids the body in using proteins, fats, and carbohydrates. Lack of vitamins in the diet can result in a **vitamin deficiency disease.** At one time, some sailors who were at sea for many months became ill with scurvy (SKUR vee). A person with scurvy has sore, bleeding gums, and lacks energy. The British Navy discovered that eating limes or other citrus fruits, such as oranges, lemons, or grapefruits, prevented scurvy. Today it is known that scurvy is caused by a lack of vitamin C. Sailors developed scurvy on long ocean voyages because they did not eat fresh fruits or other foods rich in vitamin C for long periods of time.

What is the best way to obtain the vitamins you need?

FIGURE 6–8. Citrus fruits, cabbage, and other vegetables are good sources of vitamins.

*USDA*

Rickets (RIHK uts) is also a vitamin deficiency disease. It is caused by a lack of vitamin D, calcium, or phosphorus. A person with rickets may have bones that are curved instead of straight. If a child's diet lacks any one of the three substances named above, rickets may develop.

The best way to get the vitamins you need is to eat a balanced diet. Most people who eat a balanced diet do not need to take vitamin pills. Vitamin pills should be taken only upon the advice of a doctor. Table 6–2 lists some vitamins and their sources.

Name several vitamins. Why is each required for good health?

*Table 6–2.*
Vitamins—Their Sources and Functions

| Vitamin | Food source | Function | Deficiency symptoms |
|---|---|---|---|
| A | Milk, butter, margarine, liver, leafy green and yellow vegetables | Growth, health of eyes and skin | Night blindness, slowed growth, defective tooth growth |
| $B_1$ (thiamine) | Cereals, bread, fish, lean meat, liver, milk, green vegetables | Growth, working of the heart, nerves, and muscles | Slowed growth, poor digestion, loss of appetite and weight, nerve disorders |
| $B_2$ (riboflavin) | Meat, soybeans, milk, green vegetables, eggs, poultry | Healthy skin, provides building and maintaining of tissue, prevents sensitivity of eyes to light | Premature aging, dimness of vision, sensitivity to light |
| $B_{12}$ | Green vegetables, liver | Prevents anemia | Reduction in the number of red blood cells, tiredness |
| Niacin | Meat, poultry, fish, peanut butter, potatoes, whole grain | Prevents pellagra, promotes healthy nervous system | Mental disorders, skin blemishes |
| C (ascorbic acid) | Citrus fruits, leafy vegetables, fruits | Prevents scurvy, promotes healthy blood and strong body cells | Sore gums, fatigue, tendency to bruise easily |
| D | Fish-liver oil, liver, fortified milk, eggs | Prevents rickets, aids metabolism of calcium and phosphorus | Curved bones, dental decay |
| E | Vegetable oils, wheat germ, whole grains, lettuce | Prevents infertility, muscular dystrophy | Not determined |
| K | Leafy vegetables | Aids blood clotting | Hemorrhages |

activity
### TESTING FOR VITAMIN C

**(1)** Add 10 mL of methylene blue solution to a test tube. **(2)** Use a dropper and add a drop of fresh orange juice to the test tube. Gently swirl the test tube. **(3)** Continue to add orange juice to the test tube one drop at a time. Swirl the test tube after every addition. Count the number of drops of orange juice needed to change the color of the solution from blue to colorless. **(4)** Record this number. **(5)** Repeat Steps 1–3 using lemon juice, grapefruit juice, and lime juice. **(6)** Record the number of drops of each juice needed to turn the methylene blue solution colorless. Which juice contains the most vitamin C?

## 6:8 Energy from Food

How is food's energy value measured?

The energy value of food is measured in a heat unit. The heat unit is called a Calorie. One **Calorie** is the amount of heat needed to raise the temperature of 1 kg of water 1°C. How many Calories do you need each day? This requirement depends on your age, size, sex, and daily activities. People who exercise, take part in athletics, or do hard physical work need more Calories than those who do not engage in these activities.

What factors determine the number of Calories you need each day?

Why may some persons become overweight?

When a healthy person consumes more Calories per day than the body needs for energy, the excess is stored as fat. The person gains weight. As a result, an overweight person must decrease Calorie intake to

FIGURE 6-9. Fewer calories are burned while sitting at a desk (a) than while engaging in an active sport (b).

a

*Image Workshop*

b

*Dr. E. R. Degginger*

**Table 6–3.**
Daily Calorie Requirements

| | Age (yr) | Calories |
|---|---|---|
| Boys | 9–12 | 2400 |
| | 12–15 | 3000 |
| | 15–18 | 3400 |
| Girls | 9–12 | 2200 |
| | 12–15 | 2500 |
| | 15–18 | 2300 |

lose weight. The person must consume fewer Calories than are needed so stored body fat is then broken down. Proper weight control depends upon keeping the Calorie intake equal to the Calories used for energy by the body.

## activity CALORIES

Use the Calorie Charts listed in Appendix C and the food list from the Activity on page 104. Calculate the number of Calories per day that you eat. Is this number higher or lower than the minimum requirement for your age group? What food group provides most of the calories you eat? Use the Calorie Charts and Figure 6–1 to write balanced meals for one day.

## making sure

2. Do you think the Calorie requirement of a 26-year-old person would be more or less than that of an 14-year-old person? Explain.
3. Look at the Calorie requirements for a 9-year-old boy and a 9-year-old girl. Why do you think the Calorie requirement is higher for the boy?
4. What happens when a person consumes more Calories per day than the body needs for energy?
5. How is a Calorie defined?

## 6:9 Food Additives and Food Labels

What is in food? Fresh meat, fruits, eggs, vegetables, cereal grains, and milk contain natural nutrients. Natural means the nutrient was produced by a plant or animal. Some foods, including bread and milk, have vitamins and minerals added to improve their nutritional value. These added nutrients are food additives.

Why are preservatives added to food?

There are five main classes of food additives: nutrients, preservatives, processing aids, flavorings, and colorings. Nutrients include vitamins and minerals. Preservatives are used to prevent changes in color, flavor, and texture of foods. Preservatives also are used to prevent the growth of harmful organisms in food. Calcium propionate (PROH pee uh nayt) is used to keep bread mold from growing. Processing aids are used to improve taste or texture. Gelatin makes ice cream smooth. Lecithin (LES uh thun) keeps the oil from separating in a jar of peanut butter.

Sugar and salt are the two most common flavorings. These two additives account for 93 percent of the additives a person eats in one year. Food colorings are used to make foods look appealing. Red dye is used to make strawberry jelly look red. Strawberry jelly is naturally pink. Yellow dyes are used to make cheeses look yellow. Most

Image Workshop

FIGURE 6–10. Many foods contain additives. Food additives include nutrients, preservatives, processing aids, flavorings, and colorings.

**Table 6–4.**
Some Food Additives

| Additive | Where found | Purpose |
|---|---|---|
| Iodine<br>Iron | Salt<br>Breads, cereals | To replace minerals and iron lost in processing |
| Ascorbic acid | Fruit juices | To increase vitamin C |
| Butylparaben<br>Calcium propionate<br>Sodium benzoate<br>Sodium nitrate | Cakes, pies, salad dressings<br>Breads<br>Margarine<br>Cured meats | To prevent growth of bacteria, molds, fungi, and yeasts; protect color and/or flavor |
| BHA or BHT<br>Carrageenan<br><br>EDTA<br>MSG | Cakes, pies, breads, fats, and oils<br>Whipped toppings, puddings, ice cream<br>Dressings, margarine<br>Oriental foods, soups | To prevent or delay changes in color, flavor, or texture |
| Citrus Red No. 2<br>Corn syrup<br>Fructose<br>Saccharin<br>Spices<br>Vanilla<br>Yellow No. 5 | Orange skins<br>Cereals, cakes, cookies<br>Cereals, cakes, cookies<br>Soft drinks, special dietary foods<br>Found in many products<br>Found in many products<br>Found in many products | To add color, flavor, or sweetness |

dyes are considered safe for people to eat. However, some dyes may be harmful to certain people. Table 6–4 lists some food additives.

Scientists and doctors are studying the effects of additives on human health. Eating large amounts of sugar, salt, and other chemical additives may cause changes in the behavior of some people. Many doctors recommend a diet of natural foods that do not contain any food additives. How do you know if the food you are eating contains a food additive?

Processed food is usually sold in bottles, cans, or boxes. Federal law requires processed food to have a label. Certain information must be listed on the food label. First, the name of the product must be listed. Second, the label must list the ingredients in the food. The ingredient that is used in the greatest

What information must be present on a food label?

amount must be listed first. Third, the net weight of the food must be listed. The net weight is the weight of the food, not the food and the container. Last, the name of the manufacturer must be listed.

Most food labels also include nutritional information. This information includes what nutrients are present in the food, how many servings are in the container, and the number of Calories per serving. The chemical name of any artificial flavor, color, or preservative is listed. By carefully reading the label, you can find out what is in the food you are eating. After you have read the label, you can decide if the food is nutritious. You can use the labels to compare the nutritional content of different foods, or of different brands of the same food. Reading labels will help you make healthful food choices.

Many people choose foods that are low in carbohydrates and fats. They select foods that are rich in proteins, vitamins, and minerals. By reading labels on food packages, you can select a variety of nutritious foods for a balanced diet. You can also avoid any food substance that might be harmful to your health.

FIGURE 6–11. Food labels contain information that can aid you in making healthy food choices.

## activity

### FOOD LABELS

**Objective:** To learn what information is given about food on a label

**Materials**

10 different food labels
paper
pencil

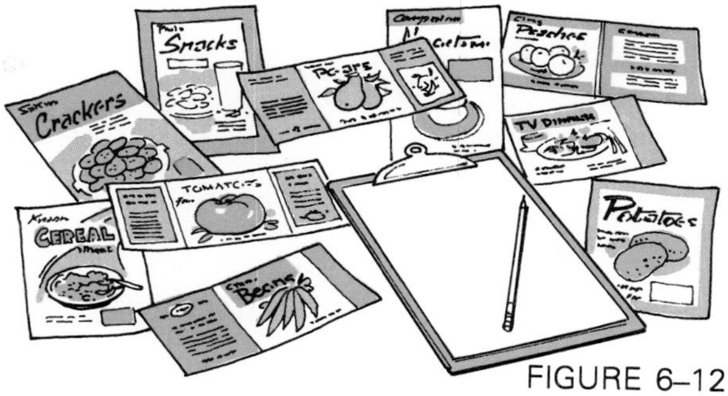

FIGURE 6–12.

**Procedure**

1. Collect the labels from 10 of your favorite processed foods.
2. Fill in the blanks in your data table with the information for each food.

**Observations and Data**

Copy the table below in your notebook.

**Questions and Conclusions**

1. What was the main natural ingredient in each food?
2. To which basic food group does each food belong?
3. If you ate portions of these 10 foods in one day, would you eat a balanced diet? Explain.
4. If you ate one serving of each of these 10 foods in one day, would you exceed the number of Calories your body needs? Explain.
5. Which foods would you recommend to a person who is trying to lose weight? Why?
6. Which food(s) contained additives?
7. What was the most common additive?
8. Did any of the foods have added vitamins? Which foods?

| Name of food | Three main ingredients | Calories/ serving | Amount | | | Artificial substances added |
|---|---|---|---|---|---|---|
| | | | Fat | Protein | Carbohydrates | |
| | | | | | | |
| | | | | | | |
| | | | | | | |

## making sure

6. Which two additives are the most common?
7. What information must be listed on a package of processed food?
8. Why are food additives used?

# PERSPECTIVES

## skills

# Using and Interpreting Tables

As you read textbooks, you have probably asked, "How can I remember all of the information in these books?" Not only do you have to remember the information, you also must understand it and relate the information to your everyday life. To do both you must be able to organize information. Organizing means that you see how the many facts relate to each other. Being able to organize increases understanding and makes remembering easier.

One way to relate facts to one another is through the use of tables. There are four tables in Chapter 6. Each table presents information in as few words as possible so that information can be located quickly. Look at Table 6-1 on page 107. Note how clearly the information about minerals is organized. Each mineral is listed with the amount needed by the body as well as how the body uses the mineral. Imagine this information in paragraph form. It probably would require two pages to present the information contained in the table.

Tables are useful only if they can be interpreted. Listed below are questions asking for information from each of the four tables in Chapter 6. See how rapidly and accurately you can locate the answers.

Use Table 6-1 to answer the following questions:

1. What mineral is needed for the formation of bone and tooth enamel? What other two minerals are needed for the same purpose? In which column would you look first to find the answers?
2. Why does the body need potassium? Which column will give you this information?
3. What should be the daily intake of chlorine? Where is this information located?

Use Table 6-2 to answer the following questions:

1. Look at the title of the table. What type of information is given in the table? Look at the column headings. What specific information will you find included in the table?
2. What types of food should be eaten in order for the body to get all the vitamins it needs? Which column provides the information to answer this question?
3. What vitamin aids the clotting of blood?

Use Table 6-3 to answer the following questions:

1. At what age do boys require the greatest Calorie intake?
2. When do girls require the greatest Calorie intake? Are the ages for boys and girls the same? Explain.

Use Table 6-4 to answer the following questions:

1. How is this table organized? What information does it offer?
2. What is one possible disadvantage of processed foods? What can you conclude about the type of information given in the table?
3. Section 6:9 presents clues to explain the reasons preservatives are needed. Can you find them? The table gives examples of food additives. What kinds of foods contain additives? Where would you look for additive information?
4. What foods contain the least amount of additives? You will need to review the information about each food type and the information in Tables 6-2 and 6-4 to answer this question.

## main ideas

1. Good nutrition means eating enough of the right kinds of food each day. Six nutrients needed for good health are water, minerals, carbohydrates, fats, proteins, and vitamins. 6:1
2. The four food groups are the milk, meat, vegetable-fruit, and bread-cereal groups. 6:1
3. Water is a nutrient required in the digestion of foods and the production of body fluids. 6:2
4. Minerals are chemically combined elements needed for good body health. 6:3
5. Carbohydrates contain energy that the body uses to carry on life activities. 6:4
6. Fats contain more energy per gram than carbohydrates. 6:5
7. Proteins contain amino acids that are needed for body repair and growth. 6:6
8. A vitamin deficiency disease is caused by lack of one or more vitamins. 6:7
9. The energy value of food is measured in Calories. 6:8
10. Many processed foods contain food additives. Labels on processed foods list the substances in the foods. 6:9

## vocabulary

*Define each of the following words or terms.*

amino acids
Calorie
carbohydrates
fats
food
minerals
nutrients
nutrition
oils
protein
vitamin
vitamin deficiency disease

## study questions

**DO NOT WRITE IN THIS BOOK.**

### A. True or False

*Determine whether each of the following sentences is true or false. If the sentence is false, rewrite it to make it true.*

1. Water makes up less than 60 percent of the body.
2. Fiber is required for a healthy digestive system.

3. Fruits and vegetables are a poor source of vitamins.
4. For a balanced diet, eat at least one food from each of the basic food groups every day.
5. Food is a substance that provides energy to carry on life activities.
6. Water yields energy in the body.
7. Fat is a source of energy for the human body.
8. Iodine is an enzyme.
9. Iron is required for the formation of hemoglobin.
10. Rickets is a vitamin deficiency disease that may result from a lack of vitamin D, calcium, or phosphorus.

**B. Multiple Choice**

*Choose the word or phrase that completes correctly each of the following sentences.*

1. Sugar is stored in the human body as (*glucose, fat, glycogen*).
2. (*Iodine, Benedict's solution, Fehling's solution*) is used to test for starch.
3. Carbohydrates are plentiful in (*cereals, meats, vegetables*).
4. Starch is a (*carbohydrate, fat, protein, vitamin*).
5. Amino acids are present in (*carbohydrates, proteins, fats*).
6. Fats contain (*more, less, the same*) energy than sugar.
7. Glucose is formed in the digestion of (*proteins, vitamins, carbohydrates, fats*).
8. A fat contains the elements carbon, hydrogen and (*nitrogen, calcium, oxygen*).
9. All proteins contain (*nitrogen, iodine, nickel*).
10. Sulfur is present in some (*carbohydrates, fats, proteins*).

**C. Completion**

*Complete each of the following sentences with a word or phrase that will make the sentence correct.*

1. Vitamin ______ is required for normal blood clotting.
2. A young person requires ______ Calories than an older person.
3. Vitamin ______ prevents scurvy.
4. Rickets is a(n) ______ disease.
5. The energy value of foods is measured in ______.
6. ______ diseases are caused by a lack of vitamins.

7. Consuming more Calories than are required each day may cause a person to gain ______.
8. Minerals needed for healthy bones are phosphorus and ______.
9. A Calorie is the amount of heat needed to raise the temperature of ______ of water 1°C.
10. ______, ______, and ______ are three nutrients containing only carbon, hydrogen, and oxygen.

**D. How and Why**

1. How can you be sure you are eating a balanced diet?
2. For what reasons is water essential to body health?
3. Why are calcium and phosphorous essential to good health?
4. How are carbohydrates and fats different?
5. Explain how the caloric content of a person's diet affects a person's weight.

## challenges

1. Visit a health food store to obtain information about health foods. Distinguish between facts and myths regarding "health" foods.
2. Visit a pet shop or feed store to learn the diets fed to different kinds of animals. Obtain information on the composition of these foods. Prepare a report.
3. Investigate the nutritional value of breakfast cereals. Compare the nutrient content of different cereals and their food value when milk and fruit are added.
4. Prepare a report on substances added to foods to increase their flavor and on substances used to preserve foods.

## interesting reading

Campbell, T. Colin, *What About the Food You Eat?* Burlington, NC: Carolina Biological Supply Co., 1981.

Serrin, William, "Let Them Eat Junk: The Triumph of Food Processing." *Saturday Review,* February 2, 1980, pp. 17-23.

Winter, Ruth, "Appetite Control—The Secret is at the Base of Your Brain." *Science Digest,* October 1980, pp. 8-13.

*With the constant activities involved in living, sometimes the body does not work properly and disease develops. Here, a doctor is using a special machine to break up fatty deposits in an artery. This technique does not require surgery. What other techniques are used in treating diseases? How can you protect yourself from disease?*

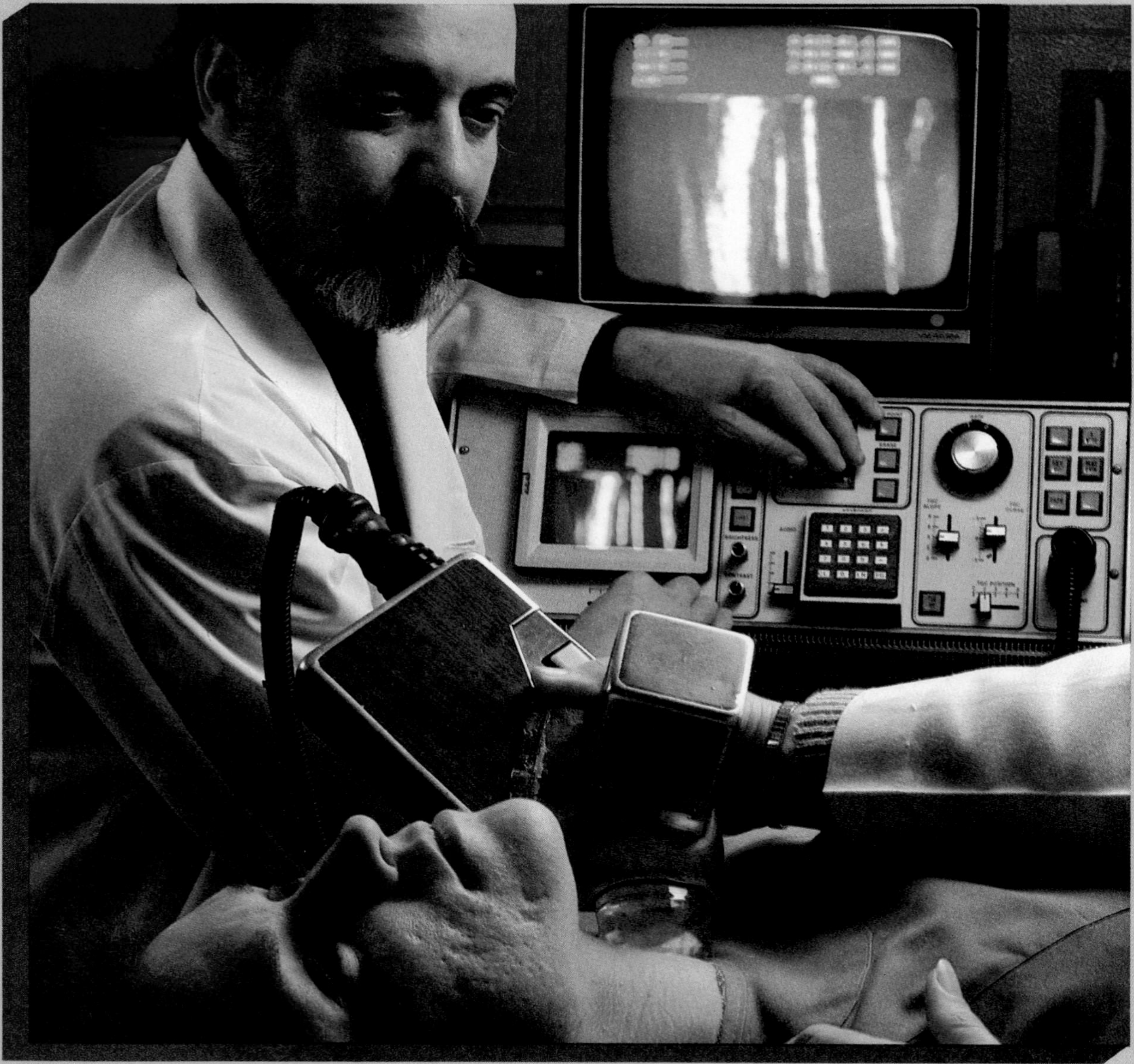

Tobey Sanford/Wheeler Pictures

# Disease

## chapter 7

## 7:1 Disease and Microbes

GOAL: You will learn what causes disease and ways to prevent and treat disease.

**Disease** is the abnormal functioning of any part of the body. Disease has many different causes. Poor nutrition can cause vitamin and mineral deficiency diseases. Disease may result from the failure of the body to produce certain enzymes or hormones. Many diseases are caused by microbes.

Name three causes of disease.

A **microbe** is a living organism or complex substance so small that it can only be seen with a microscope. **Pathogen** is a term that often is used to describe a microbe that causes a disease. Bacteria, viruses, protozoans, and fungi can all be pathogens. Bacteria are one-celled organisms that do not have nuclei and certain other cell parts. Bacteria that cause disease and those that do not cause disease all need food, warmth, and moisture to grow and reproduce. Some diseases caused by bacteria are bubonic plague, tetanus, tuberculosis, and botulism.

What kinds of organisms cause disease?

Jim Elliott

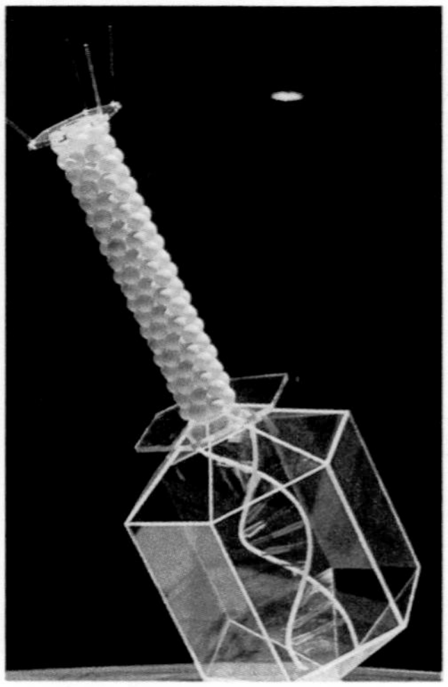

FIGURE 7–1. Viruses live only in the cells of other organisms. This is a model of a virus.

Name five diseases caused by viruses.

Some viruses also cause disease. A virus is a complex substance that can grow and reproduce inside a cell. Many viruses can live in a single human cell. Thus, viruses are parasites. A parasite lives in or on another organism and gains nourishment from that organism. Over 200 different viruses can cause the common cold and other respiratory diseases.

Protozoans cause diseases including African sleeping sickness, malaria, and amoebic dysentery. A protozoan is a one-celled organism that has a cell membrane, but no cell wall. An amoeba is one kind of protozoan. Table 7–1 lists some diseases caused by microbes.

***Table 7–1.***
Diseases Caused by Pathogens

| Disease | Cause |
|---|---|
| Anthrax | Bacteria: *Bacillus anthracis* |
| Cholera | Bacteria: *Vibrio cholerae* |
| Tuberculosis | Bacteria: *Mycobacterium tuberculosis* |
| Botulism (food poisoning) | Bacteria: *Clostridium botulinum* |
| Tetanus (lockjaw) | Bacteria: *Clostridium tetani* |
| Tonsilitis and Strep throat | Bacteria: Streptococci |
| Chickenpox | Virus: herpes zoster |
| Influenza (flu) | Virus |
| Colds | Virus |
| Rabies | Virus |
| Measles (Rubeola) | Virus |
| Polio | Virus: poliovirus |
| Mononucleosis | Virus: Epstein-Barr |
| Athlete's foot | Fungi |
| Ringworm | Fungi |
| Ameobic dysentary | Protozoan |
| Malaria | Protozoan: *Plasmodium* |

## making sure

1. What is a microbe?
2. What is a pathogen? Name three pathogens.

## 7:2 Koch's Postulates

In 1882, Robert Koch showed that bacteria caused the disease anthrax in animals and humans. He was the first person to grow anthrax organisms in the laboratory. He proved that a particular bacteria, *Bacillus anthracis*, caused a specific disease, anthrax.

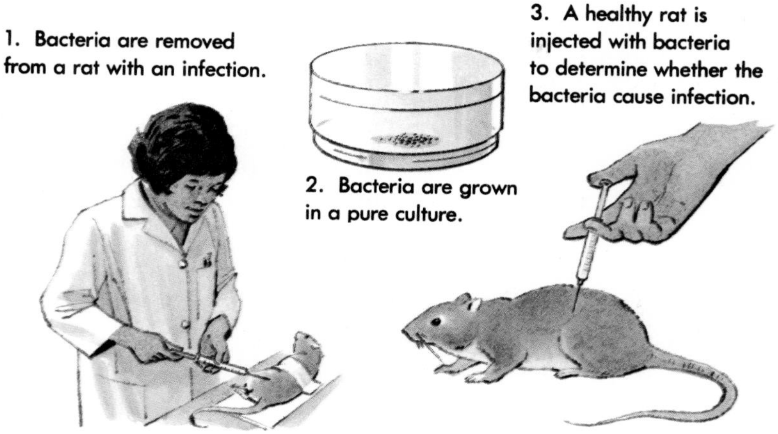

1. Bacteria are removed from a rat with an infection.
2. Bacteria are grown in a pure culture.
3. A healthy rat is injected with bacteria to determine whether the bacteria cause infection.


FIGURE 7–2. Using Koch's postulates helps prove whether or not a disease is caused by a certain microbe.

For what purpose would a scientist use Koch's postulates?

Koch's methods for proving that a disease is caused by bacteria are called Koch's postulates (PAHS chuh lutz). Koch's postulates are as follows:

(1) The bacteria thought to cause a disease must be found in the person when the disease occurs. Example: Streptococci bacteria must be in the throat of a person suffering from a throat infection.

(2) The bacteria must be isolated from the diseased person and grown in pure cultures. Example: Streptococci bacteria must be removed from the throat and grown as a pure culture. A pure culture has only one species of bacteria.

(3) When injected into a healthy organism, bacteria from the pure culture must produce the disease. Example: Streptococci from the pure culture must produce the disease when injected into a healthy organism. In modern medicine, people are not injected to prove that a bacteria causes a disease. However, bacteria suspected of causing disease are grown in cultures.

List Koch's postulates.

## activity GROWING MICROBES ON AGAR

Obtain 4 covered sterile petri dishes containing nutrient agar. Label the dishes *A, B, C,* and *D.* Open dish *A* and rub a finger of your right hand over the agar surface. Reseal the dish. Wash and dry your hands. Open dish *B* with your left hand and rub a finger of your right hand over the agar surface. Reseal the dish. Open dish *C* and leave uncovered and undisturbed overnight. Leave dish *D* sealed. The next day, reseal dish *C* and place the 4 dishes in a warm place for several days. Observe and explain any changes that occur on the surface of the agar. What is the control for this experiment? After the activity, return the dishes unopened to your teacher.

### making sure

**3.** Why might a doctor take a throat culture when you have a sore throat?

## 7:3 Microbe Carriers

What is a microbe carrier?

Microbes that cause diseases are carried by animals, people, air, water, food, and other things. A **carrier** is someone or something that carries and transmits disease microbes. Hence, a large part of disease prevention is the control of carriers. Flies, mosquitoes, and other insects can be disease carriers. Other examples of disease carriers are clothing, bedding, handkerchiefs, knives, forks, and spoons.

a

b

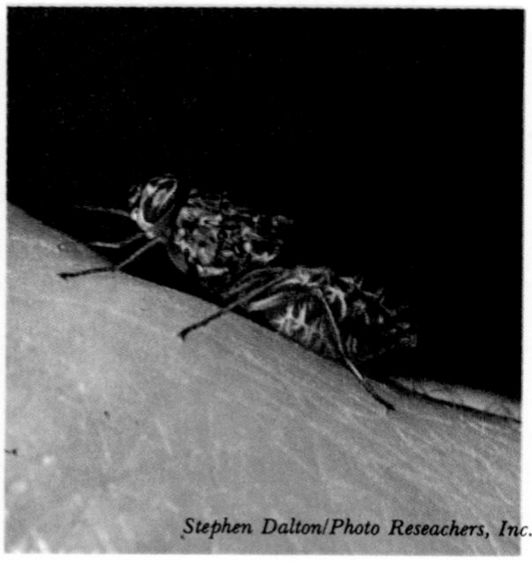


FIGURE 7–3. A mosquito (a) and a tsetse fly (b) can carry disease-causing microbes.

Bureau of Reclamation

FIGURE 7–4. When water becomes polluted it often becomes a disease carrier.

Quarantine (KWOR un teen) is an effective way to control carriers. To **quarantine** means to isolate an infected person or animal for a certain length of time. This isolation helps prevent the spread of the disease. For example, when a dog is taken to another country it is quarantined for more than a month to be sure the dog does not have rabies.

Define the term quarantine.

Water can be a major carrier in the transfer of disease. It may contain bacteria and other disease-causing microbes. Infected water can cause an outbreak of disease in a short time. Typhoid fever is one type of water-borne disease. It is caused by a species of bacteria. As a standard practice, chlorine is now added to water for drinking and swimming. The chlorine kills microbes in the water.

How is the transfer of disease through water and food prevented?

Food can transmit disease. Local, state, and federal laws govern the sanitary conditions of food stores and restaurants. Planes, trains, ships, and buses on which food is served are inspected for sanitation, too. Also, meat is checked at packing houses. Food must be destroyed if it is not disease-free or if it is processed in unsanitary conditions.

Milk can transmit disease if it has not had proper treatment. Thus, the production and sale of milk are regulated by health departments. Dairy tools are sterilized. Milk from cows is refrigerated during shipment from the dairy to the consumer. Cows are tested to be sure they are free of disease. Any cow having a disease is removed from the herd.

USDA

FIGURE 7–5. Milk is pasteurized to kill disease-causing microbes.

Most milk sold today has been pasteurized. It is heated to a specific temperature for a certain length of time and then cooled quickly. Harmful microbes are killed, but the flavor of the milk is not changed.

What is pasteurization?

## 7:4 Cancer

What is cancer?

**Cancer** is a disease in which there is abnormal cell division and a rapid increase in certain body cells. Cancer can occur in any plant or animal. Dogs, cats, fruit flies, horses, as well as humans can develop various types of cancer. What causes the abnormal, rapid growth of body cells? The DNA of a cell nucleus controls the growth and division of the cell. Normal cells grow to a certain size. For some unknown reason, some cells may continue to grow and divide. This rapid growth of cells leads to a formation of a clump of tissue called a tumor. A benign (bih NINE), non-life threatening, tumor will grow to a certain size and stop. Most moles and warts are benign tumors. A malignant (mu LIHG nunt) tumor will not stop growing. All malignant tumors are cancers. They can cause death if they are not removed or destroyed.

Cancer cells, unlike normal cells, may separate from a tumor and be carried through the blood or lymph to other organs of the body. They can invade a new body tissue and form new tumors.

FIGURE 7–6. A healthy brain (a) has no dark areas. A tumor shows up as a dark mass (b) in a cancerous brain.

a b

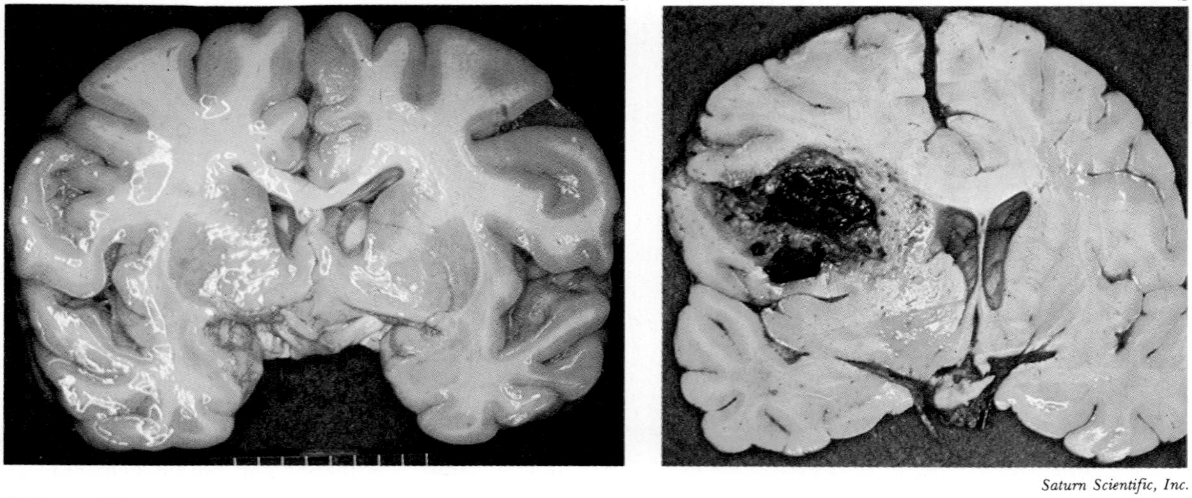

Saturn Scientific, Inc.

Cancer in many animals is known to be caused by viruses. Chickens are affected by a cancer of the connective tissue. Epstein-Barr viruses cause cancer of the lymph system in humans. Scientists are working to determine how viruses cause cancer.

What are some causes of cancer?

A **carcinogen** (kar SIHN uh jun) is a cancer-causing substance. Many different chemicals are known to be carcinogens. Certain chemicals in the environment can cause cancer. Nicotine, the chemical in tobacco, can cause lung cancer. Nitrosamines, reaction products of sodium nitrite, are carcinogens. Sodium nitrite is used to preserve meat. The nitrosamines are produced during the digestive process. Too much sunlight and overexposure to X rays and other radiation can be a physical cause of cancer.

Define the term carcinogen.

The following symptoms may indicate the presence of cancer:

(1) a sore that does not heal
(2) unusual bleeding or discharge
(3) a lump on the surface of the body
(4) a nagging cough or hoarseness
(5) a change in bowel or bladder habits
(6) indigestion or difficulty in swallowing
(7) a sudden increase in size of a wart or mole

What symptoms may indicate cancer?

Our lack of knowledge about the causes of cancer has not stopped the development of treatments for

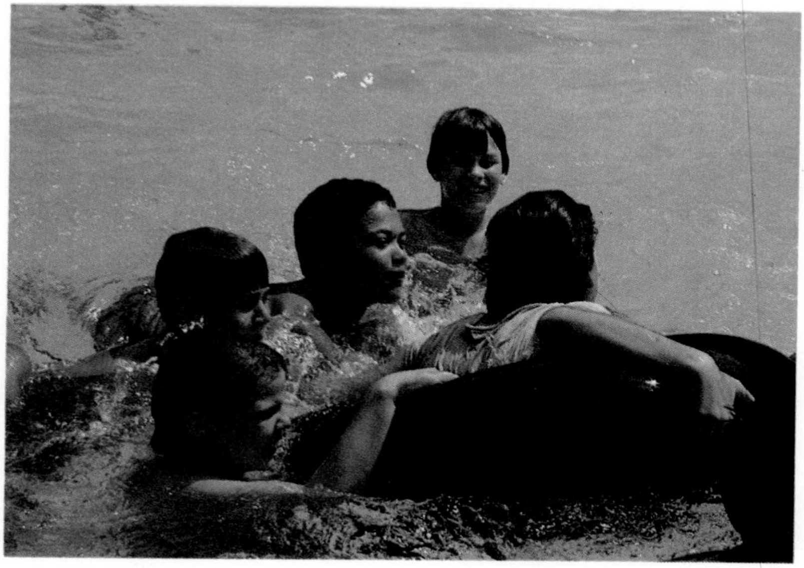

Strix Pix

FIGURE 7–7. Overexposure to sunlight can cause skin cancer.

David R. Frazier

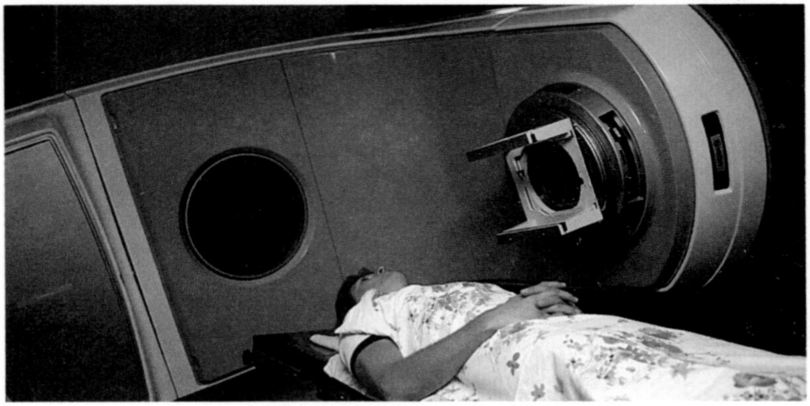

FIGURE 7–8. Radiation can be used to kill cancer cells.

How is cancer treated?

it. One way to treat cancer is to remove the cancerous growth by surgery. Another is to kill the cancer cells with radiation. Sometimes cancer can be treated with hormones or other chemicals. The use of chemicals to treat cancer is called chemotherapy. One treatment of cancer uses chemicals that stimulate the body's own defense system. The body produces cells that can kill cancer cells. This treatment, called immunotherapy, seems to work best when the number of cancer cells has been reduced by other methods such as surgery. The treatment also works well when cancer is detected early. You can aid in protecting yourself by learning habits that will reduce your risk of cancer, by recognizing the danger signals of cancer, and by seeking early treatment if necessary. Table 7–2 lists some habits that can reduce the risk of cancer.

***Table 7–2.***
Habits that Reduce the Risk of Cancer

| |
|---|
| Do not smoke |
| Avoid car fumes and factory exhausts |
| Eat a high fiber diet |
| Observe the stated precautions when working with chemicals |
| Avoid unnecessary exposure to radiation |
| Avoid overexposure to sunlight |
| Have regular dental and medical checkups |
| Do self-examinations |

## 7:5 Defenses Against Disease

Natural defenses against disease are part of the human body. Unbroken skin is a barrier to microbes. Mucous linings of the nose and throat also prevent the entry of microbes into the body. Tiny hairs line the nasal passages and trachea. They keep microbes out of the lungs. Acid in the stomach destroys many microbes in food. White blood cells or **lymphocytes** (LIHM fuh sites) are part of the immune system. The immune system is the natural defense system of the body. Every cell in the human body has a cell membrane composed primarily of protein. Lymphocytes can detect the difference between the protein in the body's cell membrane and a foreign protein. A foreign protein is called an **antigen** (ANT ih jun). Antigens may be produced by the cells of disease-causing organisms. Lymphocytes attack and destroy these cells or their poisonous products.

People can be immune to a specific disease or they can acquire immunity. **Immunity** means a person's body has a special defense against a disease. Immunity can be either naturally or artificially acquired. Natural immunity means you are born with it or you acquire it by having a disease and recovering. Artificially acquired immunity is gained in two ways. One way is to be vaccinated. Vaccines are killed or weakened microbes injected or taken

*Pfizer, Inc.*

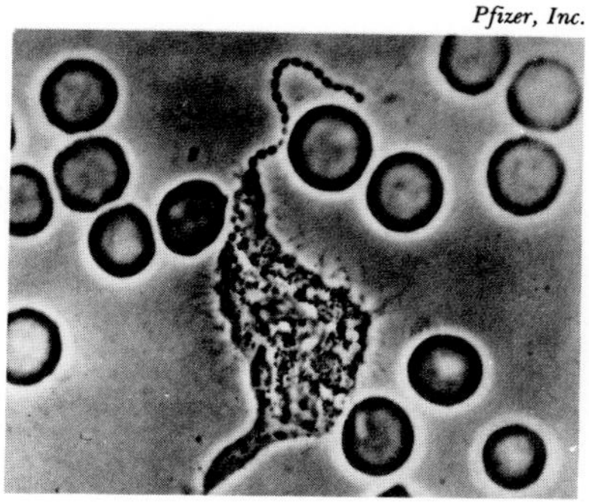

FIGURE 7–9. A white blood cell ingests a string of sphere-shaped bacteria.

Name the natural defenses against disease.

What is the difference between natural and acquired immunity?

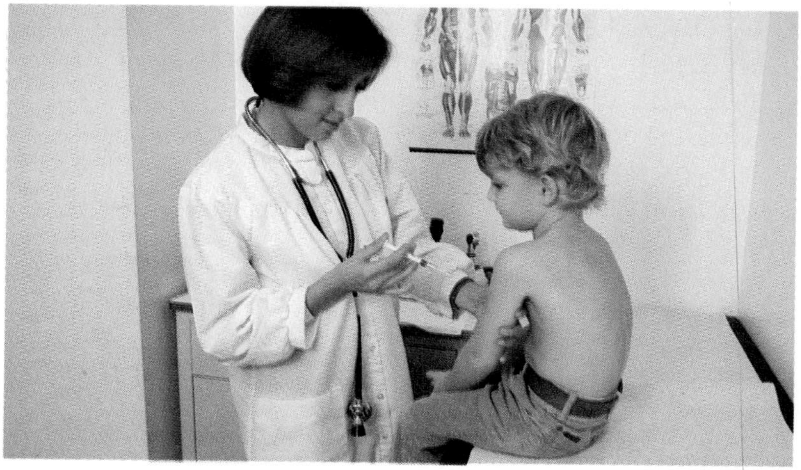

*Image Workshop*

FIGURE 7–10. A child gains immunity by receiving a shot of weakened or killed microbes.

orally into the body. The body then produces antibodies. The second way a person acquires immunity artificially is through an injection of antibodies. These antibodies are obtained from another person or animal. This kind of immunity lasts for only a few months.

***Table 7–3.***
Kinds of Immunity

| Kind | How Obtained |
|---|---|
| Natural | |
| | Present at birth; lasts for many years, perhaps for a lifetime |
| | Immunity in baby derived from mother's antibodies; lasts a few months |
| Acquired | |
| | Person has disease and recovers, or receives vaccination; both last for years |
| | Injection of antibodies; lasts for months |

## 7:6 Vaccination

How did Jenner vaccinate a boy against smallpox?

Edward Jenner (1749–1823) is credited with the discovery of vaccination. Jenner was interested in a disease called smallpox. Smallpox was responsible for many deaths in Jenner's time. Jenner observed that people who tended cows seldom had smallpox. He also observed that these people often had a disease called cowpox. Cowpox is similar to smallpox, but it is not fatal. Jenner concluded that recovery from cowpox gave a person immunity from smallpox.

Jenner injected a young boy with pus from a cowpox blister on a milkmaid's hand. The boy developed a case of cowpox. Now came the test. Was the boy immune to smallpox? Jenner injected the boy with pus from a smallpox blister. As Jenner suspected, the boy did not get smallpox. The cowpox vaccination had made the boy immune to smallpox.

FIGURE 7–11. Edward Jenner is credited with the discovery of the vaccine for smallpox.

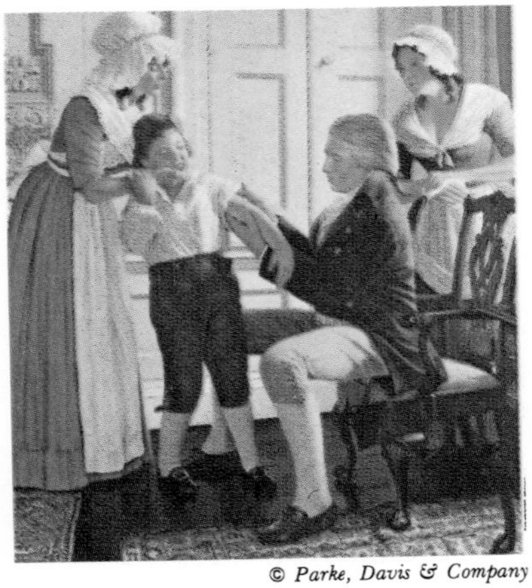

In 1953, Dr. Jonas Salk developed a vaccine for the dreaded disease, polio. Polio results in paralysis, the inability to move one or more body parts. A few years later, Dr. Albert Sabin developed another polio vaccine using weakened polio virus that could be taken orally in one dose.

### making sure

4. Why did the boy in Jenner's experiment not become ill with smallpox?
5. What kind of immunity does the polio vaccine produce?

## 7:7 Allergy

What is an allergy?

An **allergy** is an overreaction of the body's immune system to a foreign antigen. One example of an allergy is hay fever, an overreaction to pollen. Consider the case of Janet, a young girl allergic to ragweed pollen. When Janet got near ragweed in bloom, she began to sneeze and cough. Antibodies in the mucus of her nose detected the foreign antigens in the pollen and attacked them. The combination of the pollen antigen and the antibodies caused Janet's body to produce a chemical called histamine (HIHS tuh meen). Histamine caused the sneezing and coughing. Histamine could also produce hives, a skin rash, or an itchy running nose. Janet's body could release another chemical that would produce asthma.

*Jerome Wexler/Photo Researchers, Inc.*

FIGURE 7–12. Hay fever may be caused by an allergy to pollen grains from ragweed.

Herm Beck

a

FIGURE 7–13. Some people are allergic to antigens from certain fabrics (a). Other people are allergic to antigens from animal hair (b).

Michelle Wigginton

b

Asthma symptoms include shortness of breath, wheezing, and coughing. Asthma attacks can last a few minutes or a few weeks.

What causes allergies?

What causes an allergy? An allergy may be caused by antigens found in pollens, house dust, food, green plants, animals, clothing fibers, and even some medicines. The cause of some allergies may be determined through a skin test. In this test, a scratch is made on the skin and a small amount of the material being tested is placed in the scratch. A reaction such as swelling or a rash indicates the person is allergic to the substance being tested.

How are allergies treated?

There are several different methods for treating allergies. In one method, the allergic person avoids the substance that causes the allergy. Children who are allergic to milk should not drink milk or eat products containing milk. Moving to a different area may be helpful for people allergic to specific types of pollen. Some allergies are treated with medicines to prevent or relieve the symptoms. Other allergies are treated by desensitization. The allergic person receives a shot that contains a small amount of the allergic substance. Repeated injections are given and the person builds a resistance to the allergic substance. Eventually the person is no longer allergic to the substance.

## making sure

6. Are you allergic to some substance? If so, how do you know you are allergic?
7. Why might a person who is allergic to certain plants be advised to move to a different location?
8. How does a skin scratch test reveal an allergy?

## 7:8 Diseases of the Immune System

A person's immune system usually responds only to foreign antigens. An **autoimmune** (awt oh ihm YEWN) **disease** is a condition that occurs when the immune system responds to the body's own proteins. As a result, antibodies are produced that attack a person's own tissues. This type of disease is more common in older people. The disease may involve some type of infection that causes the immune system to work improperly. Some doctors believe that crippling arthritis, a disease of the joints, is an autoimmune disease. One autoimmune disease in young people is rheumatic fever. In this disease, the tissues of the heart and joints are attacked. Rheumatic fever occurs after the person has had a certain type of bacterial infection.

What is an autoimmune disease?

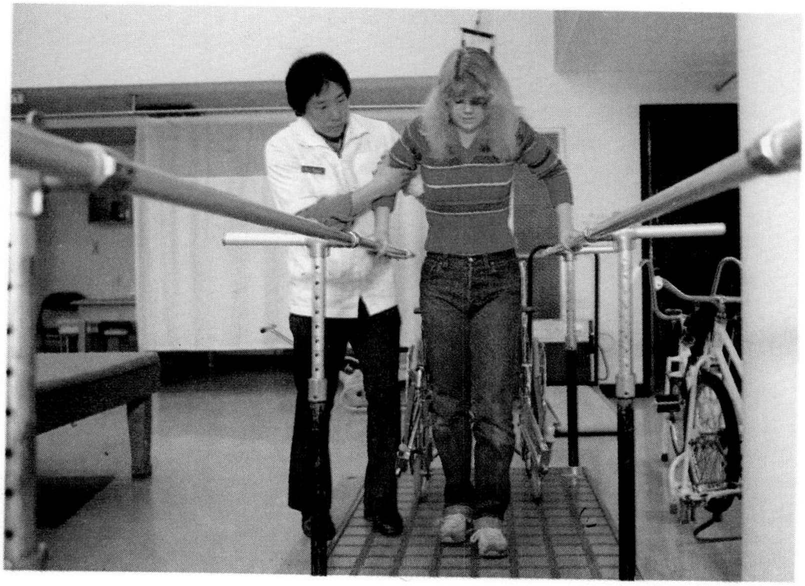

© Mike Sanderson

FIGURE 7–14. Arthritis makes activities difficult and painful.

# PERSPECTIVES

## frontiers

# Using Microbes to Fight Disease

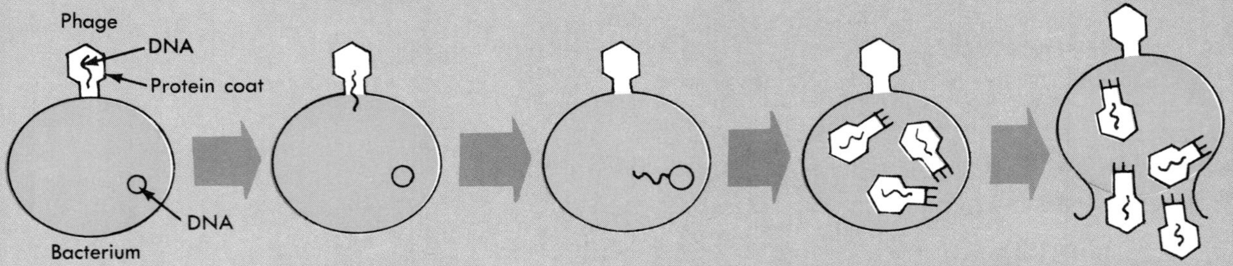


Viruses are particles that can cause diseases in both plants and animals. A virus consists of a protein shell covering DNA, a chemical strand. DNA determines a cell's structure and function. Viruses have no cellular structure and no metabolism. Some scientists do not classify viruses as living organisms because of these characteristics. Virus reproduction must be carried out within a cell of a specific organism. Thus, viruses are reproductive parasites. The organism that the virus uses for reproduction is the host. When reproducing, a virus attaches to the surface of the host's cell. The virus then injects its DNA into the cell. The viral DNA directs the host's cell to manufacture more viruses. These new viruses burst out of the cell in about an hour, destroying the host's cell. Each new virus moves on to other cells to reproduce. The destruction of the host's cells is what causes diseases.

In some cases, a virus uses a bacterial cell as its host. This virus is called a bacteriophage, or phage, meaning "bacteria eater." Since 1915, when phages were first discovered, biologists have recognized that bacteriophages might be used to destroy disease-causing bacteria. Scientists have not been able to isolate phages in pure enough form to be used effectively. Recently, however, two English biologists working with animals have isolated and used bacteriophages to destroy a strain of bacteria that caused meningitis in a child. They tested different phages they located in sewage samples to determine which one destroyed the meningitis-causing bacterial cells. When they isolated the phage they thought used that bacteria for a host, they injected the phage into infected mice. The phage cured the infection.

Using bacteriophages to fight disease has three advantages over using antibiotics. First, antibiotics are gradually used up by the body and must be administered over a period of time until the bacteria is totally destroyed. Bacteriophages need to be given only once, because they reproduce inside the body and increase in numbers with time. Second, some bacteria may be resistant to the antibiotics used and will pass this trait along to future generations. With phages, the resistant bacteria that reproduce are weaker than the original disease-causing bacteria. Third, in the past it was normal for healthy animals to be infected by the wastes of diseased animals. However, when phages are used, bacteriophages and bacteria are both acquired from wastes. Further research will be needed to determine if these disease-fighting methods will be useful in fighting bacterial infections in humans.

## main ideas

1. Disease is an abnormal functioning of any body part. 7:1
2. Many diseases are caused by bacteria and viruses. 7:1
3. Koch's postulates are used to determine whether or not a disease is caused by a specific microbe. 7:2
4. Control of disease carriers reduces the number of microbe-caused diseases. 7:3
5. Cancer is a disease in which certain body cells grow rapidly and invade healthy tissue. 7:4
6. The skin, blood, and mucous linings of the nose and throat are parts of the body's immune system. 7:5
7. Immunity to disease can be naturally or artificially acquired. 7:5
8. Vaccination produces an artificially acquired immunity. 7:6
9. An allergy is an overreaction of the body's immune system to a foreign protein. 7:7
10. An autoimmune disease is caused by the immune system of a person attacking the person's own tissues. 7:8

## vocabulary

*Define each of the following words or terms.*

| | | |
|---|---|---|
| allergy | carcinogen | lymphocytes |
| antigen | carrier | microbe |
| autoimmune disease | disease | pathogen |
| cancer | immunity | quarantine |

## study questions

**DO NOT WRITE IN THIS BOOK.**

### *A. True or False*

*Determine whether each of the following sentences is true or false. If the sentence is false, rewrite it to make it true.*

1. All diseases are caused by viruses.
2. A pathogen is a harmless microbe.
3. All bacteria cause diseases.
4. Bacteria grow best in cool, dry areas.
5. The common cold is caused by viruses.

6. Viruses are composed of cells.
7. Immunity can be either naturally or artificially acquired.
8. Only living organisms can be disease carriers.
9. Vaccination is used against bacterial and viral diseases.
10. Robert Koch developed a vaccine against polio.

**B. Multiple Choice**

*Choose the word or phrase that completes correctly each of the following sentences.*

1. A pure culture contains (*one, two, three*) kind(s) of bacteria.
2. Koch developed the idea that (*antigens, microbes, antibodies*) cause certain diseases.
3. Polio may be prevented through use of (*antigens, vaccination, histamines*).
4. Smallpox is prevented by (*quarantine, vaccination, skin test*).
5. Edward Jenner discovered (*vaccination, postulates, skin tests*).
6. (*Naturally acquired, Artificially acquired, Permanently acquired*) immunity is gained by the injection of antibodies.
7. (*Red blood cells, Hormones, White blood cells*) defend the body against disease.
8. Something that carries an organism that causes a disease is called a(n) (*quarantine, carrier, antigen*).
9. (*Tuberculosis, Common cold, Asthma*) is caused by a bacteria.
10. Dr. Jonas Salk developed a vaccine against (*polio, chickenpox, smallpox*).

**C. Completion**

*Complete each of the following sentences with a word or phrase that will make the sentence correct.*

1. Hay fever and a rash produced by eating strawberries are two kinds of ______.
2. The ______ system of the body produces antibodies.
3. An antigen is a ______ foreign to the body.
4. ______ is a chemical released by the body that produces an itchy, runny nose, hives, rash, and sneezing.
5. A skin test can be used to determine the cause of some ______.
6. A virus is a disease-causing substance that grows inside living ______.

7. A tumor is the result of an abnormal growth of ______.
8. Bacteria need ______, warmth, and moisture to grow and reproduce.
9. Most moles and warts are ______ tumors, meaning they are not cancerous.
10. Obvious change in a wart or mole can be a warning signal for ______.

**D. How and Why**

1. How are Koch's postulates used to show that a specific bacteria causes a disease?
2. What causes an allergy and how are allergies treated?
3. How is the body protected from disease?
4. What is the difference between natural and artificial immunity?
5. How is a quarantine useful in fighting some diseases?

## challenges

1. Prepare a library report on recent advances in the treatment of cancer in children.
2. Consult a branch of the Immigration and Naturalization Service to learn what vaccinations are recommended for people who travel outside the United States.
3. Many doctors and health specialists recommend a program of preventive medicine. Prepare a report on preventive methods for staying healthy.
4. Select a career in medicine and find out how you prepare for this career and what kind of work the career entails.

## interesting reading

Cohen, Daniel, *The Last 100 Years: Medicine.* New York: M. Evans, 1981.

Klein, Aaron E., *The Parasites We Humans Harbor.* New York: Elsevier/Nelson, 1981.

Nourse, Alan E. *Viruses,* revised ed. New York: Franklin Watts, Inc., 1983.

Rensberger, Boyce, Haydn Bush, and Gary Blonston, "Cancer: The New Synthesis," *Science 84.* September, 1984, pp. 28-39.

*Scientists have developed many drugs to help prevent, cure, and treat diseases. You may have taken aspirin to help ease the pain of a headache. Aspirin is a drug. A drug may affect the body in several ways. Scientists now use computers to design drugs like the one below that will have a specific effect in the body. How are drugs classified? Are all drugs helpful?*

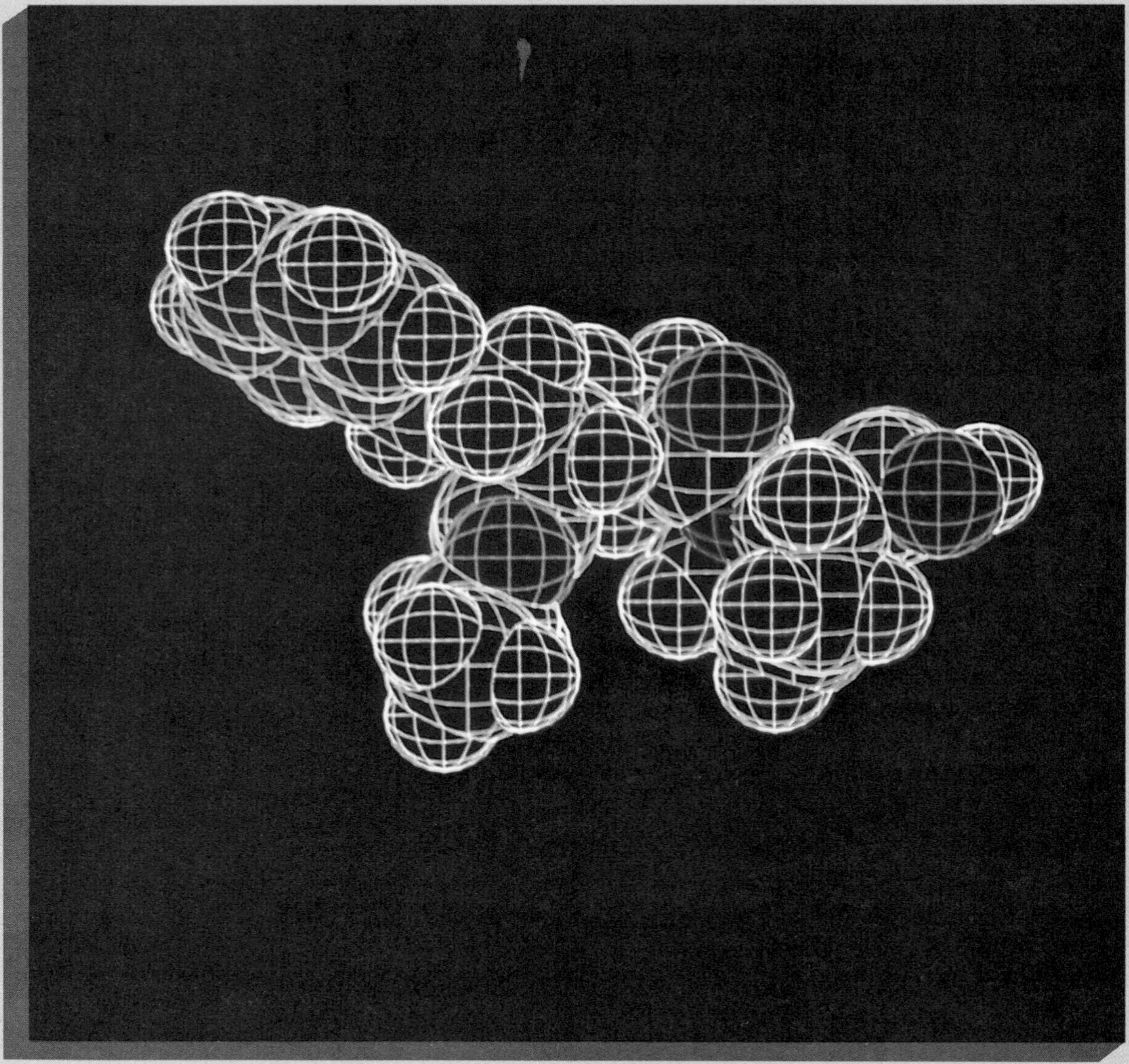

Merck & Co., Inc.

# Drugs

# chapter 8

## 8:1 Classification of Drugs

GOAL: You will learn the effects of drugs on the human body.

Many drugs are used to prevent, treat, or cure disease. These drugs are helpful. Some drugs are harmful to the body and cause poor health, disease, or death. Also, some helpful drugs taken in the wrong amounts, at the wrong time, or by the wrong person can be harmful.

How would you define the term drug? Most people would define drug as a substance given by a doctor to help cure a disease. This statement is only part of the definition. Some drugs may not be prescribed by a doctor, and they may not have anything to do with health or disease. A drug can be a substance found in the body, such as potassium salts or adrenalin. Drugs can be minerals or vitamins. A **drug** is any substance entering the body that changes the function of the body systems.

Carolina Biological Supply Co.

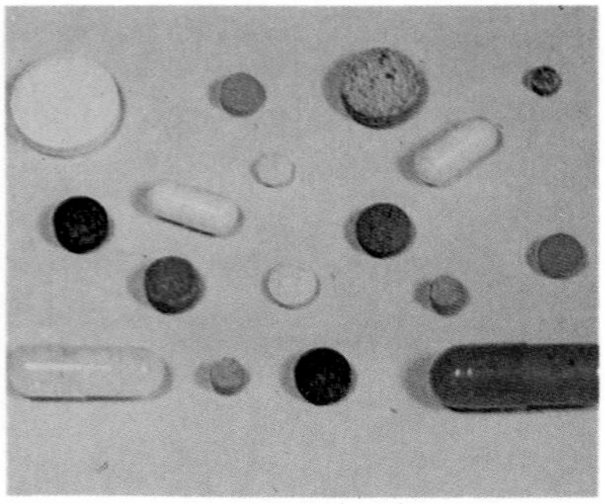

FIGURE 8–1. Drugs come in many shapes, sizes, and colors.

How are drugs grouped?

Drugs can be grouped by their general use or by their long-range effects. Drugs for general use are grouped in the following ways:

(1) Antibiotics—drugs used to treat specific microbe-caused diseases.
(2) Stimulants—drugs used to produce a temporary increase in certain body activities.
(3) Depressants—drugs used to produce a temporary slowing of certain body activities.

Drugs that have long-range effects on the body are grouped as follows:

(1) Nonhabit-forming drug—drug that does not cause a desire for the drug once the use is stopped.
(2) Habit-forming drug—drug that produces a mental or emotional need for the drug. Remember that a habit is a learned pattern of behavior. A habit can be unlearned.
(3) Addictive drug—drug that causes a physical need for the drug. An **addiction** is a physical need for a drug. This means that the body adjusts to the presence of the drug and cannot function wthout it. A person becomes ill and has pain if the drug is stopped.
(4) Hallucinogens—drugs that may act as either stimulants or depressants.

What is an addictive drug?

## activity

### DRUG SURVEY

Obtain the labels from 5 empty nonprescription drug containers. Do not open the containers. Record the name and use of each drug, the recommended dose, and any warnings on the label. Did any of the drugs have warnings on their labels? What was the most common warning?

## making sure

1. Explain the difference between a habit-forming drug and an addictive drug.

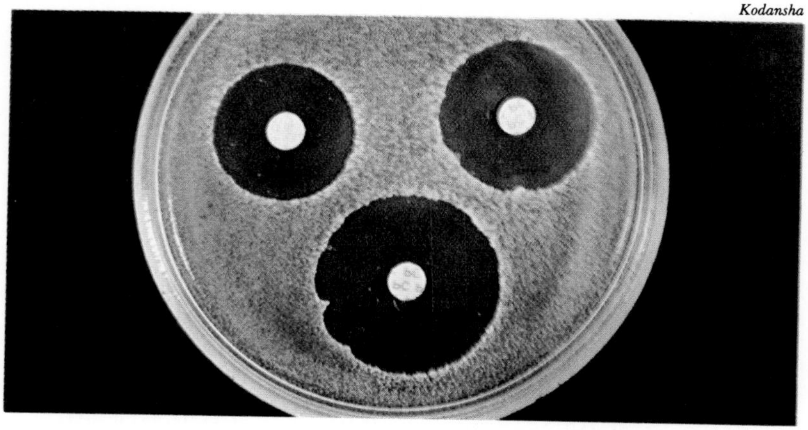

Kodansha

FIGURE 8–2. Penicillin prevented the growth of bacteria in the clear areas on this dish. Penicillin is a helpful drug.

## 8:2 Antibiotics

Define the term antibiotic.

An **antibiotic** is a chemical produced by an organism that slows or stops the growth of microbes. Antibiotics are not effective against viruses. Antibiotics come from bacteria, molds, and other organisms. Many antibiotics are now made in factories that produce drugs and other chemicals. Table 8–1 lists some antibiotics and their sources.

*Table 8–1.*
Some Antibiotics and Their Sources

| Antibiotic | Source | Used to treat |
|---|---|---|
| Bacitracin | Bacteria | Pneumonia in infants |
| Chloromycetin | Moldlike bacteria | Typhus, bacterial meningitis |
| Terramycin | Moldlike bacteria | Respiratory and urinary infections |
| Penicillin | Mold | Scarlet fever, rheumatic fever, pneumonia |
| Streptomycin | Moldlike bacteria | Tuberculosis, whooping cough, pneumonia |
| Aureomycin | Moldlike bacteria | Anthrax, Rocky Mountain spotted fever |

Penicillin is the most widely used antibiotic. It was discovered in 1928 by a British scientist, Alexander Fleming (1881–1955). Fleming saw a blue-green mold, called *Penicillium notatum*, growing in a bacterial culture. This mold is like the green molds that grow on spoiled oranges or grapefruits. He noted that bacteria did not grow where the mold was. He separated the antibiotic from the mold and named it penicillin.

Little use was made of penicillin until 1938. At this time two British biologists found a technique for producing it in large amounts. Penicillin was used during World War II to treat infections. Without it the death rate would have been about three times greater than it was.

Many antibiotics have been separated from soil-growing microbes. Streptomycin (strep tuh MISE un) is one of these. It comes from a threadlike bacterium. It is used in treating tuberculosis, whooping cough, and some forms of pneumonia.

**activity** PENICILLIN AND GROWTH OF MICROBES

Obtain a covered petri dish containing sterile nutrient agar. With a marking pencil, divide the dish into 4 quarters by marking on the outside of the dish. Label the quarters *A, B, C,* and *D.* Obtain 3 penicillin disks of differing strengths from your teacher. Open your petri dish. Use forceps to place each disk in the center of a separate quarter of your agar dish. Add a plain sterile paper disk to the remaining quarter. Record the strengths of the penicillin disk placed in each quarter. Expose the open dish to the air overnight. Cover the dish and seal it with tape. Place the dish in a warm spot or in an incubator at 37°C for several days. Observe and explain the bacteria growth patterns.

## 8:3 Stimulants

Define the term stimulant.

Name three stimulants.

Caffeine is a stimulant. A **stimulant** is a substance that increases alertness and reduces fatigue. Tea and coffee contain large amounts of caffeine. Caffeine is also present in cola drinks, chocolate, and cocoa. Some medicines including those prescribed to relieve cold symptoms, also contain caffeine.

Caffeine is thought to be safe under normal use. However, in large amounts, caffeine can be

John Swartz

FIGURE 8–3. These foods contain caffeine, a stimulant.

poisonous. About 10 grams, the amount in 70 to 100 cups of coffee, is fatal. One gram or more of caffeine can have harmful effects that include the inability to sleep, ringing in the ears, and seeing flashes of light. Decaffeinated tea, coffee, and cola drinks are available for those people who wish to avoid caffeine.

Amphetamines (am FET uh meenz) are a group of drugs that stimulate the nervous system. They come in tablet, capsule, and solution forms. Amphetamine pills are sometimes taken by people to stay awake. Some doctors prescribe amphetamines as an aid to dieters. Under certain conditions they act as an appetite suppressant.

It is not known if amphetamines cause physical addiction. However, some people develop mental or emotional dependence on these drugs. To remain effective these people require larger and larger doses.

Cocaine (koh KAYN) is a stimulant that is obtained from the cocoa plant. Cocaine can become habit-forming. Cocaine creates excitement in a person that may be followed by depression. Cocaine interferes with the transmission of nerve impulses by causing a very large number of impulses to be sent at once.

## 8:4 Stimulants: Tobacco

What is nicotine?

**Nicotine** is a chemical compound in tobacco that acts as a stimulant on the body. People can smoke, chew, or sniff tobacco. Some scientists believe that

*Ward's Natural Science Establishment*

FIGURE 8–4. Tobacco leaves contain a stimulant called nicotine.

nicotine is an addictive drug. The body is affected by the nicotine ingested when tobacco is burned, sniffed, or chewed (Table 8–2).

| ***Table 8–2.*** Effects of Nicotine |
|---|
| Increases heartbeat rate |
| Narrows blood vessels |
| Raises blood pressure |
| Cools fingers and toes |
| Interferes with digestion and decreases appetite |
| Irritates nose, throat, and lungs |

A non-smoker who inhales smoke suffers the same effects as the smoker. People with allergies and respiratory diseases are especially sensitive to smoke. For this reason, separate seating for nonsmokers is provided on airplanes and in many restaurants and theaters.

Scientific studies on tobacco completed since 1954 show a connection between smoking and lung cancer. Experiments have been performed with animals to determine the effects of cigarette smoke. It has been found that smoke damages lung tissue, stimulates blood clotting, interferes with normal formation of antibodies, and constricts the arteries.

In one experiment to study the effects of smoking, beagle dogs were taught to smoke. They smoked by inhaling cigarette smoke through a tube. During a two-year period, each of thirty-eight beagles smoked seven non-filter cigarettes a day. Of this group, 91.7 percent showed signs of lung damage. Twelve of the dogs died. In each case, the cause of death was lung tumors. A control group of eight beagles did not smoke during the two years. They did not develop lung disease. Another group of 48 beagles followed varying smoking schedules. Of this group, those that smoked half as many cigarettes had only 12.9 percent with lung damage.

Why is smoking harmful?

Tobacco smoke contains at least 15 substances identified as carcinogens. In addition to lung cancer,

Martin Rotker/Taurus Photos

Taurus Photos

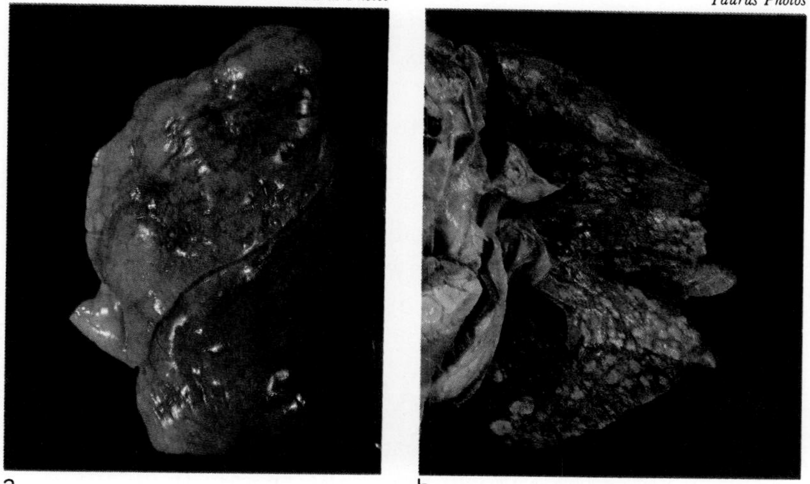

a

b

FIGURE 8–5. A healthy human lung (a) may develop lung cancer (b) when exposed to tobacco smoke.

several respiratory diseases are related to cigarette smoking. Three of these are influenza, bronchitis, and emphysema. Diseases of the blood vessels have also been linked with cigarette smoking. The largest cause of death among smokers is coronary artery disease. A nonsmoker is more likely to be healthy and live longer than a person who smokes.

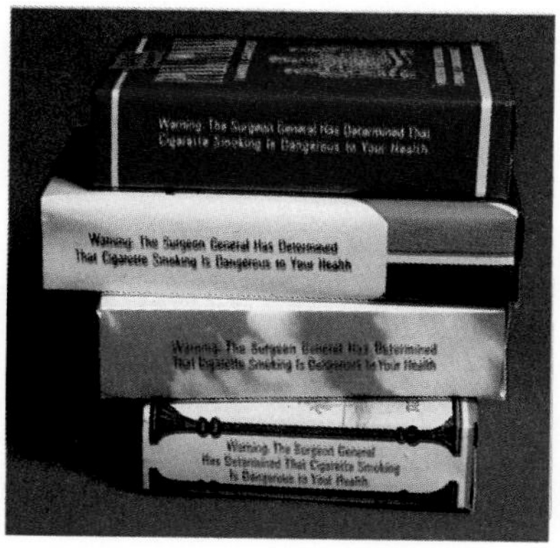


FIGURE 8–6. Cigarette packages are required by law to display a warning label.

### making sure

2. Many doctors believe that the warning on a pack of cigarettes is not accurate or adequate. How would you rewrite the warning if it were to be changed?

## 8:5 Depressants

Define the term depressant.

**Depressants** are substances that relieve pain, tension, and anxiety, and cause muscle relaxation. Thus, when used in proper amounts, they may produce a sense of well-being and contentment.

Barbiturates (bar BIHCH uh ruts) are drugs that in small doses act as depressants and produce drowsiness. They are prescribed by doctors to relieve tension and anxiety and to cause sleep. However, when too large a dose is taken, barbiturates cause a loss of mental and physical control. Judgment, vision, motor coordination, and reaction time are diminished.

Overdoses of barbiturates cause many deaths each year. Some of these deaths are accidental. Many are suicides.

Some people take barbiturates to become relaxed and free of thoughts. When they are taken along with other drugs, especially other depressants, death may result. Constant use of barbiturates can lead to addiction. Sudden withdrawal can cause death. Withdrawal from barbiturates should be done under medical supervision.

## 8:6 Depressants: Alcohol

Alcohol present in beverages is ethyl alcohol. It is produced by the fermentation of sugar in grains, fruits, and other plant material. Ethyl alcohol is a depressant. It slows the control centers of the brain and can change a person's behavior. Alcohol contains carbon, hydrogen, and oxygen. In the body, alcohol is a source of energy.

How does alcohol affect the body?

How alcohol affects people varies among individuals. Behavior in most people is changed in some way when they drink too much alcohol. Amounts of 0.05 to 0.15 percent alcohol in a person's blood may cause slurred speech and uncoordinated movements. A person responds more slowly when under the influence of alcohol. In this condition, it is dangerous for a person to drive or operate machinery. For this reason, it is against the law for a person to drink and drive. A driver who

*Ohio Department of Highway Safety*

FIGURE 8–7. A breatholater is used to measure the alcohol content of a person's breath.

has been drinking has a good chance of being involved in an accident. Alcohol is a factor in about 50 percent of the highway deaths each year. If the blood alcohol level is above a certain percent determined by law, a person is considered to be legally intoxicated. Intoxication may result in a loss of judgment and inhibitions. Death may result if alcohol in the blood exceeds 0.5 percent.

Although alcohol is a depressant, it does stimulate nerve endings in the throat and esophagus. This effect may increase the pulse rate and cause a slight rise in blood pressure. Increased blood pressure causes capillaries in the surface of the skin to expand. This expansion allows heat to leave the body at an increased rate. Thus, a person gets a warm feeling when alcohol is consumed even though body temperature does not rise.

Discuss the reasons a person may feel warm when drinking alcohol.

People who continually drink large amounts of alcohol may become alcoholics. Some scientists think that alcoholism should be listed as a disease rather than as a habit. Research is being done to find the exact causes of alcoholism.

FIGURE 8–8. Information about alcohol and alcoholism can be obtained from many sources.

Alcohol abuse may have a damaging effect on body systems. Also, nutritional diseases, caused by the lack of a proper diet, are related to alcoholism. An alcoholic gets much of the body's required daily energy from alcohol. However, many alcoholics fail to eat the proper foods. Thus, the alcoholic's diet may lack one or more nutrients. Pellagra (puh LAG ruh), a disease caused by a lack of niacin, occurs among alcoholics. A pellagra sufferer has inflamed skin and mouth and disorders of the digestive tract.

Diseases of the liver are related to alcoholism. A breakdown of liver tissue, cirrhosis (suh ROH sus), is the most well-known of these diseases. It has been shown that cirrhosis is brought on by poor diet. But, alcohol itself may also affect liver cells directly. Cirrhosis can lead to death.

*Image Workshop*

Figure 8-9. Fetal alcohol syndrome may develop in children whose mothers drank during pregnancy.

The social effects of alcoholism may be as bad as the medical problems. A drinking habit can drain a family's money reserves. Also, an alcoholic may be unable to hold a job. Many are put in jail as a result of their actions. They may become angry when intoxicated and harm others. An alcoholic in a family may lead to emotional problems for other family members. Some alcoholics are young people. They may steal alcohol or steal money to buy alcohol. Many teenage deaths are caused by driving while drinking. Malnutrition can be a more serious threat to the young alcoholic since a proper diet is necessary for growth at this age.

What is Alcoholics Anonymous?

Alcoholics Anonymous is a group that aids alcoholics in overcoming their problem. It is a voluntary group. Each alcoholic must sincerely want to give up drinking. The Alcoholics Anonymous program is one of counseling, guiding, and assisting. Members who give these services are persons who have solved their own drinking problems.

Carolina Biological Supply Co.

a

Carolina Biological Supply Co.

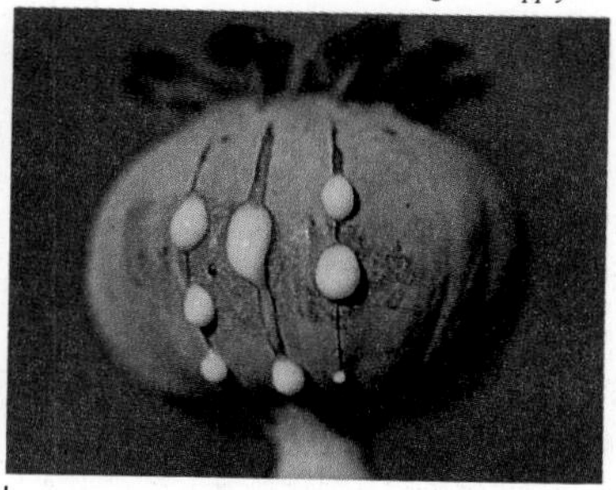

b

FIGURE 8–10. The flower of the opium poppy is the source of opium (a). Opium is prepared from the dried sap of the flower pod (b).

## 8:7 Depressants: Narcotics

What is a narcotic? Name two narcotics.

Narcotics are a group of drugs that act as depressants. Opium is a narcotic that comes from one type of poppy plant. Opium can be smoked or taken orally. Morphine and codeine are narcotics obtained from opium. They are used as pain killers. Heroin is a narcotic produced from morphine.

A narcotic addict is a person who is addicted to a narcotic such as heroin. Usually an addict must take increasingly larger doses of a narcotic to achieve the desired effect. If an addict does not get the narcotic, the addict becomes ill and suffers from a condition called withdrawal illness. Pain, nervousness, runny nose, shivers, hot and cold flashes, diarrhea, and stomach cramps are symptoms of withdrawal.

Narcotic addiction has a severe effect on health. Addicts usually lack a good appetite. They fail to eat the right foods. Thus, they suffer from deficiencies brought on by an unbalanced diet. If they are in school, they cannot concentrate on their school work. Because many addicts inject a narcotic into their veins, their arms often are covered with sores. These sores are caused by unsterile needles. An addict may also get hepatitis (hep uh TITE us) from unsterile needles. Hepatitis is a virus infection of the liver that can lead to death.

Addicts need to have a continuous supply of the drug to which they are addicted. To get the narcotic, an addict may steal money or steal objects to sell. Many burglaries are the result of narcotic addicts' need for money.

*Image Workshop, Courtesy Comp-Drug, Columbus, Ohio*

FIGURE 8–11. Local drug hotlines provide information about drugs to people.

How are narcotic addicts treated medically?

Addicts can be treated to overcome their addiction. In one method, treatment may consist of either gradual or sudden withholding of the drug. This treatment usually takes place at a hospital. The addict is given rest and good food. Any infections are treated with antibiotics. Personal counseling is given to keep the addict from returning to the narcotic. The time it takes for the addict's health to return varies. It may take a few days to many months to treat the addict successfully.

## 8:8 Hallucinogens

Some drugs change a person's thoughts, patterns, and emotions. Some of these drugs can cause a person to have illusions. An **illusion** is what a person sees that is different from what it really is. A door may appear to be wider and taller than it is. An **hallucination** (huh lews un AY shun) is what someone sees that does not exist. A person who sees and talks with a dead person, or hears strange sounds that are not present is hallucinating.

FIGURE 8–12. The arrows on the ends of the lines create an illusion that the lines are of different lengths.

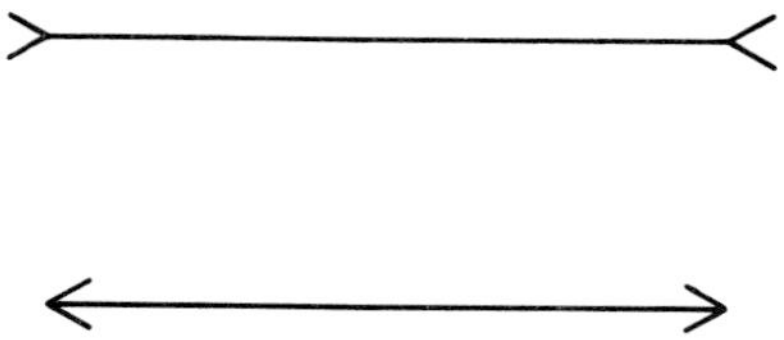

**Hallucinogens** are substances that cause illusions and hallucinations. Psilocybin (si luh SI bun), mescaline (MES kuh leen), and LSD are hallucinogens. Psilocybin is obtained from certain mushrooms. Mescaline comes from the peyote cactus plant. LSD is a tasteless, odorless, colorless compound made in a laboratory. Hallucinations produced by these drugs cannot be predicted. The symptoms may occur any time these drugs are used or months after the drugs were used.

*Larry Hamill*

FIGURE 8-13. A person has an illusion when things are seen differently than they are.

"Angel dust" is a powerful hallucinogen. The short form of the chemical name for angel dust is PCP. PCP can be eaten, snorted (inhaled into the nose), or smoked. Angel dust is a stimulant. However, in some people the drug may cause a severe depression and thoughts of suicide. A large dose can make a person very aggressive. The person may damage property or physically harm other people. A person who has taken a large dose of PCP may experience wild hallucinations in which other people may appear as monsters. PCP can be stored in body fat. The drug may be released into the bloodstream later and continue to cause harmful effects.

## 8:9 Marijuana

**Marijuana** is a nonnarcotic drug derived from the dried leaves and flowers of Indian hemp, *Cannabis sativa.* This drug is illegal to use, sell, or buy.

How does marijuana affect the body?

Marijuana can act as a stimulant or a depressant. It has an intoxicating effect on the body and may cause a loss of physical or mental control. It may affect thinking and speech. Senses can become distorted. A person can have a pleasant feeling or a frightened feeling. With a very strong dose, a person may have illusions.

Tolerance and dependence result from marijuana use. The long-range effects of steady marijuana are currently under study. Some doctors believe that steady marijuana use may result in a lack of motivation. Some doctors also believe that heavy use of marijuana may slow a person's emotional development. Marijuana causes the heartbeat rate and blood pressure to increase. This effect can harm the circulatory system over time. Marijuana may have the same effects as cigarette smoke in causing cancer and other lung diseases. Scientists continue to research the important question of marijuana's effects on the mind and body.

*Ward's Natural Science Establishment*

FIGURE 8–14. The use of marijuana may have long-range effects on the body.

## main ideas

1. All drugs can be classified by their general use or by their long-range effects. 8:1
2. Some drugs are habit-forming. Other drugs are addictive. 8:1
3. Antibiotics are chemicals that stop or slow the growth of microbes. 8:2
4. Caffeine is a common stimulant found in coffee, tea, chocolate, and cola drinks. 8:3
5. Tobacco contains nicotine that acts as a stimulant on the body. 8:4
6. Alcohol is a common depressant. Alcohol slows the body's processes. 8:6
7. Alcoholics tend to develop nutritional deficiency diseases. 8:6
8. Narcotics act as depressants on the body. Narcotics are addictive drugs. 8:7
9. Hallucinogens are drugs that cause people to have illusions and hallucinations. 8:8
10. Marijuana is a nonnarcotic drug that can act as either a depressant or a stimulant in the body. 8:9

## vocabulary

*Define each of the following words or terms.*

addiction
antibiotic
depressant
drug
hallucinogen
hallucination
illusion
marijuana
nicotine
stimulant

## study questions

**DO NOT WRITE IN THIS BOOK.**

**A. True or False**

*Determine whether each of the following sentences is true or false. If the sentence is false, rewrite it to make it true.*

1. A stimulant produces a temporary slowing of body activities.
2. Tobacco smoke is harmful to smokers and nonsmokers.

3. Statistics show that more smokers die from lung cancer than do nonsmokers.
4. Research studies show that cigarette smoking can cause cancer.
5. Several diseases are closely related to cigarette smoking.
6. Cirrhosis and hepatitis are diseases of the kidneys.
7. Marijuana is both habit forming and addictive.
8. Ethyl alcohol is present in wine and beer.
9. Narcotic addiction has a severe effect on health.
10. PCP is a hallucinogen.

**B. Multiple Choice**

*Choose the word or phrase that completes correctly each of the following sentences.*

1. (*Antibiotics, Narcotics, Vitamins*) are used to treat certain microbe-caused diseases.
2. Alcohol (*speeds, slows, does not affect*) brain functions.
3. The largest cause of death among smokers is (*lung cancer, coronary artery disease, cirrhosis*).
4. Alcohol absorbed by the body is (*used for energy, stored in body tissues, excreted immediately*).
5. If the alcohol in the blood exceeds (*0.02%, 0.03%, 0.5%*), death may result.
6. Alcohol is a (*stimulant, depressant, protein*).
7. Under the influence of alcohol, the time required for a response to a stimulus (*increases, decreases, remains the same*).
8. Pellagra is caused by a lack of (*niacin, alcohol, protein*).
9. (*Barbiturate, LSD, Heroin*) is produced from morphine.
10. (*Marijuana, Caffeine, LSD*) is classified as a hallucinogen.

**C. Completion**

*Complete each of the following sentences with a word or phrase that will make the sentence correct.*

1. ______ are drugs that are prescribed by many doctors for persons who cannot sleep.
2. Amphetamines are a group of drugs that stimulate the ______ system.
3. If a heroin ______ is deprived of the narcotic, withdrawal symptoms will be experienced.
4. All drugs can be classified by general use and by ______.

5. When given to dieters, ______ may suppress the appetite.
6. Alcoholics may contract a liver disease called ______.
7. The chemical compound in tobacco that acts as a stimulant is ______.
8. Drug addicts often acquire infections from unsterile ______.
9. Tobacco smoke contains at least 15 cancer-causing substances called ______.
10. Alcoholics often have a(n) ______ deficiency as the result of a poor diet.

**D. How and Why**

1. What evidence links lung cancer and cigarette smoking?
2. What is the relationship between cigarette smoking and life expectancy?
3. What is the difference between illusion and hallucination?
4. What are the harmful effects of alcoholism?
5. Why does a drug addict often return to drugs after having been treated and "cured"?

## challenges

1. Obtain recent information on the link between cigarette smoking and lung cancer from the American Cancer Society.
2. Obtain information about the problem of teenage alcoholism. Find out how common it is and what is being done to aid alcoholic teenagers.
3. Obtain information on local programs for treating drug addicts. Find out about local community agencies that can help addicts and their families.
4. Prepare a report on the use of drugs in treating hyperactivity in children. Identify the controversial issues involved.

## interesting reading


Casewit, Curtis W., *The Stop Smoking Book for Teens.* New York: Messner, 1980.

Comfort, Alex and Jane Comfort, *What About Alcohol?* Burlington, NC: Carolina Biological Supply Co., 1983.

Weil, Andrew and Winifred Rosen, *Chocolate to Morphine: Understanding Mind Active Drugs.* Boston, MA: Houghton Mifflin, 1982.

# SIDE ROADS

## Sports Medicine

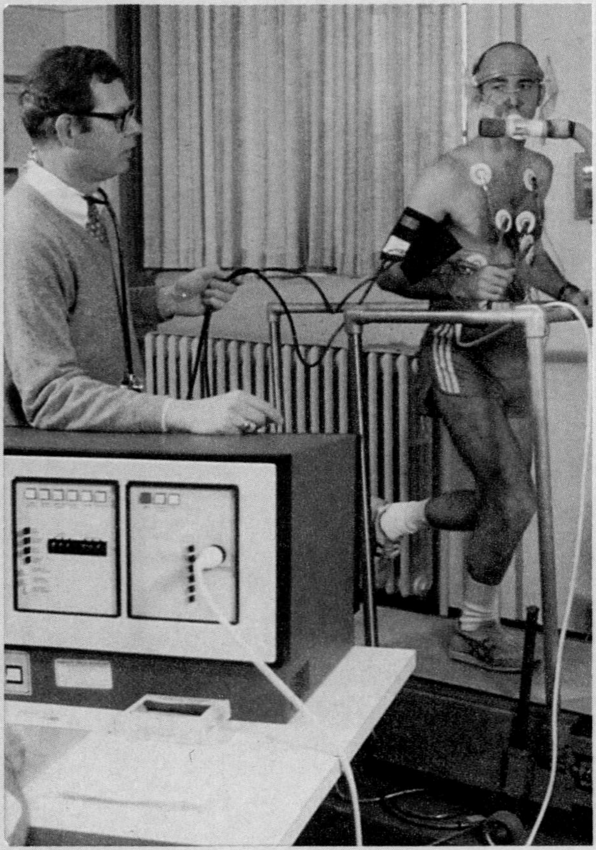

Doug Martin

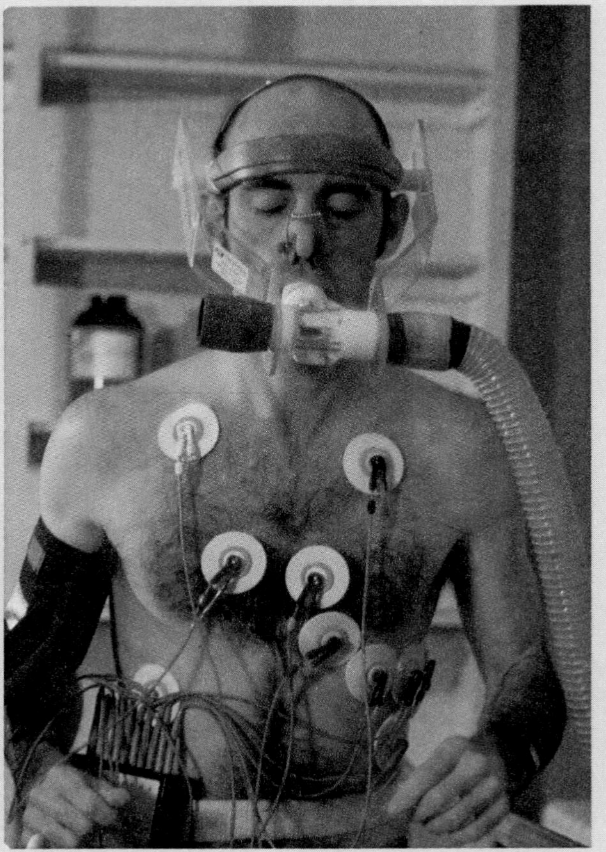

Doug Martin

*Most people realize that engaging in a sports activity is a good way to maintain their health. It strengthens muscles and burns excess calories. This activity improves lung and heart capacities and promotes a feeling of well-being.*

*Any time people take part in physical activities, there is the chance of injury. Tennis players may develop "tennis elbow." Golfers may strain their backs. Gymnasts may injure their ankles or knees. Each of these injuries may be the result of poor technique or an accident. Tennis elbow comes from an improper swing. A knee injury in gymnastics may be the result of a bad fall.*

*Treating sports-related injuries has opened a new field of medicine. It is sports medicine. Sports medicine is concerned with treating and preventing injuries that are acquired during athletic competition. It is also concerned with improving an athlete's performance.*

To meet the goals of sports medicine, scientists must understand how the body functions when engaged in a particular sport. Doctors have connected a runner to a computer by electrodes. While he runs on a treadmill, his heartbeat and breathing rates are recorded by the computer. The amount of oxygen used is also recorded. A scientist observes and records the mechanics of the runners stride. Mechanics means the way the bones and muscles move. The information gained helps scientists understand the body stress involved in running.

Another way to study the motions to an athlete is with a high-speed camera. For example, a tennis player's forehand might be filmed. The developed film is fed into a computer. The computer produces stick figures. The stick figures allow a scientist to study motions in three dimensions. The researcher can compare these motions with those of a "perfect" model stored in the computer's memory.

The information gained through these studies helps determine what kinds of motions may lead to injuries. A tennis player may injure an elbow during a forehand swing by hitting the ball when the elbow is ahead of the racquet. Using this information, doctors and trainers can more effectively prevent as well as treat injuries.

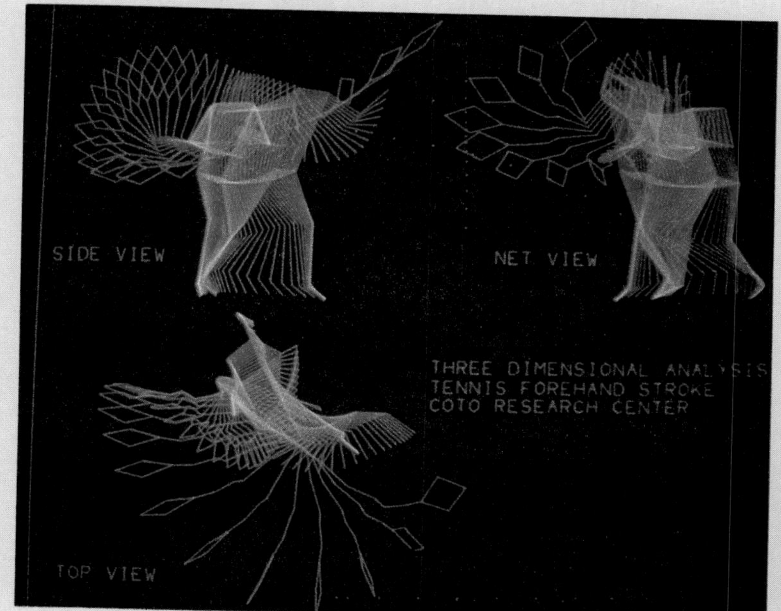


David Strick/Discover *Magazine* © *1981 Time Inc.*

David Strick/Discover *Magazine* © *1981 Time Inc.*

Another use for the information gained in these studies is technique improvement. Motion analyses can help golfers adopt better stances and swings to improve their games. This kind of analysis has been used to help figure skaters and swimmers improve their performances.

Most of the information in sports medicine has come from analyzing the performance of athletes. The information has brought changes in athletic instruction at all levels. Even a beginner learns technique that has been developed through sports medicine. The information also helps doctors recommend the proper exercise for their patients. Swimming may be recommended for an athlete with arthritis or a joint injury. A special weight training program might be used to strengthen a knee.

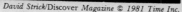

*Children inherit many characteristics from their parents. Often, people in a family share common characteristics. How are the people in this family alike? How are they different? How does life continue from generation to generation? How are traits inherited?*

*Image Workshop*

# Human Reproduction and Heredity chapter 9

## 9:1 Human Reproduction

GOAL: You will learn how humans reproduce and how inherited traits are passed from parents to children.

The survival of human beings as a species depends upon reproduction. Sexual reproduction allows for an almost endless variety of human beings.

A human female has a pair of ovaries, one on each side of her body at about hip level. Each ovary is about 3.5 cm long and 1.5 cm wide. **Ovaries** produce the female sex cell, the **egg** or ovum. Between the ovaries is a pear-shaped organ called the uterus or womb. The uterus is a hollow, muscular organ with thick walls. When an egg is released from an ovary, it enters a tube to the uterus. There are two tubes. Each one is attached to the uterus but not to the ovaries. The lower end of the uterus narrows to a small opening called the cervix. The cervix opens to the external canal, the vagina.

Where is the egg produced?

The **testes** of the male are two oval structures within an external sac called the scrotum. Sperm are produced in the testes. **Sperm** are male sex cells. Some fluids are produced by other structures. Sperm have long tails that help them swim in fluids. A human sperm is very small compared to the human egg (Figure 9–1).

What are sperm and where are they produced?

© Lennart Nilsson *from* Behold Man
—*Little, Brown and Co., Boston*

© Lennart Nilsson *from* Behold Man
—*Little, Brown and Co., Boston*

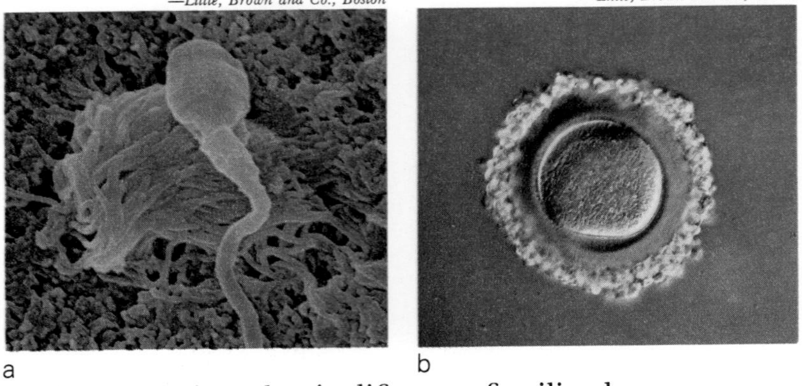


FIGURE 9–1. A human sperm cell (a) joins with a human egg cell (b) to form a fertilized egg.

How is a new human being formed from an egg and a sperm?

Human beings begin life as a fertilized egg. Fertilized means that an egg and a sperm join to form a single new cell. Normally, only one sperm can enter and fertilize an egg cell. Through repeated divisions, this single cell develops into a new human being.

## 9:2 Menstrual Cycle

Describe the menstrual cycle.

About once every month in a human female, a mature egg is released from an ovary. This process is called ovulation (ahv yuh LAY shun). At the same time, the lining of the uterus thickens in preparation for a fertilized egg. If the egg released from the ovary is not fertilized, the egg and the lining of the uterus break down. Blood and tissue pass out of the body through the vagina. This process is called menstruation (men STRAY shun). Menstruation lasts

FIGURE 9–2. The menstrual cycle repeats about every 28 days.

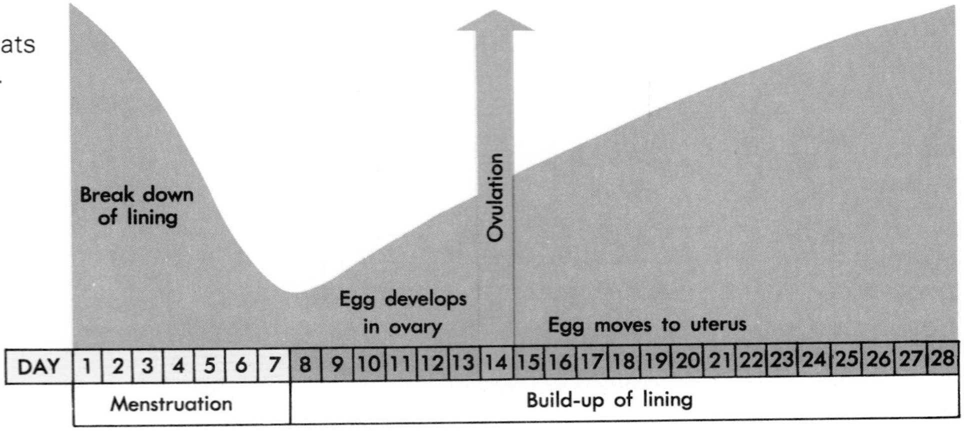

about 5 days. As menstruation is occurring, a new egg is maturing in an ovary.

Ovulation generally occurs about 14 days after the start of menstruation. This time varies from female to female. After ovulation, the egg cell lives about 24 to 48 hours. If live sperm cells are present at the time of ovulation, the egg may be fertilized.

Ovulation and menstruation are parts of the **menstrual cycle** (Figure 9–2). Menstrual cycles begin when a female is from 10 to 13 years old and continue until between the ages of 45 and 60. A female no longer ovulates when her menstrual cycles cease.

## 9:3 Pregnancy

Define the terms pregnancy, embryo, and fetus.

When an egg from a female is fertilized by a sperm from a male, **pregnancy** results. The single cell formed by the union of the sperm and egg goes through many cell divisions. In its early stages, the new organism is called an embryo (EM bree oh). Later, when it has the shape and form of a human being, it is called a **fetus** (FEET us). Pregnancy lasts about 280 days.

How is a fetus nourished?

During its development the fetus is protected by the uterus and nourished by the placenta (pluh SENT uh). The placenta is a tissue that forms in

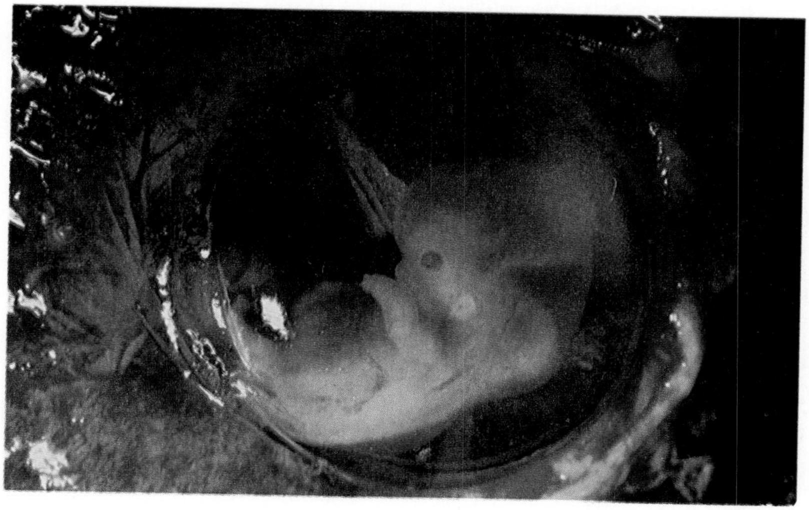

Saturn Scientific, Inc.

FIGURE 9–3. A human fetus develops in a uterus.

FIGURE 9–4. In the placenta, blood from mother and blood from the fetus exchange gases and chemicals without mixing.

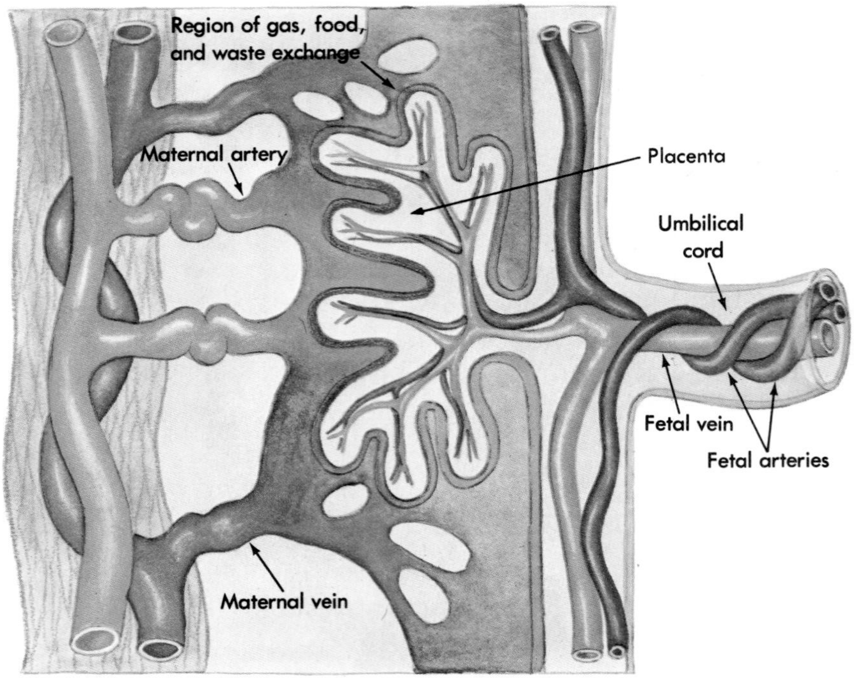


the uterine wall and has a rich supply of blood. It is connected to the embryo by a ropelike tube called the umbilical (um BIHL ih kul) cord (Figure 9–4).

The blood supply of the embryo and mother are separate. Blood does not flow from one to the other. How then is the embryo nourished? A closer look at the placenta will give you the answer.

The placenta really has two blood supplies. One belongs to the mother and the other to the embryo. Blood vessels from both closely intertwine. They lie so close together that molecules easily diffuse from one blood supply to the other. Thus, food and oxygen can diffuse from the mother's blood into the embryo's blood. Carbon dioxide and other wastes can diffuse from embryo to mother.

Birth occurs when the fetus is forced out of the uterus by strong contractions of the uterine wall. The umbilical cord is cut near its union with the newborn child. The uterine contractions continue until the placenta has also been forced out of the uterus. After birth, the child may be fed milk from the mammary glands of its mother. Some mothers may not produce enough milk for the baby. Other mothers may choose, for various reasons, not to nurse their babies. These mothers use a milk substitute called a formula to feed their babies.

## 9:4 Traits and Genes

How do children inherit traits?

**Heredity** is the passing of characteristics from parents to offspring. A **trait** is an inherited characteristic such as eye and hair color, height, and resistance to disease. Traits are carried by chromosomes. Chromosomes are threadlike structures in the cell's nucleus that become visible when the cell divides. The number of chromosomes within cells is different for each species. Humans have 46 chromosomes in each body cell. A human egg and a human sperm each contain 23 chromosomes. When an egg and a sperm join, the chromosomes pair, resulting in a total of 46 chromosomes (23 pairs) in each body cell. Thus, half a person's chromosomes come from the father, and half come from the mother.

Chromosomes are composed of genes. A **gene** is the unit of inheritance that is passed from parents to children. The total number of genes for a human being is unknown. Some scientists believe a human may have as many as 50 000 genes.

For each trait, there are at least two genes that control its inheritance. One gene for a trait is found

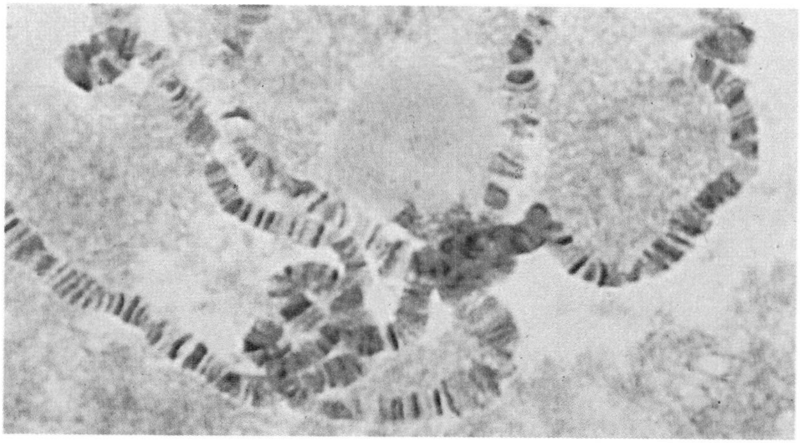

*Harris Biological Supplies Ltd.*

FIGURE 9–5. Each chromosome in your body is composed of thousands of genes. The genes on this Drosophila chromosome are responsible for the development of specific fruit fly traits.

Larry Hamill

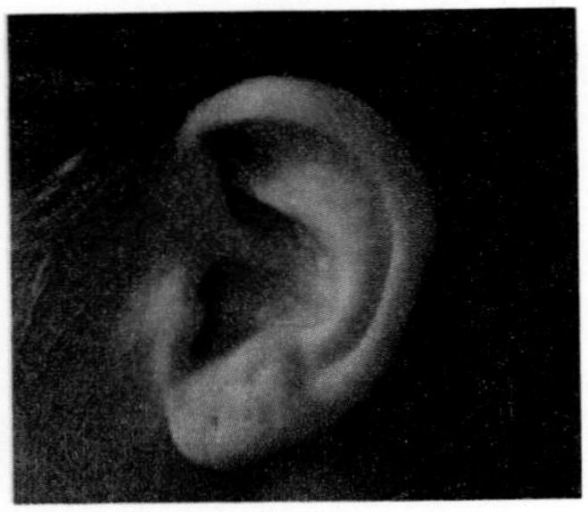

a

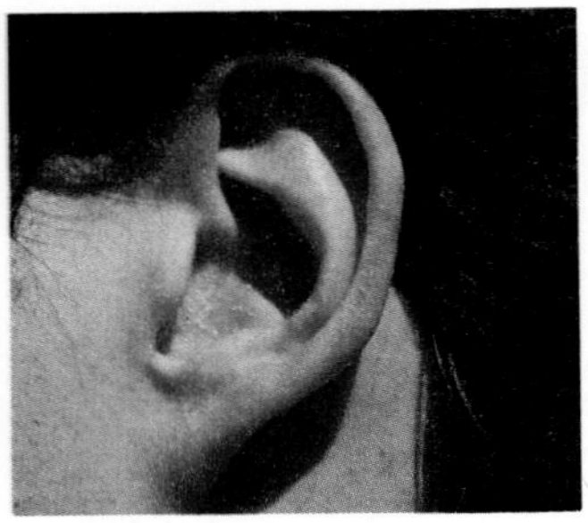

b

FIGURE 9–6. Unattached ear lobes (a) are dominant over attached ear lobes (b).

Define the terms dominant, recessive, and hybrid.

What is a gene carrier?

FIGURE 9–7. Albinism is caused by a pair of recessive genes.

Alvin E. Staffan

on each chromosome in a chromosome pair. Sometimes both genes of a pair are alike. In other cases, the genes are different. For example, a sperm could carry the genes for blue eyes, and an egg could carry the genes for brown eyes. The embryo formed from their union would have different genes for the same trait. Usually, when two different genes for a trait are present, only one gene is expressed. The gene that is expressed is **dominant.** The unexpressed gene is **recessive.** In the example above, the child would have brown eyes. The gene for brown eyes is dominant over the gene for blue eyes. A dominant trait, such as brown eyes, appears if a child has one or two dominant genes. If two dominant genes are present, the person is pure dominant for that trait. If one dominant and one recessive gene are present, the person is hybrid for that trait.

A recessive trait, such as blue eyes, appears only when a child receives two recessive genes from the parents. Recessive traits often skip generations. A parent may have a certain recessive trait that is not expressed in his or her children. Instead, the dominant form of the trait inherited from the other parent is expressed. However, the children are hybrids for this trait and carry both a dominant and a recessive gene in their chromosomes. A person who carries a gene for a recessive trait without showing the trait is a **carrier.** If a carrier later has children with another carrier or with a person who expresses the recessive trait, the children may also show the recessive trait. Thus, two brown-eyed parents can have blue-eyed children, if the children inherit two recessive genes.

Albinism is another example of a recessive trait that can skip generations. Albinos have no color pigment in their skin, eyes, or hair. The skin and hair are white, and the eyes are pink (Figure 9–7). In one family, two sons were born. One son had light brown skin, the other was an albino. The albino never married. The other son married and had children with light brown skin. In the fifth generation of this family, one child was albino. The gene for albinism had been hidden by the dominant gene. It may be a total surprise when rare recessive traits are expressed. People may not have been aware that a recessive trait was present in their family.

Why might a recessive trait skip a generation?

The chance that a carrier of a rare trait will marry another carrier of that trait is small. However, a carrier of a trait is likely to have relatives who are carriers. For this reason rare, defective hereditary traits appear most often in children from marriages between first cousins or other close relatives.

**activity**

**TONGUE ROLLING**

One dominant human trait is the ability to roll the edges of the tongue into a U-shape. Survey your classmates to see how many of them can roll their tongues. Record the number of students that can roll their tongues. How many cannot roll their tongues? On the average, about 3 out of 10 people cannot roll their tongues. How does your class compare to this figure?

David M. Dennis

FIGURE 9–8.

**making sure**

1. Two first cousins, both hybrid for albinism, marry. Could any of their children be albinos? Explain.
2. Explain how hereditary deafness may appear in a child even if the parents and grandparents hear.

## 9:5 Human Pedigrees

Heredity can be studied through pedigrees. A **pedigree** is a record of an organism's ancestors. A human's pedigree records names of ancestors, their birth dates, and any hereditary diseases, conditions, or traits exhibited by each family member. Thus, scientists may use pedigrees to determine how different traits are inherited from generation to generation. Family pedigrees are developed from

What is a pedigree?

facts taken from legal papers such as birth certificates. Other sources such as hospital records and family albums also are used.

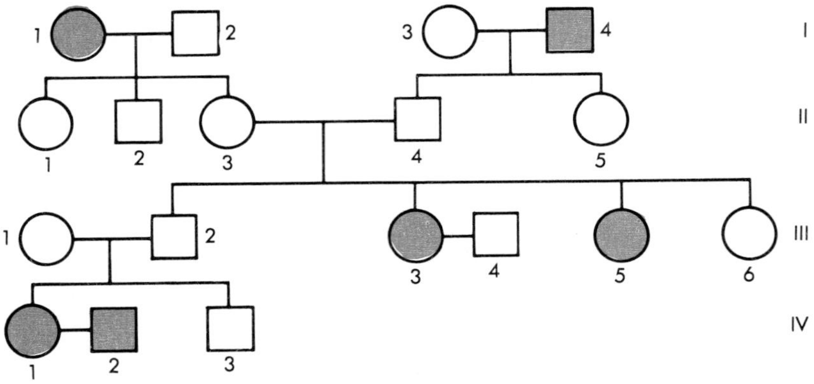


FIGURE 9–9. A pedigree may be used to trace a hereditary trait or disease in a family.

Usually a pedigree is designed to trace one family trait. Pedigrees are charted using symbols to represent people. Males are represented by squares. Circles represent females. Each generation is represented by a Roman numeral, and each person in a generation is numbered. Thus, the circle in the upper left of the pedigree in Figure 9-9 represents a female identified as I-1.

Lines on a pedigree show family relationships. A horizontal line between a circle and a square represents a marriage. A vertical line joins parents to a child. If there are several children, the vertical line ends in a horizontal line. Squares and circles that represent children are connected to this line. The children are placed left to right in order of their births. That is, the oldest child is always to the left.

How are persons who have the trait under study indicated on a pedigree?

Symbols on a pedigree are shaded to indicate which family members possess the trait under study. Figure 9–9 shows the pattern of inheritance of attached earlobes in a family. All family members with attached earlobes, a recessive trait, are shaded blue. Follow the inheritance of this trait through the generations shown.

## making sure

**3.** How do you know that the trait shown in the pedigree in Figure 9–9 results from a recessive gene?

4. Explain how the trait shown in Figure 9–9 could skip some children in generation II, yet reappear in the grandchildren in generation III.
5. If IV–1 and IV–2 have children, what type of earlobes will their children have? Explain.
6. What kind of information is needed to compile a human pedigree? Where can this information be found?
7. Both parents in a family are tongue rollers. They have three offspring—two males and one female. All three are tongue rollers. The female marries a man who is also a tongue roller. They have one boy and three girls. The boy and two of the girls are tongue rollers. Draw a pedigree for this family. Indicate the tongue rollers.

## 9:6 Sex-Linked Traits

Most physical traits, such as blue eyes and type O blood appear about equally in both men and women. These traits are determined by one or more pairs of matched genes. However, there are some traits that are more common in men than in women. These traits are called sex-linked traits. Color blindness and hemophilia are examples of sex-linked traits. Hemophilia is a rare disease in which blood does not clot properly. A cut may be fatal to a hemophiliac.

What is a sex-linked trait?

**Sex-linked traits** are believed to be controlled by genes on the chromosomes that determine the sex of a person. The determination of sex involves whole chromosomes, not just a few paired genes. There are two types of sex chromosomes. One type is the X chromosome, which is relatively large. The other is the Y chromosome, which is relatively small. Because the X chromosome is so much larger than the Y, it has more genes than the Y. As a result, a gene on the X chromosome may have no matching gene on the Y chromosome.

FIGURE 9–10. The sex of a human depends on the X and Y chromosomes.

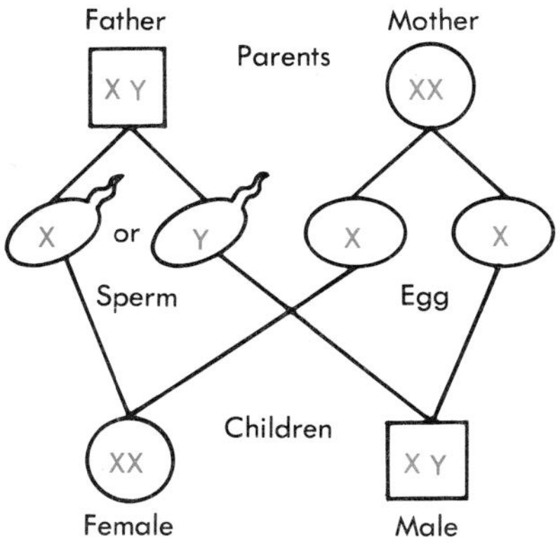


A person with two X chromosomes is a female (XX). For a female to have a recessive sex-linked trait, she must have two recessive genes. One recessive gene must be on each X chromosome. If a female has a recessive sex-linked gene on one X chromosome and not the other, she will be a carrier.

A person with an X chromosome and a Y chromosome is a male (XY). For a male to have a recessive sex-linked trait, he needs only one recessive gene. A recessive gene on the X chromosome will result in the trait if the Y chromosome does not have a gene for the trait.

Color blindness is a fairly common recessive sex-linked trait. If a color-blind woman marries a color-seeing man, all their sons but none of their daughters will be color-blind. However, all the daughters (XX) will be carriers of color blindness. A son (XY) gets his color blindness from his mother's X chromosome. The Y chromosome, that does not carry the gene, is received from his father.

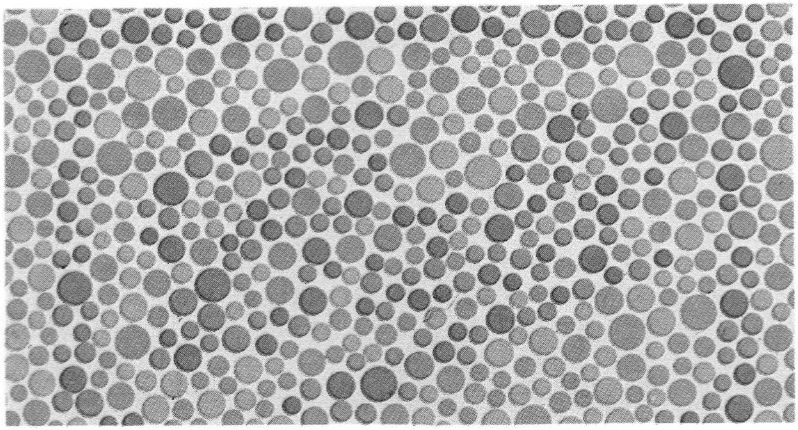

FIGURE 9–11. What word do you see in this photograph? The word would not be visible to a color-blind person.

Why do sex-linked traits appear more in males than in females?

Color blindness is much rarer in women than in men. For a woman to be color-blind, her father must be color-blind and her mother must be either color-blind or a carrier. The woman must receive an X chromosome that has a recessive gene from both parents.

## making sure

8. In a family of four sons and four daughters, two sons were born with hemophilia. The father was a hemophiliac. Was the mother normal, hemophiliac, or a carrier? Explain your answer.

9. How can a woman inherit two genes for color blindness?
10. Why is a male never a carrier of a sex-linked trait?
11. How do you know when sex-linked traits are recessive?

## 9:7 Multiple-Gene Inheritance

Few human traits are controlled by one pair of genes. Most are controlled by multiple genes. Multiple genes means that more than one pair of genes controls the trait. Multiple-gene inheritance makes the study of heredity difficult. These traits can vary from person to person, depending on the number of genes involved. Studying the effects of many gene pairs is more complex than studying the effects of only one pair.

What is multiple-gene inheritance?

With the exception of albinos, all persons have a brown pigment called melanin (MEL uh nun) in their skins. Skin color differences are due mainly to differences in the size and amount of melanin particles. The more melanin, the darker the skin.

George Anderson

FIGURE 9–12. Skin color is controlled by more than one gene pair.

The amount of melanin in the skin is controlled by genes. Scientists agree that one gene pair could not account for all the possible shades of skin color that exist. Research has shown that between four and eight gene pairs are probably involved.

## activity HANDSPAN SIZE AND ITS INHERITANCE

(1) Spread out your hand on a piece of graph paper. Make a mark at the tip of your thumb and at the tip of your little finger. Do not include length of fingernails. (2) Measure the distance between the two marks (your handspan) in millimeters. (3) Record the handspan measurements of all members of your class on the chalkboard. (4) Organize the measurements into a table showing handspans in groups of 5 mm. Also record the number of students in each group. (5) Draw a graph of the data in the table. What does the graph reveal about the differences in handspans within your class? Based on your data, do you think hand size is controlled by one or more pairs of genes? What other factors can affect hand size?

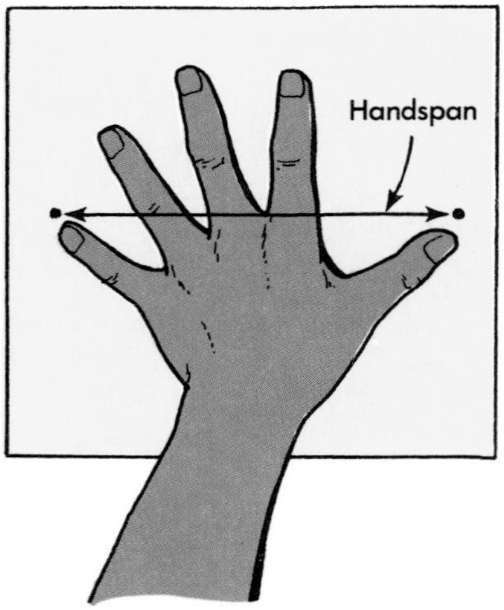


FIGURE 9–13.

## 9:8 Genetic Diseases and Disorders

Describe three genetic diseases.

Some diseases and disorders are hereditary. Huntington disease is a disease of the nervous system caused by a dominant gene. It produces uncontrollable twitching and a loss of mental ability. Signs of the disease normally do not appear until adulthood.

Sickle-cell anemia is a blood disease caused by a recessive gene. Over two million Americans are carriers of the gene for sickle-cell anemia. When two carriers marry, their children have a 25 percent chance of having the disease.

Several genetic disorders are caused by the wrong number of chromosomes in each body cell. Down syndrome is such a disorder. A child with Down syndrome has 47 chromosomes in each cell instead of the normal 46. Symptoms of the disorder include a short body, eyelid folds, and mental retardation.

FIGURE 9–14. The narrow cells are sickled red blood cells.

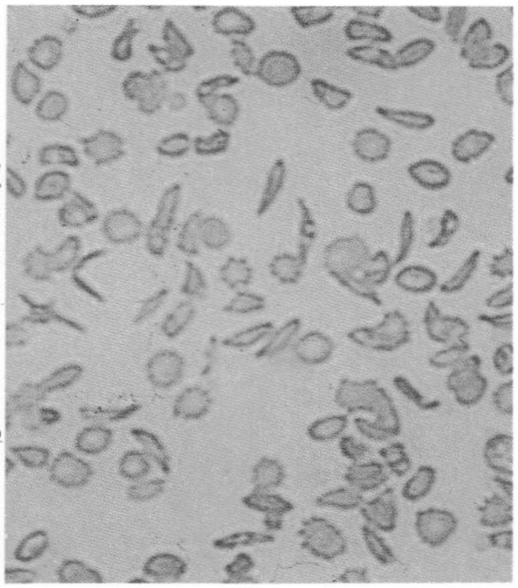

Runk, Schoenberger/Grant Heilman Photography

Couples that suspect they may carry a genetic disease should receive genetic counseling. The counselor gets facts about the couple and their families. Special blood tests or chromosome analyses may be performed. The counselor reviews all of the data and may be able to predict the couple's chances of having a normal child. If the risk of a genetic disorder is high, the couple may decide not to have children. Genetic counseling is also important in determining a couple's chances of having normal offspring if a genetic disorder is found in their first child.

A process now used to determine the genetic state of a fetus is amniocentesis (am nee oh sen TEE sus). **Amniocentesis** is a process in which some of the fluid surrounding the fetus in the mother's uterus is removed. This fluid contains cells from the fetus. These fetal cells are then grown in a special solution and examined under a microscope. Down syndrome and 80 other genetic diseases and disorders can be detected in the fetus using this process.

Why is ultrasound used?

Another process used to determine the position and size of fetal structures involves the use of ultrasound. This procedure does not require any fluid to be removed from the mother's uterus.

Tom Hutchinson

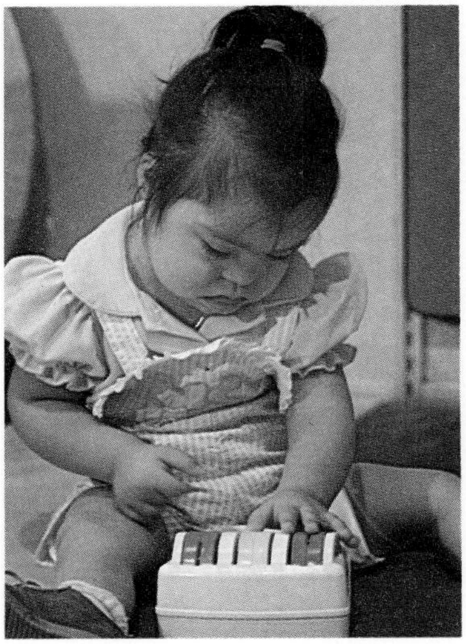

FIGURE 9–15. A child with Down syndrome has 47 chromosomes in each body cell instead of 46.

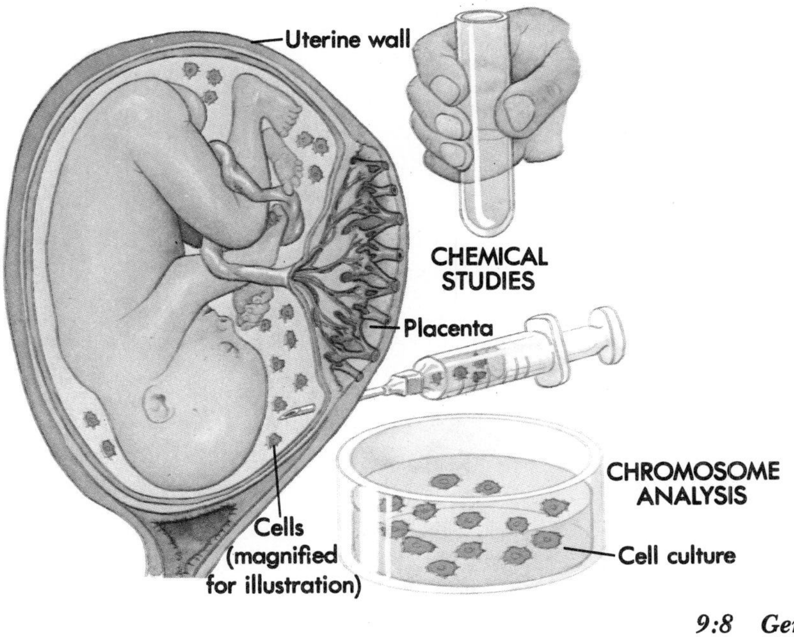


FIGURE 9–16. In amniocentesis, fetal cells are cultured and studied to uncover possible genetic diseases.

# PERSPECTIVES

skills

## Taking Notes in Outline Form

Outlining is probably the most often used form of notetaking. By outlining information, you are able to see the relationships among main ideas and the details that support them more clearly. Outlining can aid you in remembering information. When you outline, you sort and organize ideas and details and put them into your own words.

Suggestions for an outline of Chapter 9 are listed below. The types of information to be included in the outline are listed as headings and subheadings. Complete the outline by filling in the necessary information. You may find this example useful in outlining reading material in many subject areas.

**Human Reproduction and Heredity**

I. Human Reproduction
  A. Reproductive organs
    1. Male:
       two testes within the scrotum
    2. Female:
       two ovaries
  B. Sex cells
    1. Male:
       sperm
    2. Female:
       eggs
  C. Fertilization:
    1. Occurs when sperm and egg join to form a single new cell.
    2. This single cell develops into a new human being through repeated divisions.
II. Menstrual Cycle
  A. Ovulation:
  B. Menstruation:
  C. Menstrual cycle:
III. Pregnancy
  A. Occurs when:
  B. Fetus:
  C. Duration:
  D. Placenta
    1. Definition:
    2. Umbilical cord:
    3. Blood supplies:
  E. Birth:
IV. Traits and Genes
  A. Traits
    1. Definition:
    2. Chromosomes:
  B. Genes
    1. Dominant:
    2. Recessive:
    3. Carriers:
V. Human Pedigrees
  A. Definition:
  B. How to read:
VI. Sex-Linked Traits
  A. Definition:
  B. Examples:
  C. Reasons for occurrence:
VII. Multiple-Gene Inheritance
  A. Definition:
  B. Examples:
VIII. Genetic Diseases
  A. Examples:
  B. Causes:
  C. Prevention and/or treatment
    1. Reasons for counseling:
    2. Processes to determine genetic state of the fetus:

After completing the above outline, ask yourself the following: Does the outline include all the important information? Is there other information that should be included? As a class, you may wish to discuss how complete an outline should be to be useful for remembering and reviewing information.

## main ideas — Chapter Review

1. Every human being begins life as a fertilized egg. 9:1
2. Human females have a monthly menstrual cycle during which an egg matures and is released. 9:2
3. A human embryo develops inside the female uterus during pregnancy. 9:3
4. Hereditary traits are controlled by genes carried on chromosomes. 9:4
5. One half of a child's genes comes from the father and one half from the mother. 9:4
6. Scientists use pedigrees to study human heredity. 9:5
7. Some traits are inherited along with the sex of a person. 9:6
8. Most human traits are controlled by multiple genes. 9:7
9. Some diseases or disorders, including sickle-cell anemia and Down syndrome, are inherited. 9:8
10. Genetic counseling is available to couples who think they may carry a genetic disease or disorder. 9:8

## vocabulary

*Define each of the following words or terms:*

amniocentesis
carrier
dominant
egg
fetus
gene
heredity
menstrual cycle
ovaries
pedigree
pregnancy
recessive
sex-linked trait
sperm
testes
trait

## study questions

**DO NOT WRITE IN THIS BOOK.**

### A. True or False

*Determine whether each of the following sentences is true or false. If the sentence is false, rewrite it to make it true.*

1. An ovary produces eggs.
2. Each parent supplies one half of a child's heredity.
3. The menstrual cycle is about 35 days.

4. Ovulation occurs about 14 days from the start of menstruation.
5. Chromosomes carry hereditary traits.
6. A dominant gene results in a dominant trait being expressed.
7. Fathers supply two thirds of all genes to their children.
8. A human sperm cell has 23 chromosomes.
9. Females have two X chromosomes.
10. Males have two Y chromosomes.

## B. Multiple Choice

*Choose the word or phrase that completes correctly each of the following sentences.*

1. *(Color blindness, Hemophilia, Skin color)* is an example of multiple-gene inheritance.
2. The *(uterus, placenta, umbilical cord)* protects the fetus during its development.
3. A carrier of a rare trait has a *(recessive, dominant, pure)* gene.
4. Sperm are produced in the *(scrotum, testes, ovaries)*.
5. For a dominant trait to appear in a child the trait must be present in *(both parents, either parent, father only, mother only)*.
6. A carrier of albinism is *(hybrid, pure dominant, pure recessive)* for the trait.
7. Chances for the appearance of rare hereditary traits are greatest in marriages between *(unrelated people, relatives, close relatives)*.
8. *(Hair color, Eye color, Color blindness)* is a sex-linked trait.
9. A color-blind male inherited the trait from *(his father, his mother, both parents)*.
10. Albinism requires the inheritance of *(one, two, many)* genes.

## C. Completion

*Complete each of the following sentences with a word or phrase that will make the sentence correct.*

1. ______ occurs when blood and tissue pass out of the body through the vagina.
2. A man with hemophilia inherited the trait from his ______.
3. Sex-linked traits appear more often in ______ than in ______.

4. The release of an egg from the ovary is called ______.
5. ______ traits are carried by genes on the X chromosome.
6. ______ is the pigment that gives color to skin.
7. In a pedigree, squares represent ______ and circles represent ______.
8. ______ are units of inheritance that are passed from parents to children.
9. Down syndrome is caused by the presence of an extra ______.
10. ______ may be used to uncover the presence of genetic disorders and diseases in a fetus.

**D. How and Why**

1. Explain how it is possible for a genetic trait to skip a generation.
2. Describe the changes that occur during the female menstrual cycle.
3. Explain how a pedigree is constructed.
4. How are sex chromosomes responsible for the inheritance of sex-linked traits?
5. What is the purpose of genetic counseling?

## challenges

1. Prepare a report on the treatment of sickle-cell anemia.
2. Obtain information about the mapping of human chromosomes. Learn how this information may someday be used to prevent or cure certain genetic diseases.
3. Investigate genetic counseling as a career and determine the training needed to be a genetic counselor.

## interesting reading

Caveney, Sylvia and Simon Stern, *Inside Mom: An Illustrated Account of Conception, Pregnancy*. New York: St. Martin's, 1977.

Shurkin, Joel, "Operating On The Unborn," *Science 83*. May 1983, pp. 70-74.

Silverstein, Alvin and Virginia Silverstein, *The Genetics Explosion*. New York: Four Winds, 1980.

*This man is testing barrels of dye. Dyes are considered chemicals. Look around your room. Where have dyes and other chemicals been used? Chemicals affect every aspect of your life. They are in the foods that you eat, the clothes that you wear, your home, and your school. What chemicals have you used today?*

*CIBA-GEIGY Corp.*

# Chemistry unit 3

*All matter can be classified as one of four physical forms. The hang-glider is moving through air. Air is a gaseous form of matter. What form of matter is the ocean? What other forms of matter are shown in this photograph? Can matter change from one form to another? How does matter behave?*

Steve Lissau

# Matter

## chapter 10

## 10:1 Chemistry: The Science of Matter

GOAL: You will learn the properties of matter and how these properties are the result of the composition of matter.

Define chemistry and matter.

**Chemistry** is the study of the properties of matter, the changes that matter can undergo, and the laws that describe these changes. Chemists study different materials to learn their properties. Understanding the properties of matter allows us to use matter in practical ways. Look around you. The clothes you wear are different colors. These colors come from dyes made by a chemist. Certain medicines are made in the laboratory to treat diseases. New materials are being developed to build computers, space ships, and other modern inventions. Through chemistry, we change an almost endless variety of matter into other forms of matter that we use.

**Matter** has mass and occupies space. Air, brick, and ink are all classified as matter. However, each of these materials is different from the others. Each material is in a different physical state. Air is a gas, the brick is a solid, and ink is a liquid. Matter can exist in one of four physical states—solid, liquid, gas, or plasma. Each state has a specific set of properties. These properties are listed in Table 10–1.

Dick Smith

FIGURE 10-1. Helium, a gas, takes the shape of its containers, the balloons.

Define solid, liquid, gas, and plasma. Name examples.

***Table 10–1.***
Physical States of Matter

| Physical State | Property | Example |
|---|---|---|
| Solid | Definite shape and volume | Ice, wood, tree, person |
| Liquid | No definite shape; Definite volume | Water, alcohol, gasoline |
| Gas | No definite shape; No definite volume | Air, hydrogen, oxygen |
| Plasma | No definite shape; No definite volume; electrically charged particles | Star, sun's surface |

Matter can change from one state to another. When there is a change in state, energy in the form of heat is gained or lost. If a solid such as ice is heated to its melting point, it becomes a liquid. The melting point of ice is 0°C. Water freezes and becomes solid ice if it is cooled below 0°C. When matter is cooled, it loses heat. A liquid heated to its boiling point changes into a gas. The boiling point of water is 100°C. When a gas such as water vapor is cooled below its boiling point, it becomes a liquid.

Describe change of state.

List three examples of a change in state.

How does pressure affect the freezing and boiling points of water?

Let's examine the effects of pressure on the physical state of water. At sea level air pressure, water can exist as a solid, liquid, or gas. Water is a solid at temperatures below 0°C. It is a liquid at temperatures between 0°C and 100°C and a gas at temperatures above 100°C. If the pressure changes, the temperatures at which water freezes and boils change also. When air pressure is lower, such as at the top of a mountain, water freezes at a higher temperature and boils at a lower temperature. When pressure increases, water freezes at a lower temperature and boils at a higher temperature.

FIGURE 10-2. Water can be a solid, a liquid, or a gas.

Roger K. Burnard

Most solid materials will change to a liquid state if enough heat is added. Also, if enough heat is added, a liquid will change to the gas state. A few substances do not follow this pattern. Dry ice and iodine are materials that change directly from the solid state to the gas state with the addition of heat. This change is called sublimation (sub luh MAY shun). Dry ice is solid carbon dioxide. At room temperature, 21°C, carbon dioxide is a gas. When placed under high pressure and cooled, the carbon dioxide gas changes into solid dry ice. Dry ice is used to cool food or materials. The heat energy to sublimate the dry ice comes from the food or material being cooled.

### making sure

1. How is a liquid different from a solid?
2. How is a gas different from a liquid?
3. Give an example of a change of state from a solid to a liquid.
4. What happens to the freezing point of water if the pressure is reduced?
5. Why do you think solid carbon dioxide was given the name dry ice?

## 10:2 Properties of Matter

List five examples of physical properties.

Some materials such as pure sugar, pure salt, or pure carbon always have the same composition. These materials are called substances. The properties of a substance can be used to identify it and determine its use. For example, gold can be hammered into thin sheets and it reflects heat. The ability to be shaped into different forms and to reflect heat are properties of gold. Because of these properties, gold is used as the outer layer of the astronauts' space helmets.

FIGURE 10-3. Because it reflects heat and light, gold is used on an astronaut's suit.

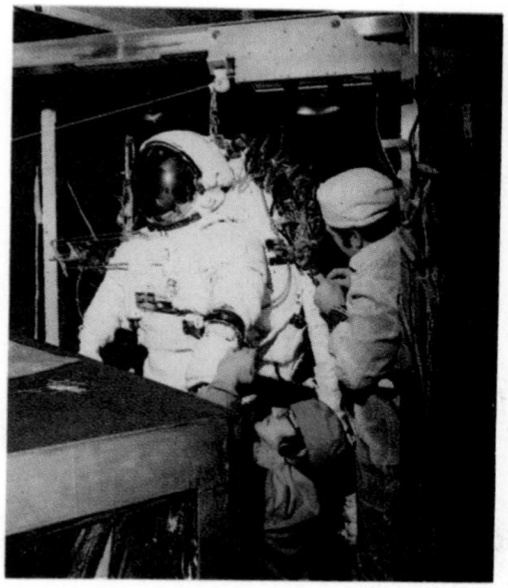

NASA

Every substance has a set of physical and chemical properties. **Physical properties** are the characteristics of a substance that may be observed without changing the composition of the substance. Some physical properties are mass, volume, color, density, and melting and freezing point. Other important properties are malleability, ductility, and conductivity. Malleability is the ability to be hammered without losing strength. Ductility is a measure of how easily a substance can be drawn into a wire. Conductivity is a measure of how easily electricity or heat flows through a substance.

Define physical change.

A **physical change** is a change in the size, shape, color, or physical state of a substance. A physical change does not affect the chemical properties or composition of a substance.

Jim Howard/FPG

FIGURE 10-4. When a metal is refined, it undergoes many physical changes.

What are chemical properties? Give two examples of chemical properties.

**Chemical properties** are characteristics that depend upon the behavior of a substance in the presence of other substances. Paper burns in the presence of oxygen. The ability to react with oxygen is a chemical property. Iron combines with oxygen in air to form rust. In both cases, a change occurs when the substance reacts with oxygen. Iron is changed to iron oxide, the chemical name for rust. When it burns, paper is changed to carbon, carbon dioxide, and water vapor. Heat and light are also produced.

The burning of paper involves more than a change in the appearance of the paper. Its chemical composition is changed. The paper no longer exists because its components have become other chemical substances. The changes in the paper are called chemical changes. In a **chemical change**, new substances with different properties are formed. Chemical changes usually involve the release of heat, light, or electricity.

FIGURE 10-5. When a match ignites, phosphorus reacts with oxygen to produce new substances. The match undergoes chemical changes.

Courtesy Diamond International Corp.

A substance can be broken down into other substances by chemical change. When an electric current is passed through water, the water decomposes into two gases, hydrogen and oxygen. Hydrogen and oxygen have properties different from water.

## activity PHYSICAL PROPERTIES

Examine and record the physical properties of samples of aluminum, iron, rubber, and wood. Use a conductivity apparatus to determine if each sample is a conductor. Touch the electrodes to each sample in a beaker. **CAUTION:** Do not touch the electrodes with your hands because you may receive a shock. Record your results. What two physical properties do aluminum and iron have in common? What two physical properties do rubber and wood have in common?

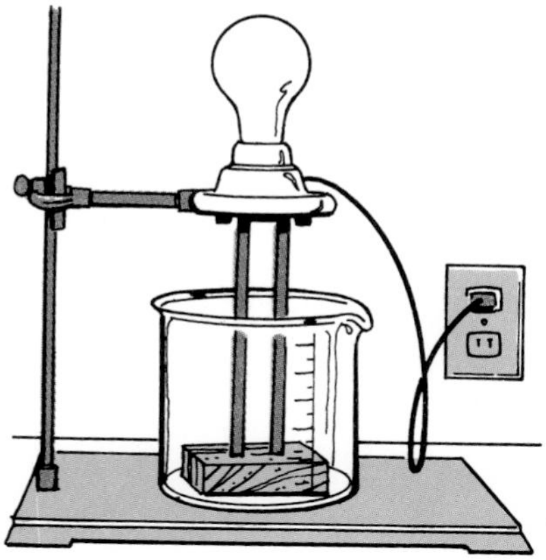

FIGURE 10-6.

## activity CHEMICAL CHANGE

Pour 5 mL of dilute hydrochloric acid into a large test tube. Touch the outside bottom of the test tube and record your impression of its temperature—cold, cool, warm, hot. Carefully add 2 small pieces of mossy zinc to the test tube. Observe and record what happens. Touch the bottom of the test tube again and record your impression of the temperature. What happened to the zinc? Was the change in zinc a physical or chemical change? How do you know?

## making sure

**6.** List three physical properties of vegetable oil.

**7.** Describe the physical properties of gold. How do its properties determine how gold is used?

**8.** Classify these as chemical or physical changes.
   a. A metal reacts with an acid.
   b. A metal is drawn into a wire.

## 10:3 Elements and Compounds

Define element and give two examples of elements.

Scientists have discovered 109 substances that they call elements. Of these elements, 90 occur naturally in our world. The rest are made by scientists in laboratories. An **element** cannot be broken down into simpler substances by a chemical change. Oxygen and hydrogen are two examples of elements.

The name of an element can be represented by a chemical symbol. When one letter is used as a symbol of an element, it is written as a capital letter. The symbol for oxygen is O. The symbol for hydrogen is H. When a symbol contains two letters, the first letter is written as a capital and the second is a small letter. The symbol for helium is He, and the symbol for chlorine is Cl. Most symbols come from the English name of the elements. Some symbols, however, come from the element's Latin name. Table 10–2 lists the Latin name and symbol for some common elements. The names and symbols for all elements are shown on pages 200 and 201.

Elements combine during a chemical change to form compounds. A **compound** is a substance formed when two or more elements are chemically joined. Water, sugar, table salt, and ammonia are chemical compounds.

Chemical compounds are represented by the combination of two or more symbols. These combined symbols used to represent a chemical compound are called a formula. Every formula contains the symbol of each element in the

***Table 10–2.***
Latin Names and Symbols for Some Elements

| Element | Symbol | Latin Name |
|---|---|---|
| Potassium | K | *Kalium* |
| Iron | Fe | *Ferrum* |
| Gold | Au | *Aurum* |
| Sodium | Na | *Natrium* |
| Silver | Ag | *Argentum* |
| Copper | Cu | *Cuprum* |
| Lead | Pb | *Plumbum* |
| Mercury | Hg | *Hydrargyrum* |

Robert Frerck/Odyssey Production

FIGURE 10–7. Iron ore is a compound of iron and other elements.

compound. Water is represented by the formula $H_2O$. The H stands for hydrogen, and the O stands for oxygen. The small number 2 in the formula is called a subscript. A subscript shows the amount of a particular element in the compound. For example, the 2 in $H_2O$ shows there are 2 parts hydrogen in water for each part oxygen. A subscript refers to the symbol before it in a formula.

How is a formula written for a compound?

Some elements are diatomic in the free state. Diatomic means occuring as two atoms. The following elements are diatomic: $H_2$, $N_2$, $O_2$, $F_2$, $Cl_2$, $Br_2$, and $I_2$.

## 10:4 Mixtures

A **mixture** consists of two or more substances that are mixed but not chemically joined. A mixture may contain elements, compounds, or both elements and compounds mixed together. Air, blood, and soil are mixtures. Air contains oxygen, nitrogen, carbon dioxide, water vapor, and other gases. Blood contains red and white cells, water, and many dissolved elements. Soil is a mixture of minerals and other materials. The fertility of soil varies because of differences in its composition.

What is a mixture?

Mixtures can be separated by physical means. No chemical changes are needed. Soil that is passed through screens of various sizes separates into small rocks, sand, and other material. To separate nitrogen from air, the air is changed to a liquid at a low temperature and high pressure. Then it is warmed

FIGURE 10-8. A bowl of vegetables is an example of a mixture. The vegetables are not chemically joined.

slowly. At the boiling point of nitrogen, −195.8°C, the nitrogen separates out as a gas. Then, it is collected and stored for later use. Blood is separated into its parts by a centrifuge. A centrifuge spins rapidly in a circular path. The rapid spinning causes the denser parts of blood to settle to the bottom leaving a clear layer of liquid over the settled parts.

## 10:5 Solutions, Suspensions, and Colloids

What is a solution?

A **solution** is a uniform mixture composed of two or more substances. A solution cannot be separated into its parts by filtering. The particles in a solution are evenly mixed throughout. Salt in water, iodine in alcohol, and oxygen in water are examples of solutions.

Sugar dissolves in water to form a sugar solution. The sugar particles separate slowly from a lump of sugar. They move to all parts of the water and mix with the water particles. After several hours, the sugar is distributed evenly throughout the water. Do not confuse the solution process with melting. The sugar has not melted as melting of sugar requires a high temperature.

Define solute and solvent.

The substance that is dissolved in a solution is the **solute** (SAHL yewt). The substance that dissolves the solute is the **solvent** (SAHL vunt). In the sugar-water solution, sugar is the solute and water is the solvent.

How does a solute affect the freezing and boiling points of a liquid?

A solute lowers the freezing point of a solvent in which it is dissolved. It also raises the solvent's

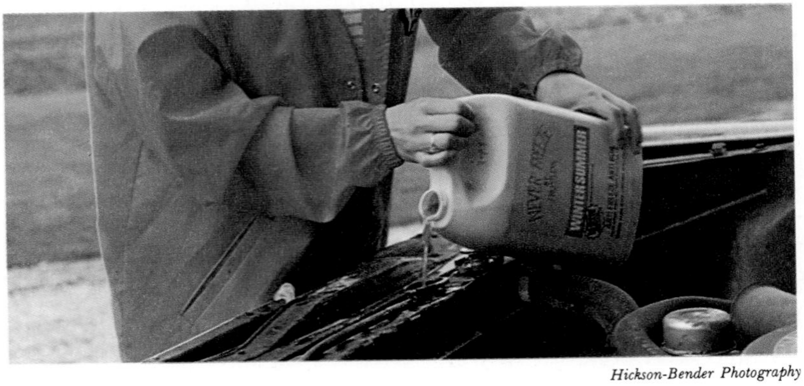

Hickson-Bender Photography

FIGURE 10-9. Antifreeze prevents the water in a radiator from freezing in winter and boiling in summer.

boiling point. Antifreeze (solute) is added to water (solvent) in automobile radiators. Motorists use antifreeze to prevent freezing in winter.

There are nine possible types of solutions. These nine combinations and an example of each are shown in Table 10–3.

*Table 10–3.*
Possible Solution Combinations

| Solvent | Solute | Example |
|---|---|---|
| Gas | Gas | Air (nitrogen, oxygen) |
| Gas | Liquid | Humidity (air, water) |
| Gas | Solid | Moth balls (air, naphthalene) |
| Liquid | Gas | Soda water (water, carbon dioxide) |
| Liquid | Liquid | Antifreeze (water, ethylene glycol) |
| Liquid | Solid | Seawater (water, salt, mineral ions) |
| Solid | Gas | Gas stove lighter (palladium, hydrogen) |
| Solid | Liquid | Dental filling (silver, mercury) |
| Solid | Solid | Jewelry (silver, copper) |

What is a suspension?

What is a colloid?

A mixture of substances does not always produce a solution. Instead, a suspension (suh SPEN chun) may be formed. In a **suspension,** particles are mixed together but not dissolved. Some suspensions may be separated by filtering. The filter traps the suspended particles and allows the liquid to pass through. Filtering a soil and water suspension traps the soil particles in the filter. Some suspensions separate when allowed to stand. If a suspension of oil and water is allowed to stand, oil rises and forms a layer on top of the water.

A **colloid** (KAHL oyd) is another mixture in which the substances do not produce a solution. A colloid differs from a suspension in particle size. Colloidal particles are so small they cannot be filtered out nor do they settle when the mixture is allowed to stand. Smoke is a colloid of solid particles in the gases of the air. Table 10–4 shows the properties of solutions, suspensions, and colloids.

FIGURE 10-10. Oil does not dissolve in water. When oil and water are mixed, they form a suspension.

*Advertising Image Photography*

**Table 10–4.**
Properties of Solutions, Suspensions, and Colloids

| Solutions | Suspensions | Colloids |
|---|---|---|
| Particles do not settle out. | Particles settle out on standing. | Particles do not settle out. |
| Particles pass unchanged through filter paper. | Particles separated by filter paper. | Particles pass unchanged through filter paper. |
| Particles smaller than 1 nm* | Particles can be seen with microscope, larger than 100 nm | Particles smaller than 100 nm but larger than 1 nm |

*1 nm (nanometer) is 0.000 000 001 m

FIGURE 10-11.

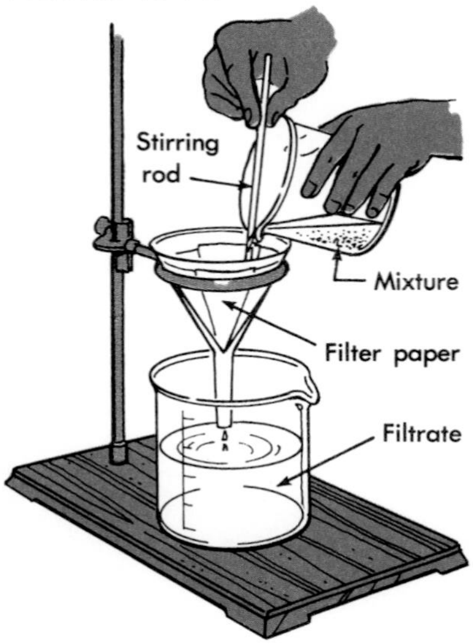


## activity MIXTURES

(1) Add 1 spoonful of soil to a small jar half full of water. **(2)** Tighten the lid and shake the jar vigorously. **(3)** Allow the jar to stand for 5 minutes. Where are the soil particles located after 5 minutes? **(4)** Pour half of the liquid through a filter. **(5)** Describe the material in the filter and the liquid that has passed through. What kind of mixture is soil and water? How do you know? **(6)** Add 1 drop of iodine solution to a jar containing 10 mL of water. Record your observations. **(7)** Put a very small amount of cornstarch in a clean jar containing 10 mL of water. Add 1 drop of iodine solution. Record your observations. **(8)** Put the same amount of cornstarch into a second clean jar containing 10 mL of water. Mix the cornstarch and water and filter the mixture. Describe the mixture before and after filtering. **(9)** Add 1 drop of iodine solution to the filtered liquid. Record your observations. What kind of mixture is cornstarch and water? Explain.

## making sure

**9.** What is a solution?

**10.** How is a suspension different from a solution?

**11.** Why can suspensions be separated by filtration while solutions cannot?

## 10:6 Solubility

A substance that dissolves in a solvent is soluble (SAHL yuh bul). A substance that does not dissolve in a solvent is insoluble. The most common liquid solvent is water. Some substances dissolve in water. Others do not. Salt is soluble in water. Oil and mercury are insoluble in water.

How much of a solid can be dissolved in a solvent? It depends upon the solid and the temperature of the solvent. At 20°C, a maximum of 360 g of table salt (NaCl) will dissolve in 1 L of water. This quantity of salt is called the solubility of the salt at 20°C. The solubility can be changed by changing the temperature. Usually, the solubility of a solid in water increases as temperature of the water increases.

Explain the meaning of solubility.

How does temperature affect the solubility of a solid in a liquid?

When a solution contains the maximum amount of solute for that temperature, it is saturated. If more solute is added, it does not dissolve; it sinks to the bottom of the solution. Larger amounts of solute can be dissolved at temperatures higher than room temperature. If the hot solution is cooled slowly, an unstable solution is formed. This solution contains more of the solute than would normally dissolve. The solution is called a supersaturated solution. If a crystal is added to a cooled supersaturated solution, the excess solute crystallizes out of the liquid.

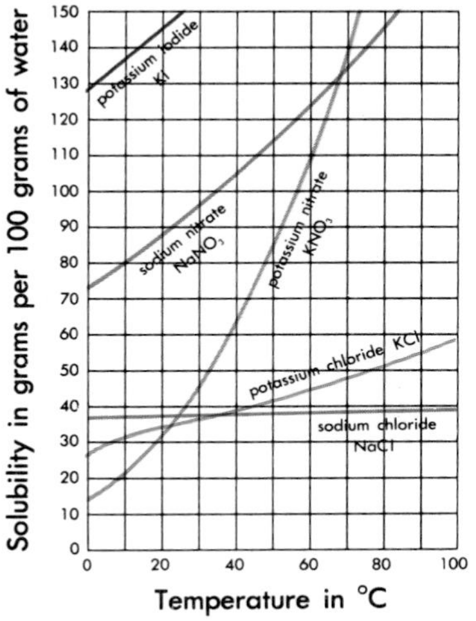


FIGURE 10-12. Different compounds have different solubilities. Each compound's solubility changes with temperature.

Hickson-Bender Photography

FIGURE 10-13. As a carbonated drink warms, the gas escapes.

The solubility of gases in liquids is affected by pressure, temperature, and the gas dissolved. Increased pressure increases the solubility of a gas. As temperature increases, the solubility of a gas decreases.

**activity** SOLUBILITY

(1) Label three beakers *A, B,* and *C.* **(2)** Pour 30 mL of distilled water into each beaker. **(3)** Measure and record the temperature of the water in each beaker. **(4)** Measure 2 g of table salt and add it to beaker *A.* Stir and record your observations. **(5)** Add more table salt, 2 g at a time, until no more salt will dissolve. Be sure to stir after each addition of salt. **(6)** Record the total mass of salt that was added. **(7)** Repeat Steps 4 and 5 using potassium nitrate and beaker *B.* **(8)** Repeat Steps 4 and 5 using boric acid and beaker *C.* **(9)** Record all data. What was the solubility for each substance at the recorded temperature? Which substance was most soluble? Least soluble?

## 10:7 Atoms

What are atoms?

Name three particles that make up atoms.

Suppose you take some sulfur and use a hammer to break it into smaller and smaller pieces. What would you have? Eventually, you would reach the point where you have the smallest possible pieces of sulfur. The smallest piece of an element that has the properties of that element is an **atom.** The smallest piece of sulfur you can have is an atom of sulfur. All elements are composed of atoms. Every atom is composed of tiny particles. Three of these particles are the proton, neutron, and electron. Atoms and the particles of which they are composed are too small to be seen by the unaided eye.

A **proton** is a positively charged particle. A **neutron** has about the same mass as a proton. It does not have an electric charge. An **electron** has a negative charge and has a very small mass. It takes 1837 electrons to equal the mass of one proton. The number of protons in an atom equals the number of electrons.

FIGURE 10-14. An atom of sulfur is the smallest particle that has the properties of sulfur.

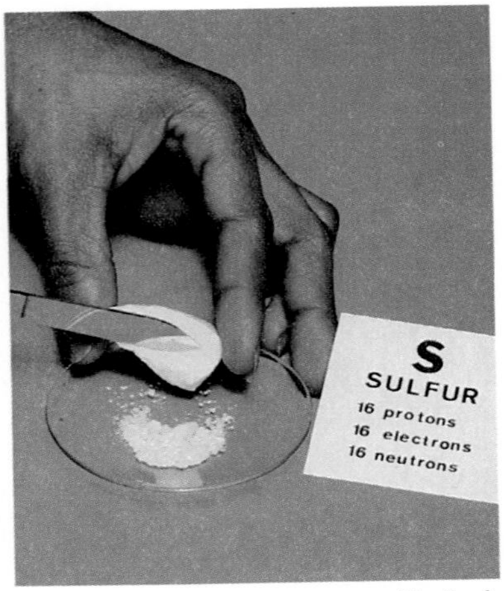


Tim Courlas

Protons and neutrons are located in the nucleus, or core, of an atom. Electrons are present outside the nucleus. The nucleus is only a small part of the total volume of an atom. Most of the volume of an atom consists of a cloud of negative electricity composed of electrons.

All atoms of an element have the same number of protons. For example, every hydrogen atom has one proton in its nucleus. The number of protons in an atom determines what the element will be and is the **atomic number.** The table on pages 200 and 201 is keyed to show the atomic number of each element.

An atom is electrically neutral. Therefore, the number of protons in the atom must equal the number of electrons.

Scientists often use models to explain the structure of an atom. In 1913, Neils Bohr, a Danish scientist, proposed a model of the structure of the atom. His idea of an atom pictured the electrons moving around the nucleus. The electrons were in definite paths, or orbits, just as planets move in orbits around the sun.

A modern model of atomic structure is called the **electron cloud model**. Scientists have shown that electrons do not remain in fixed orbits. The path of an electron may be close to the nucleus or far from the nucleus. Each electron in an atom has a certain amount of energy. Electrons occupy certain regions outside the nucleus based on their energy. The energy level indicates the path around the nucleus where an electron is most of the time. The lowest energy level is near the nucleus. Energy levels farther from the nucleus are regions of higher energy. The exact location of an electron at any specific time cannot be plotted. Scientists can only calculate the percentage of time an electron is in a certain region.

a

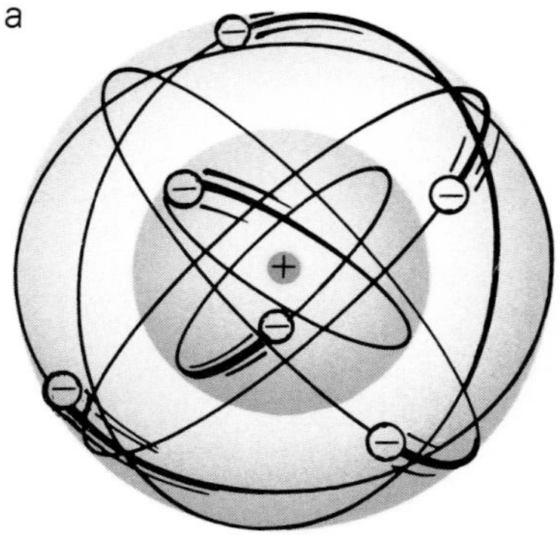

Bohr 1913

b

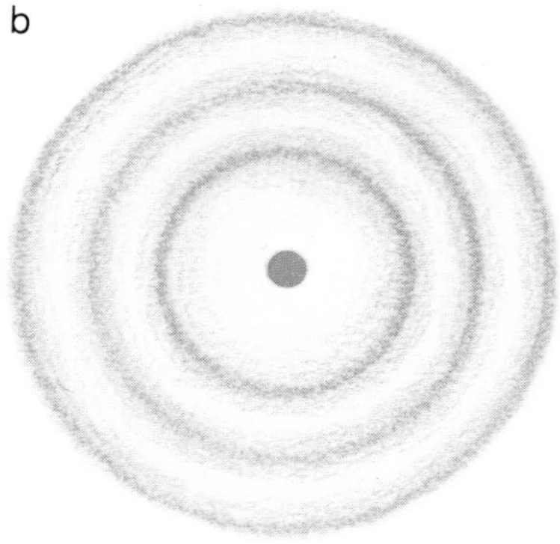

Modern Electron Cloud Model

FIGURE 10-15. In the Bohr model of the atom (a), electrons have fixed orbits around the nucleus. In the electron cloud model (b), electrons occupy certain energy levels.

Explain the electron cloud model of the atom.

## making sure

**12.** What information does the atomic number of an element represent?

# Using and Interpreting Graphs

Getting information from graphs is a quick way of learning new ideas and concepts. Graphs show information in a diagram form. Graphs have a main idea, give you specific facts, and make it possible for you to draw conclusions about specific ideas. Three types of graphs will be examined to determine the kind of information that can be obtained.

Line graphs often show a change or the rate and extent of development of a concept. A line graph may also show comparisons. Use the line graph on page 191 to answer the following questions:

1. What is the main topic of the graph?
2. What is the main idea?
3. What is the solubility of potassium chloride at 70°C?
4. Looking at the graph critically, how could you determine its accuracy?

Bar graphs may be used to show comparisons. Use the bar graph below to answer the following questions:

1. What is the main idea of the graph?
2. What is being compared?
3. Do men or women use a greater number of Calories in each activity?
4. What conclusion can you draw about the food needed by men as compared to women?

Circle graphs are very useful in enabling you to see how various parts add up to the whole. As in most circle graphs, the parts are expressed as percents. Use the circle graph below to answer the following questions:

1. What is the main idea of this graph?
2. What source provides the greatest amount of electric energy?
3. Using the graph, list the energy sources in order from greatest to least percentage.
4. In the graph, what does the term "other" include?

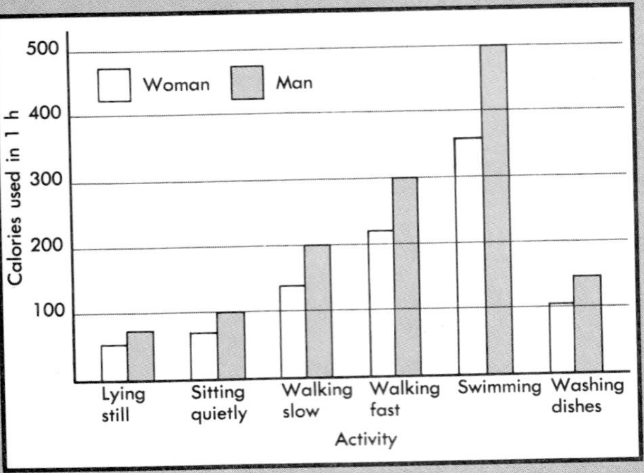


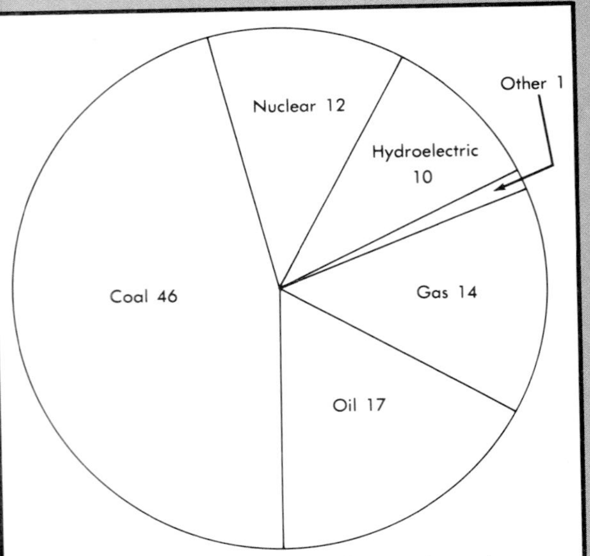


Energy sources for generating electricity (percent)

## main ideas — Chapter Review

1. Chemistry is the study of matter. 10:1
2. Matter has mass and occupies space. 10:1
3. Matter can be changed from one physical state to another. 10:1
4. Every substance has two sets of properties—physical and chemical. 10:2
5. An element is a substance that cannot be broken into simpler substances by a chemical change. 10:3
6. The substances in a mixture are not chemically joined. 10:4
7. Mixtures include solutions, suspensions, and colloids. Particle solubility and size determine how the mixture is classified. 10:5
8. The amount of a substance that will dissolve in a specific amount of solvent at a specific temperature is called the solubility of the substance. 10:6
9. All elements are composed of atoms. An atom is the smallest piece of an element that has the properties of that element. 10:7
10. Three kinds of particles present in atoms are the proton, neutron, and electron. 10:7

## vocabulary

*Define each of the following words or terms.*

atom
atomic number
chemical change
chemical properties
chemistry
colloid
compound
electron
electron cloud model
element
matter
mixture
neutron
physical change
physical properties
proton
solute
solution
solvent
suspension

## study questions

**DO NOT WRITE IN THIS BOOK.**

### A. True or False

*Determine whether each of the following sentences is true or false. If the sentence is false, rewrite it to make it true.*

1. Water, $H_2O$, is composed of hydrogen and oxygen.
2. Freezing is a change of state.

3. Cl is the symbol for carbon.
4. Carbon dioxide and dry ice are two different chemical states of the same substance.
5. Burning is a chemical change.
6. Color is a chemical property of a substance.
7. A solution is a uniform mixture.
8. The most common liquid solvent is alcohol.
9. Compounds have the same properties as the elements that compose them.
10. A substance can be broken into simpler substances by a physical change.

### B. Multiple Choice

*Choose the word or phrase that completes correctly each of the following sentences.*

1. For a solid to change to a liquid, energy must be (*added, removed, unchanged*).
2. A solute (*raises, lowers, does not change*) the freezing point of the solvent.
3. (*Melting, Freezing, Burning*) is a chemical change.
4. Air is a(n) (*mixture, compound, element*).
5. Matter in the stars is in the (*liquid, gas, plasma*) state.
6. (*Soil, Air, Table salt*) is a compound.
7. (*Protons, Neutrons, Electrons*) are located outside the nucleus of an atom.
8. As temperature increases, the solubility of a gas (*increases, decreases, remains the same*).
9. The number of protons in an atom is (*greater than, less than, the same as*) the number of electrons.
10. An atom is the smallest piece of a(n) (*compound, element, mixture*).

### C. Completion

*Complete each of the following sentences with a word or phrase that will make the sentence correct.*

1. ______ is the amount of solute a solvent can hold at a given temperature.
2. The atomic number of an element is the number of ______ in every atom of the element.
3. An electron has a ______ electric charge.

4. Oxygen gas is ______ soluble in warm water than cold water.
5. According to the ______ model of the atom, electrons do not travel in fixed orbits.
6. Soil mixed with water produces a ______.
7. In a solution of salt water, water is the ______ and salt is the ______.
8. Matter is anything that has ______ and ______.
9. Matter can exist in one of ______ states.
10. Protons and neutrons are located in the ______ of an atom.

**D. How and Why**

1. Compare the properties of solids, liquids, and gases.
2. Explain why it takes longer to boil an egg on a mountaintop than at sea level.
3. Compare the properties of a solution, suspension, and colloid.
4. Explain how an atom is electrically neutral when it is composed of positive and negative charges.
5. Explain the difference between elements and compounds.

## challenges

1. Prepare a report on common household compounds. Begin by making a list of compounds used in the home. Check the labels on containers for the names of compounds. In your report list the properties, composition, and uses of each compound.
2. Prepare a report on the history of the periodic table.
3. Find out about the plasma state of matter. Prepare a short report for your class.

## interesting reading

Grey, Vivian, *The Chemist Who Lost His Head: The Story of Antoine Laurent Lavoisier.* New York: Coward, McCann and Geoghegan, 1982.

Hansen, James, "The Delicate Architecture of Cement." *Science 82,* December 1982, pp. 48-55.

Trefil, James, "Matter vs. Antimatter." *Science 81,* Sept. 1981, pp. 66-69.

*Flowers can be classified into groups by their common characteristics. Studying many objects is made easier by classifying them into small groups. One class of matter, the elements, can also be divided into groups. What properties are used to classify the elements? Is there more than one way to classify them?*

Richard W. Brown

# Elements

## chapter 11

### 11:1 Elements and the Periodic Table

GOAL: You will learn how the elements are classified and some properties of each family of elements.

By the middle of the 19th century, a number of elements had been discovered. Some way of classifying these elements was needed. While looking for relationships among the elements, Dmitri Mendeleev (DMEE tree•men duh LAY uf), a Russian scientist, made an important discovery. When arranged in a table, certain chemical properties were repeated regularly. These properties were related to the sum of the protons and neutrons in an atom. Mendeleev's table contained the 65 elements then known and some blank spots. He predicted the properties of elements not yet discovered to fill in these blanks.

How are elements classified in the periodic table?

As more elements were discovered, some problems occurred with Mendeleev's arrangement. As a result, today's classification system of the elements is based on the atomic numbers of the elements. Look at the **periodic table** on pages 200 and 201. Note that it has 7 rows called **periods**, and 18 columns called **groups**, or **families**. Two rows are separated from the table so it can be shortened to a more readable form. These two rows fit into the table as shown by the arrows.

*Table 11–1.*

## The Periodic Table

(Based on Carbon 12 = 12.0000)

Metals

Transition Metals

| | IA | IIA | IIIB | IVB | VB | VIB | VIIB | VIIIB | VIIIB |
|---|---|---|---|---|---|---|---|---|---|
| 1 | 1 **H** Hydrogen 1.0079 | | | | | | | | |
| 2 | 3 **Li** Lithium 6.941 | 4 **Be** Beryllium 9.01218 | | | | | | | |
| 3 | 11 **Na** Sodium 22.98977 | 12 **Mg** Magnesium 24.305 | | | | | | | |
| 4 | 19 **K** Potassium 39.0983 | 20 **Ca** Calcium 40.08 | 21 **Sc** Scandium 44.9559 | 22 **Ti** Titanium 47.90 | 23 **V** Vanadium 50.9414 | 24 **Cr** Chromium 51.996 | 25 **Mn** Manganese 54.9380 | 26 **Fe** Iron 55.847 | 27 **Co** Cobalt 58.9332 |
| 5 | 37 **Rb** Rubidium 85.4678 | 38 **Sr** Strontium 87.62 | 39 **Y** Yttrium 88.9059 | 40 **Zr** Zirconium 91.22 | 41 **Nb** Niobium 92.9064 | 42 **Mo** Molybdenum 95.94 | 43 **Tc** Technetium 96.90639 | 44 **Ru** Ruthenium 101.07 | 45 **Rh** Rhodium 102.9055 |
| 6 | 55 **Cs** Cesium 132.9054 | 56 **Ba** Barium 137.34 | 71 **Lu** Lutetium 174.97 | 72 **Hf** Hafnium 178.49 | 73 **Ta** Tantalum 180.9479 | 74 **W** Tungsten 183.85 | 75 **Re** Rhenium 186.207 | 76 **Os** Osmium 190.2 | 77 **Ir** Iridium 192.22 |
| 7 | 87 **Fr** Francium 223.09176 | 88 **Ra** Radium 226 | 103 **Lr** Lawrencium 256.099 | 104* 257 | 105* 260 | 106* 263 | 107* 258 | 108* 265 | 109* 266 |

| | | | | | | |
|---|---|---|---|---|---|---|
| LANTHANIDE SERIES | 57 **La** Lanthanum 138.9055 | 58 **Ce** Cerium 140.12 | 59 **Pr** Praseodymium 140.9077 | 60 **Nd** Neodymium 144.24 | 61 **Pm** Promethium 144.91279 | 62 **Sm** Samarium 150.4 |
| ACTINIDE SERIES | 89 **Ac** Actinium 227.0274 | 90 **Th** Thorium 232.0381 | 91 **Pa** Protactinium 231.03590 | 92 **U** Uranium 238.029 | 93 **Np** Neptunium 237.04819 | 94 **Pu** Plutonium 244.06424 |

Key: 12 **Mg** Magnesium 24.305 — Atomic number (12); Element symbol (Mg); Average atomic mass (24.305)

SYNTHETICS—orange SOLIDS—blue GASES—green LIQUIDS—yellow

| | IB | IIB | IIIA | IVA | VA | VIA | VIIA | Noble Gases VIIIA |
|---|---|---|---|---|---|---|---|---|
| | | | | | | | | 2 He Helium 4.00260 |
| | | | 5 B Boron 10.82 | 6 C Carbon 12.011 | 7 N Nitrogen 14.0067 | 8 O Oxygen 15.9994 | 9 F Fluorine 18.998403 | 10 Ne Neon 20.179 |
| | | | 13 Al Aluminum 26.98154 | 14 Si Silicon 28.0855 | 15 P Phosphorus 30.97376 | 16 S Sulfur 32.06 | 17 Cl Chlorine 35.453 | 18 Ar Argon 39.948 |
| 28 Ni Nickel 58.70 | 29 Cu Copper 63.546 | 30 Zn Zinc 65.38 | 31 Ga Gallium 69.72 | 32 Ge Germanium 72.59 | 33 As Arsenic 74.9216 | 34 Se Selenium 78.96 | 35 Br Bromine 79.904 | 36 Kr Krypton 83.80 |
| 46 Pd Palladium 106.4 | 47 Ag Silver 107.868 | 48 Cd Cadmium 112.41 | 49 In Indium 114.82 | 50 Sn Tin 118.69 | 51 Sb Antimony 121.75 | 52 Te Tellurium 127.60 | 53 I Iodine 126.9045 | 54 Xe Xenon 131.30 |
| 78 Pt Platinum 195.09 | 79 Au Gold 196.9665 | 80 Hg Mercury 200.59 | 81 Tl Thallium 204.37 | 82 Pb Lead 207.2 | 83 Bi Bismuth 208.9804 | 84 Po Polonium 208.98244 | 85 At Astatine 209.98704 | 86 Rn Radon 222 |

Nonmetals: IIIA–VIIA

**Rare Earth Elements**

| | | | | | | | |
|---|---|---|---|---|---|---|---|
| 63 Eu Europium 151.96 | 64 Gd Gadolinium 157.25 | 65 Tb Terbium 158.9254 | 66 Dy Dysprosium 162.50 | 67 Ho Holmium 164.9304 | 68 Er Erbium 167.26 | 69 Tm Thulium 168.9342 | 70 Yb Ytterbium 173.04 |
| 95 Am Americium 243.06139 | 96 Cm Curium 247.07038 | 97 Bk Berkelium 247.07032 | 98 Cf Californium 251.07961 | 99 Es Einsteinium 254.08805 | 100 Fm Fermium 257.09515 | 101 Md Mendelevium 258 | 102 No Nobelium 255.093 |

*Names for elements 104 through 109 have not been approved by the IUPAC.

The periodic table is one of a chemist's most important tools. You can learn much about an element from its position in the table. Look at the key for the periodic table on page 200. The atomic number is the number of protons in the nucleus. The average atomic mass is the relative mass of the element compared to carbon as a standard. For example, the carbon standard has a mass of 12.000 and hydrogen has a mass of 1.0079. Hydrogen has about 1/12 the mass of carbon.

Define atomic number and atomic mass.

## making sure

1. Write the symbol for each of the following elements.
   (a) helium (b) chromium (c) boron
2. Using the periodic table, locate two elements that are liquids at room temperature. List their symbols and names.
3. Which element has the largest atomic mass? The smallest?

## 11:2 Metals, Nonmetals, and Metalloids

How are metals different from nonmetals?

Most of the elements are classified as metals. **Metals** usually have three or less electrons in their outer energy levels. Metals give up electrons when forming compounds. They usually have a luster or shine. Most metals are good conductors. They are also malleable and ductile.

FIGURE 11-1. Silver (a) is a metal. Iodine (b) is a nonmetal. The metallic properties of silver make it suitable for jewelry.

a

*Gerard Photography*

b

*Tim Courlas*

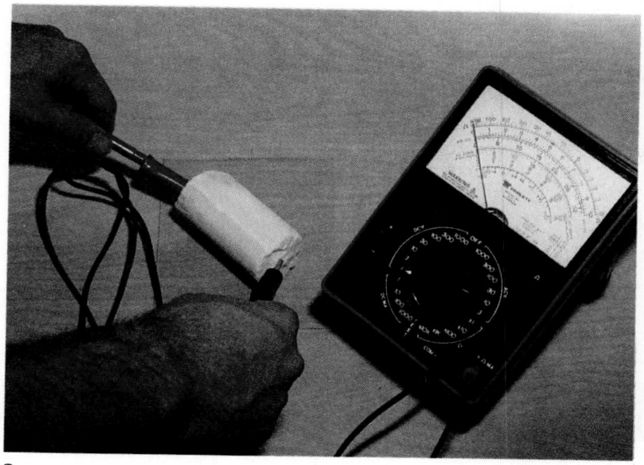

a

b

FIGURE 11-2. Nonmetals are poor conductors of electricity (a). They cannot be hammered into shapes (b).

**Nonmetals** are elements that have five or more electrons in their outer energy levels. Nonmetals can share or gain electrons when forming compounds. Nonmetals generally have dull surfaces, and the solids are brittle. They are poor conductors.

Some elements have properties of both metals and nonmetals. These elements are called **metalloids** (MET ul oydz). As you might expect, the metalloids are found along the dotted stairstep line in the periodic table. Some metalloids have a luster like metals. Metalloids are conductors, but they are poor conductors. Boron, silicon, germanium, arsenic, antimony, tellurium, polonium, and astatine are the metalloids.

What are metalloids? Name five examples.

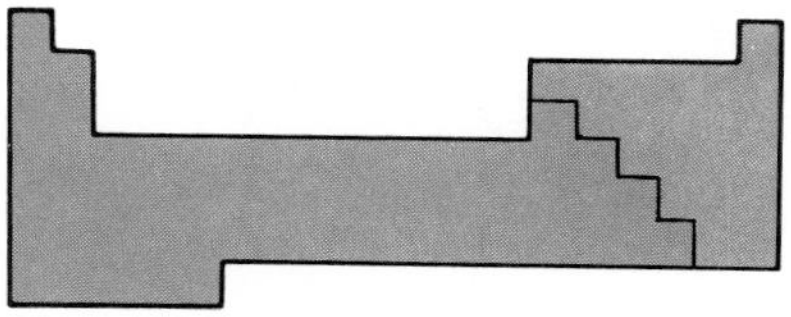

FIGURE 11-3. Metals are located in the blue area. Nonmetals are located in the pink area. The elements at the border are metalloids.

### making sure

4. Classify the following elements as metals, nonmetals, or metalloids.
   (a) calcium (b) carbon (c) germanium

## 11:3 Alkali Metals

Elements in Group IA of the periodic table, with the exception of hydrogen, are called the **alkali** (AL kuh li) **metals**. Alkali metals have one electron in their outer energy levels. Alkali metals are shiny and good conductors. Group IA elements are the most chemically active of all metals. Chemically active

FIGURE 11-4. Group IA is the alkali metal family.

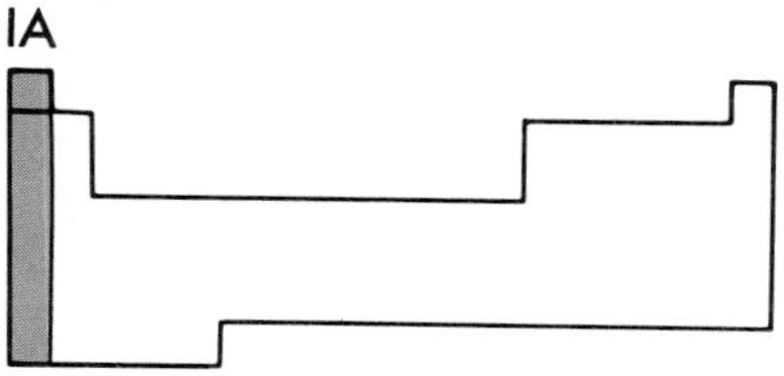

FIGURE 11-5. Sodium burning in chlorine gas gives off a bright light (a). Sodium is stored under kerosene (b).

*Hickson-Bender Photography* *Mr. Floridia/River Valley High School*

a b

means an element readily combines with other substances to form compounds. Alkali metals are never found in pure form in nature. These elements react violently with oxygen in air and water. For this reason, these metals are stored covered in oil.

Why are the alkali metals not found in pure form in nature?

Alkali metals form compounds by losing electrons. Most of the compounds formed are white. Table salt is a common alkali metal compound. Table salt is sodium chloride, NaCl. One way to identify alkali metals is by flame tests (Figure 11–6). When an alkali metal compound is heated in a flame, the metal produces a colored flame. This color is a characteristic of the metal in the compound. For example any salt containing sodium will color the flame yellow. However, it is important that the substance being tested is pure.

How are flame tests used to identify alkali metals?

FIGURE 11-6. Flame tests of sodium (a), potassium (b), rubidium (c), and cesium (d) each produce a different color.

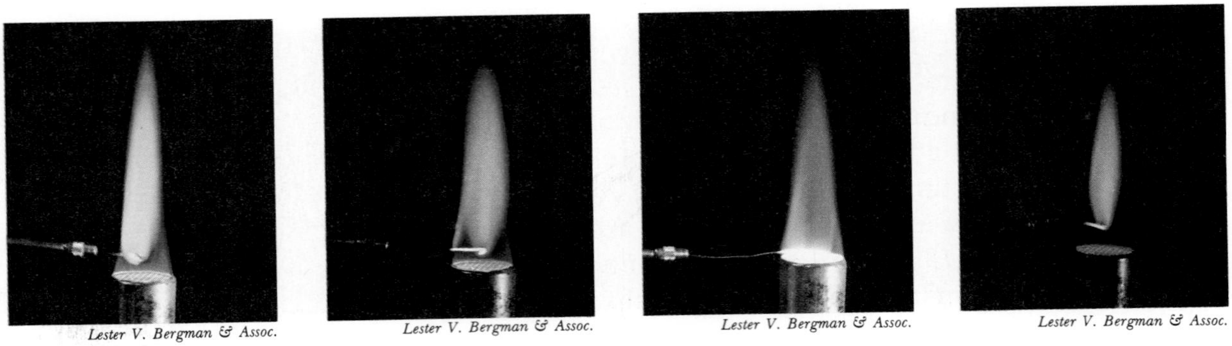

*Lester V. Bergman & Assoc.* *Lester V. Bergman & Assoc.* *Lester V. Bergman & Assoc.* *Lester V. Bergman & Assoc.*

## activity FLAME TESTS

(1) Obtain chloride solutions of the following alkali metals: lithium, potassium, sodium, cesium, and an unknown metal. (2) Clean a platinum or nichrome wire by dipping it into hydrochloric acid and then into distilled water. Dry the wire by heating it in the burner flame. Repeat this procedure until the wire no longer colors the burner flame. (3) Dip the clean wire into the lithium chloride solution. (4) Hold the wire at the tip of the inner cone of the burner flame. What color is produced? (5) Clean the wire according to Step 2. (6) Repeat Steps 3–5 for each solution. Record the color formed for each compound. How can you be sure the chloride was not causing the color? Why did you clean the wire between tests? What was your unknown alkali metal? How do you know?

### making sure

5. Make a table and record the name, symbol, melting point, boiling point, and density for each alkali metal. Obtain your data from Appendix E.
6. List three chemical properties of alkali metals.

## 11:4 Alkaline Earth Metals

Elements in Group IIA are called **alkaline** (AL kuh lun) **earth metals**. Alkaline earth metals have two electrons in their outer energy levels. They have the same metallic properties as the alkali metals, but they are slightly less chemically reactive.

List the properties of the alkaline earth metals.

Alkaline earth metals give up electrons when forming compounds. Some of these elements, including barium and calcium, react with water. Most alkaline earth metal compounds are white.

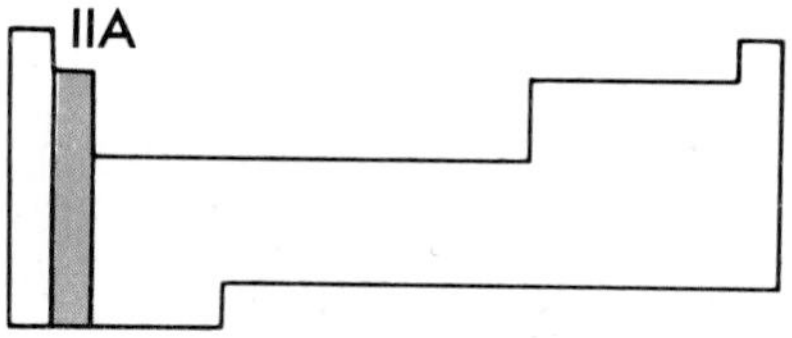


FIGURE 11-7. Group IIA is the alkaline earth metal family.

Magnesium and calcium are the two most common alkaline earth metals. Magnesium is found in seawater and in mineral deposits as an ore. It is used in the construction of lightweight aircraft and in some medicines. Magnesium sulfate ($MgSO_4$) is sold under the name Epsom salt.

Calcium sulfate ($CaSO_4$) is called gypsum. Gypsum is used to make brick and stone. It is also used to make drywall panels for interior wall construction. When gypsum is heated, a white powder is formed called plaster of paris. Calcium oxide (CaO), called lime, is important to agriculture. Lime is used to treat soils that are too acid for plants to grow. Lime is also used to make mortar and plaster.

Name four alkaline earth metals.

Barium and strontium compounds are used to produce some of the colors in fireworks. Strontium produces a red color and barium a green color. Barium sulfate ($BaSO_4$) is used in a dye that helps doctors study the digestive tract.

Radium is used in the treatment of cancer. Once, radium was used to make dentures and watch dials. It was later discovered that radium emits rays that are hazardous to people's health. Radium is no longer used in teeth and watches.

## making sure

**7.** Make a table and record the name, symbol, melting point, boiling point, and density for each alkaline earth metal. Use Appendix E to obtain your data.

FIGURE 11-8. Drywall panels contain calcium sulfate (a). Fireworks may contain barium or strontium (b).

a

*Latent Image*

b

*Hickson-Bender Photography*

## 11:5 Transition Metals and Synthetic Elements

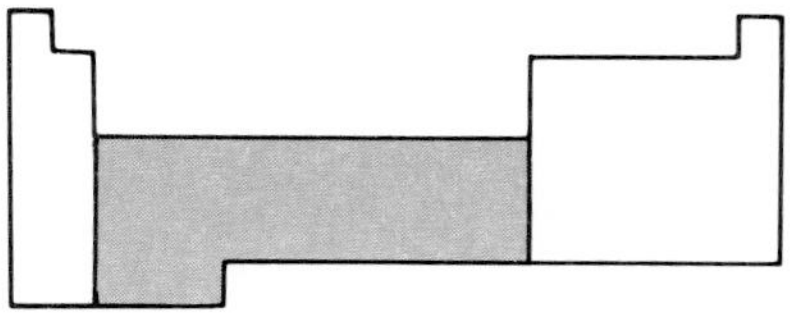

FIGURE 11-9. Groups IB through VIIIB are the transition metals.

Where are the transition metals located in the periodic table?

How do transition metals form compounds?

Elements in Groups IB through VIIIB are the **transition metals**. These groups contain the metals with which you are most familiar. Iron, copper, silver, and gold are all transition metals. Transition metals may have one or two electrons in their outer energy levels. They can lose one or both of these electrons, or they can lose an electron from a lower energy level. Transition metals can also share electrons when forming compounds. A Roman numeral is used after the element's name to show how many electrons are given up or shared in a compound. For example, in copper(II) sulfate, the II means that copper gives up two electrons.

Transition metal compounds are usually colored. For example, iron(III) oxide, $Fe_2O_3$, is red, and copper(II) sulfate, $CuSO_4$, is blue.

Transition metals are good conductors. Gold is the best conductor, followed by silver. Transition metals also form alloys. An alloy is a mixture composed of two or more metals or a metal and a nonmetal. Alloys have properties that the pure metals composing them do not have. An alloy of iron and chromium does not rust, but iron does. Steel is an alloy composed mainly of iron and carbon. Other steel alloys are formed from iron, carbon, and other elements. Table 11–2 lists some alloys and their uses.

*Dan McCoy/Rainbow*

FIGURE 11-10. Some transition metals and their alloys, such as steel, have great strength. They are often used for the frames of buildings.

*Table 11–2.*
Some Alloys and Their Uses

| Alloy | Metals | Uses |
|---|---|---|
| Wood's metal | Bi, Pb, Sn, Cd | Automatic water sprinklers |
| Bronze | Cu, Sn | Jewelry, nuts, and bolts |
| German silver | Cu, Zn, Ni | "Silver" plating, jewelry |
| Gold, 14 karat | Au, Cu, Ag | Jewelry, heat shields |
| Dentist's amalgam | Ag, Hg, Cu, Zn, Sn | Dental fillings |
| Nichrome | Ni, Cr | Electric heating elements |
| Stainless steel | Cr, Ni, Fe | Surgical instruments, flatware |
| High speed steel | Fe, Cr, W, or Fe, Cr, Mo | Cutting tools, drill bits, saw blades |
| Solder | Sn, Pb | Electric wire solderings |

What is a synthetic element?

Elements with atomic numbers 43, 61, and higher than 92 are **synthetic elements.** These elements are produced in nuclear reactions. All of the synthetic elements break down into other elements. Nuclear scientists believe that elements with atomic numbers as high as 126 may be produced by nuclear reactions.

## activity
### TRANSITION METALS

Obtain samples of the following compounds: iron(II) sulfate, iron(III) sulfate, iron(II) chloride, iron(III) chloride, copper(II) chloride, and copper(II) sulfate. Record in a table, the name and the color of each compound. What color do iron(II) compounds have? Iron(III) compounds? Copper(II) compounds? What color would you predict for copper(II) nitrate? Why? What color would you predict for iron(II) nitrate? Why?

## making sure

**8.** Design a table to record the name, symbol, melting point, boiling point, and density for the following transition metals: chromium, manganese, iron, cobalt, nickel, copper, silver, zinc, and gold. Use Appendix E to obtain your data.

## 11:6 Boron and Aluminum

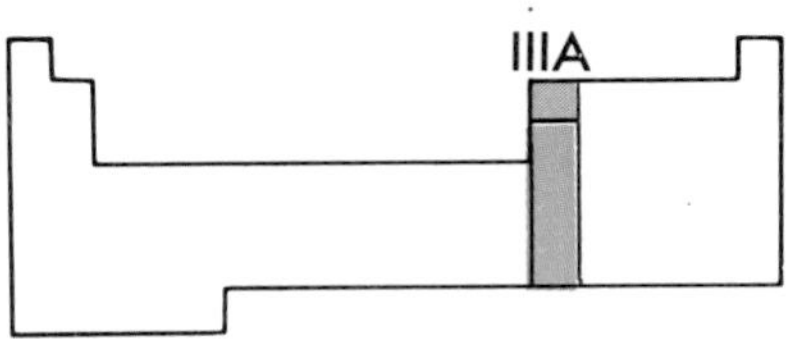


FIGURE 11-11. Group IIIA is the boron family.

Boron and aluminum are members of Group IIIA. Boron is a metalloid; aluminum, gallium, indium, and thallium are metals. Boron shares its electrons when forming compounds. Boron is essential in small amounts for proper plant growth and development. A compound of boron, boric acid, is a weak acid used in eyewash solutions. The best known compound of boron is borax ($Na_2B_4O_7 \cdot 10H_2O$). Borax is used to remove certain minerals from water.

Aluminum is the third most abundant element in the earth's crust. Only oxygen and silicon exist in greater quantities. Aluminum is not found as a free element in nature. It is generally found as an ore. Aluminum is silvery in appearance and light in weight. A common form of aluminum is aluminum foil used to wrap and store foods and some

FIGURE 11-12. Aluminum is a light, strong element that has many uses in homes.

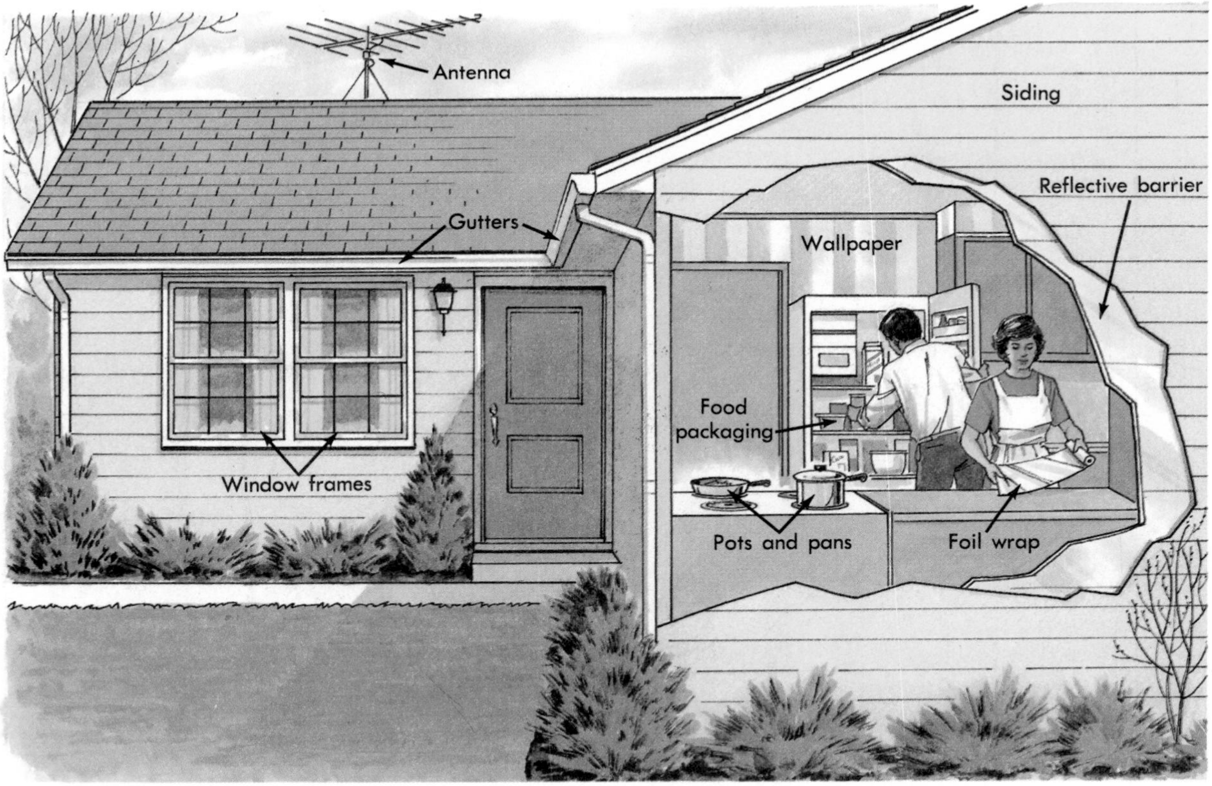

Laird/FPG

FIGURE 11-13. The outside walls of the World Trade Center towers are aluminum.

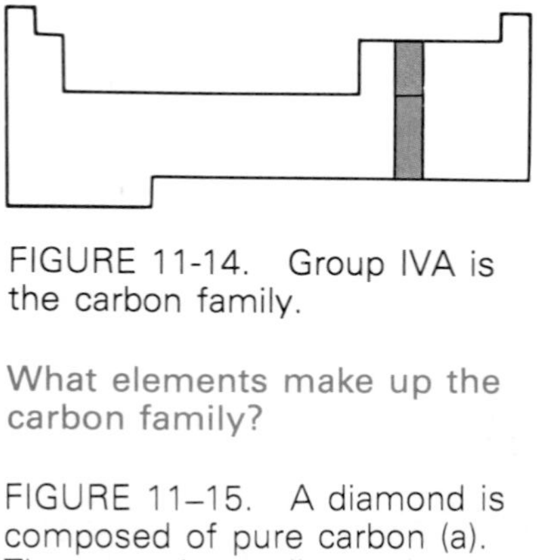

FIGURE 11-14. Group IVA is the carbon family.

What elements make up the carbon family?

FIGURE 11–15. A diamond is composed of pure carbon (a). These products all contain the carbon compound graphite (b).

a

Image Workshop

medicines. Aluminum is used to make pots and pans for cooking because it is a good conductor. It is also used to build airplanes and frames for windows and doors. Aluminum siding is used to cover the outside of houses and other buildings. The outside walls of the World Trade Center towers in New York City contain over 4100 metric tons of aluminum.

## 11:7 Carbon Family

Group IVA is the carbon family. It contains both metals and nonmetals. Carbon is a nonmetal; silicon and germanium are metalloids; and tin and lead are metals. Carbon, silicon, and germanium share electrons when forming compounds. Tin and lead can share or give up electrons when forming compounds.

Graphite, the "lead" in pencils, is one form of the element carbon. Diamond is another form of carbon. These two substances have very different properties because of the way the carbon atoms are arranged. Graphite is black, soft, and slippery. It is used to reduce friction between moving machine parts. Diamond is the hardest natural substance known. It is used in drill bits, saw blades, abrasives, and jewelry.

b

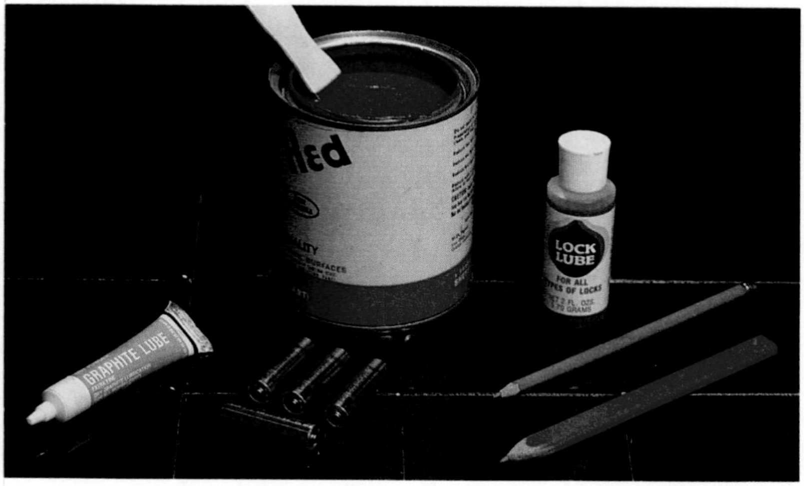


Gerard Photography

Carbon is one of the most important elements in living organisms. Carbon compounds serve as fuel for our bodies in the form of carbohydrates. Amino acids, the components of proteins, are carbon compounds that contain nitrogen. Carbon dioxide, a gas, is used by plants to make food.

Over 80 percent of all known compounds contain carbon. The study of the chemistry of carbon compounds is called organic chemistry. Many carbon compounds exist as long chains or rings that contain hundreds of atoms. These long molecules are called **polymers** (PAHL uh murz). The properties of a carbon compound depend upon the number and type of atoms in the compound and the pattern in which the atoms are joined. You will learn more about **organic compounds** in Chapter 13.

Silicon is the second most common element in the earth's crust. Sand is a compound of silicon and oxygen. Silicon is used to make glass, abrasives, solar cells, and electronic circuits. Silicon is used in electronics because it conducts electricity. Germanium, like silicon, conducts electricity. For this reason, it is also used extensively in the electronics industry.

Tin and lead are used mainly in alloys. Tin is used to make bronze and metal bearings. Lead is used in the manufacture of batteries and as a coating for pipes used to transport chemicals.

*Elaine Comer*

FIGURE 11–16. Many of our foods contain organic compounds. A major part of an organic compound is carbon.

Which element is the basic element in living things?

How does carbon form carbon compounds?

Name a use for silicon, tin, germanium, and lead.

FIGURE 11–17. Sand is a compound of silicon (a). Silicon chips are used in computers (b).

a

*James Westwater*

b

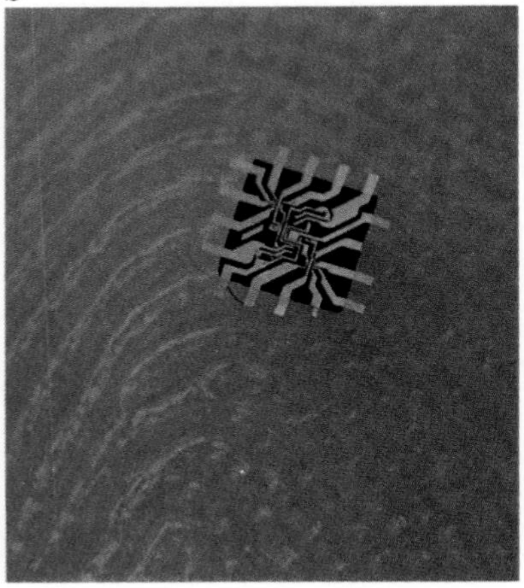

## activity A PRODUCT OF BURNING

Light a candle and hold a cool glass square above it. What happens? Describe the substance that forms on the glass above the flame. **CAUTION:** Let the glass cool. Then, use cold water and try to wash the substance off the glass. What happens? Candles are made of wax that contains carbon. What substance formed on the glass?

## 11:8 Nitrogen Family

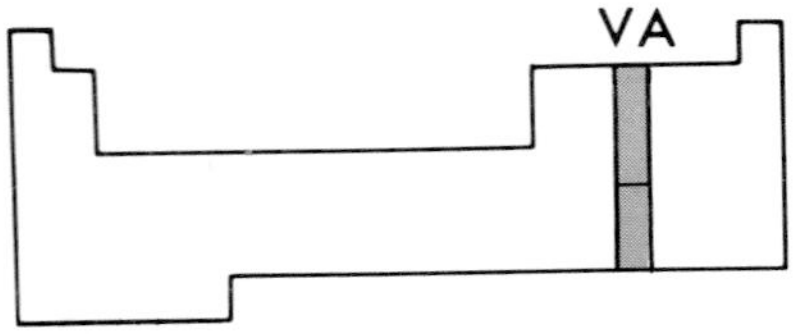


FIGURE 11-18. Group VA is the nitrogen family.

Why is nitrogen an important element?

About 78 percent of the air around you is nitrogen gas ($N_2$). Nitrogen is in Group VA of the periodic table. Phosphorus and arsenic are also members of the nitrogen family. Group VA elements have five electrons in their outer energy levels. They tend to share electrons when forming compounds.

Nitrogen is a nonmetal. It is a colorless, tasteless, odorless gas. Nitrogen does not combine easily with other elements. Yet, nitrogen is needed by all living organisms. Nitrogen is a basic element in protein used by living organisms to maintain tissues.

Phosphorus is also needed by living organisms. Phosphorus is an important nutrient for plants. It is also used in some water softeners and detergents.

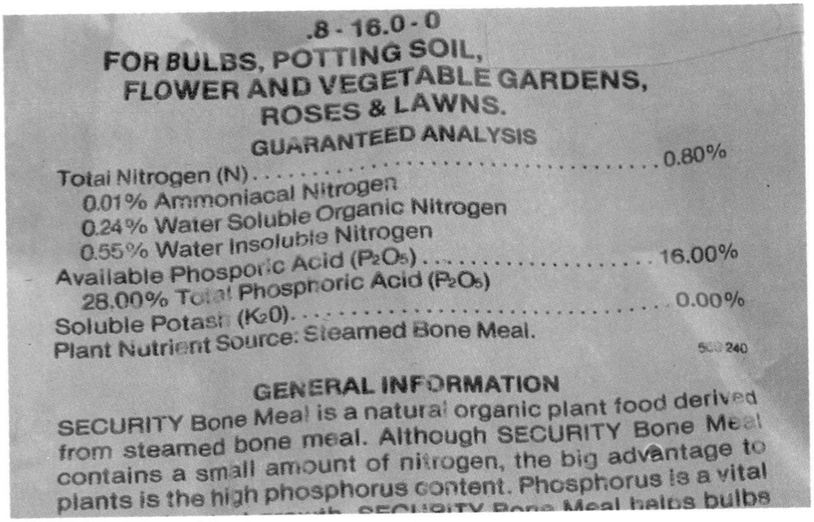

.8 - 16.0 - 0
FOR BULBS, POTTING SOIL,
FLOWER AND VEGETABLE GARDENS,
ROSES & LAWNS.
GUARANTEED ANALYSIS
Total Nitrogen (N) .......... 0.80%
0.01% Ammoniacal Nitrogen
0.24% Water Soluble Organic Nitrogen
0.55% Water Insoluble Nitrogen
Available Phosphoric Acid (P2O5) .......... 16.00%
28.00% Total Phosphoric Acid (P2O5)
Soluble Potash (K20) .......... 0.00%
Plant Nutrient Source: Steamed Bone Meal.
GENERAL INFORMATION
SECURITY Bone Meal is a natural organic plant food derived
from steamed bone meal. Although SECURITY Bone Meal
contains a small amount of nitrogen, the big advantage to
plants is the high phosphorus content. Phosphorus is a vital


FIGURE 11–19. Nitrogen and phosphorous are two of the major nutrients in fertilizer.

Arsenic forms a wide variety of compounds. It is used in some medicines. Because it is a poison, arsenic also is used in insecticides and weed-killers.

Antimony and bismuth are metals. Antimony is used in alloys to increase their hardness. The alloy pewter contains antimony. Antimony is used in paints and plastics as a fire-retarding agent. Bismuth is used in alloys to produce a low melting point. These alloys are used in fire detecting equipment and in sprinkler systems.

### making sure

**9.** Which members of the nitrogen family are metals?

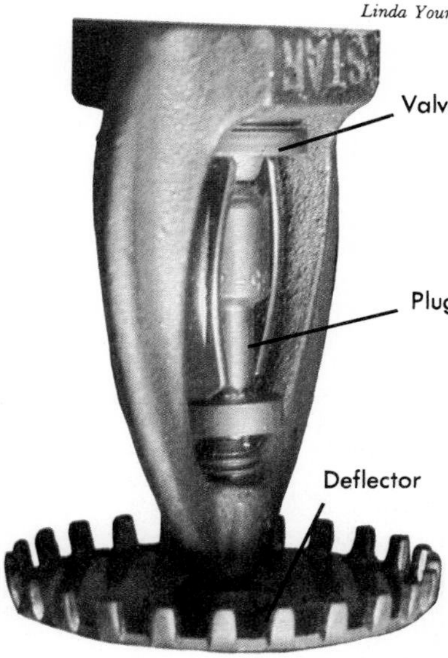


FIGURE 11-20. Water sprinklers in buildings are made with a bismuth alloy as a plug.

## 11:9 Oxygen Family

Group VIA of the periodic table is called the oxygen family. These elements have six electrons in their outer energy levels. Most members of this family share electrons when forming compounds. Elements in this family may be found free in nature or chemically combined. Oxygen and sulfur are nonmetals. Selenium has some metallic properties. Tellurium and polonium are metalloids.

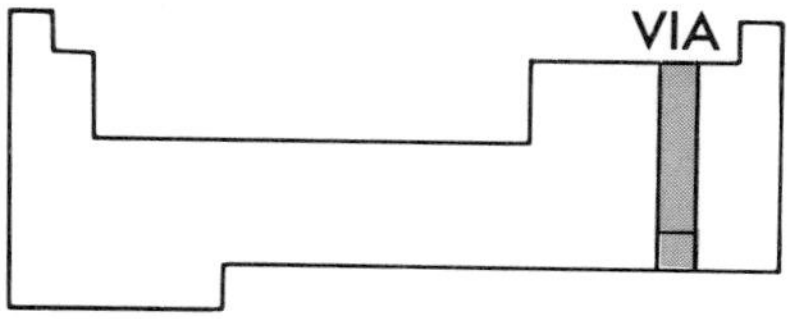


FIGURE 11–21. Group VIA is the oxygen family.

Oxygen is the most abundant element in Earth's crust. About 21 percent of air is oxygen. Oxygen is necessary for life. It is used by plants and animals in chemical changes that release energy from food. Oxygen is also needed to burn fuels.

What elements are in the oxygen family?

Why is oxygen an important element?

Oxygen can exist in two forms. In the air, it has the formula $O_2$. Under certain conditions, $O_3$, called ozone, is formed. Lightning causes $O_2$ to combine and form $O_3$. Ozone has a strong odor and is often detected near electric machinery or during electric storms.

Compounds of oxygen are oxides. Water is an important oxide of hydrogen. Another oxide of hydrogen, hydrogen peroxide ($H_2O_2$), is used as a disinfectant and bleach. Rust ($Fe_2O_3$) is an oxide of iron.

What important acid is made from sulfur?

Sulfur is vital to modern industry. It is used to make sulfuric acid, which is used to make fertilizers and refine petroleum. Sulfuric acid is also used to manufacture steel, paints, and fabrics. Egg protein and many other proteins contain sulfur. When these proteins break down, hydrogen sulfide gas ($H_2S$) is released. This gas is released when eggs rot. Sulfur combines with metals to form metallic **sulfides**. Metallic sulfides include CuS, ZnS, and FeS. Hydrogen sulfide causes the tarnish on silver.

How are sulfides like oxides?

a

*Tim Courlas*

b

*NASA*

FIGURE 11–22. Selenium compounds are used in developing film (a). Pure oxygen in the liquid state is used with rocket fuel (b).

## activity IDENTIFYING SULFIDES

**(1)** Pour 5 mL of each of the following solutions into separate test tubes: lead nitrate, zinc sulfate, bismuth nitrate, and antimony(III) chloride. **(2)** Label each test tube with the name of the compound. **(3)** Cover the labels with a piece of paper. **(4)** Have someone rearrange the test tubes in the rack. **(5)** Add 5 drops of hydrogen sulfide solution to each test tube. What happens? **(6)** What metal is present in each test tube? Lead sulfide is black; zinc sulfide is white; bismuth sulfide is brown; and antimony sulfide is orange. Uncover the labels and check your results. What did you use to identify the metal in the sulfides?

## 11:10 Halogens

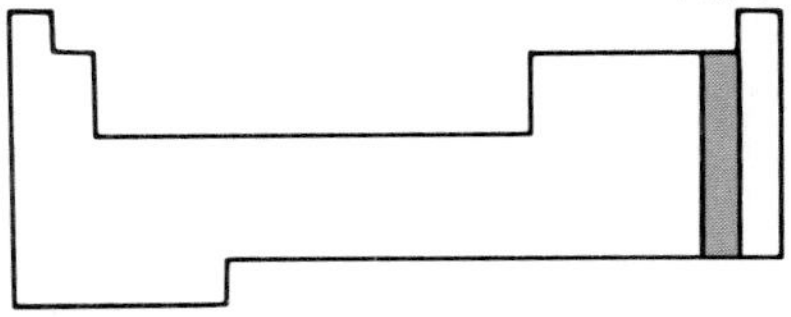


FIGURE 11-23. Group VIIA is the halogen family.

Group VIIA in the periodic table is called the halogen family. **Halogens** are the most chemically active nonmetals. Each halogen has seven electrons in its outer energy level. One more electron is needed to complete the outer energy level. When a halogen combines with a metal, the halogen gains that electron. Halogens can also share electrons when forming compounds.

How are the halogens alike?

Fluorine is the most chemically active of all nonmetals. Its compounds are called fluorides. Fluorides are added to drinking water and to toothpastes to prevent tooth decay. Nonstick surfaces of cooking utensils are composed of a compound containing fluorine and carbon. Fluorine is never found free in nature.

Name a use of fluorides.

Chlorine is the most common halogen. It does not occur free in nature either. It is usually obtained by passing an electric current through molten sodium chloride. Chlorine compounds are called chlorides. Many bleaches contain chlorine compounds. Sodium hypochlorite is one common chlorine compound used in bleach. The ability to bleach fabrics is a

a

Diane Graham-Henry/Click, Chicago

FIGURE 11–24. Chlorine is used as a disinfectant for water in swimming pools (a). A chlorine compound called muriatic acid is used for cleaning (b).

b

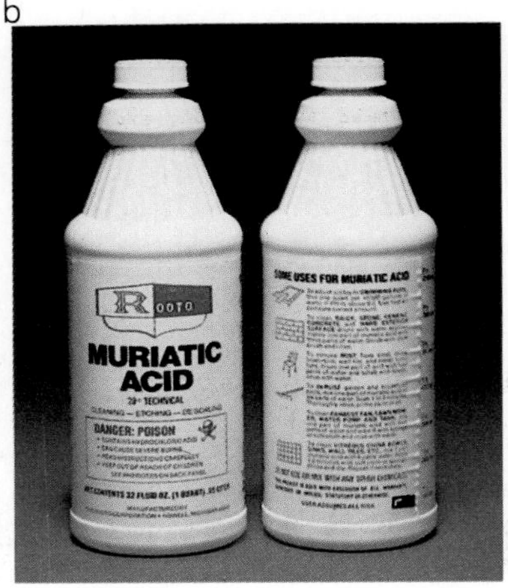


Tim Courlas

Why are chlorine compounds used to purify water?

chemical property of these compounds. Chlorine compounds are also used as disinfectants and in purifying water. These compounds destroy microscopic living things that may be hazardous to health.

Hydrogen chloride gas dissolved in water forms hydrochloric acid ($HCl$). Hydrochloric acid is used for many processes including cleaning metals. During the refining process, many metals become covered with an oxide scale. This substance is actually a compound of the metal and oxygen from water or the air. Hydrochloric acid removes this scale.

Doug Martin

FIGURE 11–25. Photographic film contains silver bromide. When the film is exposed to light, chemical changes occur. When the film is developed, another chemical change produces the image you see on the negative.

Which halogen is a liquid at room temperature?

Bromine is a liquid that vaporizes easily at room temperature. If you examine a closed bottle of bromine, you should notice that the bottle is filled with bromine vapor. Bromine is found in compounds called bromides. Silver bromide ($AgBr$) is used to coat photographic film. Ethylene bromide is used in gasoline to remove lead compounds formed during fuel combustion.

Iodine, like the other halogens, is not found free in nature. Iodine has many of the physical properties of a metal. Iodine compounds are vital to the human diet. They are also used in medicines. All of the halogens are poisonous in pure form.

Astatine is made in a laboratory. It has properties similar to iodine, but it breaks down into other elements. Note the position of astatine in the periodic table. It is close to the stairstep line separating the metals from the nonmetals. Astatine has some metallic properties. Astatine can form compounds with the other halogens.

## 11:11 Noble Gases

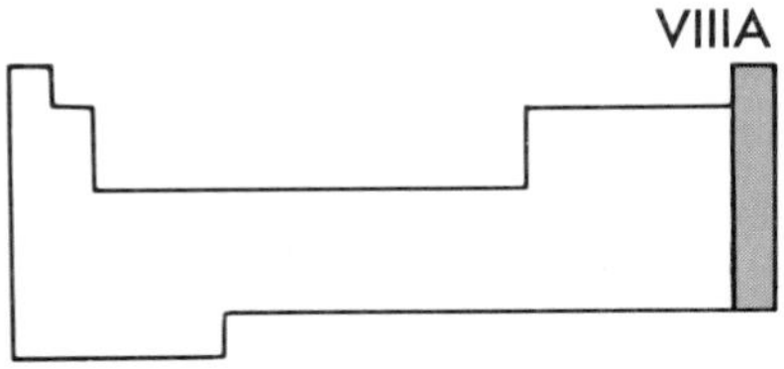


FIGURE 11-26. Group VIIIA is the noble gas family.

How are the noble gases alike?

Describe some uses for the noble gases.

Group VIIIA of the periodic table contains the **noble gases**. These elements do not combine chemically except under special conditions. Each element in this family has a complete outer energy level. This completed outer energy level makes each element stable.

Helium was discovered in the sun in 1868. Scientists had analyzed the light from the sun and predicted the existence of a new element. In 1895, helium was found in the earth's air. Helium comes from the Greek word "helios" meaning sun. Helium is less dense than air. It is used to fill balloons and airships. Helium is also used to cool substances to extremely low temperatures.

Helium, neon, and argon are used in lighted display signs. Krypton is added to light bulbs to extend the life of the filaments. Xenon is used in flashtubes for high-speed photography.

*Rich Brommer*

FIGURE 11-27. This light display is made of tubes containing noble gases.

# PERSPECTIVES

## skills

# Taking Notes in Table Form

As you read about elements in Chapter 11, you may wonder how you can remember each element in its proper classification. The first step is to read the section titles. They aid in organizing the chapter. For example, Section 11:1 introduces elements and the periodic table. Section 11:2 gives an overview of the main groups of elements. Section 11:3 begins a discussion of one important group of metals by presenting the alkali metals. As you read the chapter you will note that there are sections for each major group of metals, nonmetals, and metalloids.

How can you keep this information organized and in a form that is useful for studying and reviewing? You can make your own table of information about elements by grouping facts about metals, nonmetals, and metalloids. To give you an example, a partially completed table is shown below. The table lists the metallic elements. The first column lists the groups of metals. The other columns divide the information into useful topics. Copy the table and fill in each part of the table that is blank.

This table can be expanded to include information about nonmetals and metalloids. You may obtain additional information for your table from the periodic table on pages 200-201 and from class discussions. In this way, your notes in table form can include more information than can be found in the chapter.

Taking notes in table form is a useful study aid if you have a lot of information to remember. Tables can help you organize information so that it can be easily reviewed. Remember, however, that this form of taking notes can only be done once you have identified your topics.

| Metal Groups | Examples | Properties, uses | Compound formation |
|---|---|---|---|
| Alkali metals | Sodium<br>Rubidium<br>Lithium | Shiny, good conductors, not found in pure form, react violently with oxygen | One electron in outer energy levels, readily form compounds that are white in color, form compounds by losing one electron |
| Alkaline earth metals | Barium<br>Calcium<br>Magnesium<br>Strontium<br>Radium | | |
| Transition metals | | | |

## main ideas

# Chapter Review

1. The periodic table is a system of classification that groups the elements according to their atomic numbers. 11:1
2. Elements are classified as metals, metalloids, or nonmetals. 11:2
3. The alkali metals in Group IA are chemically active. 11:3
4. The alkaline earth metals in Group IIA are slightly less chemically active than the alkali metals. 11:4
5. Transition metals include common metals such as gold, iron, copper, and silver. Synthetic elements, with atomic numbers greater than 92, are produced in a laboratory. 11:5
6. Aluminum in Group IIIA is the third most abundant element in Earth's crust. 11:6
7. Carbon in Group IVA is an abundant nonmetal that forms many compounds. 11:7
8. Nitrogen in Group VA is not chemically active, but it is important to living organisms. 11:8
9. Oxygen in Group VIA combines with other elements to form oxides. Sulfur combines with metals to form sulfides. 11:9
10. The halogens, Group VIIA, are the most chemically active nonmetals. 11:10
11. Noble gases are nonmetals that are not chemically active. They have completed outer energy levels in their atoms. 11:11

## vocabulary

*Define each of the following words or terms.*

alkali metals
alkaline earth metals
families
groups
halogens
metals
metalloids
noble gases
nonmetals
organic compounds
periods
periodic table
polymers
sulfides
synthetic elements
transition metals

## study questions

**DO NOT WRITE IN THIS BOOK.**

### A. True or False

*Determine whether each of the following sentences is true or false. If the sentence is false, rewrite it to make it true.*

1. Alkali metals are the most chemically active of all metals.

2. Elements in the periodic table are arranged according to their atomic numbers.
3. The atomic number of an element is always equal to the number of protons in the nucleus.
4. Sodium is a chemically active metal.
5. Most elements can be classified as metals or metalloids.
6. Calcium is an alkaline earth metal.
7. Nonmetals have three or less electrons in their outer energy levels.
8. Synthetic elements are found in nature.
9. Most compounds of alkali metals are blue.
10. Compounds containing sodium are organic compounds.

**B. Multiple Choice**

*Choose the word or phrase that completes correctly each of the following sentences.*

1. The alkali metals are (*never, always, sometimes*) found in pure form in nature.
2. Ozone is a form of (*chlorine, oxygen, hydrogen*).
3. ($O_3$, *NaCl, FeO*) is a formula for an oxide.
4. Boron and silicon are (*metals, metalloids, nonmetals*).
5. Iodine is a (*metal, noble gas, halogen*).
6. (*Fluorine, Chlorine, Bromine*) is the most chemically active halogen.
7. CdS is the formula for a(n) (*sulfide, oxide, chloride*).
8. Graphite and diamond are two natural forms of (*sulfur, carbon, iron*).
9. The (*color, smell, shape*) produced in a flame test can be used to identify certain metals.
10. Each halogen has (*five, six, seven*) electrons in its outer energy level.

**C. Completion**

*Complete each of the following sentences with a word or phrase that will make the sentence correct.*

1. ______ and ______ are two forms of oxygen found in the air.
2. Compounds of ______ are called organic compounds.
3. Sodium is a chemically active ______ metal.

4. Many ______ compounds exist in long chains or rings.
5. Iron and copper are ______ metals.
6. Metalloids have some properties of ______ and ______.
7. Hydrogen oxide has the formula ______.
8. The noble gases are in Group ______ of the periodic table.
9. ______ is an element discovered on the sun before it was discovered on Earth.
10. The most abundant element in Earth's crust is ______.

**D. How and Why**

1. How are metals different from nonmetals?
2. Give three reasons why oxygen is an important element.
3. How are the halogens alike? How are they different?
4. Compare the properties of the halogens with those of the noble gases.
5. How are the alkali metals different from other metals?

## challenges

1. Prepare a report on the noble gases.
2. Make a large periodic table for a bulletin board display. Include the name and symbol for each element. You may wish to use different colors for different groups or families. Also, you may wish to look up the year of discovery for each element and add these dates to your table. Prepare a short talk on the use of the periodic table by chemists.
3. Obtain information on careers in chemistry. Prepare a report for your class on this topic.

## interesting reading

Hansen, James, "Metals that Remember." *Science 81,* June 1981, pp. 44-49.

Walters, Derek, *Chemistry.* New York: Franklin Watts, 1983.

# SIDE ROADS

## On the Trail of New Elements

Achim Zschau

*Scientists have been on the trail of new elements since 1869, when Mendeleev arranged the elements into a periodic table. Theoretically, scientists should be able to create the elements "missing" from the periodic table by adding protons and neutrons to the nuclei of an existing atom, thus creating a new, heavier element. However, protons and atomic nuclei both have positive charges, and so repel each other. This repulsion can be overcome only if the particles are pushed close enough together so that the nuclear force takes over and binds the particles. By the 1930s, scientists were smashing nuclei together in an effort to create new atoms. In 1940, this effort resulted in the creation of element 93, neptunium.*

*Most of the synthesized elements have been made by smashing the nuclei of a light element such as oxygen into the heavy nuclei of an artificially created element. However, because artificially created nuclei were scarce, it was difficult for scientists to obtain them. A new process for synthesizing elements was devised. In this process, new heavy elements* would be made by combining entire nuclei of stable, naturally occurring atoms. Scientists went to work to make a new machine that would accelerate the nuclei to a speed fast enough for them to join, but not so fast that smashing nuclei would shatter.

In 1971, physicists at Germany's Institute for Heavy Ion Research (GSI) began building the UNILAC accelerator. This instrument bombards a target element with particles of a second element. If the two types of elements fuse, a new element is formed. They also designed an instrument to detect the new element. A problem encountered by scientists in the past was that newly created elements decayed too quickly to be detected. This decay occurred in one of two ways. They either spontaneously split, or they emitted an alpha particle. The properties of new elements that emit alpha particles are easier to determine than those that split because the energy that escapes during alpha decay indicates the mass of the parent compound.

UNILAC created its first synthetic element, 107, in 1981. Then in August, 1982, GSI physicists produced element 109. For ten days, they smashed a beam of billions of iron ions against a layer of bismuth foil. When the iron and bismuth nuclei merged, a new element was formed. The resulting element lasted less than five-thousandths of a second before it decayed by emitting an alpha particle. In order to confirm the creation of this element, the detecting device used electric and magnetic fields to filter out particles traveling at the velocity predicted for element 109. The energy emitted during the decay of these particles was measured, and the presence of 109 confirmed.

Gerard Photography

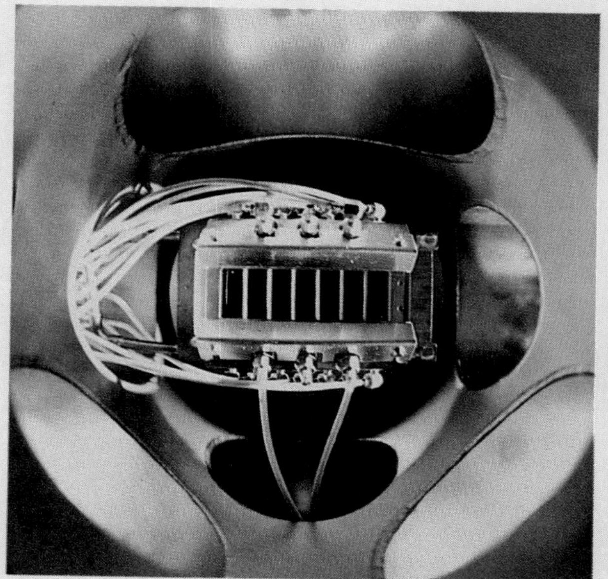

Achim Zschau/Discover Magazine

Synthetic elements have some practical uses. Plutonium is the fuel used in "breeder" nuclear reactors. The element americium is used in most home smoke detectors. Other synthetic elements have uses in medicine, especially in diagnosis and in the treatment of tumors.

Scientists are continuing to search for new elements. Recently, element 108 was produced. In the future, scientists expect to make elements with atomic numbers over 300.

Bruce Schecter © DISCOVER Magazine December, 1982, Time Inc.

*The man cleaning the bricks is using a special material. The cleaning material removes dirt from the bricks without harming the bricks themselves. When the cleaning material reacts chemically with the dirt, the characteristics of the resulting material are different from the original materials. What is a chemical reaction? How do chemical reactions differ?*

Greg Sailor

# Reactions

# chapter 12

## 12:1 Bonding

GOAL: You will learn how atoms bond, how to write chemical equations, and how reactions are classified.

Atoms combine to complete an outer energy level of electrons. An atom with a complete outer energy level is said to be stable. Stable atoms generally have eight electrons in their outer energy level. Atoms may share, gain, or give up electrons to become stable. When atoms combine chemically, the force that holds the atoms together is called a bond.

One type of bond is called a **covalent bond.** In a covalent bond, electrons are shared. Hydrogen bromide (HBr) is a compound in which electrons are shared. Hydrogen has one electron in its outer energy level. The addition of another electron results in a more stable condition. Bromine has seven electrons in its outer energy level. If bromine had another electron, it would be stable also. Its outer energy level would contain eight electrons. When hydrogen and bromine combine, two electrons are shared. Hydrogen now has two electrons in its outer energy level—its original electron and one that it shares with bromine. Bromine has eight electrons in its outer energy level. Seven are its original electrons; one is shared with hydrogen. These two atoms combine by forming a covalent bond.

FIGURE 12-1. In a hydrogen bromide molecule, electrons are shared between the hydrogen and bromine atoms.

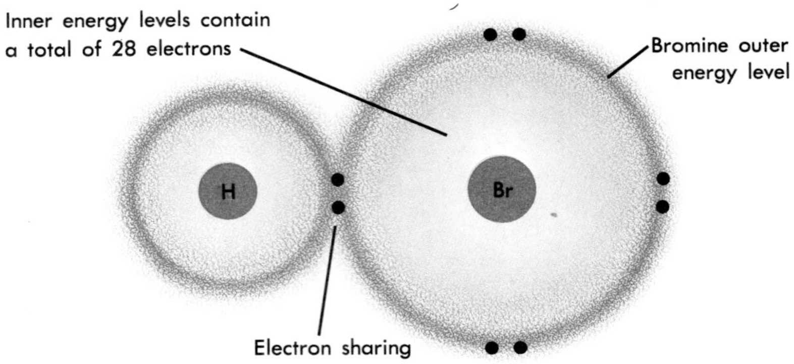


The particle formed by a covalent bond is called a **molecule.** A molecule usually contains two or more atoms. Some elements exist in nature only as molecules. Oxygen gas in air exists as a molecule. The molecule is composed of two oxygen atoms. The formula for oxygen gas is $O_2$. Other elements occur as molecules composed of two atoms. These elements include nitrogen ($N_2$), hydrogen ($H_2$), chlorine ($C_2$), and fluorine ($F_2$).

An atom that gains or loses one or more electrons, thereby acquiring a charge, is an **ion.** The charge of an ion is positive if an electron is lost. The charge of an ion is negative if an electron is gained.

How is an ionic bond formed?

Some compounds form bonds by transferring electrons between atoms. Potassium chloride is formed by the transfer of an electron from potassium to chlorine. Potassium has one electron in its outer energy level. When potassium gives up this electron, its preceding energy level is already filled and the ion is positively charged. When the chlorine atom gains an electron from the potassium, the ion is negatively charged. Both atoms have now formed ions with opposite electric charges. Because opposite charges attract each other, the ions are held together in a chemical bond. Bonding that occurs between ions is called **ionic bonding.** Ionic compounds, such as potassium chloride (KCl), exist as ions, not as molecules. Molecules are uncharged particles.

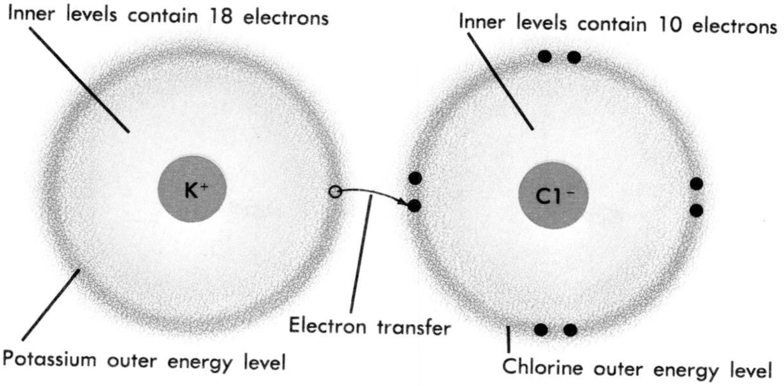


FIGURE 12-2. Potassium chloride is an ionic substance. One electron is transferred from the potassium atom to the chlorine atom.

Compounds have properties different from the properties of the elements that compose them. For example, the element sodium is a soft metal. It can be cut with a knife. It is very reactive and must be stored in oil. Chlorine is a greenish gas that is very poisonous. The ionic compound formed by these two elements is sodium chloride (NaCl). Sodium chloride is used to flavor and preserve foods. The common name for sodium chloride is table salt.

Solid ionic compounds, such as sodium chloride, have high melting points. These compounds will conduct a current when they are in solution or in a molten stage. Covalent compounds have low melting points and do not conduct a current. Water is an example of a covalent compound. What is its melting point?

## making sure

1. What is an ion? Name two examples of ions.
2. What is the difference between a covalent bond and an ionic bond?
3. How do the properties of compounds compare with the properties of the elements that compose them?
4. What is the charge of an ion if two electrons are lost by an atom?
5. What is the charge of an ion if two electrons are gained by an atom?

## 12:2 Oxidation Numbers

How are oxidation numbers used to write chemical formulas?

The **oxidation number** of an atom is the number of electrons an atom transfers or shares in forming compounds. An oxidation number is either positive or negative. For example, the oxidation number for bromine is 1−. It transfers or shares one electron when forming compounds. Some elements have more than one oxidation number. Copper can have oxidation numbers of 1+ or 2+. Copper transfers or shares either one or two electrons when forming compounds. Roman numerals are used to show the oxidation numbers for an element that has more than one oxidation number.

Oxidation numbers are used to write correct chemical formulas. Atoms and ions always combine in definite ratios. Oxidation numbers aid you in determining these ratios. If the oxidation numbers of the elements in a compound add to zero, the formula is correct. To write the formula for sodium chloride, begin by determining the oxidation numbers for these elements. Table 12–1 shows an oxidation number of 1+ for sodium and 1− for chlorine. When you add these oxidation numbers, you get zero (1+ + 1− = 0). Therefore, the formula for sodium chloride is NaCl. The combining ratio is one to one. Note that the element or ion with the positive oxidation number is written first. Note also that the name for chlor*ine* is changed to chlor*ide*. In a compound composed of two different elements, the name of the element with the negative oxidation number takes on the *-ide* ending.

FIGURE 12-3. Compounds formed from different oxidation states of the element chromium have characteristic colors.

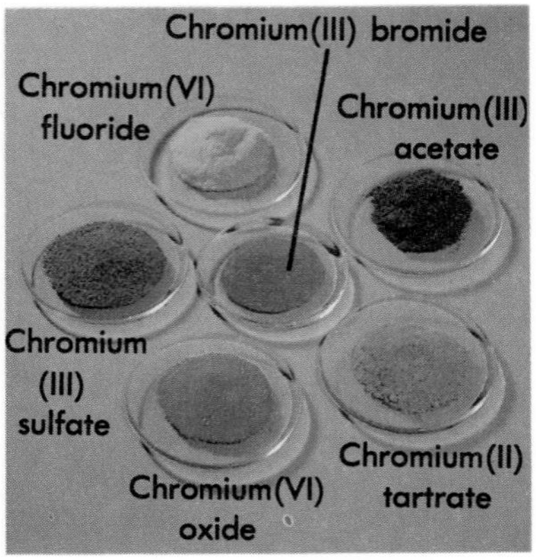


*Hickson-Bender Photography*

The correct formula for calcium chloride is $CaCl_2$. The oxidation number of calcium is 2+. The oxidation number of chlorine is 1−. Two chloride ions are needed to balance the oxidation number of the calcium. The subscript 2 indicates the two chloride ions.

Hydrogen has an oxidation number of 1+. Oxygen (oxide) has an oxidation number of 2−. Two atoms of hydrogen are needed for every atom of oxygen to form the compound $H_2O$, water.

Some compounds contain polyatomic ions. A **polyatomic ion** is a group of atoms that acts as one ion. Examples of polyatomic ions are carbonate ($CO_3^{2-}$), ammonium ($NH_4^+$), and sulfate ($SO_4^{2-}$). Formulas for compounds containing polyatomic ions are written in the same way as other formulas. The positive part of the compound is written first. For example, the formula for copper (II) nitrate is $Cu(NO_3)_2$. The parentheses are used to show that the nitrate ion is to be treated as a single unit. The subscript 2 shows that two nitrate ions are in the formula. *Parentheses must be used whenever a formula shows more than one polyatomic ion.* The subscript indicating the number of polyatomic ions is always written outside the parentheses. Table 12–1 also includes some polyatomic ions.

***Table 12–1.***
Common Oxidation Numbers

| 1+ | 2+ | 3+ |
|---|---|---|
| Hydrogen, $H^+$ | Barium, $Ba^{2+}$ | Aluminum, $Al^{3+}$ |
| Lithium, $Li^+$ | Calcium, $Ca^{2+}$ | Chromium(III), $Cr^{3+}$ |
| Potassium, $K^+$ | Cobalt(II), $Co^{2+}$ | Iron(III), $Fe^{3+}$ |
| Silver, $Ag^+$ | Copper(II), $Cu^{2+}$ | |
| Sodium, $Na^+$ | Iron(II), $Fe^{2+}$ | |
| Ammonium, $NH_4^+$ | Magnesium, $Mg^{2+}$ | |
| Copper(I), $Cu^+$ | Zinc, $Zn^{2+}$ | |
| **1−** | **2−** | **3−** |
| Bromide, $Br^-$ | Oxide, $O^{2-}$ | Nitride, $N^{3-}$ |
| Chloride, $Cl^-$ | Sulfide, $S^{2-}$ | Phosphate, $PO_4^{3-}$ |
| Iodide, $I^-$ | Carbonate, $CO_3^{2-}$ | |
| Acetate, $C_2H_3O_2^-$ | Sulfate, $SO_4^{2-}$ | |
| Hydroxide, $OH^-$ | | |
| Nitrate, $NO_3^-$ | | |

## making sure

**6.** Use Table 12–1 to write correct formulas for compounds formed from each of the following:
(a) silver and chlorine (c) potassium and iodine
(b) calcium and chlorine (d) iron(III) and sulfur

## 12:3 Naming Compounds

How are compounds named?

Some compounds have both scientific and common names. The scientific name for a compound is based on the names of the elements or ions it contains. Compounds containing two elements are **binary compounds.** When naming binary compounds, first write the name of the element having the positive oxidation number. Then add the name of the element having the negative oxidation number. The name of the element with the negative oxidation number is changed to end in *-ide.*

Naming compounds that contain polyatomic ions is similar to naming binary compounds. The positive part of the compound is named first followed by the name of the polyatomic ion. However, the name of the polyatomic ion is not changed. For example, $K_3PO_4$ is potassium phosphate and $Al_2(SO_4)_3$ is aluminum sulfate. Do not be confused by the parentheses. They are not part of the name.

***Example 1***

What is the name of the compound BaS?

Solution

Using Table 12–1 or the periodic table, determine the names of the atoms in the compound. Since BaS is binary, sulfur has an -ide ending. Therefore, the name of the compound is barium sulfide.

***Example 2***

What is the name of the compound $MgSO_4$?

Solution

Using Table 12-1 or the periodic table, determine the names of the atoms and ions. The name of the compound is magnesium sulfate.

### making sure

**7.** Use Table 12–1 and the periodic table to name each of the following:

(a) $Ca(NO_3)_2$
(b) $FeCl_2$
(c) HI
(d) $Na_2S$
(e) $NaC_2H_3O_2$
(f) $CuSO_4$
(g) $CaCO_3$
(h) $CrPO_4$

## 12:4 Equations for Chemical Reactions

A chemical equation is written to show the changes that occur during a chemical reaction. This equation can be written using words or a shorthand composed of chemical symbols and formulas. "Carbon plus oxygen yields carbon dioxide" is the word equation for the formation of carbon dioxide. The shorthand for this word equation is

$$C + O_2 \rightarrow CO_2.$$

Substances to the left of the arrow in the shorthand equation are the starting substances or **reactants.** Substances to the right of the arrow are the **products.**

Atoms are rearranged in a chemical reaction, never created or destroyed. The same number and kind of atoms present at the beginning of a reaction must be present at the end of the reaction. Thus, a chemical equation must be balanced to maintain the same number and kinds of atoms on both sides of the arrow. An equation is balanced by adding numbers, coefficients (koh uh FIHSH unts), in front of symbols and formulas. To balance a chemical equation, add or change the coefficients. Never change a formula. When you change a formula, you have a new substance with different properties and the reaction is no longer correct. To write a balanced equation, follow the four steps below.

(1) Write a word equation.

(2) Write the shorthand equation. Use symbols or formulas for the substances in the word equation.

(3) Check the number and kinds of atoms on each side of the arrow to see if the equation is balanced.

(4) If the atoms are not in balance, add coefficients.

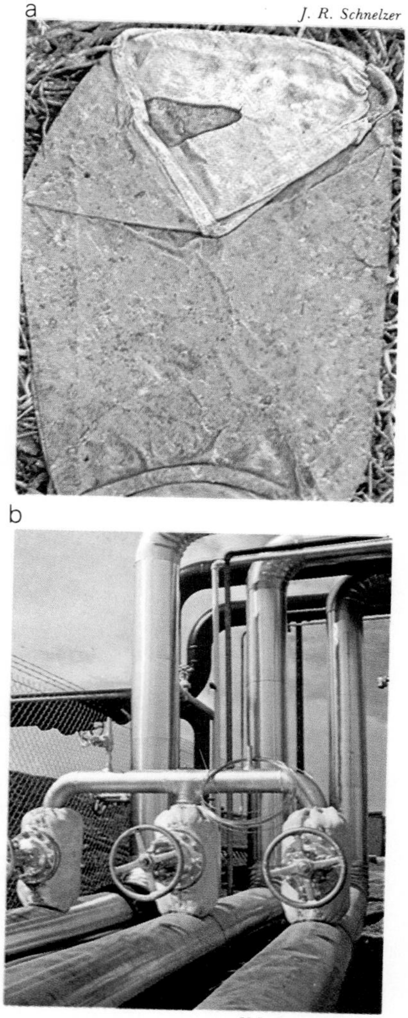

a J. R. Schnelzer

b U.S. Dept. of Energy

FIGURE 12–4. Rust occurs when iron reacts with oxygen in air or water (a). Valves, pipes, and faucets protected by a zinc coating or a zinc-base paint do not rust easily (b).

What is a chemical equation?

Define reactant, product, and coefficient.

***Example***

Hydrogen and oxygen combine to form water. Write the balanced equation for this reaction.

Solution

*Step 1*: Write the word equation.

hydrogen plus oxygen yield water

*Step 2:* Write the symbols and formulas for each part of the word equation.

$$H_2 + O_2 \rightarrow H_2O$$

Do not forget that hydrogen and oxygen exist in nature as diatomic molecules.

*Step 3:* Check the numbers of atoms on each side of the → to see if the equation is balanced.

Hydrogen: 2 → Hydrogen: 2
Oxygen: 2 → Oxygen: 1

The equation is not balanced. Why?

*Step 4:* Add coefficients to balance the equation. In order to get two oxygen atoms on the right, the coefficient 2 is placed before $H_2O$. Then, check the numbers of atoms again.

$$H_2 + O_2 \rightarrow 2H_2O$$

Hydrogen: 2 → Hydrogen: 4
Oxygen: 2 → Oxygen: 2

Add a coefficient of two before $H_2$ on the left.

$$2H_2 + O_2 \rightarrow 2H_2O$$

Hydrogen: 4 → Hydrogen: 4
Oxygen: 2 → Oxygen: 2

A chemical equation should show the state of each substance in the reaction. Symbols are used to show the state of matter. The symbol (g) means gas; (c) means solid or crystal; (l) means liquid. Some substances will not react unless they are dissolved in water. Aqueous means a compound is dissolved in water. The symbol for aqueous is (aq). The completed equation for the reaction that produces water is

$$2H_2(g) + O_2(g) \rightarrow 2H_2O(l)$$

**making sure**

8. Write a balanced chemical equation for each of the following reactions:
   (a) silver plus oxygen yield silver oxide
   (b) potassium plus bromine yield potassium bromide
   (c) sodium chloride yields sodium plus chlorine
   (d) hydrogen plus chlorine yield hydrogen chloride

## 12:5 Types of Chemical Reactions

There are four general types of chemical reactions. A synthesis (SIHN thuh sus) reaction occurs when two or more substances combine to form one new substance. The formation of sodium chloride is a synthesis reaction.

List four types of reactions.

$$2Na(c) + Cl_2(g) \rightarrow 2NaCl(c)$$

A single displacement reaction occurs when one element displaces another in a compound. If a piece of zinc is added to a beaker containing hydrochloric acid, the zinc displaces the hydrogen and sets it free. Gas bubbles are seen in the beaker. Zinc chloride is formed in the reaction also. The zinc chloride is dissolved in solution. The solid can be obtained by boiling off the liquid.

$$Zn(c) + 2HCl(aq) \rightarrow ZnCl_2(aq) + H_2(g)$$

Englehard Industries

FIGURE 12-5. The silver plating process is an example of a single displacement reaction.

*Hickson-Bender Photography*

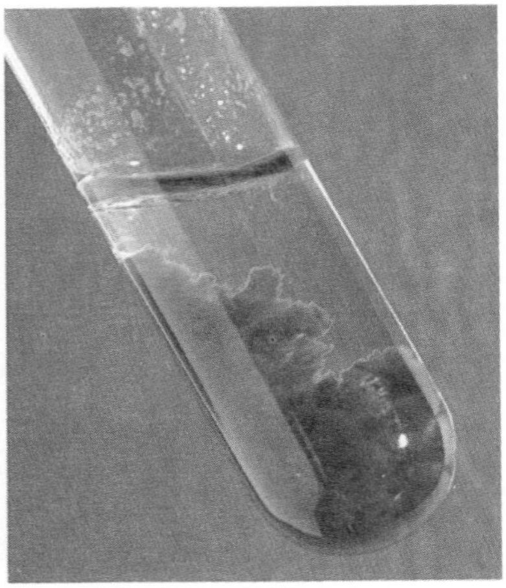

FIGURE 12-6. A precipitate forms in a double displacement reaction.

In a double displacement reaction, the positive and negative parts of two compounds are exchanged. An example of a double displacement reaction is given below.

$$3NaOH(aq) + FeCl_3(aq) \rightarrow 3NaCl(aq) + Fe(OH)_3(c)$$

When the aqueous solutions of NaOH and $FeCl_3$ are mixed, a red precipitate (prih SIHP uh tayt) forms. A precipitate is a solid substance that does not dissolve in water. In this case, the precipitate is iron(III) hydroxide, $Fe(OH)_3$.

The fourth type of chemical reaction is the decomposition reaction. In a decomposition reaction, a substance breaks into simpler substances when energy is added. The energy may be in the form of heat, light, or electricity. Free chlorine gas is prepared by passing an electric current through liquid sodium chloride. The equation for the decomposition of sodium chloride is given below.

$$2NaCl(l) \rightarrow 2Na(l) + Cl_2(g)$$

## making sure

**9.** Name the type of chemical reaction represented in each equation below.

(a) $Pb(OH)_2(aq) \rightarrow PbO(c) + H_2O(l)$
(b) $Cl_2(g) + 2KBr(aq) \rightarrow 2KCl(aq) + Br_2(l)$
(c) $ZnBr_2(c) + 2AgNO_3(aq) \rightarrow Zn(NO_3)_2(aq) + 2AgBr(c)$
(d) $SO_3(g) + H_2O(l) \rightarrow H_2SO_4(l)$
(e) $S(c) + O_2(g) \rightarrow SO_2(g)$
(f) $MgCl_2(aq) + H_2SO_4(aq) \rightarrow MgSO_4(aq) + HCl(aq)$

**10.** Complete and balance the following equations. Use Table 12–1 to find the oxidation numbers and charges.

(a) $AgNO_3(aq) + NaCl(aq)$ → ______Cl(c) + ______$NO_3$(aq)
(b) $KCl(aq) + Pb(NO_3)_2(aq)$ → K______(aq) + Pb______(c)
(c) $2C_2H_2(g) + 5\ O_2(g)$ → 4C______(g) + 2______O(l)
(d) $H_2SO_3(aq)$ → ______O(l) + S______(g)

## 12:6 Chemical Change and Energy

Define endothermic and exothermic.

Chemical changes always involve a change in energy. Energy is either gained or lost in a chemical change. If energy must be added during a reaction, the reaction is **endothermic** (en duh THUR mihk). If energy is released, the reaction is **exothermic** (ek soh THUR mihk). The decomposition reaction that frees chlorine gas from liquid sodium chloride is endothermic. Energy in the form of electricity must be added during the reaction. Burning wood in a fireplace is an exothermic reaction. Once the fire has been lighted, the chemical reaction continues and energy is released as heat and light.

The time it takes for a chemical reaction to occur varies greatly. The rusting of iron can take months. When sodium metal combines with water, the reaction is very quick. In order to speed up some chemical reactions, chemists use catalysts (KAT ul usts). A catalyst is a compound that speeds up a reaction without being permanently changed.

What are the properties of acids?

## 12:7 Acids and Bases

An **acid** is a substance that has a sour taste, reacts with metals, and contains hydrogen. When dissolved in water, an acid produces hydronium ions ($H_3O^+$) in solution. The presence of $H_3O^+$ gives acids their

a

*Larry Hamill*

b

FIGURE 12-7. Oranges and lemons contain citric acid; vinegar contains acetic acid (a). An automobile battery can be corroded by the acid it contains (b).

*Hickson-Bender Photography*

characteristic properties. Most acids contain hydrogen and a nonmetal. Since most acids contain hydrogen, it is customary to write the hydrogen first in the formula for an acid. The formula for hydrochloric acid is written HCl. Many common foods contain acids. Buttermilk contains lactic acid, and vinegar contains acetic acid. Carbonated beverages contain carbonic acid. Citrus fruits contain citric acid.

Sulfuric acid ($H_2SO_4$), hydrochloric acid (HCl), and nitric acid ($HNO_3$) are used often in industry as well as in the laboratory. Sulfuric acid is used to make paints, plastics, and fertilizers. It is also used in storage batteries and in the iron and steel industry. Sulfuric acid is important in industry as a drying agent. It can remove water from some organic compounds that contain no free water. If you put sulfuric acid on a cube of table sugar ($C_{12}H_{22}O_{11}$), hydrogen and oxygen are removed. Carbon is left. The same reaction occurs when sulfuric acid comes in contact with human skin. Therefore, it is important to always handle an acid with care.

*Kodansha* *Kodansha*

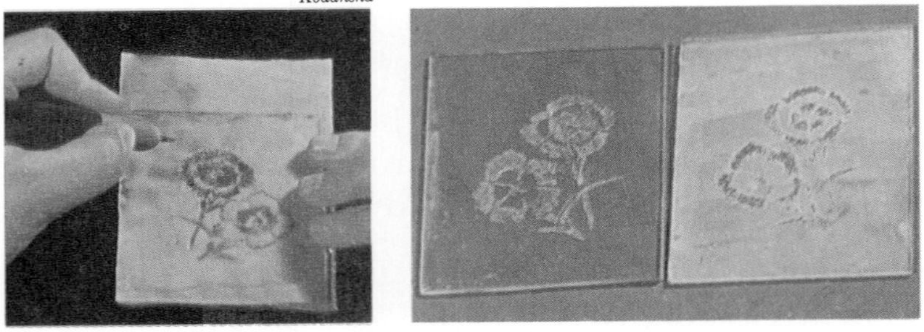

FIGURE 12-8. Hydrofluoric acid is used to etch glass.

Hydrochloric acid is used in the steel industry to clean metal. It, too, can cause burns and damage clothing. In addition, fumes from hydrochloric acid can harm lung tissue.

Nitric acid combines with protein in the skin and turns the skin yellow. This color will gradually fade. Nitric acid will also damage clothing.

A **base** is a substance that tastes bitter, feels slippery, will dissolve fats and oils, and may dissolve in water. When a base dissolves, hydroxide ions

(OH⁻) are released. The presence of $OH^-$ ions gives a base its characteristic properties.

Milk of magnesia, ammonia, and lye are examples of common bases. Milk of magnesia is a stomach antacid. Milk of magnesia contains $Mg(OH)_2$. Ammonia solution ($NH_4OH$) is used as a household cleaner, especially for windows. Lye (NaOH) dissolves oils and grease readily and is used to unclog sink drains. Strong bases, like lye, will also dissolve the fats in human skin. Always handle bases with care.

### making sure

**11.** What happens when an acid dissolves in water? A base?

Larry Hamill

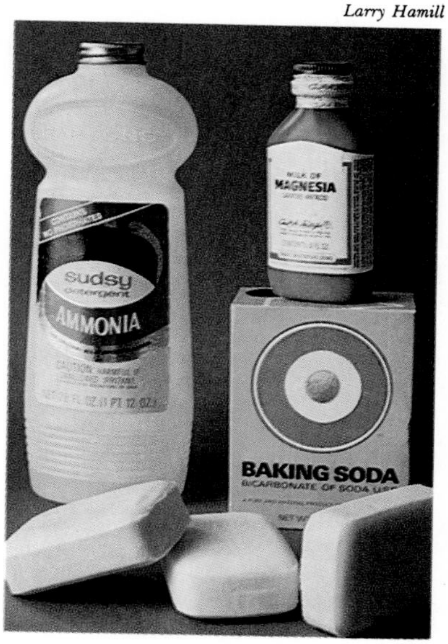


FIGURE 12-9. Many everyday household products contain bases.

## 12:8 Ions in Acids and Bases

Pure water contains water molecules and ions. The ions formed are the hydronium ion ($H_3O^+$) and the hydroxide ion ($OH^-$).

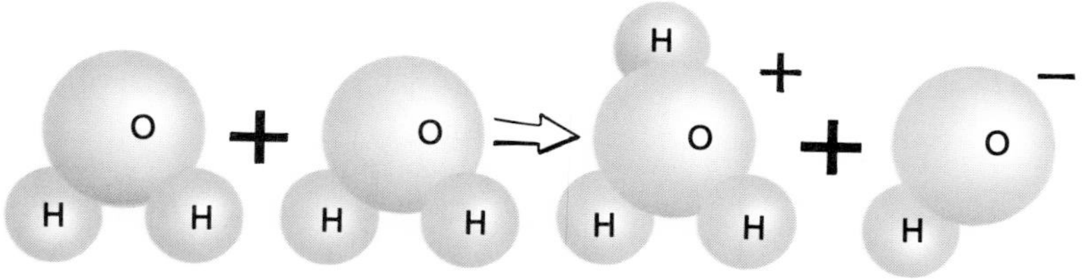


FIGURE 12-10. Two water molecules can form a hydronium ion and a hydroxide ion.

In pure water, there are equal numbers of hydronium and hydroxide ions. Therefore, pure water is neutral. The ratio changes if an acid or base is added to the water. Additional $H_3O^+$ ions come from the hydrogen in the acid that combines with water molecules. When hydrogen chloride, HCl, is added to water, the number of $H_3O^+$ ions in the solution increases.

$$HCl(aq) + H_2O(l) \rightarrow H_3O^+(aq) + Cl^-(aq)$$

The addition of a base increases the number of $OH^-$ ions in water. When sodium hydroxide, NaOH, is added to water, it dissolves. The additional $OH^-$ ions come from the base.

$$NaOH(aq) \rightarrow Na^+(aq) + OH^-(aq)$$

Not all compounds that contain an OH group are bases. Some carbon compounds called alcohols contain an OH group. However, alcohols do not release $OH^-$ ions in water so they are not classified as bases. Some metal hydroxides, such as $Zn(OH)_2$ and $Al(OH)_3$, can act as either an acid or a base in water. Reaction conditions determine how these compounds are classified.

How is a strong acid or base different from a weak acid or base?

Acids and bases can be classified as strong or weak depending upon how completely they ionize (form ions) in water. Strong acids and bases generally break up completely into ions. Hydrochloric acid is a strong acid. A weak acid or base does not break up completely in water.

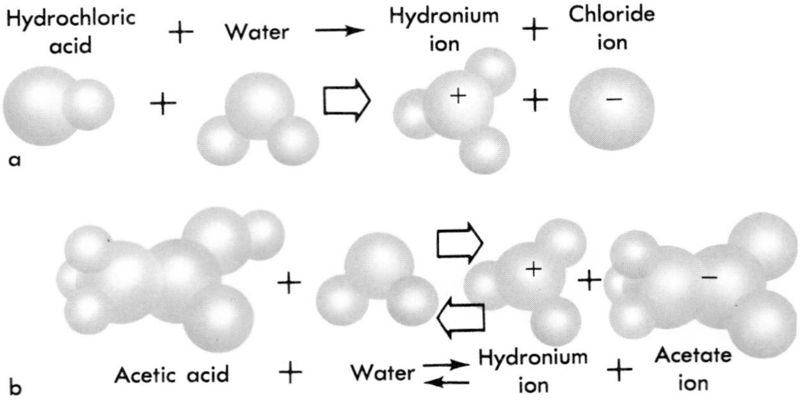


FIGURE 12-11. In water, a strong acid breaks up completely into ions (a). A weak acid produces some hydronium ions (b).

A double arrow (Figure 12–11) indicates that all the particles shown in the equation are present in the solution. For the strong acid, only ions are present in the solution with water. There are no HCl molecules. A weak acid or base solution will contain some ions as well as the acid or base in molecular form. Since there will be fewer $H_3O^+$ or $OH^-$ ions, the acid or base is labeled weak.

## 12:9 Indicators and pH Scale

How do you test for an acid or base?

The presence of an acid or a base may be shown by an indicator. Litmus paper and phenolphthalein (feen ul THAYL een) are two common indicators. Blue litmus paper will turn red in an acid solution. Red

Hickson-Bender Photography Hickson-Bender Photography George Anderson

FIGURE 12-12. Indicators can be used to detect acids and bases. Phenolphthalein is colorless in an acid (a) and turns pink in a base (b). Litmus paper turns red in an acid and blue in a base (c).

litmus paper will turn blue in a base solution. If a solution does not change the color of either paper, the solution is neutral. Phenolphthalein is an indicator that is generally used in solution form. It is colorless in an acid solution and bright pink in a base solution.

What is the pH scale and how is it used?

The **pH scale** is used to measure the number of hydronium ions in an acid or base solution. The pH scale ranges from 0 to 14. Seven is the neutral point. A pH above seven indicates a base. A solution with a pH below seven is an acid. Indicators can be used to measure pH over a specific range. A piece of pH paper is composed of several indicators. It shows colors from red to orange in acidic solutions ($pH<7$). The pH paper shows colors from blue to green in basic solutions ($pH>7$).

There are limitations to the use of indicators. In order to see color changes, the solutions tested must be colorless. Another problem is the ability of the human eye to detect small changes in color. A pH meter is used for accurate determination of pH. A pH meter is an electronic device that can provide very precise measurements.

FIGURE 12-13. pH paper can be used to find the approximate pH of a solution because it is composed of several indicators.

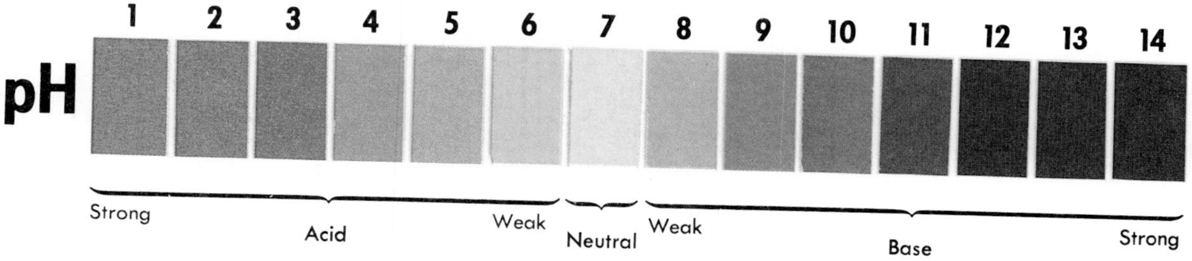

## activity ACIDS AND BASES

**(1)** Label 4 small jars *A, B, C,* and *D.* **(2)** Pour 10 mL buttermilk into jar *A.* Pour 10 mL vinegar into jar *B.* Pour 10 mL milk of magnesia into jar *C.* Pour 10 mL distilled water into jar *D.* **(3)** Use litmus paper to test each solution. Determine which solutions are acids, bases, or neutral. Record the results and explain. **(4)** Label 2 beakers *E* and *F.* **(5)** Pour 100 mL distilled water into each beaker. **(6)** Add 40 mL ammonia solution to beaker *E.* **(7)** Add 40 mL vinegar to beaker *F.* Add about 2 g petroleum jelly to each beaker. **(8)** Allow the beakers to stand undisturbed overnight. **(9)** Observe the contents of each beaker. Record and explain your observations.

## activity pH VALUES

**(1)** Obtain 10-mL samples of each of the following substances: lemon juice, ginger ale, apple juice, orange juice, sauerkraut juice, tomato juice, milk, corn syrup, salt water, milk of magnesia, and shampoo. **(2)** Use a separate piece of pH paper for each sample and determine the pH value of each. Record all values. **(3)** Rank the substances in order of pH values from the lowest to the highest. Which of the substances tested has the lowest pH? Which has the highest pH? Classify your samples as acids, bases, or neutral substances.

## 12:10 Neutralization and Salts

When an acid and a base are mixed together, a chemical reaction occurs. This reaction is called **neutralization** (new truh luh ZAY shun). In neutralization, properties of both the acid and the base are changed. Neutralization produces a salt and water. A salt is neither an acid nor a base. Neutralization explains why bases are used to counteract acid spills.

In neutralization, hydronium ions from the acid combine with hydroxide ions from the base. The ions form water. Sodium chloride is formed in the neutralization reaction between hydrochloric acid and sodium hydroxide.

$$HCl(aq) + NaOH(aq) \rightarrow NaCl(aq) + H_2O(l)$$

Sodium chloride is a salt compound. **Salts** are compounds that contain at least one metal and one nonmetal. Some salts are used to flavor and preserve foods.

Salts are also formed when metals react with acids. If zinc is added to hydrochloric acid, zinc chloride, a salt, and hydrogen gas are produced.

Solutions of acids, bases, and salts all contain ions. These solutions can conduct electricity. Therefore, you should not touch an electric appliance with wet hands. Ions in the water can conduct electricity from the appliance to you. As a result, you feel a shock. Electricians wear insulated clothing and take special precautions when working on electric lines.

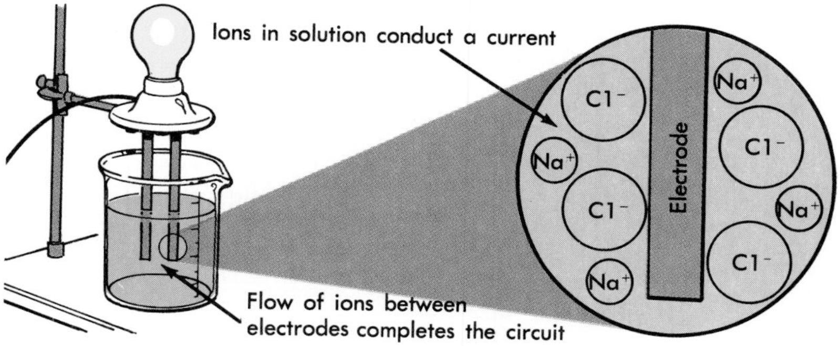


FIGURE 12-14. Solutions of acids, bases, or salts conduct electricity.

## activity NEUTRALIZATION

(1) Add 5 drops of phenolphthalein to 50 mL of water in a beaker. (2) Add 10 mL of vinegar to the beaker. Is this solution an acid or base? How do you know? (3) To the same beaker, add ammonia water, 1 drop at a time, until a color change occurs. Is this solution an acid or base? How do you know? Was the pH of the solution above 7 or below 7 before you added the final drop? How does this activity relate to neutralization?

# PERSPECTIVES

## frontiers

# Quick-setting Polymers

*Image Workshop*

Imagine that a water line breaks late at night under a major highway. When the repair crew arrives, the road is blocked and traffic detoured. The crew removes a section of the road, exposes the pipe, and replaces the broken section. One hour before the morning traffic rush, the crew pours a mixture of gravel, sand, and a clear liquid into the hole. The mixture hardens in ten minutes and the road is reopened.

The quick-setting concretelike material the repair crew used is a substance recently developed by Una Nandi at Battelle Memorial Institute and chemists at other laboratories. It hardens in five to ten minutes, is five times stronger than regular concrete, can be used at temperatures ranging from $-31°C$ to $55°C$, and will harden in rain, snow, or under water. Its composition can also be varied slightly so that it will bend or absorb strong shocks.

Dr. Nandi explained that two substances are used in the reaction resulting in the quick-setting material—a monomer and an activator. One end of a monomer is highly reactive. The highly reactive end bonds with a second monomer to form a dimer. The reactive end of the dimer bonds with a third monomer. This bonding process continues until no monomers remain. The activator provides a "push" that enables the monomers to bond. The long chain formed by the monomers is called a polymer. Some common polymers are nylon, plexiglas, vinyl, and latex paints.

Both the activator and the monomer are liquids. When the two liquids are mixed together and a filler such as gravel is added, the quick-setting material used for road repair is made. Repairing roads is not the only proposed use of the polymer. In the future, the material may be poured over an oil spill or a hazardous material that is dangerous for humans to touch. After the mixture hardens, the spilled material can be hauled away. The polymer may also be used as a sealant for certain types of leaks. Boats could be repaired without having to drydock them. Because the polymer adhers well to other substances, it has been suggested for use as a bone or dental cement. Dr. Nandi believes that the uses for the quick-setting polymer are limited only by the imagination.

# Chapter Review

## main ideas

1. Atoms form bonds by transferring or sharing electrons. 12:1
2. A particle formed by a covalent bond is a molecule. An atom that gains or loses an electron forms an ion. 12:1
3. Oxidation numbers are used to write chemical formulas. 12:2
4. Compounds are written and named starting with the positive part of the compound first. 12:3
5. A chemical equation is used to show the changes that occur during a chemical change. 12:4
6. The number and kind of atoms present at the beginning of a reaction must be present at the end of the reaction. 12:4
7. There are four general types of chemical reactions. Chemical changes always involve a change in energy. 12:5, 12:6
8. Acids and bases form hydronium ($H_3O^+$) ions and hydroxide ($OH^-$) ions in a water solution. 12:7, 12:8
9. The presence of an acid or a base in a solution can be shown by an indicator. 12:9
10. Neutralization is the reaction that occurs when an acid and a base are combined. A salt and water are produced. 12:10

## vocabulary

*Define each of the following words or terms.*

acid
base
binary compounds
covalent bond
endothermic
exothermic
ion
ionic bonding
molecule
neutralization
oxidation number
pH scale
polyatomic ion
products
reactants
salts

## study questions

**DO NOT WRITE IN THIS BOOK.**

**A. True or False**

*Determine whether each of the following sentences is true or false. If the sentence is false, rewrite it to make it true.*

1. Molecules are formed when atoms form a covalent bond.
2. A charged atom is called a molecule.

3. A binary compound contains two elements.
4. A subscript shows the amount of a particular element in a compound.
5. Every element has only one oxidation number.
6. Vinegar contains an acid.
7. Strong acids produce fewer ions than weak acids in water solutions.
8. The formula for sulfuric acid is $H_2SO_4$.
9. An indicator can be used to determine if a solution is an acid or a base.
10. A solution with a pH of 7 is an acid.

## B. Multiple Choice

*Choose the word or phrase that completes correctly each of the following sentences.*

1. The compound $Cu(NO_3)_2$ contains (*mercury, neon, nitrate*).
2. Sodium chloride is a(n) (*element, mixture, compound*).
3. The compound iron(II) oxide has the formula ($Fe_2O$, $FeO$, $FeO_2$).
4. Nitrate, $NO_3^-$, is a (*compound, molecule, polyatomic ion*).
5. ($H_2O$, $MgO$, $HCl$) is the formula of an acid.
6. An acid could have a pH of (*3, 7, 11*).
7. Neutralization reactions produce a salt and (*acid, base, water*).
8. The pH of an NaOH solution is (*more than 7, 7, less than 7*).
9. If the concentration of a strong acid in water increases, the number of hydronium ions (*increases, decreases, remains the same*).
10. The compound $Fe_2(SO_4)_3$ contains (*3, 4, 12*) atoms of oxygen.

## C. Completion

*Complete each of the following sentences with a word or phrase that will make the sentence correct.*

1. Oxygen has an oxidation number of ______.
2. In forming compounds, oxygen transfers or shares ______ electrons.
3. A binary compound contains atoms of ______ elements.
4. The elements in a compound are always combined in the same ______.

5. $H_3O^+$ is the formula for the ______ ion.
6. Bases can be tested by using a(n) ______.
7. The presence of acids and bases gives food distinctive ______.
8. A salt is formed when an acid reacts with a(n) ______.
9. The name of the compound represented by the formula AgCl is ______.
10. The sour flavor of a lemon is due to the presence of a(n) ______.

**D. How and Why**

1. How is covalent bonding different from ionic bonding?
2. How can copper form these two compounds, CuCl and $CuCl_2$?
3. Write formulas for the following compounds: calcium phosphate, aluminum sulfate, and magnesium sulfate.
4. How are acids different from bases?
5. Explain neutralization and give an example.

## challenges

1. Use pH paper to measure the pH of aquarium water, drinking water, soapy water, saliva, and several moist soil samples. Prepare a table of your results.
2. Using information from gardening books, make a list of three plants that require acid soil and three plants that require basic soil. Write a report on the methods used to make soil acidic or basic.
3. Check the labels on ten household items, such as medicines, cleaners, and foods. Record how many contain an acid or a base.

## interesting reading

Alper, Joseph, "The Stradivarius Formula." *Science 84*. March 1984, pp. 36-43.

Dunkle, Terry, "The Cold Facts About Ice Cream." *Science 81*, July/August, 1981, p. 54.

Preuss, Paul, "The Shape of Things to Come." *Science 83*. December 1983, pp. 80-87.

*Research in chemistry has led to many new products that you use every day. Detergents are a product of chemical technology that are used in cleaning fabrics and other substances. What properties of matter made the development of detergents possible? What other advances in chemical technology have improved your life?*

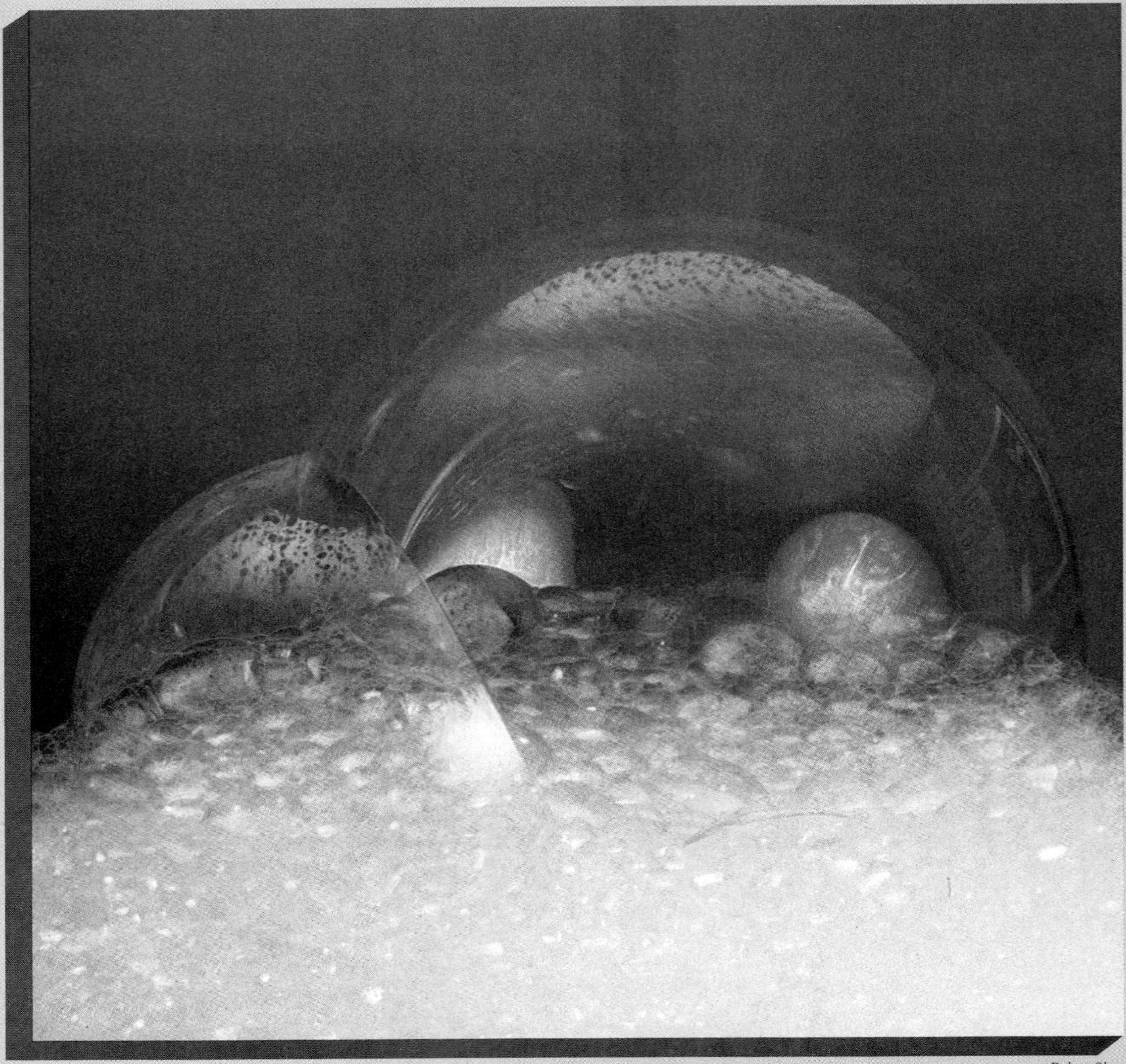

Robert Shay

# Chemical Technology

chapter 13

## 13:1 Chemical Technology

GOAL: You will learn some of the practical applications of chemical laws.

Technology is the application of science for practical purposes. Chemical technology is using our knowledge of matter to make new products. You use the results of chemical technology every day.

What is chemical technology?

What color clothing are you wearing today? Is it made of a natural fiber such as cotton, wool, or silk? Is it made of a synthetic fiber such as nylon, polyester, or acrylic? Dyes used in textiles are developed in laboratories. Many fibers, like nylon, are produced from coal or oil. Vinyl floor coverings, nylon carpets, and plastic pipes are synthetic substances. They are often used in place of more expensive materials in the construction of houses.

If you use water from a central supply system, you are using the results of chemical technology. Chemicals are used to purify water. Impurities are removed by chemical and physical changes. Technology is used to pipe the water to your home.

FIGURE 13–1. Plants can be grown in properly balanced chemical solutions.

Some chemicals are used to make our clothes, homes, and furnishings fire resistant. Other chemicals are used to smother fires. Soils are often enriched by chemical fertilizers. People use the plants grown in fertilized soil for food. Pesticides and herbicides are chemicals used to control animal and plant pests that destroy crops. Other chemicals are used to flavor, color, and preserve food.

Many medicines are a result of chemical technology. New body parts are manufactured from alloys and plastics. The use of chemical technology makes our lives easier and safer in many ways.

### making sure

1. Describe two ways that chemical technology has made your life easier or more enjoyable.

## 13:2 Carbon and Chemical Technology

Why are some carbon compounds important?

Most of the substances you use contain the element carbon. Nylon clothing, gasoline, and aspirin all have one element in common—carbon. Carbon forms millions of compounds. Over half of all chemicals manufactured are carbon compounds. Carbon is a vital part of chemical technology.

Name some carbon compounds.

One group of carbon compounds is called hydrocarbons. **Hydrocarbons** are compounds that contain only the elements hydrogen and carbon. The simplest hydrocarbon is methane, $CH_4$. Nylon is a hydrocarbon containing hundreds of carbon atoms. Hydrocarbons can be changed into compounds that contain elements such as oxygen, nitrogen, sulfur, phosphorus, and the halogens. These elements are substituted for part of a hydrocarbon molecule. For example, carbon tetrachloride, $CCl_4$, contains chlorine atoms in place of hydrogen atoms.

## 13:3 Petroleum

**Petroleum** is a liquid mixture of hydrocarbons obtained from wells drilled deep into the ground. Another name for petroleum is crude oil. Petroleum is the major source of fuels, including propane, gasoline, kerosene, and diesel fuel. Compounds in petroleum are used to make plastics, synthetic fibers, cosmetics, medicines, and many other products.

Is petroleum an element, a compound, or a mixture? Why?

The mixture of hydrocarbons in petroleum is separated by a process called **fractional distillation**. Each part of the mixture is called a fraction. In fractional distillation, the petroleum is heated slowly. The hydrocarbons in the mixture have different boiling points (Table 13–1). As the temperature increases, each fraction changes to a gas at its boiling point. The fractions rise to different points in the fractionating tower. Each fraction is collected at different levels in the tower and cooled to reform a liquid. A pipe still and a fractionating tower used in this process are shown in Figure 13-2b.

How is petroleum separated into different compounds?

a

*The Standard Oil Co.*

FIGURE 13-2. Crude oil is distilled into many fractions at a refinery (a). A pipe still and fractionating tower are used to separate the fractions (b).

b

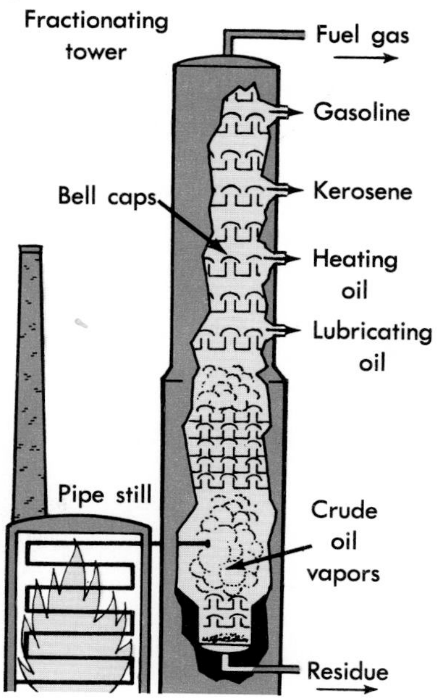

*Table 13–1.*
Petroleum Fractions

| Name | Boiling Range (°C) | Principal Uses |
| --- | --- | --- |
| Gas | Below 40 | Cooking, heating |
| Gasoline | 40–180 | Gasoline for cars, trucks |
| Kerosene | 180–230 | Heating, jet fuels |
| Light gas oil | 230–305 | Home heating fuel |
| Heavy gas oil | 305–405 | Diesel fuel |
| Residue | 405–515 | Asphalt for road construction, waxes for candles and cosmetics, coke for the steel industry |

Each petroleum fraction may be distilled again to further purify it. Other chemicals may be added to remove impurities. A fractionating tower may distill as much as 2 000 000 liters of petroleum per day.

One petroleum fraction is gasoline. Gasoline is the primary fuel used in highway transportation. Gasoline production can be increased by a process called cracking. Cracking splits the large molecules of other fractions of petroleum into smaller gasoline molecules. Thermal cracking uses heat to break large molecules into gasoline molecules. Catalytic cracking uses a catalyst.

### making sure

2. Name three fractions obtained from petroleum.
3. Which of the three fractions has the highest boiling point? The lowest?
4. Explain how cracking can increase gasoline production.

## 13:4 Plastics

What are plastics?

**Plastics** are polymers made from petroleum compounds. These compounds exist as long chains or rings that contain hundreds of atoms. Plastics have many uses and each use depends upon the properties of the plastic. Polystyrene is a soft, flexible plastic that is water resistant. It is used to make plastic bottles and tubing. Table 13-2 shows some common plastics and their uses. There are two types of plastics—thermoplastics and thermosetting plastics. A **thermoplastic** may be changed in shape by heating and molding. The plastic softens when it is heated. It hardens again when it is cooled. Some eyeglass frames are made from a thermoplastic. They are adjusted to fit the wearer by careful heating and molding.

How is a thermosetting plastic different from a thermoplastic?

Lucite® and Plexiglas® are trade names for two clear plastics. Both of these thermoplastics are strong and shatterproof. Each may be cut with a saw. Lucite® and Plexiglas® are used to make lenses for glasses, airplane windows, jewelry, safety glasses, and musical instruments. Both plastics can be dyed and are used to make dental plates.

A **thermosetting plastic** cannot be heated and remolded once it has hardened. Plastic radio and television cabinets are made from these plastics. Bakelite® is the trade name for one thermosetting plastic. Bakelite® is made by combining two organic compounds. When the compounds are mixed and

How is Bakelite® produced?

*Tim Courlas*

FIGURE 13-3. Plastics such as polystyrene, Lucite, and Plexiglas are used in many products.

*Table 13–2.*
Some Common Plastics

| **Thermoplastics** | **Uses** |
|---|---|
| ABS | Football helmets, telephones |
| Acrylic | Car lights, windows, television screens |
| Nylon | Combs and brushes, stockings, fabrics, parachutes, gears, tires, fish nets, tennis rackets, artificial grass |
| Polyethylene | Pipes, toys, adhesives, artificial snow, automobile gasoline tanks, radiation shielding, baby bottles, garbage bags |
| Polypropylene | Rope, baby bottles, storage batteries, carpets, molded parts of appliances, lids for food storage containers, printing plates |
| Vinyl | Records, garden hoses, floor coverings, car tops, upholstery fabrics |
| **Thermosetting** | |
| Alkyd resin | Light switches, car bodies |
| DAP | Handles, knobs |
| Epoxy resin | Glues, base for stained glass, road paving used with asphalt, coatings for glass |
| Melamine resin | Dishes, table and counter tops, leather processing, boilproof adhesives |
| Polyester | Jewelry, fabrics, boat hulls, upholstery fabrics |
| Silicone | Adhesives, electric insulation, gaskets, surgical membranes, replacement body parts |
| Polyurethane | Switch plates, mattresses, pillows, insulation, adhesives, shoe uppers, material used to soak up oil spills on seawater |
| Urethane | Pesticides, fungicides, biomedical research |

heated, the mixture slowly thickens. As it cools, Bakelite® is formed. Bakelite® is used to make telephones, camera bodies, and handles for cooking pots and pans.

## activity PLASTICS

Make a list of 10 items in your home that are made of plastic. Use Table 13–2 to determine if each plastic is a thermoplastic or a thermosetting plastic. Were most of the plastics thermoplastics? Why do you think these items were made of plastic? What properties does each plastic have that make it suitable for that item? Of what natural substance could each item be made?

## making sure

5. ABS is used to make football helmets. What properties must this plastic have to be suitable for this use?
6. What properties must a plastic have if it is to be used for making ropes?
7. What is the difference between thermoplastics and thermosetting plastics?
8. Why is polypropylene unsuitable for use as handles for pots and pans?
9. What is a polymer?

## 13:5 Synthetic Fibers

Of what are synthetic fibers made?

**Synthetic fibers** are polymers. Molecules of polymers have long chains of carbon atoms. Most clothes manufactured today contain some synthetic fibers. These clothes are more wrinkle resistant than clothes made from natural fibers. Synthetic fibers are also more resistant to wear.

List four examples of synthetic fibers.

Synthetic fibers are made from petroleum products. Rayon, nylon, Acrilan®, polyester, and Orlon® are common synthetic fibers.

a b

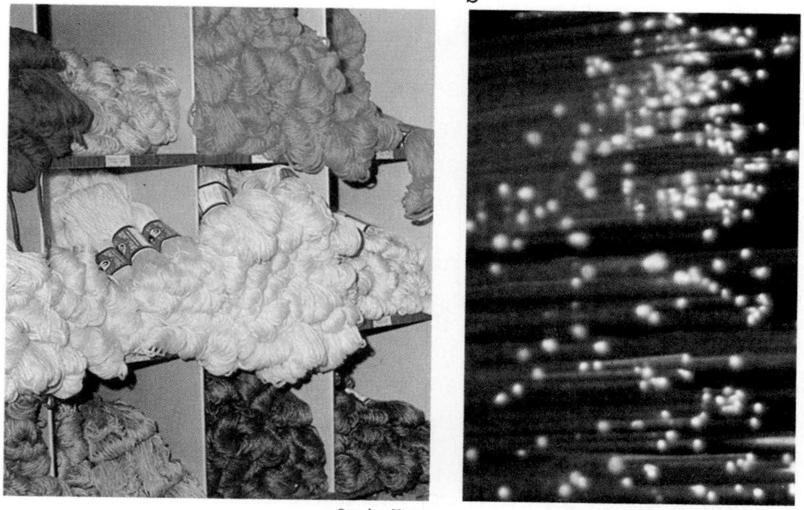

*Stanley Kayne* *E. I. DuPont de Nemours & Co.*

FIGURE 13-4. Synthetic fibers range from yarns used to make clothes (a) to fibers used to carry light (b).

# activity

## SYNTHETIC FIBERS

**Objective:** To determine the properties of synthetic fibers and contrast these with the properties of natural fibers.

### Materials

6 beakers, 250 mL
hair dryer
1 laundry marker
1 roll paper towels
chlorine bleach
water
watch or clock

fabric samples, red (15 cm x 15 cm)
- nylon
- polyester
- acrylic
- cotton
- wool
- cotton-polyester blend

FIGURE 13-5.

### Data and Observations

| Fabric sample | Drying time (min) | Wrinkles | Ravels | Tears | Bleach affects |
|---|---|---|---|---|---|
| | | | | | |

### Procedure

1. Using the laundry marker, label each sample with the fabric type.
2. Soak the nylon sample in water for 3 minutes. Remove this sample and place it on a paper towel.
3. Dry the sample with the hair dryer. Record the time it takes to dry.
4. Take the nylon sample and wad it into a ball. Hold the ball for 1 minute and then open the sample. Record the appearance of the sample.
5. Try to remove 1 thread from the side of the nylon sample. Record whether or not it ravels easily. Also record the appearance of the sample after the thread is removed.
6. Try to tear the nylon sample. Record the results.
7. Place the nylon sample in a beaker and cover it with chlorine bleach. **CAUTION:** Bleach is a strong base. Do not spill on skin or clothes. Rinse all spills with water. Let the beaker stand overnight.
8. Repeat Steps 2 through 7 with the other fabric samples.
9. The next day observe the bleached fabric samples and record your observations.

### Conclusions and Questions

1. Which of the samples are synthetic? Which are natural?
2. What are the differences between the properties of synthetic and natural fibers?
3. What do you think are the advantages of blended fibers over pure fibers?

## 13:6 Soap and Detergent

What is soap?

**Soap** is a long chain of carbon atoms. Hydrogen atoms are bonded to each carbon atom. A metal, either sodium or potassium, is bonded to one end of the chain. The organic part of soap comes from animal fat. The metal part comes from a strong base. Sodium soap is hard and is made into cakes and bars. Potassium soap is soft or liquid.

Soap is a good cleaning agent because the metal end of the soap dissolves in water. The carbon end of the soap dissolves in grease or oil. Since grease does not dissolve in water, soap is used to dissolve grease and wash it away. However, soaps are not effective cleaning agents if minerals are present in the water. The mineral ions attach to the soap and form precipitates. These precipitates are seen as soap scum.

How is a detergent different from a soap?

A **detergent** is a synthetic soap. Detergents are hydrocarbon chains that break particles of grease or oil into smaller particles. The smaller particles are more easily washed away by water. A detergent is an effective cleaning agent because it makes water "wetter." That is, a detergent reduces the attraction between water molecules. Thus, water can penetrate fabrics and dirt more easily. Detergents are not affected by minerals in the water. Thus, they do not leave a soaplike scum.

a

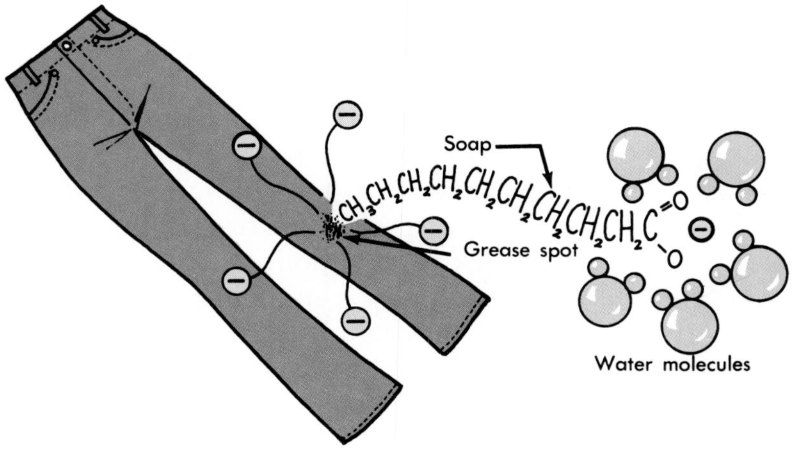


FIGURE 13–6. The carbon end of soap can dissolve grease and carry it away (a). If minerals are present, they combine with the metal end of the soap and form a precipitate (b).

b

*Kevin Fitzsimons*

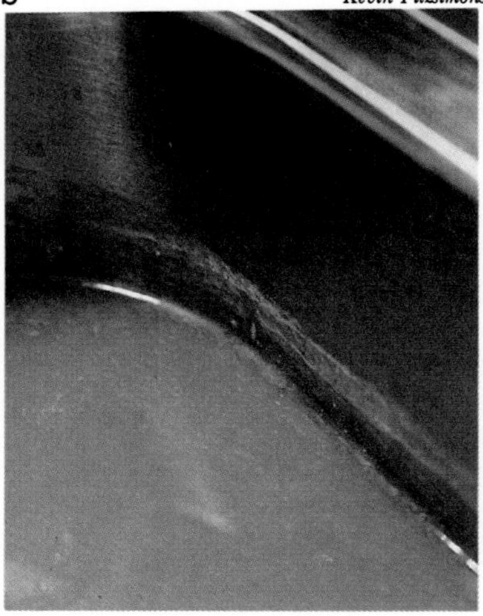

FIGURE 13-7. In some places, seawater is distilled into pure water for drinking and agriculture.

U.S. Dept of the Interior

## 13:7 Water Purification

What is distillation and how is it used?

Pure water can be obtained from the process of **distillation.** The water obtained is distilled water. The process is similar to fractional distillation except there is only one fraction. In distillation, water is heated and changed to a gas. Boiling the water kills most of the bacteria present. Soil particles and dissolved minerals remain in the container. Water vapor passes through a pipe or tube and is cooled. As the water vapor cools, it changes state to pure liquid water.

Distilled water is used in the laboratory, home, and some industries. Chemists use distilled water to prepare solutions. The solutions do not contain any minerals that might affect the reaction.

Distillation can be used to purify seawater. Salts, especially sodium chloride, make seawater unfit for drinking and for use in irrigating crops. Distillation removes the sodium chloride from the seawater. This process is very expensive on a large scale.

Why may water from natural surroundings be unsuitable for drinking?

Water from your natural surroundings is seldom safe to drink. It often contains pollutants. Water from lakes and rivers usually contains suspended solids. It may also contain dissolved minerals, dust, particles of plant and animal material, and bacteria.

Communities must purify water from lakes and rivers to make it safe to drink. This process may occur in many steps. For example, aluminum sulfate, $Al_2(SO_4)_3$, may be added to water to remove suspended solids. Aluminum sulfate reacts with water to form aluminum hydroxide, $Al(OH)_3$, a sticky, jellylike substance. Aluminum hydroxide traps fine sediments as it settles to the bottom of the water. This process is called **settling**. Aluminum hydroxide also traps many bacteria, carrying them along as it sinks.

How is water purified for drinking?

Sediment may be removed from water by filtering. Water may be filtered by passing it through layers of sand, gravel, and charcoal inside large tanks. Some water filtering tanks are larger than your classroom. Fine sediment particles are trapped by the sand and gravel, thereby increasing the water's purity. Charcoal absorbs any vapors and odors.

Why is chlorine added to drinking water?

In many cities, chlorine is added to drinking water to kill harmful bacteria. This process is called chlorination. The amount of chlorine added is carefully controlled in order to kill bacteria while not harming people.

Why is wastewater sent through a sewage treatment plant?

To prevent water pollution, wastewater from homes and industries is treated before it is released into rivers and lakes. In a sewage treatment plant, some types of bacteria aid in purifying the water.

a

*Lawrence Migdale*

FIGURE 13–8. Wastewater from cities and industries often is treated in plants similar to this one before it is released into rivers and lakes (a). Bacteria that break down compounds into simpler substances are used in sewage and water treatment (b).

b

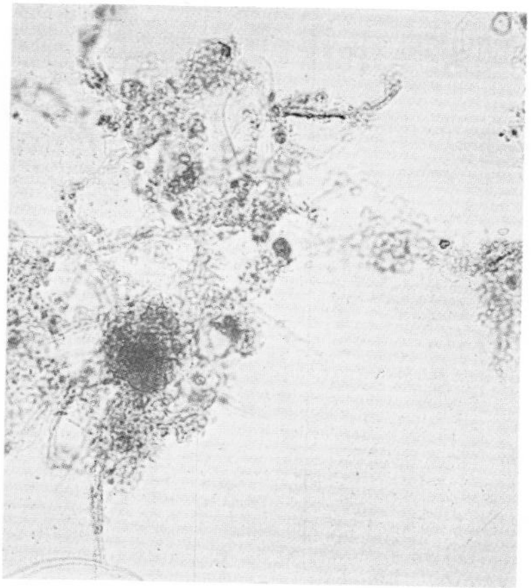

What is a biodegradable substance?

These bacteria act on compounds that are hard to remove. They break these compounds down into simpler substances that can be removed more easily. Substances broken down by bacteria are **biodegradable** (bi oh dih GRAYD uh buhl). Some detergent packages state that the contents are biodegradable. These detergents contain chemicals that can be broken down into harmless substances.

Why is aeration important?

If you went to a sewage treatment plant, you might see water spraying into the air. During this process, called **aeration** (er AY shun), oxygen in the air dissolves in the water. Adding oxygen to the water speeds up the breakdown of biodegradable materials by bacteria.

*Brian Parker/Tom Stack & Associates*

FIGURE 13-9. Aeration adds oxygen to water at a sewage treatment plant. The added oxygen helps bacteria break down wastes.

FIGURE 13-10.

## activity PRECIPITATION

**(1)** Moisten a piece of filter paper with water and put it in a supported funnel. **(2)** Dissolve 20 g aluminum chloride ($AlCl_3$) in 100 mL water in a beaker. **(3)** Slowly add 10 mL dilute sodium hydroxide ($NaOH$) solution. **(4)** Pour the solution through the filter into another beaker. What is the material in the filter? Write a chemical equation for the reaction that took place.

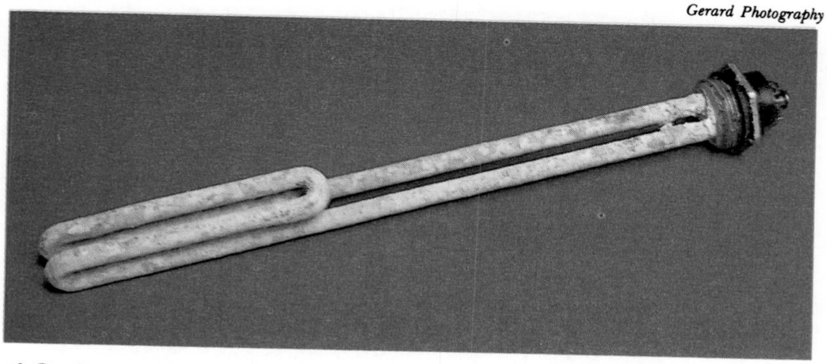

Gerard Photography

FIGURE 13-11. Hard water can ruin the element in an electric hot water heater.

## 13:8 Hard Water

Have you ever seen a ring around the inside of your bathtub? The ring is the product of a chemical reaction between soap and bath water. When soap dissolves in bath water, it reacts with certain minerals in the water to form a precipitate. This precipitate is the ring that you see around the tub. This same reaction also can occur in a clothes washer, and may leave a deposit inside a water heater and on cooking utensils.

What minerals cause water to be hard?

Calcium, magnesium, and iron are minerals that produce a precipitate in soapy water. They also cause mineral deposits in water heaters, tea kettles, and steam irons. Water having one or more of these mineral elements dissolved in it is called hard water. Carbonate compounds of the mineral elements may be left as deposits when hard water is heated. For example, boiling of water containing calcium hydrogen carbonate produces a precipitate of calcium carbonate that settles out of the water.

$$Ca(HCO_3)_2(aq) \xrightarrow{heat} H_2O + CO_2\,(aq) + CaCO_3\,(c)$$

calcium hydrogen carbonate → water + carbon dioxide + calcium carbonate

What is soft water?

Water that is free of calcium, magnesium, and iron is soft water. Soft water, because it lacks these minerals, does not leave deposits. Hard water may be softened through the use of chemicals that remove the minerals from the water. Washing soda has been used for many years to remove minerals from wash water. Washing soda is sodium carbonate, $Na_2CO_3$. It

How does washing soda soften hard water?

FIGURE 13–12. Sodium zeolite is used in many water softeners to remove mineral ions from the water. Eventually, the zeolite becomes saturated with mineral ions and must be restored by soaking in a sodium chloride solution.

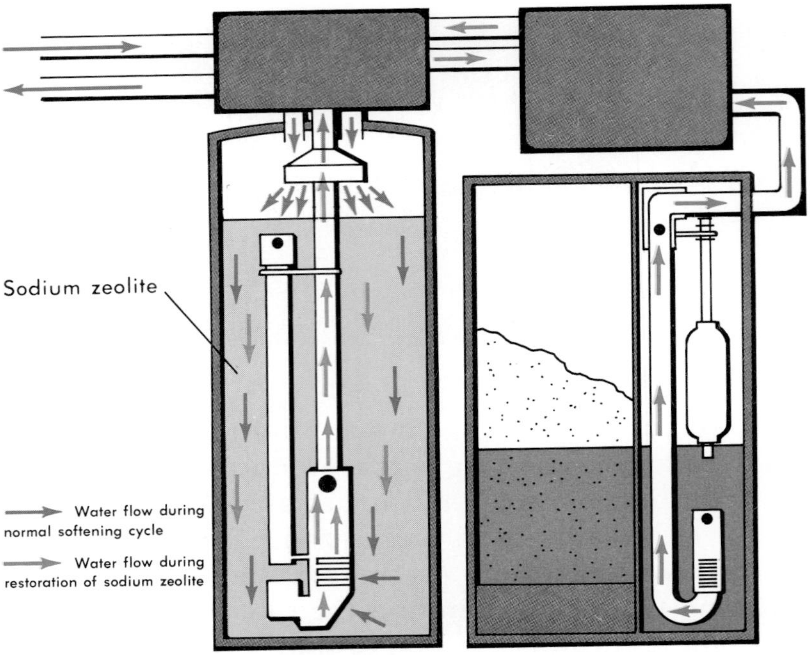


is added to the water before adding soap. Washing soda reacts with calcium, magnesium, and iron, forming precipitates that remove these minerals from hard water, thereby softening it.

How is water softened with zeolite?

Another method used to soften water involves the displacement of iron, magnesium, and calcium ions by sodium ions. The chemical used in most water softeners is **sodium zeolite** (ZEE uh lite). This chemical looks like little red beads. When hard water passes over sodium zeolite, calcium in the water is absorbed and replaced by sodium. For each calcium ion removed from the water, two sodium ions are added. The water containing sodium is soft.

When zeolite becomes saturated with calcium, the ion exchange no longer occurs. The zeolite must be restored. To restore the zeolite, it is soaked for a period of time in a concentrated sodium chloride solution. Sodium ions from the solution replace calcium ions in the zeolite. Once restored, the zeolite can be used to soften more hard water.

## making sure

**10.** List three advantages of soft water over hard water.

## main ideas

1. Technology is the application of science for practical purposes. 13:1
2. Hydrocarbons contain only the elements hydrogen and carbon. 13:2
3. Petroleum is a mixture of hydrocarbons. It can be separated by fractional distillation. 13:3
4. Plastics and synthetic fibers are polymers made from petroleum compounds. 13:4, 13:5
5. Soap and detergents dissolve grease and oil. 13:6
6. Distillation is used to separate mixtures by differences in boiling points. 13:7
7. Water is purified using physical and chemical processes. 13:7
8. Biodegradable substances can be broken down by bacteria into simpler substances. 13:7
9. Water that contains ions of calcium, magnesium, or iron is called hard water. Water free of these ions is called soft water. 13:8

## vocabulary

*Define each of the following words or terms.*

aération
biodegradable
detergent
distillation
fractional distillation
hydrocarbons
petroleum
plastics
settling
soap
sodium zeolite
synthetic fibers
thermoplastic
thermosetting plastic

## study questions

**DO NOT WRITE IN THIS BOOK.**

**A. True or False**

*Determine whether each of the following sentences is true or false. If the sentence is false, rewrite it to make it true.*

1. Methane contains water and carbon.
2. Water can be purified by distillation.
3. Aeration increases the chlorine content of water.
4. Distillation involves two chemical changes.

5. Filtration kills harmful bacteria.
6. Aluminum hydroxide, $Al(OH)_3$, is used to purify water.
7. Aeration speeds up the breakdown of biodegradable materials by bacteria.
8. Adding washing soda is one way to soften hard water.
9. Few compounds contain carbon.
10. Water containing calcium carbonate, $CaCO_3$, can be softened by boiling.

**B. Multiple Choice**

*Choose the word or phrase that completes correctly each of the following sentences.*

1. The organic part of soap comes from (*carbon dioxide, animal fat, petroleum*).
2. Soap contains (*calcium, magnesium, carbon*).
3. Soaps containing (*calcium, potassium, sodium*) are soft or liquid soaps.
4. (*Hydrogen, Oxygen, Carbon*) atoms bond to form long chains and rings.
5. Petroleum is a (*mixture, compound, ion*).
6. Polymers contain (*one, a few, many*) atoms.
7. A synthetic fiber is a (*polymer, natural substance, mixture*).
8. Aeration is the process of adding (*hydrogen, oxygen, chlorine*) to water.
9. Hard water contains ions of (*calcium, copper, gold*).
10. (*Wool, Nylon, Silk*) is a synthetic fiber.

**C. Completion**

*Complete each of the following sentences with a word or phrase that will make the sentence correct.*

1. Petroleum is separated into compounds by ______.
2. ______ and ______ are the two main types of plastics.
3. Two fuels obtained from petroleum are ______ and ______.
4. Synthetic fibers and plastics are both composed of large molecules called ______.
5. Fractional distillation is a(n) ______ change.
6. A chemical used to remove mineral ions from water is called a water ______.
7. ______ and ______ are used to dissolve grease and oil.

8. In softening water with sodium zeolite, ______ are exchanged.
9. ______ is used to kill bacteria in water.
10. Detergents clean in either ______ or ______ water.

**D. How and Why**

1. How is water purified for drinking?
2. How is hard water softened?
3. Explain how soap is made.
4. How is gasoline obtained from petroleum?
5. Why is a synthetic detergent a good cleaner?

## challenges

1. Obtain some sodium zeolite from a hardware store. Construct a water softener with the zeolite that can be attached to a water faucet.
2. Chemicals are important in gardening and farming. Prepare a library report on the use of chemicals to grow plants.
3. Prepare a report on the use of petroleum to make useful products.
4. Do library research on the storage of chemical wastes, and prepare a report for your class.

## interesting reading

Gunston, Bill, *Coal.* New York: Franklin Watts, 1981.
Olney, Ross R., *Offshore! Oil and Gas Platforms in the Ocean.* New York: Dutton, 1981.

*Burning fuel provides the energy used to heat our homes. Because of a limited supply of fuel, energy should be conserved. The red portions of this thermogram show where heat is escaping from these houses. What can be done to prevent heat loss and conserve energy?*

*Vascam Thermogram by Daedalus Enterprises, Inc.*

# Energy
# unit 4

*Without heat from the sun, life could not exist. Heat from within the earth explodes onto the surface during this eruption of the Hawaiian volcano Mauna Loa. Humans use heat for many things. It is used to cook food, distill water, and obtain metals from ores. Why do some objects feel cold while others feel warm? How does heat travel from place to place? What is insulation?*

Dan McCoy/Rainbow

# Heat

chapter 14

## 14:1 Energy

GOAL: You will learn the relationship between heat and energy and some uses of heat.

**Energy** is defined as the capacity to do work. Energy is either potential or kinetic. Potential energy is the energy of position. Suppose you lift a book off the floor and lay it on top of your desk. The book gains potential energy due to its change in position. What happens if the book falls off the desk? During its fall the potential energy changes to kinetic energy. Kinetic energy is the energy of motion. Just before the book hits the floor, all of the potential energy it had gained has changed to kinetic energy. What happens to the kinetic energy? Some of the kinetic energy becomes the sound you hear when the book hits the floor. The rest becomes heat.

What is energy?

When something is moved, work is done. Work is equal to force multiplied by distance. Under ideal conditions, the energy used to do work is equal to the work that is done. For this reason, work is a measure of energy. Energy is measured in the same unit as work, the **joule** (JEWL), J.

What is the unit for energy?

## making sure

1. How are energy and work related?
2. What is the unit of energy?
3. How would you calculate a value for work given a force and distance?
4. Does a ball on the edge of a table have potential or kinetic energy?

## 14:2 Temperature and Heat

What is temperature?

All matter is composed of particles that are in constant motion. Even the particles of a solid are in constant motion. These particles have kinetic energy. The average kinetic energy of particles is measured as **temperature**. If energy is added to a substance, the particles in the substance move at a faster rate. Thus, the temperature of the substance would be increased.

What is heat?

How is mass related to the amount of heat in an object?

**Heat** is the total internal energy of a substance. Heat depends upon the mass of the substance and its temperature. Imagine a cup of hot chocolate and a pot of hot chocolate. If both liquids are at the same temperature, which liquid has more heat? The mass of hot chocolate is greater in the pot than in the cup. There are more particles in the pot than in the cup. Therefore, the total internal energy of the hot chocolate in the pot is greater than that in the cup. The pot of hot chocolate has more heat.

Heat and temperature are related. When the internal energy of a substance is increased, its particles move faster. This increase in kinetic energy is shown by a rise in temperature. As a substance's kinetic energy is decreased, its particles move more slowly. The temperature of the substance falls.

## making sure

5. How are temperature and heat related?
6. Which has more energy, an ice cube or the ice in a frozen pond? Why?

## 14:3 Effects of Heat and Matter

Most substances expand when heated and contract when cooled. This expansion and contraction causes changes in volume. Expansion and contraction can be understood if you recall that all matter is composed of particles in motion.

What effect does heat energy have on the molecules of a substance?

In solids, the particles in a substance vibrate around fixed positions. When a solid absorbs heat energy, its particles vibrate more rapidly. The increased vibration causes the substance to expand. An iron ball and ring can be used to show expansion due to heating. When the ball and ring are at room temperature, the ball slips through the ring. After the ball is heated, it will not go through the ring.

How does the loss or gain of heat affect the size of an object?

Solids expand at different rates. Engineers must consider these expansion rates when designing a structure. Concrete is used as a road surface over many steel bridges. If the concrete does not expand and contract at the same rate as steel, some allowance must be made in the design. Otherwise, the road will crack and split.

A practical application of the different rates of expansion is the bimetallic (bi muh TAL ihk) strip. A bimetallic strip consists of iron and brass bonded together. When the strip is heated, the brass layer expands more than the iron layer. The strip curves

FIGURE 14-1. Concrete driveways are often made with spaces or strips to allow expansion (a). Repeated expansion and contraction of street pavement can cause potholes (b).

a

Kevin Fitzsimons

b

Kevin Fitzsimons

Hickson-Bender Photography

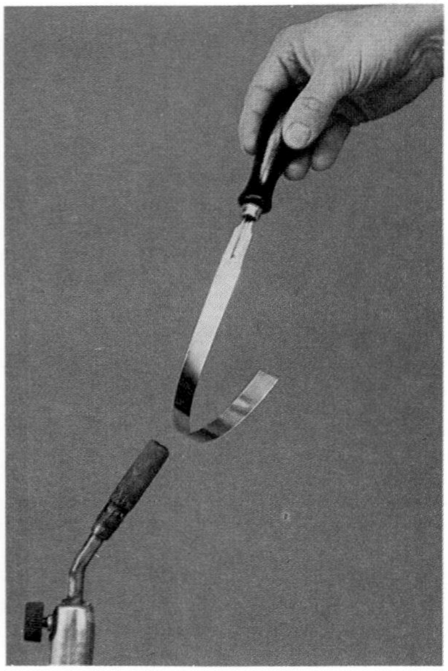

FIGURE 14-2. A bimetallic strip bends when heated because one metal expands more than the other.

How does a thermostat work?

with the brass on the outside of the curve. Some home furnace controls contain a bimetallic strip that turns the furnace on and off automatically.

Particles of fluids (liquids and gases) move freely. As a fluid absorbs heat, the particles hit each other with more force and more often. The harder collisions cause the particles to move farther apart. Thus, the volume of the fluid increases. In general, fluids expand at greater rates than do solids.

The expansion properties of mercury are used in making thermometers. The scale of a thermometer is designed to give an accurate temperature reading based on how much the mercury in the column has expanded. The red liquid you see in many outdoor thermometers is a tinted alcohol solution. Alcohol thermometers work the same way as mercury thermometers.

Modern home thermostats also contain mercury. A small amount of mercury is sealed in a glass tube. The tube is balanced much like a seesaw. When the temperature in the room rises, the mercury expands. The tube moves like a seesaw as one end becomes heavier than the other. An electric connection is broken and the furnace shuts off. If the room becomes too cold, the mercury in the tube contracts. The tube moves in the other direction because the other end is now heavier. The electric connection is restored and the furnace turns on.

FIGURE 14-3.

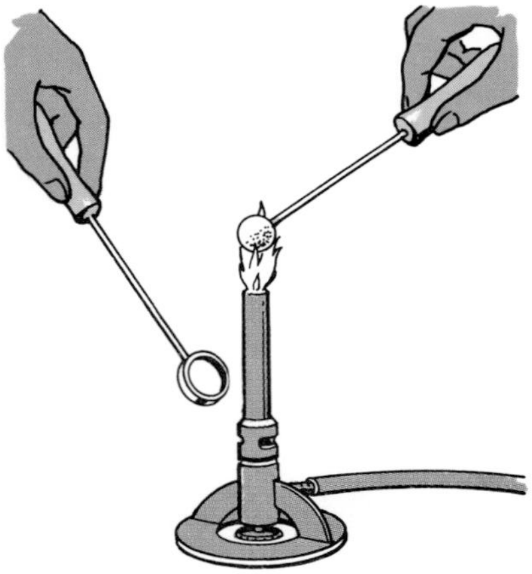

## activity

### HEAT AND METALS

**(1)** Obtain an iron ball and ring, and a bimetallic strip. **(2)** Try to pass the ball through the ring. What happens? **(3)** Heat the ball in a flame for 30 s. Try to pass the ball through the ring again. What happens? What effect does heat have on the metal? **(4)** Observe the bimetallic strip and record which side of the strip is toward the desk. Heat this side of the strip over a flame. What happens? **(5)** Let the strip cool, and then heat the other side. What happens?

## 14:4 Heat and Changes of State

How does a substance keep its shape? There must be a force or forces that hold the particles of matter together. What happens to these forces as heat energy is absorbed by a substance?

Suppose you measure the temperature of ice in a beaker and find it to be −10°C. Next you gently heat the ice, recording the temperature every 30 s until all the ice is melted. You graph the changes in temperature, Figure 14–4. What do you observe? The temperature rises to 0°C and then remains constant until all the ice has melted. What happens to the energy that is added to the ice? The energy is used to do work on the water molecules frozen in the ice. The work overcomes the forces holding the ice particles together as a solid. The energy needed to change a solid to a liquid is the **heat of fusion** (FYEW zhun). It takes 334 J of energy to melt one gram of ice.

Define heat of fusion and heat of vaporization.

What happens when water changes to a gas? As water is heated, the temperature rises steadily until it reaches 100°C. The temperature remains constant until all the water is changed to water vapor. This process takes more energy than melting. The energy needed to change a liquid to a gas is the **heat of vaporization** (vay pruh ZAY shun). At 100°C, 1 g of water absorbs 2260 J of energy to become a gas.

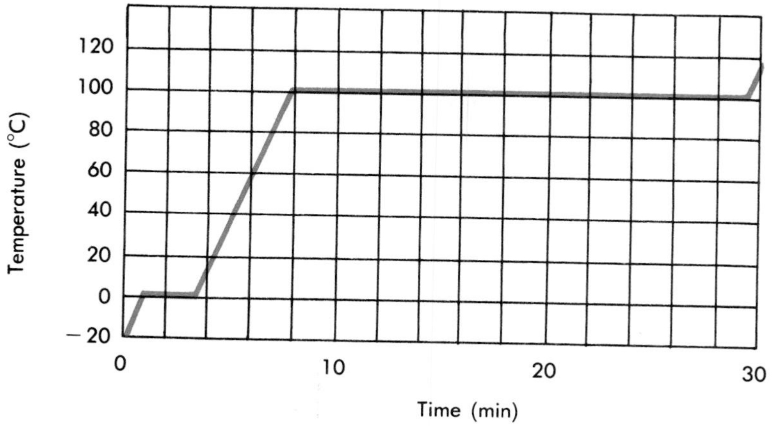


FIGURE 14-4. When heated at a constant rate, the temperature of ice rises steadily until it reaches the melting point. Heat is absorbed until all of the ice is melted. Then, the temperature rises steadily again. At the boiling point, the heat is absorbed until all of the water becomes a gas.

What is the connection between heat and change in state?

When a solid changes to a liquid, it gains energy to overcome the forces of attraction between its particles. As a gas condenses to a liquid, heat is released. Heat is also released when a liquid changes to a solid.

### activity — HEAT AND CHANGES IN STATE

**(1)** Fill a beaker one-half full of ice. Record the temperature of the ice. **(2)** Gently heat the beaker of ice on a hot plate. **(3)** Record the temperature of the icewater every 2 min until the water boils. **(4)** Draw a graph of temperature versus time. Why does the temperature rise at first and then remain constant? What does the graph look like at 100°C when the water boils? What process occurs at 0°C? at 100°C? How does your graph compare with Figure 14–4?

### making sure

**7.** An ice cube is placed in a glass of tap water.
  (a) What happens to the temperature of the water?
  (b) Does the ice cube release or absorb heat? Explain.

**8.** Why does ice melt faster in the sun than in the shade?

**9.** Why does the temperature of a substance remain the same during a change of state if heat is being added?

**10.** Which are stronger—the forces holding water particles together in a liquid or in a solid?

## 14:5 Specific Heat

Some substances can absorb heat better than others. If you heat a metal pan containing water on a stove, the temperature of the pan increases at a faster rate than the water temperature. It takes more

Tim Courlas

FIGURE 14-5. Cooking utensils are made from metals because they are good conductors and have low specific heats.

energy to raise the temperature of water one degree than it does for the metal. Therefore, the pan heats faster than the water.

Define specific heat.

**Specific heat** ($C_p$) is the amount of heat needed to raise the temperature of 1 g of a substance 1°C. The unit used to express specific heat is the joule per gram Celsius degree, J/g·C°. Different substances have different specific heats. Water has a specific heat of 4.18 J/g·C°. This fact explains why water is used to cool car engines. Water can absorb a large amount of heat as its temperature rises.

***Table 14–1.***
Specific Heat (J/g·C°)

| | | | |
|---|---|---|---|
| Alcohol (ethanol) | 2.45 | Ice | 2.06 |
| Aluminum | 0.903 | Iron | 0.450 |
| Brass | 0.376 | Silver | 0.235 |
| Carbon | 0.710 | Steam | 2.02 |
| Copper | 0.385 | Water | 4.18 |
| Glass | 0.664 | Zinc | 0.388 |

## activity SPECIFIC HEAT

(1) Obtain two empty soup cans. (2) Place a thermometer in each can. (3) Fill one can ⅔ full of water. Fill the second can ⅔ full of sand. (4) Place both cans in bright sunlight or under a lamp. (5) Record the temperature of each substance every 2 min for 15 min. In which can did the temperature increase faster? Which substance, sand or water, has the higher specific heat?

## making sure

**11.** Which metal has the higher specific heat, aluminum or copper? Which metal heats up faster?

**12.** A piece of iron and a piece of copper with equal masses are heated to 150°C. Both are placed on a block of ice. Which piece of metal will melt more ice? Explain.

## 14:6 Measuring Heat Changes

How is the amount of heat calculated?

The amount of heat absorbed or released by a substance can be measured. When a substance absorbs heat energy, its temperature rises. When a substance releases heat energy, its temperature falls. To calculate the heat absorbed or released, you must know how much the temperature changes. You must also know the mass of the substance and its specific heat. Heat absorbed or released can be calculated using the equation:

Heat change = change in temperature × mass × specific heat

$$\Delta H = \Delta t \times m \times C_p$$

△ means change.

***Example***

One hundred grams of water is cooled from 50°C to 40°C. How much heat is released by the water?

Solution

*Step 1:* Write the equation for the change in heat.

$$\Delta H = \Delta t \times m \times C_p$$

*Step 2:* Calculate the change in temperature, $\Delta t$.

$$\Delta t = t_2 - t_1$$
$$\Delta t = 50°C - 40°C = 10°C$$

*Step 3:* Substitute the values given in the problem.

$$\Delta H = 10°C \times 100\ g \times 4.18\ J/g \times C°$$

*Step 4:* Solve the equation.

$$\Delta H = 10°C \times 100\ g \times 4.18\ J/g \times C° = 4180\ J$$

Explain the use of a calorimeter.

A **calorimeter** (kal uh RIHM ut ur) is a device used to measure heat changes (Figure 14–6). In the calorimeter, the substance being tested is burned. When the substance burns, it releases heat. This heat is absorbed by a known mass of water in the outer chamber. The change in the temperature of the water can be used to calculate the heat released by the substance. The amount of heat absorbed by the water is equal to the amount of heat released by the substance.

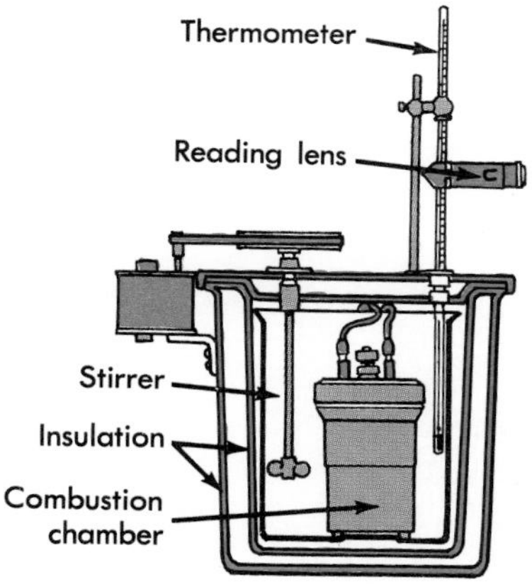


FIGURE 14-6. Calorimeters are used to measure the energy value of foods, coal, wood, trash, gasoline, and many other materials.

## activity CALORIMETER

**(1)** Obtain a large can and a small can that fits inside the larger can. Fill the bottom of the larger can with vermiculite. **(2)** Place the smaller can inside the larger one and fill the space between the cans with more vermiculite. **(3)** Cut a cardboard cover for the cans. Make two small holes in the center of the cardboard cover. **(4)** Insert a wooden rod through one hole and a thermometer through the other hole. **(5)** Add 200 mL water to the inner can and record its temperature. **(6)** Heat a thick piece of aluminum in boiling water for 5 minutes. **(7)** Add the aluminum to the water in the calorimeter. Replace the lid. **(8)** Stir the water and record the temperature every 2 minutes for 10 minutes. What happened to the temperature of the water? What happened to the temperature of the metal? How do you know? Calculate the joules of heat absorbed by the water. How do you determine the number of joules of heat released by the aluminum?

FIGURE 14-7.

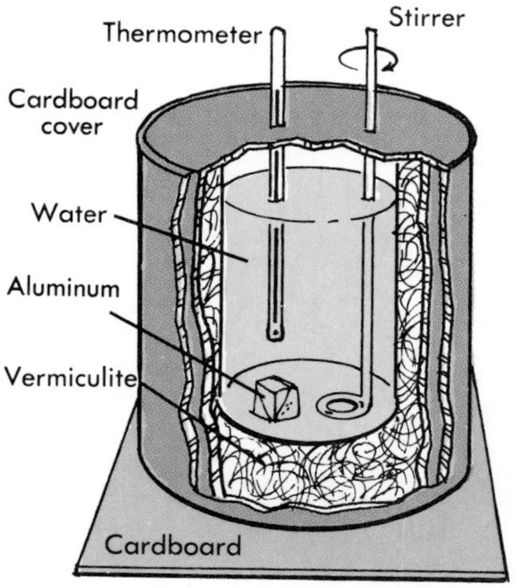

## making sure

**13.** How much heat is absorbed by 125 g of water when it is heated from 10°C to 75°C?

**14.** A 40-g bar of silver is heated from 15°C to 65°C, then cooled in water to 20°C. How much heat is absorbed by the water?

## 14:7 Heat Transfer

Heat is transferred from one place or object to another in three ways: conduction, convection (kun VEK shun), or radiation. In everyday situations, any two or three of these methods may be operating at the same time. If you leave a metal poker in a hot fire, the poker becomes too hot to touch even though the handle is not in the fire. Heat energy was conducted from one end of the poker to the other end. **Conduction** is the transfer of heat energy through collisions that occur between particles. Particles of the poker in the fire absorb heat energy. As a result, the kinetic energy of the particles increases and they vibrate faster. When these particles hit other particles, some of the heat energy is transferred. Heat can be conducted through solids, liquids, or gases.

Name the three ways in which heat is transferred.

In conduction, how does heat pass through a substance?

Solids are the best conductors of heat. Metals are the best solid heat conductors. Wood, some plastics, rubber, and cork are poor heat conductors. Because plastics are poor heat conductors, they are used as handles on cooking utensils.

How is heat moved through a liquid or gas?

Liquids and gases transfer heat rapidly by convection. **Convection** is the transfer of heat by the movement of large numbers of particles from one place to another. Convection can involve the movement of particles over large distances. When a pan of water is heated on a stove, the density of the water on the bottom of the pan decreases. The molecules absorb heat energy and move farther apart. The warmer water is pushed upward and replaced by the cooler surface water. This motion of the water is called a convection current. Winds and

Explain how a convection current is formed.

FIGURE 14-8. Heat is transferred through water in a pan by convection.

ocean currents, such as the Gulf Stream, are examples of convection currents on a large scale. Weather is generally a result of convection currents in the atmosphere that move over Earth.

Both conduction and convection transfer heat energy through matter. Heat energy from the sun powers the convection currents of air and water on the earth and provides energy for plants. How does the sun's energy reach Earth through "empty" space?

How does energy travel through space?

**Radiation** is the transfer of energy such as heat without the presence of matter. Energy from the sun radiates to Earth in the form of electromagnetic (ih lec troh mag NET ihk) waves. Electromagnetic waves consist of various types of radiation including heat and visible light.

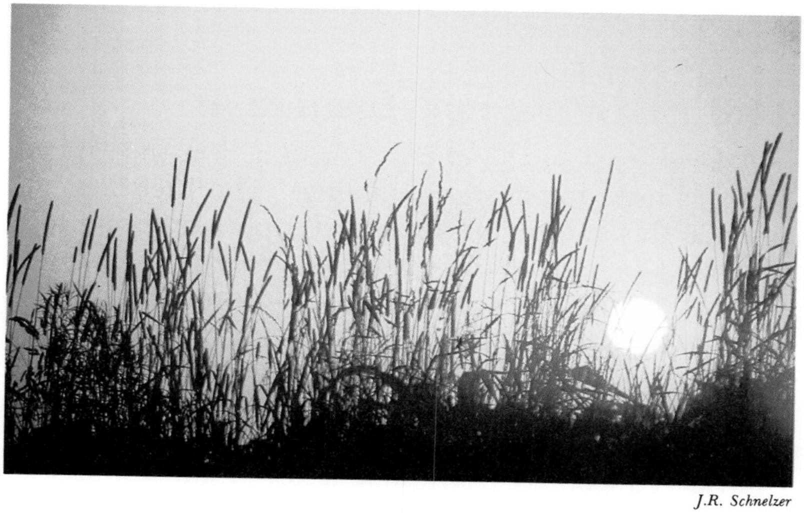

J.R. Schnelzer

FIGURE 14-9. Heat from the sun reaches Earth through radiation.

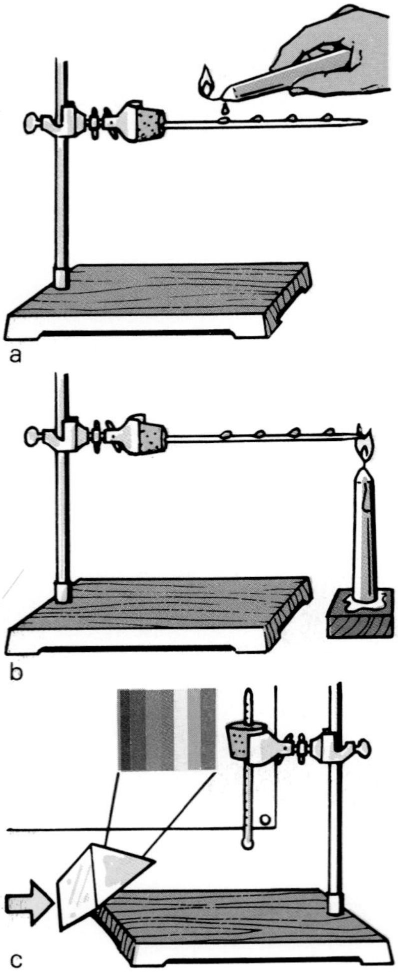

FIGURE 14-10.

## activity HEAT TRANSFER

(1) Push one end of a metal knitting needle into a cork. Clamp the cork to a ring stand. (2) Light a candle and allow 4 small pieces of wax to drip about 3 cm apart on the knitting needle. See Figure 14–10a. (3) Place the lighted candle under the pointed end of the knitting needle. **CAUTION:** Be sure to keep your hair and clothes away from the flame. (4) Record the time it takes for all the wax to drip off the needle. Which method of heat transfer is demonstrated by this procedure? (5). Place a drop of glycerol on the tip of a glass rod 15 cm long. Using a towel to hold the rod, carefully insert it into a 1-hole stopper. Clamp the stopper to a ring stand. (6) Place 4 pieces of wax about 3 cm apart on the glass rod (see Step 2). (7) Use the lighted candle to heat the glass rod the same length of time you heated the needle. What happened to the wax? Explain. Compare the difference in heat transfer between the knitting needle and the glass rod. (8) Using a light source, produce a rainbow with a prism. (9) Using the procedure described in Step 5, insert the top of a thermometer into a 1-hole stopper and clamp it to a ring stand. (10) Position the thermometer to the right of the red band of color. Record the temperature. Wait 5 minutes. Record the temperature again. Explain any changes in recorded temperature. What type of heat transfer does this procedure illustrate? Explain.

## 14:8 Heating and Insulation

A large part of the energy consumed in the United States is used for heating buildings. The fuels that provide this energy are limited. People are trying to find ways to reduce the amount of energy used for heating. Insulation (ihn sul LAY shun) can help decrease the amount of energy used for heating.

What is insulation and how is it used?

**Insulation** is any substance that slows or controls the movement of heat energy. Most of the heat lost from buildings goes out through the roof. Heat loss can be reduced by using insulation. Some insulation

Image Workshop

FIGURE 14-11. Insulation in the hollow spaces of floors, ceilings, and outside walls greatly reduces heat loss.

consists of long glass fibers pushed close together. The glass fibers trap air between them. Trapped air prevents heat transfer by convection and conduction. Plastic foam is also used to prevent heat loss. Plastic foam contains tiny air bubbles. Air is a poor conductor of heat and the bubbles are so small that convection currents do not form. Plastic foam is used on the outside walls of buildings and in cups and picnic coolers. Heat loss by radiation can be reduced by using shiny metal foils. Aluminum and other shiny surfaces reflect heat. Light-colored surfaces also reflect heat. Metal foils are used on the surfaces of buildings between the interior walls and the exterior siding.

Name three kinds of insulation.

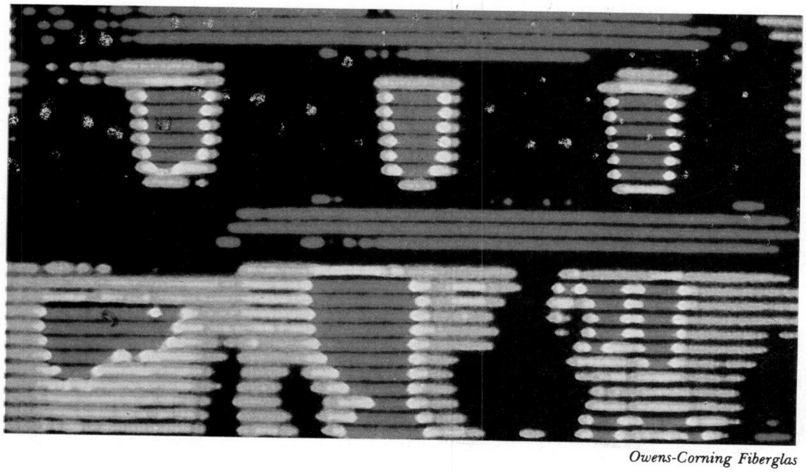

Owens-Corning Fiberglas

FIGURE 14-12. A house with little insulation loses large amounts of heat. The red areas represent maximum heat loss.

FIGURE 14-13. Metal foil is often used to help insulate new houses.

Russ Lappa

## activity INSULATION

**(1)** Obtain 4 small cans, 1 large can, and a bag of vermiculite. **(2)** Using tap water and a graduated cylinder, add 400 mL water to one can. Mark the 400-mL level. Use this water to determine and mark the 400-mL level in each can. Then pour the water into a sink. **(3)** Cover one small can with aluminum foil, shiny side toward the can. **(4)** Cover another small can with aluminum foil, shiny side out. **(5)** Leave the third small can uncovered. **(6)** Set up the last small can and the large can like a calorimeter (page 275). **(7)** Heat 2 L water to 100°C in a tea kettle on a hot plate. Use protective gloves to handle the teakettle. Pour hot water into each container to the 400-mL mark. Put a thermometer into each container and record the temperatures every 2 minutes for 20 minutes. Draw a graph of temperature versus time for each container. In which container did the water cool fastest? Slowest? How was heat transferred from the containers? Which container had the best insulation for this type of heat transfer? Why was one can left uncovered?

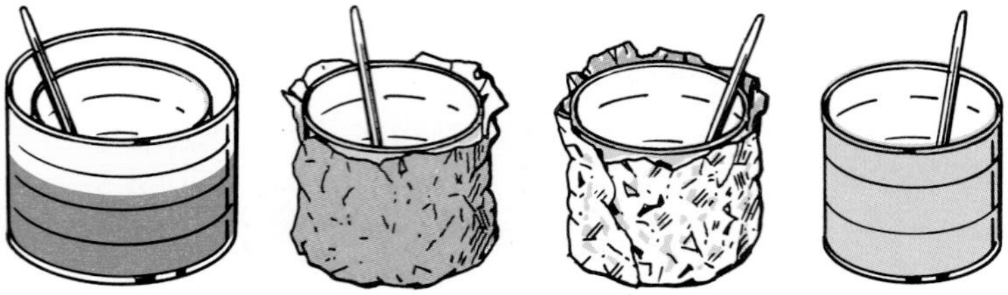

FIGURE 14-14.

## 14:9 Central Heating Systems

Most heating systems produce heat for an entire building at one place and then transfer the heat to the different rooms. There are two main types of central heating systems, direct and indirect. A direct heating system circulates warm air throughout a building. An indirect heating system circulates a hot fluid through pipes to radiators that release the heat. Both types of heating systems may use electricity, gas, oil, or coal as the source of energy.

A forced air heating system, used in many houses, is a direct heating system. This system has a furnace, pipes to carry the hot air to the rooms, registers, and cold air returns to carry the air back to the furnace. A fan helps to move the air to and from the furnace efficiently. This movement of air also helps to equalize the temperature within the rooms.

Steam heat is an indirect heating system. Many houses and buildings are heated by hot steam. This system contains a furnace, steam boiler, pipes, and radiators. Heat from the furnace is used to boil water in the boiler. Pipes carry the steam to the radiators where the heat is radiated into the rooms. Steam systems are efficient because steam contains more energy than does liquid water at 100°C.

How is a steam heating system different from a hot-water system?

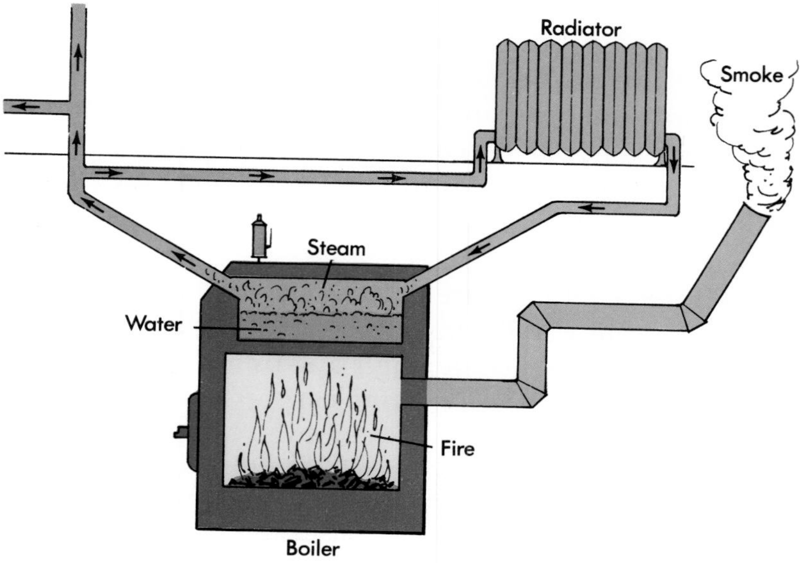


FIGURE 14-15. A steam heating system is an indirect heating system.

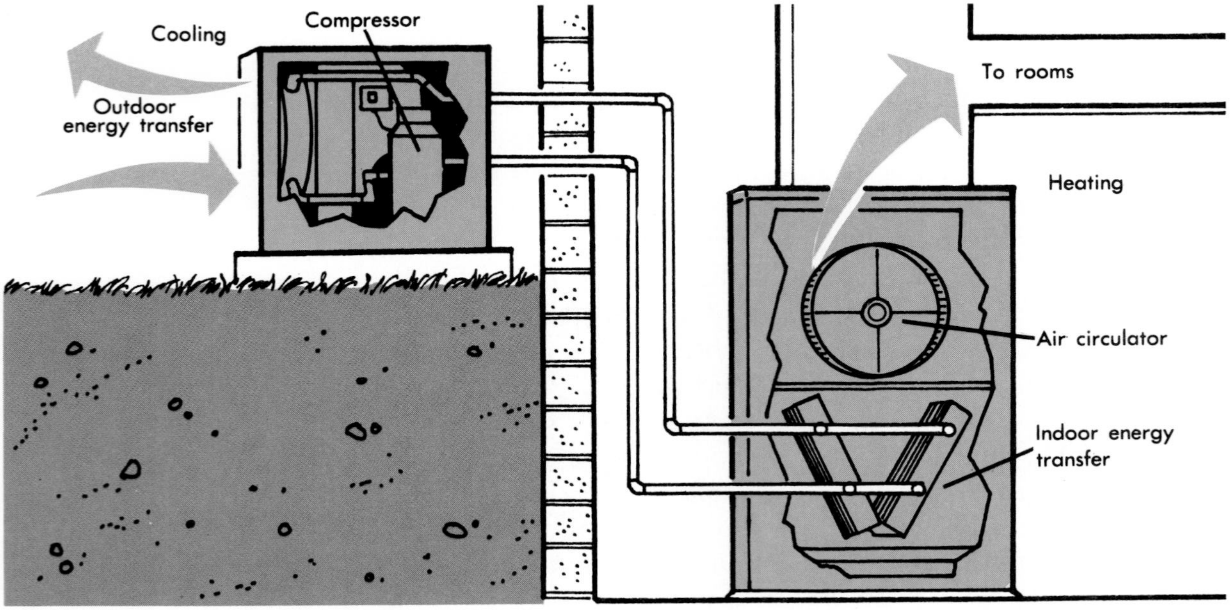


FIGURE 14-16. A heat pump transfers heat from one area to another. It can be used to heat or cool a house.

Explain how a heat pump works.

One heating system that does not require a furnace is the heat pump. The heat pump was invented in 1851 by Lord Kelvin. A heat pump system has a coil and compressor outside the building and a coil, fan, and pipes inside the building. A heat pump circulates a liquid in the coil outside the building. This liquid absorbs heat from the air or ground and changes to a gas. The gas passes through a compressor that increases the temperature and pressure of the gas. The hot gas passes into the building in the inside coil. The cool air around the inside coil cools and condenses the gas. As the gas condenses, heat is released into the air. The liquid is then moved to the outside coil and the cycle repeats.

Another heating system that does not require a furnace is electric heating. Electric heat is produced by passing electricity through a substance that resists its flow. Electric heating units can be placed in ceilings, floors, walls, or baseboards. Most portable room heaters and appliances like toasters are electric heating units.

Solar heating does not require a furnace or electricity. In a solar heating system, pipes carrying water are located in contact with a large black surface. The black surface absorbs the sun's radiation and transfers it to the water. The water is moved through pipes to a storage tank, usually in the basement, where the heat is radiated to the rest of the building. The collecting surface and the pipes are covered by clear glass to prevent heat loss. Some form of backup system is needed in areas where there are many cloudy days.

Describe one kind of solar heating system.

*Hank Morgan/Rainbow*

a

*© St. Petersburg Times & Evening Independent*

b

FIGURE 14–17. Solar panels (a) may be used to absorb heat for buildings (b).

## making sure

**15.** Which of the systems described in this section are direct heating systems? Which are indirect?

**16.** Many engineers consider a heat pump to be an inefficient method of heating. Why do you think the engineers say this? *Hint:* Electricity supplies energy for the compressor and pump.

**17.** The specific heat of water is high. Explain why this property makes water a good choice for use in heating systems.

## 14:10 Cooling Systems

Why does ice have a cooling effect?

An ice cube melts when you hold it in your hand. What is the heat source? Heat moves from your hand to the ice cube. Your hand feels cooler. To change ice to water, heat must be added. In general, to change a solid to a liquid or to change a liquid to a gas, heat must be added. This heat comes from the surroundings. **Refrigeration** is the process of removing heat energy from a substance. Refrigerators, air conditioners, and some heat pumps are mechanical devices used to remove heat.

Why is evaporation a cooling process?

Modern refrigeration is based on the cooling effect produced when a liquid changes into a gas. This change of state is called evaporation. When a liquid evaporates, it removes heat from the surroundings.

Freon is used as a coolant in many refrigerators and air conditioners. Freon, $CCl_2F_2$, absorbs 167 J

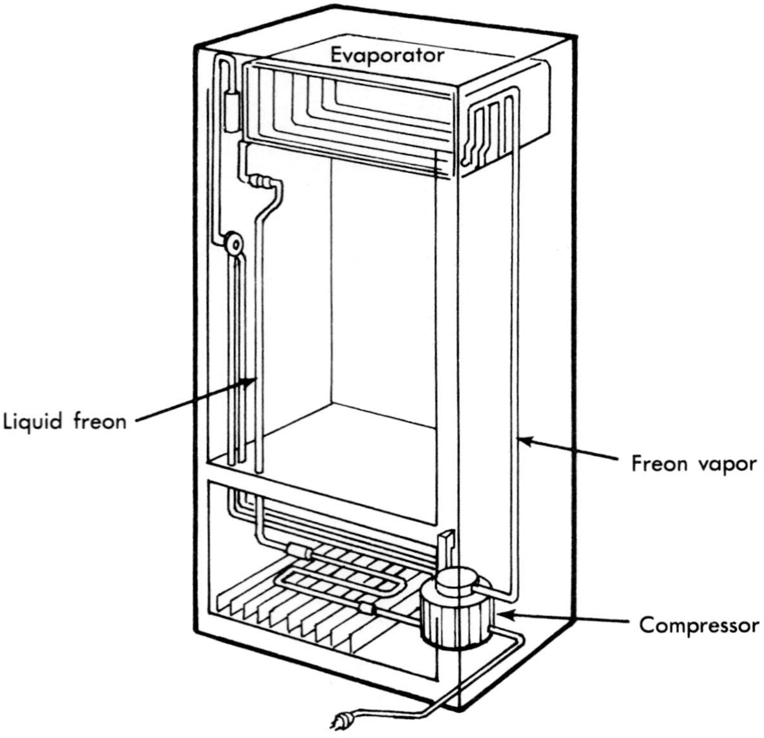


FIGURE 14-18. Evaporation of freon is used to cool food in a refrigerator.

of energy per gram to change to a gas. In a refrigerator, liquid freon is stored in a tank under high pressure. The liquid freon passes through a series of coils in the refrigerator. In these coils, the pressure is reduced and the freon evaporates. Heat from the food inside the refrigerator provides the energy for this change of state. As a result, the food is cooled. The freon gas is pumped to an area where it loses heat and becomes a liquid again. Then the freon is pumped back to the storage tank.

Explain how a refrigerator works.

A heat pump can cool the same way a refrigerator does. Heat from inside the building evaporates the gas in the inside coil. The gas carries the heat out of the building and transfers it to the outside coil where it is released to the air or ground.

*Image Workshop*

FIGURE 14–19. Frozen foods can be transported long distances by using refrigerated trucks.

## making sure

**18.** Why must there be a space between the back of a refrigerator and a wall?

**19.** How is a change of state related to refrigeration?

**20.** How does pressure affect the evaporation of a substance?

# PERSPECTIVES

## people

# High Temperature Corrosion

Electricity is one source of energy used to produce home heat. Most of the electricity in the United States is generated by burning some type of fuel such as coal or gas in a high temperature combustion chamber. Burning is a chemical reaction in which oxygen combines with carbon, hydrogen, sulfur, and other substances. The products of this reaction are heat, light, and hot gases. Pipes containing water are positioned close to the heat. The heat changes the water in the pipes to steam. As the temperature of the steam rises, it builds up pressure in the pipes. The pressurized steam turns generators to produce electricity.

The pipes that contain the water and pressurized steam are called heat exchangers. Heat exchangers are exposed to very high temperatures and hot gases. The metals in the heat exchangers react with the hot gases and form metal oxides and sulfides, which are called corrosion products. The sulfur in the fuel that forms the sulfides can severely corrode the heat exchanger. When the pipes become severely corroded, it is necessary to shut down the power plant and replace the heat exchangers, which is expensive and inconvenient.

The amount of oxygen and sulfur in the gases determines the types of corrosion products that will be produced. Thus, when engineers design combustion chambers many factors must be considered to ensure reliability.

Mike Rocazella is a metallurgist. A metallurgist is a scientist who studies metals. His research involves studying high temperature combustion chambers and determining the best way to burn fuels to minimize corrosion of heat exchangers. He places probes in the combustion chamber to determine the concentrations of oxygen. A map is then constructed showing the distribution of oxygen concentrations in the chamber. Samples of heat exchange pipes are also placed in the chamber. The pipes are examined under light microscopes and scanning electron microscopes to determine the damage caused by corrosion. Scientists have found that low oxygen concentrations cause severe corrosion. By carefully controlling the amount of oxygen and the design of the combustion chamber, electricity can be produced more efficiently. Thus, a constant supply of heat producing electrical energy is ensured.

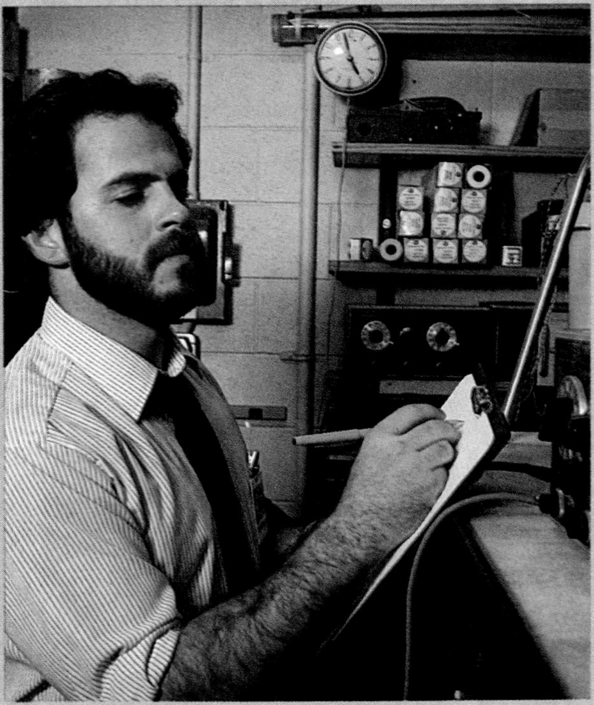

*Image Workshop*

## main ideas

1. Energy is the capacity to do work. The unit of energy is the joule (J). 14:1
2. Temperature is the average kinetic energy of particles. Heat is the total internal energy of a substance. 14:2
3. Fluids expand at greater rates than do solids when heat energy is absorbed. 14:3
4. Heat energy absorbed by a solid when it melts is called heat of fusion. Heat energy absorbed by a liquid when it changes to a gas is called heat of vaporization. 14:4
5. Specific heat is the amount of heat needed to raise the temperature of 1 g of a substance 1 C°. 14:5
6. The amount of heat absorbed or released by a substance depends upon the substance's mass, specific heat, and temperature change. 14:6
7. Heat is tranferred by conduction, convection, and radiation. 14:7
8. Insulation is any substance that slows down or controls the movement of heat energy. 14:8
9. Central heating systems include hot air, hot water, steam, electric, solar, and heat pump systems. 14:9
10. Modern refrigeration uses the change of state from a liquid to a gas to remove heat from the surroundings. 14:10

## vocabulary

*Define each of the following words or terms.*

calorimeter
conduction
convection
energy
heat
heat of fusion
heat of vaporization
insulation
joule
radiation
refrigeration
specific heat
temperature

## study questions

**DO NOT WRITE IN THIS BOOK.**

**A. True or False**

*Determine whether each of the following sentences is true or false. If the sentence is false, rewrite it to make it true.*

1. Heat and temperature are the same quantity.

2. The specific heat of copper is greater than the specific heat of water.
3. Heat is the total internal energy of a substance.
4. When heat is absorbed by a gas, the gas particles move more slowly.
5. Metals are poor heat conductors.
6. A good heat conductor is a good heat insulator.
7. A thermometer measures the total internal energy of a substance.
8. Heat energy can be transferred through a liquid by convection.
9. A unit of heat energy is the joule.
10. When ice melts, it absorbs heat energy.

**B. Multiple Choice**

*Choose the word or phrase that completes correctly each of the following sentences.*

1. When the temperature of water is increased the molecules of water move (*faster, slower, at the same speed*).
2. Heat is transferred through a solid mainly by (*conduction, convection, radiation*).
3. A (*thermometer, barometer, calorimeter*) is used to measure the amount of heat absorbed or released by a substance.
4. (*Specific heat, Density, Temperature*) is the amount of heat needed to raise the temperature of 1 g of a substance 1 C°.
5. (*Water, Aluminum, Carbon*) increases in temperature fastest when heat is added.
6. Heat loss from buildings is reduced by (*conduction, convection, insulation*).
7. (*Iron, Steel, Plastic foam*) is a good insulator.
8. When ice changes to water, it (*absorbs, releases, produces*) heat.
9. A heat pump (*produces, transfers, condenses*) heat.
10. Evaporation (*lowers, raises, has no effect on*) the temperature of a material.

**C. Completion**

*Complete each of the following sentences with a word or phrase that will make the sentence correct.*

1. Winds are examples of ______ currents.

2. ______ is the capacity to do work.
3. Heat is transferred through a piece of metal by ______.
4. A bimetallic strip will ______ when heated.
5. A(n) ______ can warm or cool the inside of a building.
6. When a material expands, the amount of space it occupies ______.
7. Energy is transferred through space by ______.
8. Air currents transfer energy by ______.
9. ______ is a cooling process in which a liquid changes to a gas.
10. ______ are the best solid conductors of heat.

**D. How and Why**

1. What is the difference between heat and temperature?
2. Radiation occurs in space, but conduction and convection do not. Explain.
3. How does glass fiber insulation reduce heat loss?
4. Compare the transfer of heat in a refrigerator and in a steam heating system. How are they alike? Different?
5. How would you produce convection currents in the air in a room?

## challenges

1. Obtain a discarded thermostat from a heating and air conditioning company. Sketch the inside of the thermostat and label the parts. Explain how the thermostat works.
2. Obtain information on the latest solar heating systems. Draw a design of a solar heating system for your home.

## interesting reading

Butti, Ken and John Perlin, *A Golden Thread: 2500 Years of Solar Architecture and Technology*. New York: Van Nostrand Reinhold/Cheshire, 1980.

Consumers Union, "Saving Energy Dollars." *Consumer Reports,* October 1981, pp. 563-594.

Satchwell, John, *Energy at Work*. New York: Lathrop, Lee, and Shepard, 1981.

*You can see evidence of light traveling through the fibers, but you see no evidence of sound. Both light and sound travel through the fibers as waves. Light and sound are two of many forms of energy. What is energy? What other forms of energy are there? How do the various forms of energy differ? How do we use energy?*

Carl Fischer Photography, Inc.

# Sound and Light

# chapter 15

## 15:1 Waves

GOAL: You will learn the properties of waves and some uses of light and sound.

How is energy transferred from one place to another? Heat energy may move from place to place through matter by conduction or convection. A hammer driving a nail into wood transfers energy from the hammer to the wood. Energy also moves from one place to another as waves. Heat energy transfer by radiation is one example of the transfer of energy by waves. Sound waves transfer the energy of a vibrating piano string to your ear. Water waves have enough energy to destroy beaches during storms. Electromagnetic waves transfer energy from the sun to the earth. All waves transfer energy.

How are mechanical waves different from electromagnetic waves?

There are two kinds of waves: mechanical and electromagnetic. **Mechanical waves** transfer energy as they travel through matter. Water and sound waves are mechanical waves. We can directly observe the behavior of most mechanical waves. **Electromagnetic waves** do not need matter to transfer energy. Light is the best known form of electromagnetic wave. X rays, radio waves, microwaves, and infrared waves are other examples of electromagnetic waves. We cannot directly observe electromagnetic waves. However, we can use information about mechanical waves to understand electromagnetic waves.

Kodansha

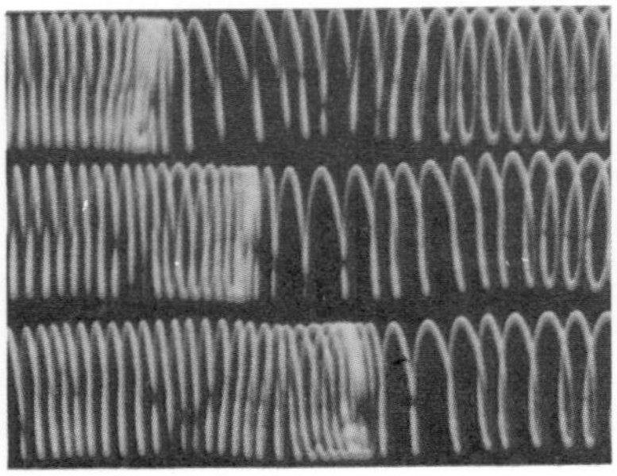

a

Larry Hamill

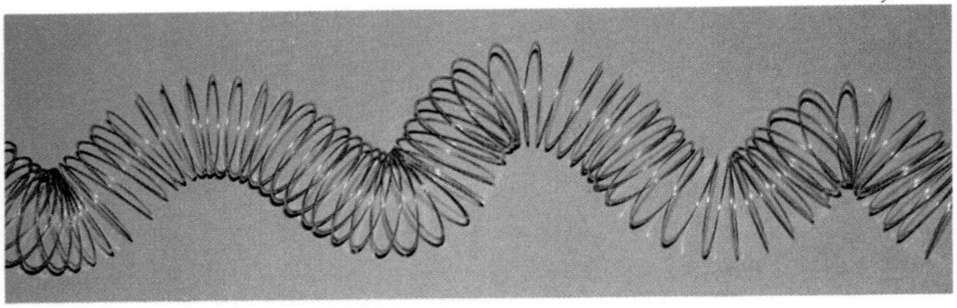

b

FIGURE 15-1. Two types of waves are longitudinal (a) and transverse (b).

What is the difference between transverse and longitudinal waves?

Waves can also be classified by the way they displace matter. The kind of wave produced in the coil spring in Figure 15-1a is called a longitudinal wave. The coils of the spring move back and forth as the energy moves through the spring. In a longitudinal wave, the matter moves in the same direction as the wave travels. In the coil spring, a longitudinal wave is produced by pinching together several coils and then quickly releasing them. A wave then travels along the spring. As the wave reaches a new part of the spring, new coils are pushed together. As the wave moves on, these coils move apart. The coils of the spring continue to move back and forth. Sound waves are longitudinal waves.

Figure 15–1b illustrates a transverse (tranz VURS) wave. The coils of the spring move up and down as energy moves through the spring. Hills and valleys are formed in the coil. In transverse waves, matter moves at right angles to the direction in which the waves travel. Light and radio waves are understood to behave in the manner of transverse waves.

### making sure

1. How is a mechanical wave different from an electromagnetic wave?

## 15:2 Characteristics of Waves

All waves have certain characteristics. The **wavelength** of a wave is the distance between two corresponding points on consecutive waves (Figure 15–2). The top of the wave is called the crest and the bottom is called a trough.

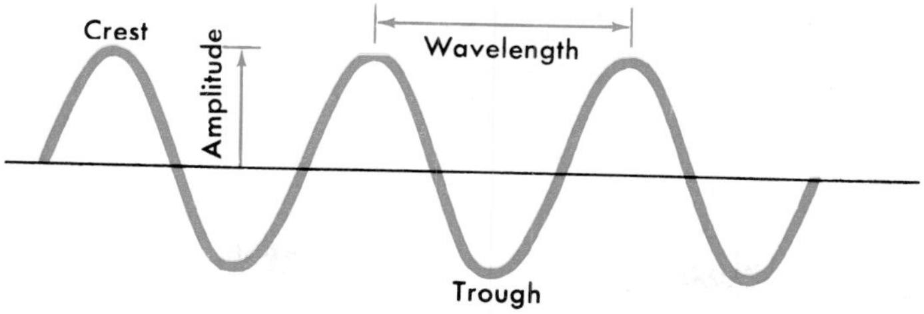


FIGURE 15-2. Waves have certain characteristics including wavelength and amplitude.

Diagram a wave and label its wavelength and amplitude.

**Amplitude** is the distance a wave rises or falls from its rest position. The amplitude of a wave depends upon the amount of energy in the wave. As the amount of energy increases, the amplitude of the wave increases. A large rock dropped into a pond creates a larger wave than a pebble. The amplitude of the wave created by the rock is greater.

What is wave frequency?

All waves have a frequency (FREE kwun see). **Frequency** is the number of waves that pass a given point in a second. Suppose you were at a beach watching ocean waves. Four waves pass a rock in 12 s. What is the frequency? The frequency is ⅓ wave per second.

$$\frac{4 \text{ waves}}{12 \text{ s}} = \frac{1 \text{ wave}}{3 \text{ s}} = 0.33 \text{ w/s}$$

Have you ever watched a floating object? When a wave passes through the water, the object bobs up and down. You can count the number of up and down movements in a unit of time to determine the wave frequency. Long waves have low frequencies. Fewer waves pass a given point each second. Short waves have high frequencies.

Steve Lissau

FIGURE 15-3. Frequency is determined by counting the number of waves that pass a point in one second.

In what unit is frequency expressed?

Frequency is measured in a unit called the hertz. One hertz, Hz, equals one wave per second (1 Hz = 1 w/s). The speed of a wave can be calculated if you know the wavelength and the frequency. The speed of the wave is given by the following equation:

$$\text{speed} = \text{wavelength} \times \text{frequency}$$

**making sure**

2. How is the frequency and amplitude of ocean waves related to surfboarding?

## 15:3 Sound Waves

What causes sound?

Ring a bell or strike a tuning fork and it begins to vibrate. Sound waves are produced. When a person speaks, vibrating vocal cords produce waves. These waves move through air or other matter. They are received by the ear and interpreted by the brain as sound. Certain devices, including the telephone, can convert sound waves to electricity that moves through wires to a receiver.

How does temperature affect the speed of sound?

Sound waves generally move faster through solids than through liquids and gases. The average speed of sound in air is about 332 m/s. Sound travels faster through warm air than through cold air. The speed of sound increases about 60 cm/s for each Celsius degree rise in temperature. At sea level and 20°C, sound travels through air at 344 m/s. Table 15–1 shows the speed of sound through various substances.

There are many sound waves around you. Some you cannot hear. Most people hear sound waves if the frequency is between 20 Hz and 20 000 Hz.

FIGURE 15–4. Sound waves are produced when a musical instrument causes the air to vibrate.

*Joseph DiChello*

***Table 15–1.***
Average Speed of Sound

| Substance | Speed of sound (m/s) |
|---|---|
| Air | 332 |
| Water | 1454 |
| Wood | 3828 |
| Iron | 5103 |
| Stone | 5971 |

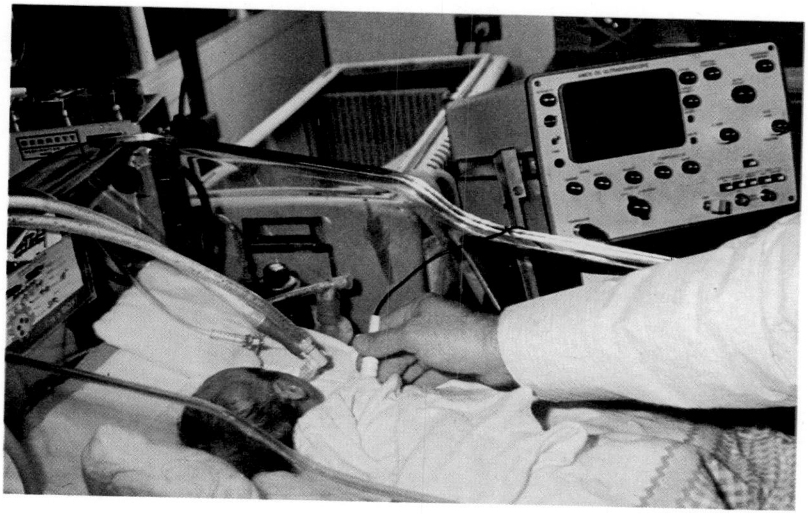

FIGURE 15-5. Ultrasonic sound waves can be used to monitor a baby's heartbeat.

Sounds with frequencies above 20 000 Hz are called ultrasonic (ul truh SAHN ihk) sounds. Ultrasonic sounds cannot be heard by humans. They can be heard by some animals. Dogs can hear sounds with frequencies up to 25 000 Hz.

**making sure**

3. Why could you not hear a sound in a vacuum?
4. What frequencies can most people hear?
5. Do sound waves move faster through a liquid or a gas? Explain.
6. When the speed of sound is known, an echo can be used to measure distance. How far away is a mountain if you hear an echo 2 s after you speak?

## 15:4 Volume and Pitch of Sound

Define volume and pitch.

When you shout, you increase the volume or loudness of your voice. More energy is needed to make a louder sound. Volume depends upon the amplitude of the sound waves. As amplitude increases, loudness increases. The volume of sound is often measured in a unit called decibels, dB. Sounds that are loud enough to cause pain in the ear range from 110–120 dB depending upon frequency.

How are sounds of different pitch produced?

The **pitch** of a sound is determined by the sound's frequency. If you sing a musical scale, you change the pitch. High pitch sounds have high frequencies. Low pitch sounds have low frequencies. A good way to remember the relative wavelength is to remember the letters LLSS—longer, lower; shorter, shriller.

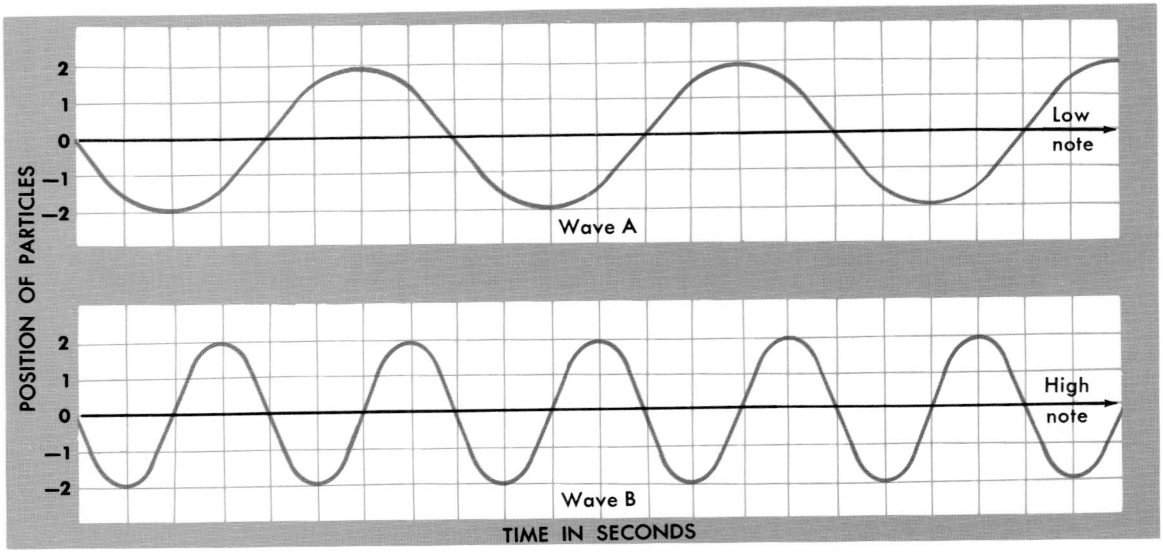


FIGURE 15-6. The frequency of wave B is twice the frequency of wave A. Thus, wave B has a higher pitch than wave A.

Musical instruments produce sounds of different pitch. The instruments have strings or tubes of various sizes. Drums have different amounts of air trapped inside. Different sizes produce different frequencies. Each note is produced by a vibration of a string or by the vibration of air within a tube. A musical sound is produced by matter that vibrates over and over at the same frequency.

What is the Doppler effect?

The Doppler effect is a change in the frequency or pitch of a sound wave caused by the motion of the wave source. For example, sound from the siren of an approaching police car increases in pitch. Why? As the car approaches, its movement crowds the sound waves closer together. The crowded waves have a higher frequency and a higher pitch. As the car passes and moves away, the pitch of the sound decreases. The sound waves are farther apart. Both the frequency and the pitch of the sound waves decrease.

FIGURE 15-7. Musical sounds are produced when matter vibrates at constant frequencies.

*© 1978, Michael Philip Manheim*

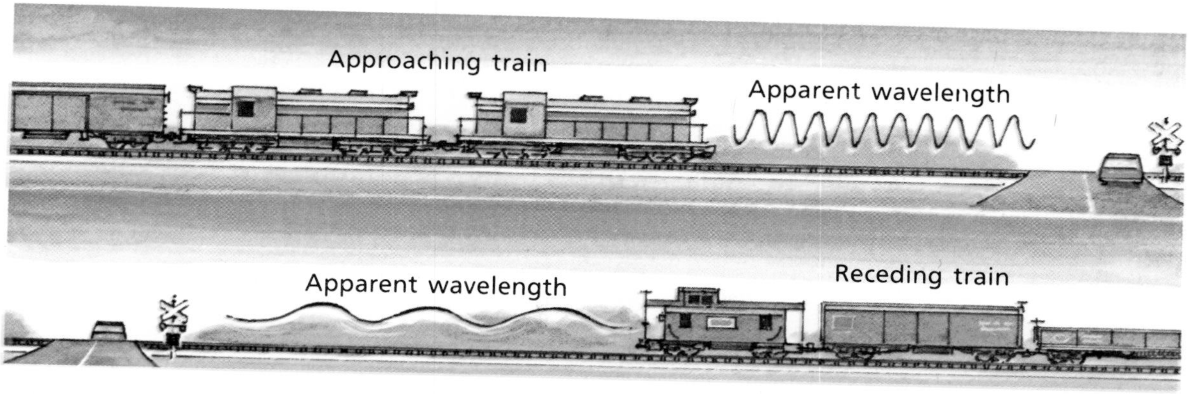


The Doppler effect is also noticed when a person moves toward or away from the source of sound. If you ride a train moving toward a warning bell at a crossing, the sound of the clanging bell increases in pitch. After you pass the bell and are moving away, the pitch decreases.

FIGURE 15-8. As a train approaches, the frequency of its whistle seems to be high. As the train moves away, the frequency seems to be low. This effect is called the Doppler effect.

A practical application of the Doppler effect is in radar speed-detecting devices. Radar waves are sent out from a transmitter. The waves bounce off a car and are picked up by a receiver. Changes in the frequency of the radar waves are caused by the car moving toward the receiver. The change in frequency is used to determine if the car is moving faster than the legal speed limit.

FIGURE 15–9. The speed detecting radar used by police officers can be attached to a car (a) or held by hand (b). The Doppler effect is used to determine a car's speed, which is indicated on the radar unit.

a

Larry Hamill

b

E. Johnson/PHOTRI

## making sure

7. How does pitch differ from volume?
8. What is the relationship between pitch and frequency?
9. What is the relationship between volume and amplitude?

## 15:5 Reflection and Refraction

Define reflection.

Water waves in a ripple tank can be used as models to show the behavior and properties of sound, light, and other waves. **Reflection** is the bouncing of waves from an object. Waves that strike the object are called incident waves. Waves that bounce off are called reflected waves. Waves are reflected from an object at the same angle at which they strike the object.

As water waves move into shallow water, their wavelengths become shorter. The speed of the waves decreases. Why? Remember that the speed of a wave is equal to the wavelength times the frequency. If the

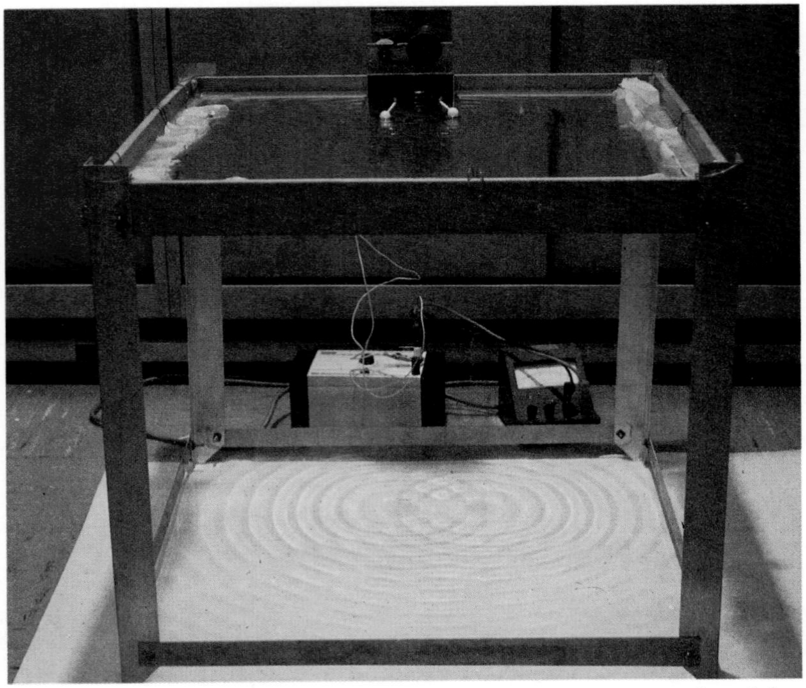

George Anderson

FIGURE 15-10. A ripple tank can be used to study wave behavior.

Steve Lissau

FIGURE 15-11. When water waves enter shallow water at an angle, they are refracted.

frequency remains the same and the wavelength decreases, the speed must decrease.

When water waves enter shallow water at an angle, the waves are refracted (Figure 15–11). **Refraction** is the bending of waves. Refraction always occurs toward the area in which the speed of the wave slows down. Any type of wave can be refracted. Whenever a wave passes from one substance into another substance, its speed changes. If the wave approaches the boundary between the two substances at an angle, the wave is refracted.

Define refraction.

When is a wave refracted?

## activity

### REFLECTION AND REFRACTION

**(1)** Roll a ball so that it strikes a wall at a 90° angle. At what angle is it reflected? **(2)** Roll a ball toward the wall at another angle. **(3)** Repeat Step 2 by rolling the ball toward the wall at several different angles. Mark the path of the ball with chalk. Measure and compare the angle of incidence and the angle of reflection. How do these angles compare? **(4)** Mount 2 toy wheels on an axle. Roll the axle at an angle toward a soft cloth that is on a smooth surface. What happens to the wheel that hits the cloth first? What happens to the speed and direction of the other wheel and the axle? How is this example similar to refraction?

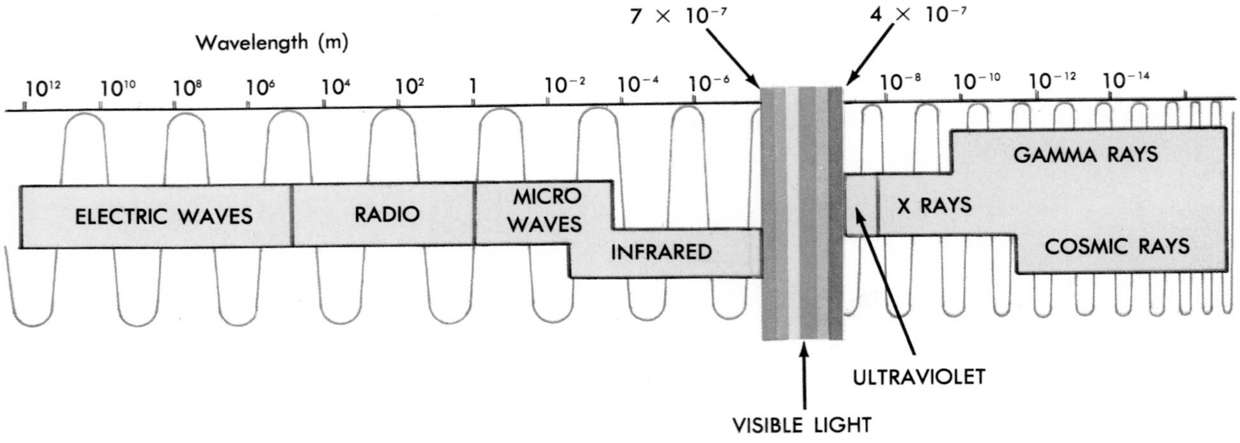


FIGURE 15-12. The electromagnetic spectrum ranges from very long wavelength electric waves to very short wavelength gamma rays. Visible light covers a very small portion of this spectrum.

List the kinds of waves that make up the electromagnetic spectrum.

How do electromagnetic waves differ from each other?

## 15:6 Electromagnetic Waves

Electromagnetic waves are all around you. Visible light can be detected by your eyes, but most waves cannot be seen. Radio, television, radar, infrared, ultraviolet, X ray, and gamma ray waves are part of your environment, too. All of the waves listed here are electromagnetic waves. These waves do not need to travel through matter to transfer energy. They all travel at the speed of light—300 000 000 m/s in a vacuum.

Each kind of electromagnetic wave has a different wavelength and frequency. Arranged in order of their wavelength and frequency, the waves form an electromagnetic spectrum (Table 15–2). Electromagnetic waves are transverse waves.

Visible light is only a small part of the electromagnetic spectrum. Yet, it is vital to the survival of most living organisms. Life on Earth would be very different without light from the sun.

Light appears to travel in straight lines. If you turn on a flashlight in a dusty room, you see a beam of light. The small beam of light contains many individual waves of different wavelengths. These waves travel together in straight lines. A straight line, called a ray, can be used to represent the direction in which light waves travel.

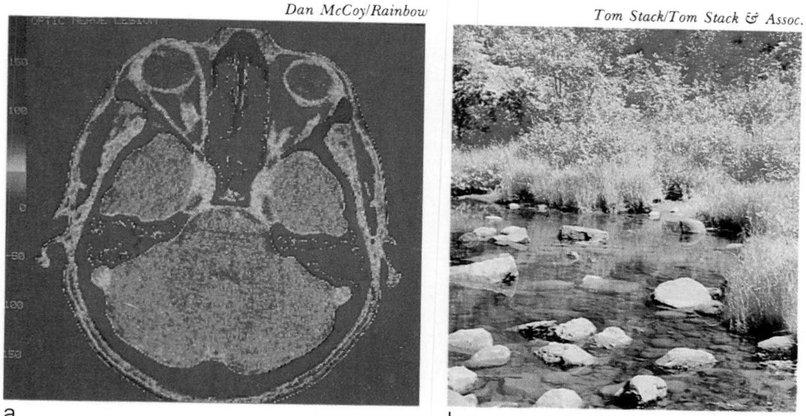

Dan McCoy/Rainbow — a

Tom Stack/Tom Stack & Assoc. — b

FIGURE 15-13. Technology makes use of many parts of the electromagnetic spectrum such as X rays in CAT scans (a) and infrared waves in infrared photography (b).

***Table 15–2.***
**The Electromagnetic Spectrum**

| Type of Radiation | Wavelength (m) | Comments |
|---|---|---|
| Radio | $10^{4}$ to 1 | Used in communications: AM and FM radio and TV broadcasts. AM waves are longer than FM waves. TV waves and FM waves are the same length. |
| Microwaves<br>Radar | 1 to $10^{-4}$ | Used in communication because they can travel through smoke, fog, and rain. Used in microwave ovens to cook food. Radar waves are used to track satellites, speeding vehicles, and airplanes. |
| Infrared | $10^{-4}$ to $10^{-6}$ | Used in lamps to dry and warm things. All living organisms emit infrared waves. Military applications include heat-seeking missiles. Used in medicine to detect tumors. Used in photography to detect mineral deposits and to make foliage maps of areas. |
| Visible light<br>Ultraviolet | $10^{-6}$ to $10^{-7}$<br>$10^{-8}$ to $10^{-9}$ | The light we see. Used to identify objects.<br>Present in sunlight. Light that tans humans. Used in hospitals to kill germs. Overexposure to ultraviolet radiation can cause skin cancer. |
| Gamma radiation<br>X rays | $10^{-10}$ to $10^{-14}$ | Gamma radiation is produced when the nucleus of an atom breaks up. X rays are produced by beams of electrons hitting a metal target. X rays are used in medicine to diagnose diseases and to kill cancer cells. Used to build lasers and to determine the structure of new compounds. |
| Cosmic rays | $10^{-14}$ to $10^{-17}$ | Cosmic rays come from outer space. They are produced when the nuclei of atoms break up. |

FIGURE 15-14. The transparent glass windows allow people on the street to see the crystal in the store. The crystal is also made of transparent glass.

Define transparent, opaque, and translucent.

Matter affects light in different ways. Some substances let light pass through them. We call these substances transparent. A glass window, clear water, and air are transparent substances. A substance that does not allow any light to pass through is called opaque (oh PAYK). Light that strikes an opaque substance is either reflected or absorbed. Wood, steel, and bricks are opaque substances. Some substances allow light to pass through but scatter the waves in all directions. These substances are called translucent (trans LEW sunt). You cannot see distinct shapes through a translucent substance.

### making sure

10. What type of substance would you use in a bathroom window—transparent, opaque, or translucent? Explain your choice.

## 15:7 Mirrors and Reflection

What is an image?

A **mirror** is a smooth, shiny surface. It reflects light waves in a regular pattern. When you look into a mirror, you see an image of yourself. An **image** is a visual likeness of an object. The mirror reflects light from your body back to your eyes. The angle at which the light is reflected from the mirror is the same angle at which the light strikes the mirror.

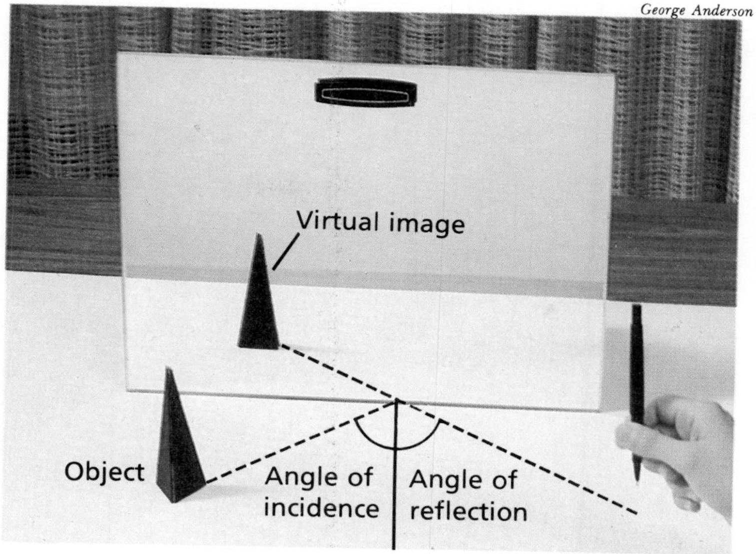


a

b

FIGURE 15-15. The image of the cone appears to be behind the mirror (a). Some mirrors magnify an image (b).

When you look at your image in a plane mirror, your image appears to be behind the mirror. Your image appears to be as far behind the mirror as you are in front of the mirror. It appears that light waves are being reflected from the image. However, no light waves actually reach the image. When an image is formed without light waves passing through it, the image is a **virtual** (VURCH wal) **image**. A virtual image cannot be projected onto a screen. A piece of paper held where the image appears to be would be blank.

How does a mirror form a virtual image?

Reflecting surfaces may also be curved. Curved mirrors form images also. A concave mirror has a curved surface in which the center of the mirror is farther away from the viewer than are the edges (Figure 15–15). A concave mirror can form a real image. In a **real image**, light waves actually pass through the image. A real image may be projected onto a screen. Concave mirrors are used in makeup mirrors to magnify the image.

Explain how a convex mirror is different from a concave mirror.

Convex mirrors are also curved. The center of a convex mirror extends outward. The image formed by a convex mirror is a virtual image that cannot be projected onto a screen. Convex mirrors are used in some rearview mirrors on car and truck doors.

FIGURE 15-16. The rearview mirror on a car reflects the image of vehicles approaching the car from behind. The mirror helps the driver avoid accidents.

## activity

## LOCATING A VIRTUAL IMAGE

**Objective:** To form a virtual image and locate its position

FIGURE 15–17.

### Materials

clay
2 identical candles
2 identical candle holders
matches
metric ruler
mirror, plane

### Procedure

1. Use the clay as a base to make the mirror stand vertically on a table (Figure 15–17).
2. Place each of the candles securely into a candle holder.
3. Using the ruler, position the center of one of the candles 5 cm in front of the mirror.
4. Place the second candle behind the mirror. Light the second candle. CAUTION: Secure hair and loose clothing before lighting the candle.
5. Watch the image of the unlit candle in the mirror. Have your partner carefully move the lighted candle behind the mirror until you observe that the image of the front candle appears to be lighted also. The candle image should appear to remain lighted from any viewing position.
6. Measure the distance from the reflecting surface of the mirror to the center of the lighted candle. Record your observations in a table similar to the one shown in Data and Observations.
7. Repeat Steps 2 through 6 with the center of the unlit candle at 10 cm and 20 cm from the reflecting surface of the mirror. Extinguish the candle as soon as you finish the procedure.

### Data and Observations

| Distance From Mirror | |
|---|---|
| Unlighted candle | Lighted candle |
| 5 cm | |
| 10 cm | |
| 20 cm | |

### Questions and Conclusions

1. What type of image was formed by the mirror? What observations support your answer?
2. Where was the candle image located? How do you know?
3. If you placed a piece of paper where the candle image appeared to be, what would you observe?
4. A candle is placed 1 meter in front of the reflecting surface of a plane mirror. How far from the reflecting surface will the image appear to be? Explain.
5. In a small room, why might a decorator use mirrors to panel one wall?

# 15:8 Refraction of Light

Did you ever dive for a coin at the bottom of a swimming pool? It is better to dive in front of where you see a coin than to dive directly at it. Light reflected from the coin is bent as it leaves the water. Thus, it does not follow a straight path from the coin to your eye.

Refraction is caused when the speed of light changes as it passes at an angle from one substance into another. When light passes at an angle from water into air, its speed increases. The light bends at the surface between the two substances. The index of refraction tells how much light is refracted by a substance. The greater the change in the speed of light, the larger the index of refraction. Table 15–3 gives the index of refraction and the speed of light for various substances.

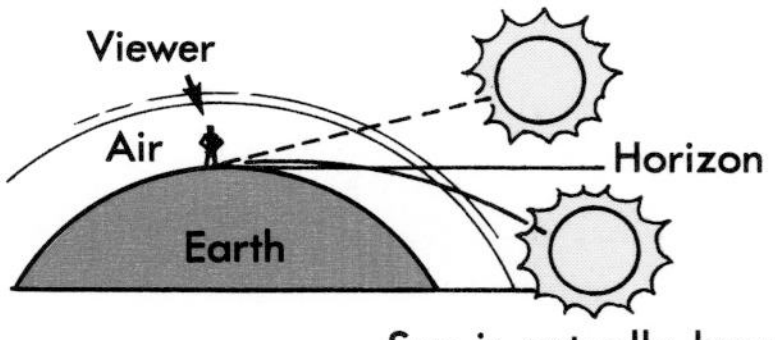


FIGURE 15-18. Air refracts sunlight making the sun appear to be above the horizon even though it is actually just below. Because of this refraction, the sun seems to linger on the horizon at dawn and at dusk.

When is light refracted?

What is the index of refraction of a substance?

***Table 15–3.***
Index of Refraction and Speed of Light

| Substance | Index of refraction | Speed of light (m/s) |
|---|---|---|
| Air | 1.00 | $3.00 \times 10^8$ |
| Water | 1.33 | $2.23 \times 10^8$ |
| Ethanol | 1.36 | $2.21 \times 10^8$ |
| Glass | 1.50 | $2.00 \times 10^8$ |
| Plexiglas | 1.51 | $1.98 \times 10^8$ |
| Diamond | 2.42 | $1.24 \times 10^8$ |

## activity
### REFRACTION OF LIGHT

Place a coin in the bottom of a shallow baking pan. Have a partner stand so that the edge of the pan just blocks the view of the coin. Now carefully fill the pan with water. Do not change the position of the pan or the coin. What does your partner observe? How is this observation an example of refraction?

## making sure

**16.** Diamond has a large index of refraction. How does this property explain the fact that cut diamonds sparkle?

## 15:9 Lenses, Prisms, and Color

Light travels in a straight line. However, light waves are refracted as they enter or leave a transparent substance at an angle. A **lens** is any transparent substance that refracts light so it is focused. A curved piece of glass is an example of a lens. The point where the light waves meet after leaving a lens is the **focal point.**

Draw a diagram of a convex lens and a concave lens.

How do lenses produce images?

There are two kinds of lenses: convex and concave. A convex lens is thicker in the middle than at the edges. A convex lens can form a real image when light passes through it. A real image formed by a convex lens is upside down and on the opposite side of the lens. The image formed on a movie screen is a real image formed by a convex lens. An

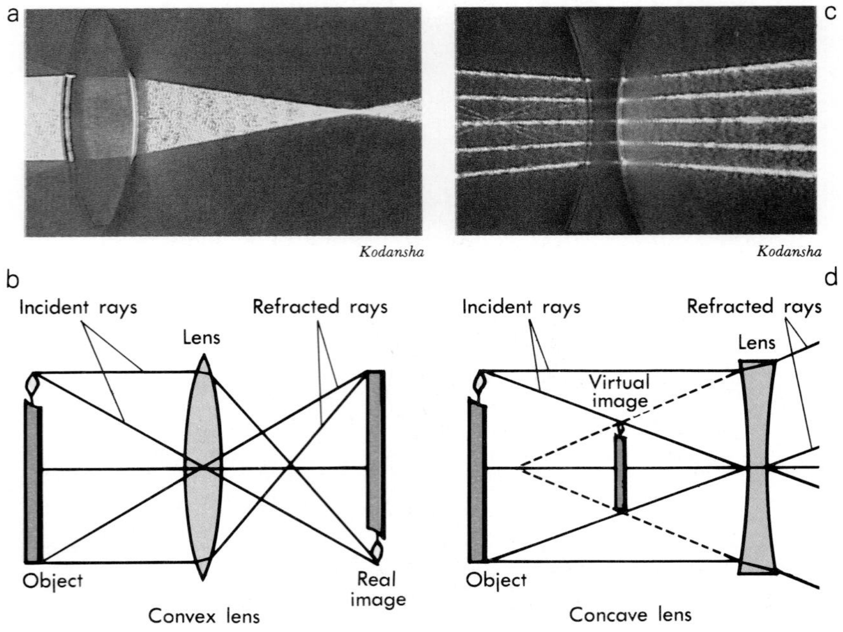


FIGURE 15-19. A convex lens (a and b) forms a real image by refracting light to a focus. A concave lens (c and d) forms a virtual image by refracting light away from a focus.

USDA

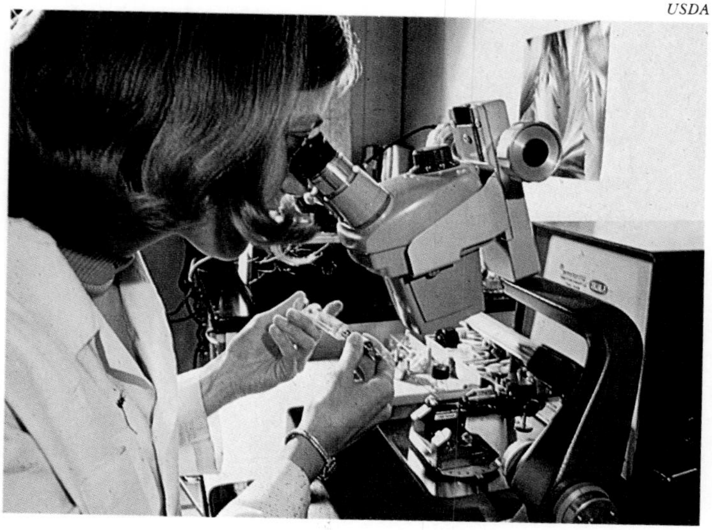

FIGURE 15-20. Convex lenses in a microscope magnify the image.

image produced by a convex lens may be larger, smaller, or the same size as the object. Microscopes, telescopes, and binoculars contain convex lenses. A convex lens is used to correct farsighted vision in people.

A concave lens is thinner in the middle than at the edges. A concave lens forms an image that is right side up and smaller than the object. The image formed is always a virtual image. A concave lens is used to correct nearsighted vision in people.

White light is a mixture of all wavelengths of visible light (Figure 15–21). When white light strikes a prism, the light "mixture" is separated into its parts by refraction. A **prism** is a solid triangular piece of transparent material that refracts light. Light is refracted as it passes at an angle from air into the

How does a prism produce a color spectrum?

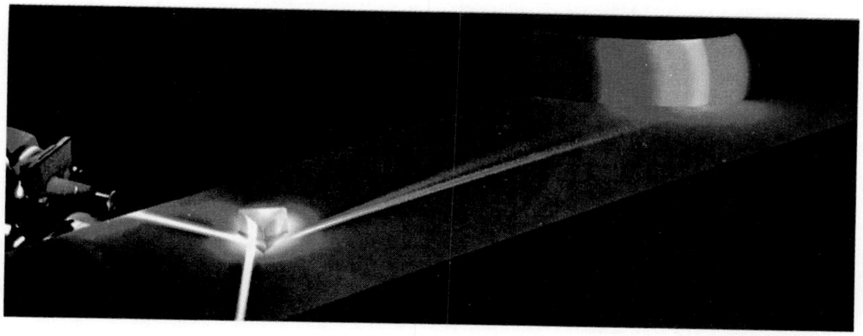

Eastman Kodak Company

FIGURE 15-21. A prism separates white light into the colors of the visible spectrum.

William D. Popejoy

a

John Swartz

b

FIGURE 15-22. A rainbow is a result of sunlight being refracted by raindrops (a). The shirt appears red because it reflects red light (b).

How are rainbows produced?

How does light produce the color of an object?

prism. The colors of visible light have different wavelengths and frequencies. Therefore each color is bent at a slightly different angle. Violet light is refracted much more than red light. A rainbow is an example of light refracting when it passes through water drops.

White objects reflect all the colors of light. Colored objects reflect only part of the colors of light. The color of an object depends upon the color of the light that it reflects. A red shirt in a white light reflects only red light to your eyes. Therefore, it appears red. The other colors of light are absorbed by the shirt. In the same way, a blue rug reflects blue light. When an object does not reflect any light, it appears black.

### making sure

**17.** Is the image on a movie screen a real or virtual image? Why?

## 15:10 Polarized Light

How is polarized light different from ordinary light?

Light waves can vibrate in all directions. Some vibrate up and down, others vibrate from side to side. **Polarized light** is light that vibrates in only one plane. How is polarized light produced? One way is to pass light through a polarizing filter. The filter contains a series of fine slits. Only those waves vibrating in the same plane as the slits will pass

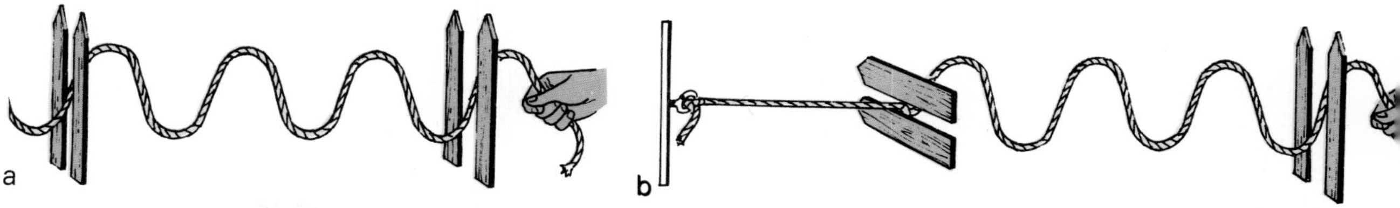

FIGURE 15-23. These parallel sticks act like a polarizing filter. Waves vibrating in the same plane as the slit will pass through (a). Waves vibrating at right angles to the slit are blocked (b).

through the filter. The other waves are blocked. You can compare this filter to a set of parallel sticks with a rope vibrating between them (Figure 15–23). If the sticks are rotated 90°, the waves are no longer in the same plane as the sticks. The sticks stop the wave motion. One of the most common applications of polarized light is in polarized sunglasses. These sunglasses reduce the glare of bright light. Polarizing filters are used in photography to reduce the intensity of light that enters the camera. There is more contrast between the colors in the photograph when a polarizing filter is used.

## 15:11 Sources of Light

Describe four ways in which light is produced.

Most of the light on Earth comes from the sun. Moonlight at night is the sun's light reflected to Earth by the moon. Another source of light on Earth is a burning fuel, such as the wax in a candle. Other sources of light are the result of technology. Light can be produced when certain substances are heated to high temperatures. The heated substances do not burn, instead they glow and produce light. This process of producing light is called incandescence (ihn kun DES unts). Many lights in homes are incandescent lights. The light bulbs contain a tungsten metal filament that is heated by electricity. The hot, glowing filament emits white light.

Some light is produced when certain substances are relatively cool. This process of producing light is called luminescence (lew muh NES unts). Neon lights, fluorescent lights, and television and X-ray fluoroscope screens are examples of this type of light. Luminescence is also found in nature. Glowworms and fireflies produce luminescent light.

Luminescent light can be produced when certain substances absorb energy from X rays, ultraviolet

FIGURE 15-24. The lights of a city are both incandescent and luminescent.

*Vince Streano, 1983*

Dan McCoy/Rainbow

FIGURE 15-25. Luminescent light is produced by some chemical reactions.

How is laser light produced?

List some uses of the laser.

rays, or other kinds of radiation. For example, a fluorescent tube has a coating on the inside. When radiation strikes the inside coating of the tube, it causes the coating to glow. As a result, light is emitted. Different colors of light are produced by adding dyes to the coating materials of the tube.

Laser light can be produced when atoms of certain substances are excited. Excited atoms contain electrons that have been raised to a higher than usual energy level. The atoms in a laser can be put into the excited state in different ways. When the atoms in some lasers are exposed to an intense flash of light, a brief flash of laser light is emitted. This flash is called a pulse. An electric discharge can also be used to put atoms in the excited state. This type of laser is continuous rather than pulsed. The lasers often seen in classrooms are continuous lasers that use a mixture of helium and neon gas atoms. All the individual waves in a beam of laser light have the same frequency.

Lasers have many practical applications. In medicine, lasers are used to repair torn retinas in eyes and to destroy cancer cells. In photography, laser light is used to photograph extremely high-speed objects. Laser light carries telephone messages over long distances. Lasers also are used to operate some video-disc players. These machines enable you to view a movie or other program at home using your television set. Supermarket checkout counters use lasers to "read" the price of grocery items. Lasers are an excellent example of technology.

FIGURE 15-26. A laser produces a beam of high-energy light.

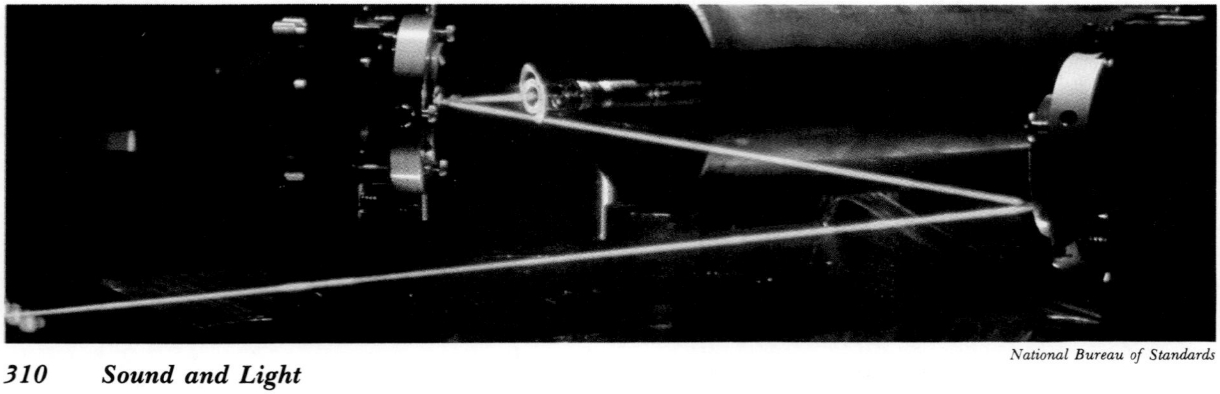

National Bureau of Standards

# main ideas



1. Waves transfer energy. Electromagnetic waves can transfer energy through matter and a vacuum. 15:1
2. The properties of a wave include its wavelength, amplitude, and frequency. 15:2
3. Sound waves are mechanical energy waves. 15:3
4. The volume of sound depends upon the amplitude of the sound waves. Pitch is determined by a sound's frequency. 15:4
5. Reflection occurs when a wave strikes an object and bounces off it. Refraction is the bending of waves as they pass from one substance into another. 15:5
6. Electromagnetic waves travel at the speed of light in a vacuum. 15:6
7. Images can be virtual or real. 15:7
8. The index of refraction tells how much light is refracted by a substance. 15:8
9. A lens is any transparent substance that bends light so it is focused. 15:9
10. Polarized light vibrates in only one plane. 15:10
11. Light is produced by burning and by heating certain substances to a high temperature. Light is also produced by bombarding certain substances with high energy radiation. 15:11

# vocabulary

*Define each of the following words or terms.*

amplitude
electromagnetic waves
focal point
frequency
image
lens
mechanical waves
mirror
pitch
polarized light
prism
real image
reflection
refraction
virtual image
wavelength

# study questions

**DO NOT WRITE IN THIS BOOK.**

## A. True or False

*Determine whether each of the following sentences is true or false. If the sentence is false, rewrite it to make it true.*

1. Sound waves can travel through a vacuum.

2. The pitch of a sound wave depends upon its frequency.
3. Sound waves travel faster in glass than in air.
4. Most people hear sounds with frequencies above 20 000 Hz.
5. High pitch sounds have low frequencies and low pitch sounds have high frequencies.
6. Water waves entering shallow water at an angle are refracted.
7. Visible light is the entire electromagnetic spectrum.
8. A virtual image can be projected onto a screen.
9. Infrared waves and ultraviolet waves are invisible to the human eye.
10. Polarized light vibrates in all directions.

**B. Multiple choice**

*Choose the word or phrase that completes correctly each of the following sentences.*

1. The unit of frequency is the (*joule, hertz, pascal*).
2. Short waves have frequencies (*higher than, shorter than, the same as*) long waves.
3. When a wave is reflected, it (*bounces off an object, changes speed, changes frequency*).
4. The reflection of an object in a mirror is called a(n) (*optical illusion, mirage, image*).
5. A visible light spectrum is produced by a (*polarizing filter, plane mirror, prism*).
6. The wavelength of infrared radiation is (*longer than, shorter than, the same as*) that of ultraviolet radiation.
7. The color of an object depends upon the color of light it (*refracts, polarizes, reflects*).
8. Producing light by heating a substance to a high temperature is called (*luminescence, lasing, incandescence*).
9. Laser light is produced when certain substances are bombarded by (*light, X rays, ultraviolet radiation*).
10. An object appears (*black, white, colorless*) when it does not reflect any light.

**C. Completion**

*Complete each of the following sentences with a word or phrase that will make the sentence correct.*

1. You cannot hear ______ sounds.

2. An increase in the pitch of a sound results from an increase in the ______ of the sound.
3. Sound ______ travel through matter.
4. One hertz is one vibration per ______.
5. Sound waves are produced when a tuning fork ______.
6. Each color of light has a different wavelength and ______.
7. A lens ______ light waves so they are focused.
8. A concave lens forms a(n) ______ image.
9. A(n) ______ lens is used to correct nearsighted vision.
10. White objects reflect ______ colors of light.

**D. How and Why**

1. How does the frequency of sound change when you change the pitch of your voice?
2. Draw a simple sketch to show how a light wave is reflected by a wall.
3. Draw a simple sketch to show how a convex lens brings parallel rays of light to a focus.
4. Draw a sketch of a prism. Show how it separates white light. Name the colors of the visible light spectrum formed.
5. How is polarized light produced?

## challenges

1. Find out how bats use sound waves to navigate and to find food.
2. Write a report on the uses of sonar.
3. Find out how color photography works. You may wish to do a project on color film, color dyes, or color printing.

## interesting reading

Burroughs, William, *Lasers.* New York: Warwick, 1982.

Knight, David C., *Silent Sound: The World of Ultrasonics.* New York: Morrow, 1980.

Simon, Hilda, *The Magic of Color.* New York: Lathrop, Lee, and Shepard, 1981.

*The volume of water that Hoover Dam holds back equals the volume of water that flows in the Colorado River in two years. The stored water has a large amount of potential energy. Power plants use the kinetic energy of falling water to generate electricity. What is electricity? How is electricity related to magnetism? Are there different kinds of electricity and magnetism?*

C. Reaves/Alpha

# Magnetism and Electricity

chapter 16

## 16:1 Magnets

GOAL: You will learn how magnetism and electricity are produced, measured, and used.

Long ago, people in an eastern region of the earth called Magnesia found stones that would attract each other. The stones also attracted iron and some other substances. These stones were called magnets. Most natural magnets contain a mineral called magnetite, $Fe_3O_4$.

Magnetism is a property of matter. However, in only a few elements is the magnetic effect strong. Iron, nickel, and cobalt are naturally magnetic elements. Other substances can be made to act as magnets.

Name three elements that are naturally magnetic.

Most magnets have two ends where the magnetic effects are strongest. These ends are called the poles. If a magnet is allowed to swing freely, one end will always point toward the north. This pole of a magnet is called the north pole. The other pole is called the south pole.

When two magnets are brought close together, they exert a force on each other. Two magnetic north poles repel each other. Two magnetic south poles also repel each other. A magnetic north pole attracts a magnetic south pole. Like poles repel and unlike poles attract.

Which poles of magnets repel each other?

Bell Telephone Laboratories

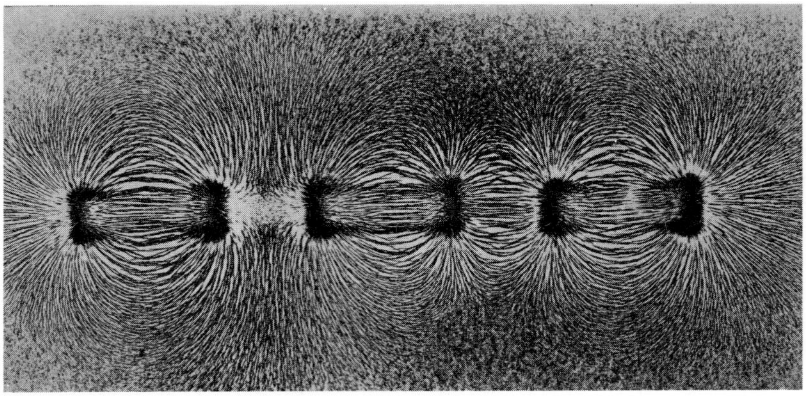

FIGURE 16-1. The magnetic field around a magnet can be shown using iron filings. The empty space between the left and middle magnets shows that both poles are the same. They repel each other.

A magnetic field exists in the area around a magnet. The magnetic field can be thought of as lines of magnetic force. Within the magnetic field, attraction and repulsion occur. The lines of magnetic force always point from the north pole to the south pole of a magnet.

## activity MAGNETS AND MAGNETIC FIELDS

**(1)** Tie a thin string around the center of a magnet, and hang it from support. **(2)** Tie a second piece of string around the center of a second magnet. **(3)** Hold the string so the magnet swings freely. Be sure there is no metal in the area. In which direction do the magnets point? **(4)** Bring the two north poles of the magnets close together. What happens? **(5)** Bring both south poles together. What happens? Why? **(6)** Bring one north pole close to one south pole. Describe what happens. **(7)** Place one magnet under a piece of white paper. Sprinkle iron filings on the paper above the magnet. Tap the paper lightly. What kind of pattern is formed? **(8)** Place both bar magnets under the paper with their north poles close to each other. Sprinkle iron filings on the paper. What kind of pattern is formed? **(9)** Repeat Step 8 with one north pole facing one south pole. What pattern is formed?

## making sure

1. How could you use a magnet to help you find directions if you were lost?

## 16:2 Theory of Magnetism

The magnetic properties of an object are determined by its atomic structure. Electrons move about the nucleus of an atom. Each electron spins as it moves about the nucleus. The spinning causes each electron to be a tiny magnet.

In the atoms of iron, cobalt, and nickel, there are unpaired electrons. These unpaired electrons act like tiny magnets. In unmagnetized pieces of these metals, the magnetic fields of the atoms extend in many directions. There is no orderly arrangement. When the metal is magnetized, the individual magnetic fields align so that all of the north poles face the same direction. The strength of the magnetic field is thereby increased in one direction.

In nonmagnetic substances, the electrons usually occur in pairs. One electron spins in a clockwise direction, and the other electron spins counterclockwise. The magnetic effect of the electrons is canceled. When all electrons in the atom are paired, the substance shows no strong magnetic properties.

A magnet can lose its magnetism if it is heated or hammered. The individual magnetic fields return to random positions. Magnetized steel, unlike iron, tends to remain magnetized longer. Steel's internal structure keeps the magnetic fields aligned. Many

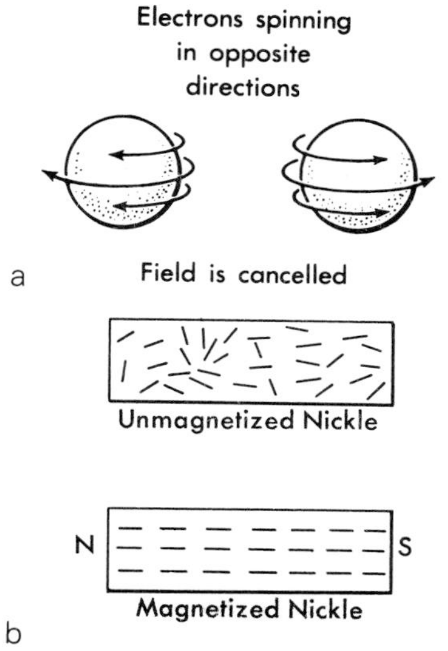


FIGURE 16-2. When the electrons in an atom are in pairs, they spin in opposite directions (a). Atoms with unpaired electrons have a magnetic field. When these fields line up, the total magnetic field of the material increases (b).

Explain how a magnet can lose its magnetism.

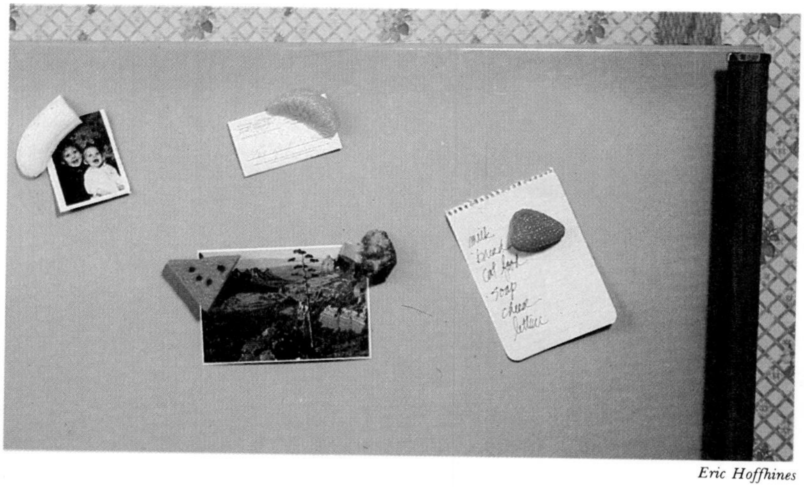

Eric Hoffhines

FIGURE 16-3. Magnets are often used to hold notes and other items on a refrigerator.

Dykstra/Image Finders Photo Agency

FIGURE 16-4. Electromagnets are made from a coil of wire around a metal core.

Hickson-Bender Photography

magnets are made of steel. These magnets are called permanent magnets. Alnico, an alloy of aluminum, nickel, and cobalt is also used in permanent magnets.

## 16:3 Electromagnets

How can electricity be used to produce magnetism?

Electricity produces magnetic fields. This fact is used to make electromagnets. An **electromagnet** is a piece of metal, usually iron or steel, surrounded by a coil of wire. Electricity in the wire magnetizes the metal. The metal acts like a magnet when electricity passes through the wire.

Electromagnets are used to operate many devices including doorbells and telephones. When you push a doorbell button, a flow of electricity magnetizes an electromagnet in the bell. The electromagnet attracts a steel knob, causing the knob to strike the bell. As it strikes, the electricity is turned off and the knob springs back to its original position. The electricity flows again and the cycle repeats.

Explain how an electromagnet works in a telephone.

A telephone contains electromagnets. When a person talks to you on the telephone, the voice pattern is carried by electricity. This electricity produces magnetism in an electromagnet inside the telephone receiver. The electromagnet makes a thin metal strip vibrate back and forth. The vibrations stimulate receptors in the ear. Impulses are sent to the brain, and you hear the person speak.

## activity ELECTROMAGNETS

(1) Obtain an iron nail, 1½-volt battery, and a 20-cm length of bell wire. (2) Wrap the wire tightly in a coil around the iron nail. (3) Connect the two ends of the wire to the battery. Attempt to pick up pins, tacks, and paper clips with the nail. Is the nail magnetic? (4) Remove the cover from an electric bell. Identify the electromagnet and metal striker. (5) Connect the bell and switch to a 1½-volt battery. (6) Use the switch to turn the bell on and off a few times. Observe the movement of the metal striker. How does the electromagnet operate the bell?

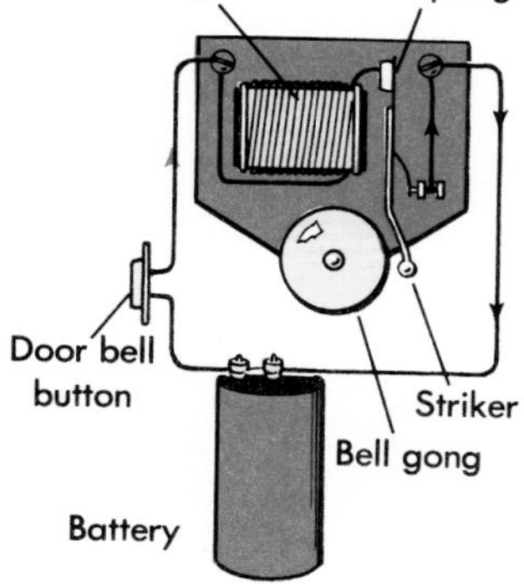


FIGURE 16-5.

## 16:4 Static Electricity

Magnetism may be caused by electricity. The word electricity comes from a Greek word that means amber. Amber is the hardened sap from a tree. When rubbed, it attracts small pieces of paper and dust. This effect is called **static electricity**.

Describe three examples of static electricity.

What causes static electricity?

Have you ever pulled your clothes out of the dryer and found your socks stuck to your jeans? Have you ever felt a shock when you touched a metal doorknob after you walked across a carpet? If you have had these experiences you were exposed to static electricity. In each case, an object has been "charged" with static electricity. The charge is produced by the object either gaining or losing electrons.

Static electricity is caused by the transfer of electrons. If an object gains electrons, it develops a negative electric charge. An object that loses electrons develops a positive electric charge. Because the charge is not moving, it is called static, meaning at rest. A static charge of electricity remains for a short time and is gradually lost. A charge can be eliminated by touching the charged object to the earth. Since the earth is so large, no net charge develops on it.

Walk across a wool rug, then touch a metal doorknob, and you may feel a shock. You gain a negative electric charge as your feet rub the wool

FIGURE 16–6. Static electric charges can be produced in a clothes dryer, causing articles of clothing to cling.

*Image Workshop*

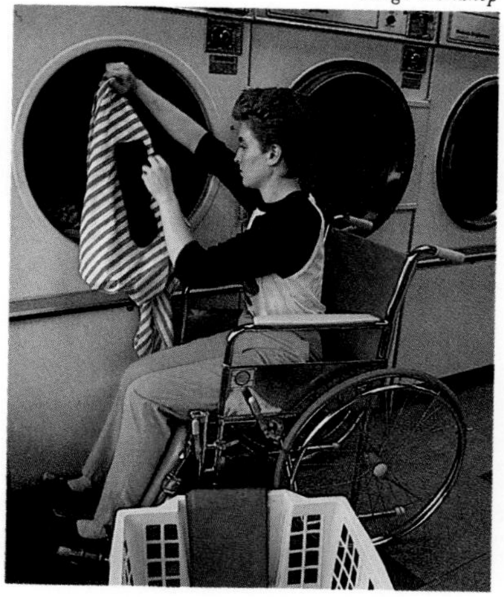

Larry Hamill

FIGURE 16-7. The conductors in this cable are metal wires. They are surrounded by plastic insulators.

Distinguish between conductor and insulator.

carpet. When you touch the doorknob, the electrons move from you to the metal.

Now suppose you walk across the carpet and touch the doorknob with a metal pen. You see a small flash of light between the pen and the knob. Electrons move through the pen to the doorknob. The flash of light, or spark, is produced when the electrons combine with atoms. This combining changes electric energy to heat and light.

The metal pen in the example above is called a conductor. A **conductor** is a substance through which electricity flows easily. Metals are excellent conductors. Some substances do not conduct electricity well. These substances are called **insulators**. Wood and rubber are good electric insulators.

Explain how lightning is produced.

The sudden transfer of a large electric charge from one object to another is called an electric discharge. Lightning is an electric discharge. It is a giant spark between two clouds of opposite charge or between the cloud and the earth. The electric field pulls electrons from the air molecules. When the electrons recombine with the molecules, light and heat are produced. The intense heat makes the air expand suddenly. This rapid expansion produces a loud noise called thunder.

Bob Hamburg/Tom Stack & Associates

FIGURE 16-8. Lightning is an electric discharge.

A lightning discharge from a cloud to the ground is very dangerous. Many people have been killed by lightning. Lightning can also start fires. Buildings may be protected from lightning by lightning rods. An electric discharge always takes the shortest path to the ground. A lightning rod is connected to the ground by a wire. The lightning rod is said to be grounded. A lightning bolt striking the building will travel down the rod into the wire and into the ground. Usually, there is no damage. If lightning strikes a steel frame building, the electrons travel through the steel to the ground. Metals are good conductors of electricity. Lightning rods and ground wires are made of metals.

There are two important facts to remember about electric charges.

(1) Electric charges can be positive or negative.

(2) Like charges repel each other; unlike charges attract each other.

There are many practical applications of static electricity. Copy machines use static charges and dry inks in copying material. Electronic air filters in homes and industries use static charges to remove dust and particles from the air.

Doug Martin

FIGURE 16-9. A lightning rod is used to protect a building by grounding the electric discharge of lightning.

How does a lightning rod protect a building against lightning?

What two important facts should you remember about electric charges?

## activity

### STATIC ELECTRICITY

**(1)** Obtain two pith balls, each attached to a thread. Suspend the balls so they are about 2 cm apart. Do they attract or repel each other? Do they have the same charge? Explain. **(2)** Charge a hard rubber rod with wool. Touch the rod to both pith balls. Do the balls attract or repel each other? Explain. **(3)** Repeat Step 2 using a glass rod and wool. Explain your observation. **(4)** Charge one pith ball with the rubber rod and the other ball with the glass rod. Do the balls attract or repel each other. Why?

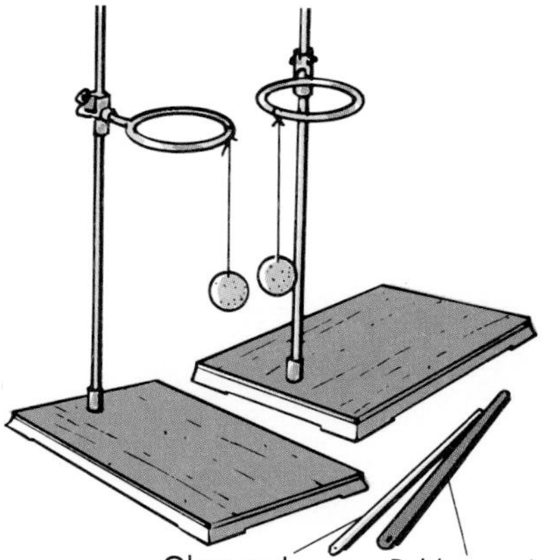


FIGURE 16-10.

## making sure

**2.** What is meant by the term electric discharge?

**3.** Why does a steel skyscraper not need a ground?

## 16:5 Electric Potential Energy

Compare the flow of electrons to a falling rock.

Electricity can transfer energy. Let us look at a model to help us understand how this process occurs. A large rock rests on the edge of a cliff that rises 50 m above a lake. The rock has potential energy because of its height. If the rock falls, this potential energy will be changed to kinetic energy. Kinetic energy is transferred to the water in the lake when the rock strikes it and makes the water splash. The rock falls because it is attracted by gravity.

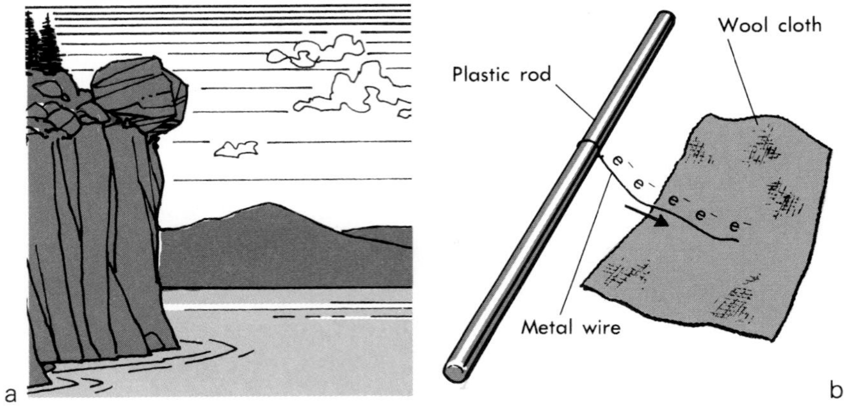


FIGURE 16-11. The rock has potential energy due to its position above the lake (a). When a rod is rubbed with wool, it gains potential energy in the form of electrons. The potential energy is changed to kinetic energy if the rod and wool are connected by a wire through which electrons can flow (b).

Now suppose a plastic rod is rubbed with wool. Electrons are transferred from the wool to the rod, making the rod negatively charged. This situation is similar to the rock and water above. The electrons in the rod have electric potential energy. If the charged rod is connected to the wool by a metal wire, electrons will flow through the wire from the rod to the wool. The electric potential energy of the electrons is changed to kinetic energy. Electrons flow from the negative rod to the positive wool because they always flow from areas of higher concentration to areas of lower concentration. If a wire or other conductor connects two charged objects, electrons will flow from the object with more electrons to the object with fewer electrons.

What unit is used to measure electric potential energy?

The difference in electric potential energy between two points is called potential difference and is measured in **volts** (V). Potential difference is also called voltage (VOHL tihj).

FIGURE 16-12. The electric potential difference between two points can be measured using a voltmeter.

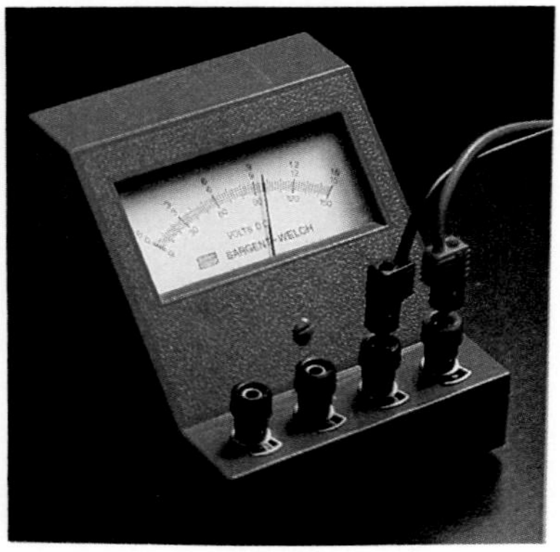

## making sure

4. What is electric potential energy? Describe one way that it can be produced.

# 16:6 Electric Current

An **electric current** is a flow of electrons. When two objects having a potential difference are connected together by a conductor, a flow of electrons occurs. For an electric current to be useful, a constant flow of electrons must be maintained. There must be a device that can "pump" electrons from one object to another object so a potential difference is maintained. The most common "pumps" are batteries and generators. The battery in a portable radio creates a potential difference that causes an electric current.

What is an electric current?

How is an electric current produced?

a

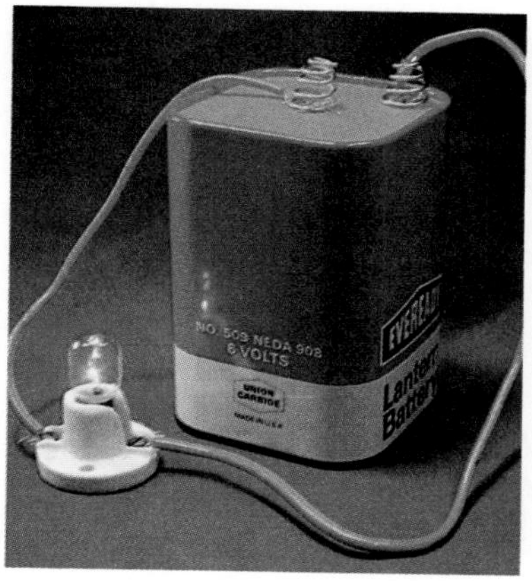


Craig Kramer

b

Hickson-Bender Photography

FIGURE 16-13. The terminals of a battery have a potential difference. When they are connected by a wire, current flows (a). Batteries and dry cells have many sizes and shapes (b).

There are two types of batteries: those made of wet cells and those made of dry cells. Both types of batteries use chemical energy to generate electric current. The wet cell contains two different metals in a solution containing an acid, base, or salt. When an acid, base, or salt dissolves in water, ions are released (Section 12:10). Recall that ions are charged particles. The solution contains an equal number of positive and negative charges. When a wire connects the two metals, electrons move from one metal to the other. One metal becomes negatively charged. The other becomes positively charged. Ions move through the

Draw a diagram of a wet cell and explain how it works.

FIGURE 16-14. Electrons flow from the zinc strip through the wire to the copper strip. The copper(II) sulfate solution transfers the electrons back to the zinc strip in this wet cell.

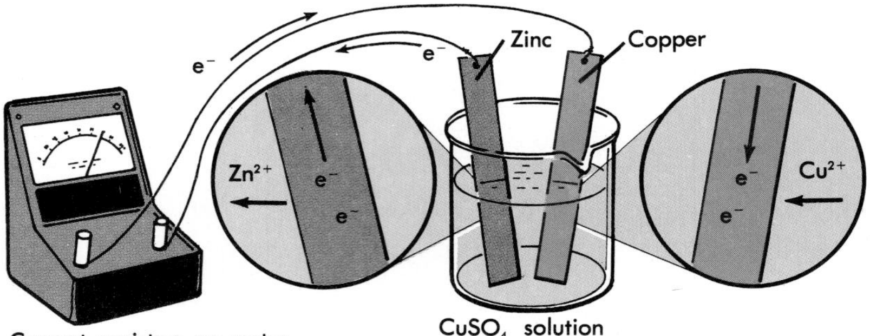


solutions because they are attracted by the charged metals. The flow of electrons is a current. If the wire is removed from one metal, the flow of electrons stops. A battery contains one or more cells connected together. For example, the storage battery in a car contains wet cells connected together to produce a potential difference of 6 volts or 12 volts.

Describe how electric current is generated in a dry cell.

Electric current is also generated by a dry cell. A dry cell is a zinc can containing a moist, pastelike mixture of chemicals. In the center of the can is a solid carbon rod. Chemicals in the paste react with the zinc and release electrons that flow through a conductor to the carbon rod (Figure 16-15).

What is the unit for measuring electric current?

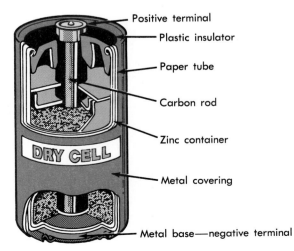

Electric current is defined as the rate of flow of electric charge. Electric current is measured in a unit called the **ampere** (AM pihr). The current produced by batteries is called direct current, DC. In **direct current,** the electrons flow in one direction.

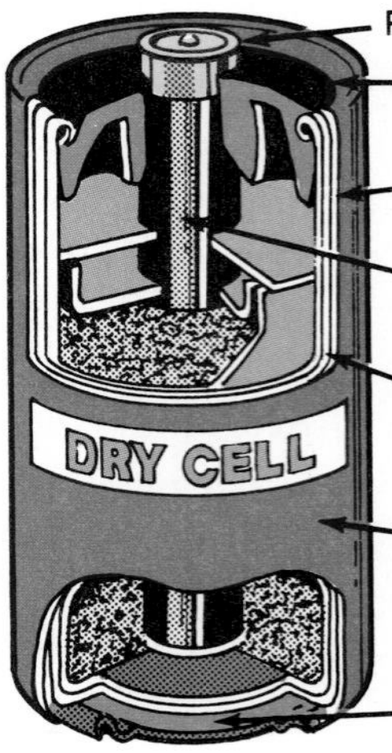


FIGURE 16-15. A dry cell contains a moist paste between a zinc case and a carbon rod. The zinc and the carbon are the electrodes.

## making sure

5. One kind of battery in a car contains four wet cells connected together. Each cell has a potential difference of 1½ volts. What is the voltage of the battery?

## 16:7 Electric Generators

Some generators produce an electric current called an alternating current (AC). Alternating current is produced by magnetism. Pushing a magnet through a coil of wire causes electrons in the wire to move. Pulling the magnet in the opposite direction reverses the direction of the electron movement. Pushing and pulling generates an alternating current in the coil. In an **alternating current**, the direction of electron flow changes. Electrons reverse their directions many times in one second.

How is alternating current different from direct current?

A simple electric generator is shown in Figure 16–16. When the handle is turned, the coil rotates. When the coil rotates, the magnetic field at all points in the wire changes direction. Because the magnetic field constantly changes direction, the current in the coil constantly changes direction.

Explain how a generator produces an electric current.

A strong magnet produces more current than a weak magnet. Increasing the number of loops in the coil also increases the current.

a

b

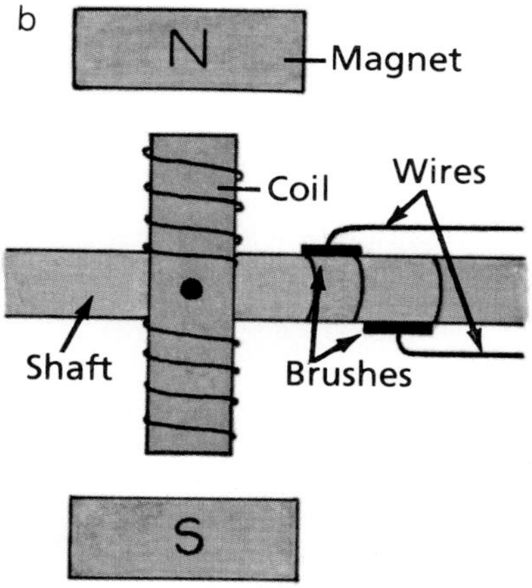


FIGURE 16-16. When the handle of this simple electric generator (a) is turned, the coil rotates. The magnetic field in the wire changes direction(b), producing alternating current.

Alternating current is designated as a number of cycles per second, or hertz. In the United States, most current supplied to homes and businesses is alternating current. Generators that produce the electricity usually operate at 60 Hz.

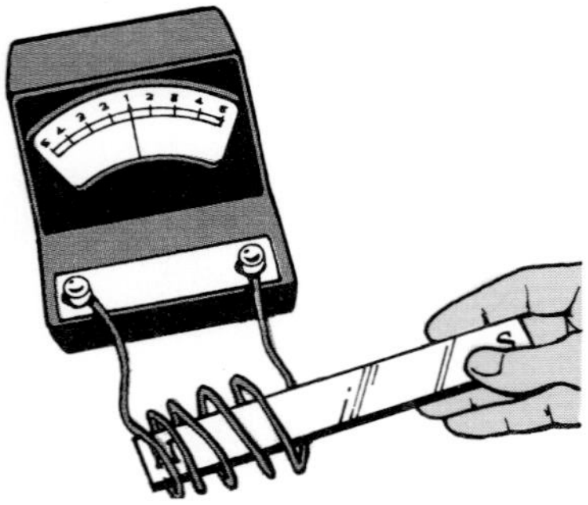


FIGURE 16-17.

## activity MAGNETISM AND ELECTRIC CURRENTS

Obtain a 1-m piece of wire. Twist the wire into a coil having 5 loops, each with a diameter of 5 cm. Attach the two ends of the wire to a galvanometer. Move a bar magnet back and forth through the coil. Is an electric current formed? How does the speed of the magnet's movement affect the quantity of electric current?

## 16:8 Resistance and Ohm's Law

What is resistance and what unit is used to measure it?

Every substance offers some resistance (rih ZIHS tunts) to the flow of electrons. **Resistance** is the opposition of a conductor to the movement of electrons through it. Resistance is measured in **ohms** (Ω). Wires have different resistances to the flow of electrons. For example, a copper wire has less resistance than an iron wire. Electrons flow more easily through a wire of low resistance.

How are the thickness and length of a wire related to its resistance?

The electric resistance of a wire is affected by its length and thickness. A long copper wire has more resistance than a short copper wire. A copper wire with a large diameter has less resistance than a copper wire with a small diameter. Comparing the wire to a water pumping system is helpful in understanding resistance. The size of the pipe affects the quantity of water that can flow through it. More water can flow through a 10-cm pipe in 1 min than through a 5-cm pipe, providing the pressure is the same in both. In effect, the pipe with the larger diameter has less resistance to water flow. A wire with a larger diameter has less resistance to electron flow than one of smaller diameter.

FIGURE 16–18. A small wire or metal strip serves as a resistor in an automobile fuse.

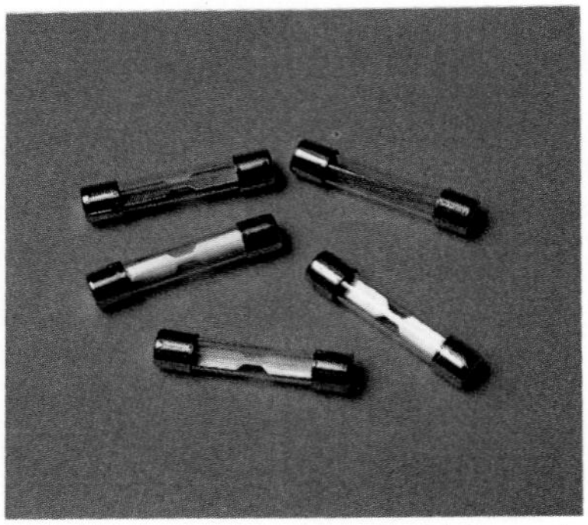

*Gerard Photography*

When electrons flow through a substance, they lose energy. The electrons do work, which is changed to heat. The relationship among potential difference, current, and resistance is known as Ohm's law. Ohm's law states that current is equal to the potential difference divided by the resistance.

$$\text{current (amperes)} = \frac{\text{voltage (volts)}}{\text{resistance (ohms)}}$$

$$I = \frac{V}{R}$$

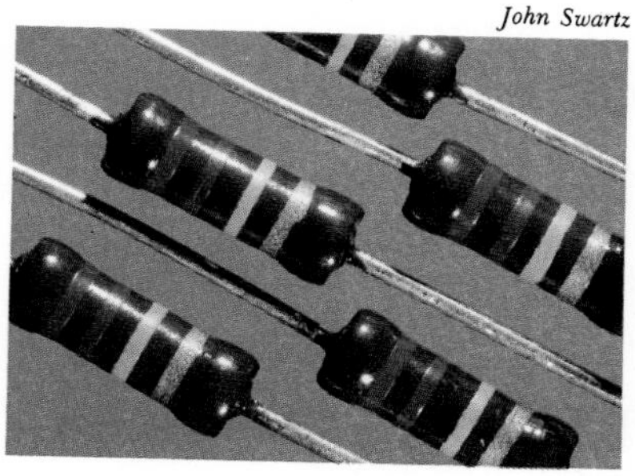
John Swartz

FIGURE 16–19. Resistors are used to control the voltage and current in different parts of many electric devices. Resistors usually have four color bands that indicate the amount of resistance.

State Ohm's law.

***Example***

A circuit has a potential difference of 6 V. The resistance is 2 Ω. What current flows through the wire?

Solution

*Step 1*: Write the equation for Ohm's Law.

$$I = \frac{V}{R}$$

*Step 2*: Substitute the values given in the problem.

$$I = \frac{6\ \text{V}}{2\ \Omega}$$

*Step 3*: Solve the mathematical equation.

$$I = 3\ \text{A}$$

***Example***

The current passing through the taillight of a car is 4 A. The resistance is 2 Ω. What is the potential difference?

Solution

*Step 1*: Write the equation for Ohm's law.

$$I = \frac{V}{R}$$

*Step 2*: Rearrange $I = \frac{V}{R}$ to find $V$.

$$V = I \times R$$

*Step 3*: Substitute the values given in the problem.

$$V = 4\ \text{A} \times 2\ \Omega$$

*Step 4*: Solve the mathematical equation.

$$V = 8\ \text{V}$$

***Example***

A wire has a current of 2 A flowing through it. If the potential difference is 14 V, what is the resistance?

Solution

*Step 1*: Write the equation for Ohm's law.

$$I = \frac{V}{R}$$

*Step 2*: Rearrange to find *R*.

$$R = \frac{V}{I}$$

*Step 3*: Substitute the values given in the problem.

$$R = \frac{14\ \text{V}}{2\ \text{A}}$$

*Step 4*: Solve the mathematical equation.

$$R = 7\ \Omega$$

## making sure

**6.** Use Ohm's law to find the unknown for each example.

| Volts | Ohms | Amperes |
|---|---|---|
| 1.5 | 2 | *I* |
| 6.0 | *R* | 3 |
| 12.0 | 6 | *I* |
| *V* | 0.22 | 2.2 |
| 220.0 | 10.0 | *I* |

## 16:9 Types of Circuits

The path formed by the conductors for the electrons is called a **circuit** (SUR kut). There are two kinds of circuits: series and parallel. In a **series circuit**, there is only one path for the electrons (Figure 16–19). When any part of the circuit is disconnected, the current no longer flows. A switch is used to open and close circuits. When the switch is open, there is no current in any part of the circuit.

How is a parallel circuit different from a series circuit?

In a **parallel circuit**, there are two or more paths for the electrons. The voltage is the same in each branch. If one branch of the circuit is opened, the current still flows through the other branches.

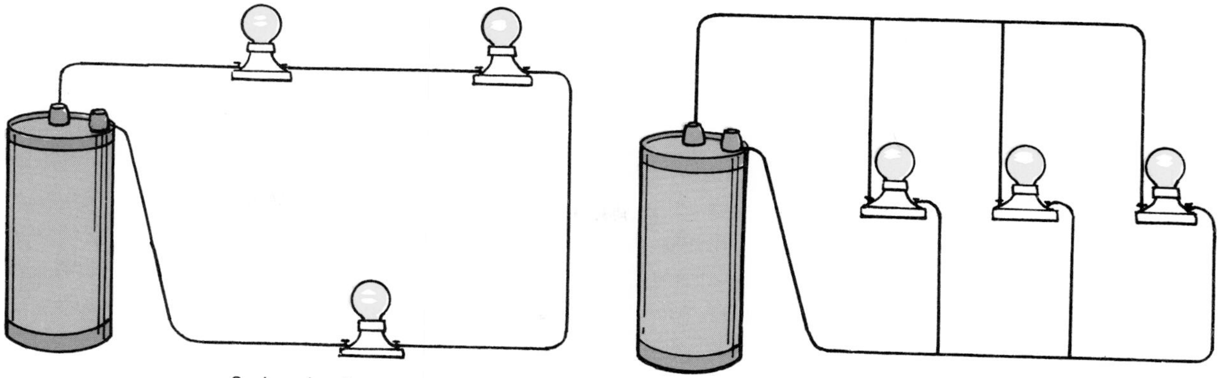


FIGURE 16-20. In a series circuit, there is only one path for the current (a). In a parallel circuit, there is more than one path for the current (b).

The current in a circuit is equal to the sum of the currents required by each appliance in the circuit. When the number of appliances is increased, the total current in the circuit is increased too. If the current becomes too large, the circuit cannot meet the demand. The wires can overheat and start a fire.

Why are fuses and circuit breakers used in circuits?

To prevent overloading a circuit, fuses or circuit breakers are built into most circuits. A fuse is made with a metal wire that has a low melting point. When the current is greater than the rating of the fuse, the wire melts and the flow of electricity is stopped. The flow of electricity will not begin again until a new fuse is put into the circuit. However, the cause of the overload must be found and corrected first. Many house circuits contain 20-A fuses.

Define a short circuit.

In newer houses, circuit breakers are used instead of fuses. The circuit breaker looks like a light switch. When too much current flows through the breaker, the circuit is opened. When the circuit has cooled, the breaker can be reset. Never reset a breaker without locating the cause of the overload and correcting it.

Fuses and circuit breakers protect a building from short circuits. A short circuit occurs when the current takes a "short cut" and does not follow its intended path. When a short circuit occurs, there is a large increase in current. The wire in the fuse melts, or the circuit breaker is activated and the circuit is broken.

FIGURE 16–21. Circuit breakers protect a building from fires that could be caused by short circuits.

*John Swartz*

## activity CIRCUITS

**(1)** Obtain a dry cell, pieces of bell wire, a switch, a screwdriver, and several small lamp receptacles. **(2)** Using the screwdriver and the wire, connect three 1½ volt lamps as shown in Figure 16–22a to the dry cell. **(3)** Complete the wire circuit so that the lamps are lighted. Unscrew one of the lamps. What happens? Is this a series or parallel circuit? **(4)** Connect the three lamps as shown in Figure 16–22b. Connect the wire so the circuit is complete. **(5)** Unscrew one of the lamps. Is this a series or parallel circuit?

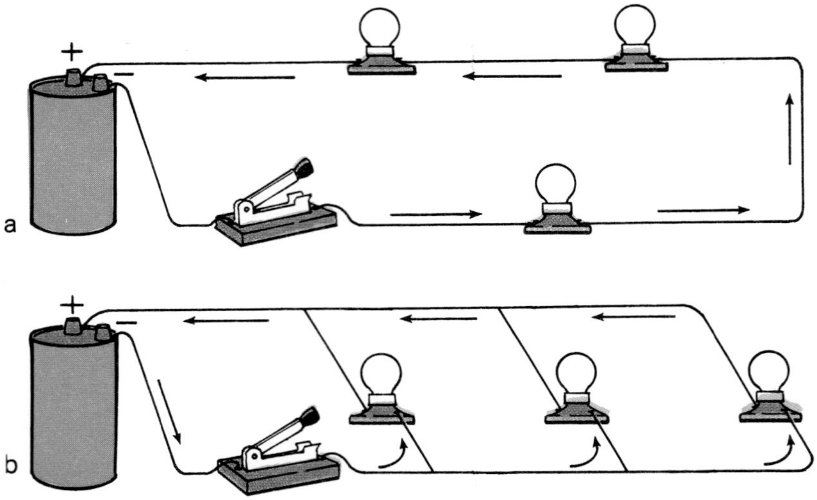


FIGURE 16–22.

### making sure

**7.** Why is it important to find the cause of an overloaded circuit?

**8.** A kitchen circuit has appliances that draw the following current: light bulb, 0.8 A; electric heater, 15 A; and an electric skillet, 11 A. If the circuit has a 20-A fuse, will the fuse blow? Explain.

## 16:10 Electric Energy and Power

Electric appliances such as a toaster and a television use energy. Electric energy is transformed into heat and light in the toaster and into visible light in the television. These appliances are rated in watts of power. Power is defined as the work done (energy used) per unit of time. The power in a circuit is the voltage of the source multiplied by the current produced by the source. The unit for power is the **watt**, W.

What is the unit used to measure electric power?

How is the amount of electric energy calculated?

$$\text{power} = \text{voltage} \times \text{current}$$

$$P = V \times I$$

***Example***

A toaster uses 7 A of current when it is plugged into a 110-V circuit. How many watts of power does this toaster use?

Solution

*Step 1*: Write the equation for power.

$$P = V \times I$$

*Step 2*: Substitute the values given in the problem.

$$P = 110 \text{ V} \times 7 \text{ A}$$

*Step 3*: Solve the mathematical equation.

$$P = 770 \text{ W}$$

Electric light bulbs are stamped with the number of watts of power they use. Many 100-watt bulbs are used in home lamps. An electric toaster uses about 800 watts of power.

When you use electric current, you are using energy. The amount of electric energy that you use depends upon the amount of energy required and the length of time the energy is used. To measure electric energy, you must measure the power and the time. Electric companies sell energy in units called kilowatt hours. A **kilowatt hour** (kWh) is the energy of 1000 W delivered constantly for 1 h.

FIGURE 16–23. An electric meter is used to measure the kilowatt hours used in a home.

*Aaron Haupt*

## making sure

9. How many watts of power are used by an electric stove that draws 5 A of current on a 220-V line?
10. An electric blanket uses 2 A of current on a 110-V line. How much power does it use?

# Conducting Plastics

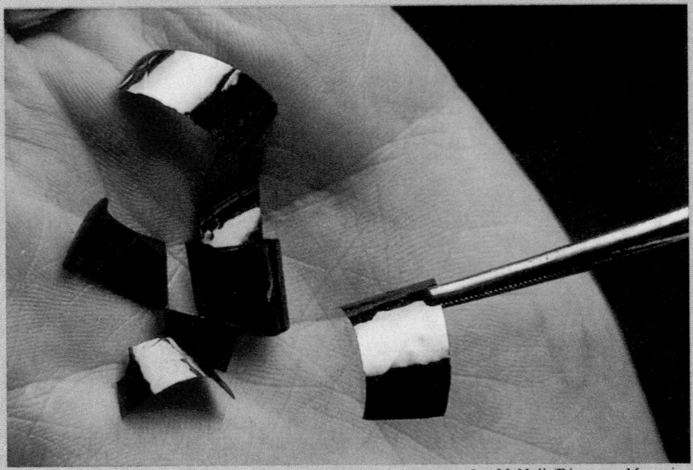

*Joe McNally*/Discover *Magazine*

In 1970, an assistant to a chemist in Japan was asked to prepare a polymer from acetylene. While making the plastic, the assistant used too much of a certain chemical catalyst. Instead of producing a black powder, a silvery film formed. When treated with iodine, the properties of the plastic altered. The iodine produced a plastic that could conduct electricity.

The discovery of a plastic that could conduct electricity was a surprise to the researchers. Unlike metals, plastics have always been considered excellent electrical insulators. Metals conduct electricity because they have loosely bonded electrons that easily pass from atom to atom. This movement of electrons is an electric current. Plastics have electrons that are tightly attached to their nuclei. Because the electrons are not free to move, an electric current cannot pass through a plastic.

In the new plastic, iodine acts as a "crowbar" to pry electrons from the atoms that make up the polymer. When an electrical field is applied to the plastic, electrons move into the "holes" left in the atoms by the iodine. These electrons in turn leave "holes" behind them, which are filled by still other electrons. Thus, the plastic becomes a conductor and allows the passage of an electric current.

Scientists are now researching practical applications for these plastics. One promising use is in making a super-lightweight battery for electric cars. Researchers have already produced experimental electric batteries that not only weigh less than conventional batteries, but also can be charged and discharged much faster than conventional lead-acid batteries. These batteries also can be recharged an indefinite number of times. Scientists foresee these batteries being used in appliances or by public utilities to store electricity from hydroelectric or wind generators. They may also be used to fabricate inexpensive solar panels. Scientists hope that in the future, these plastics may be used in place of more expensive metals in motors, wires, and other manufactured products that contain conductors.

# main ideas — Chapter Review

1. Like magnetic poles repel and unlike poles attract. 16:1
2. The magnetic properties of an object are determined by its atomic structure. 16:2
3. An electromagnet is made by passing electricity through a wire coiled around a piece of metal. 16:3
4. An object develops a negative electric charge when it gains electrons and a positive electric charge when it loses electrons. 16:4
5. Electricity transfers energy. Electrons always flow from areas of high concentration to areas of low concentration. 16:5
6. An electric current is a flow of electrons through a conductor. Electric current is measured in amperes (A). 16:6
7. In direct current (DC), the flow of electrons is continuous in one direction. In alternating current (AC), the electron flow reverses many times per second. 16:6, 16:7
8. Ohm's law states that current, $I$, is equal to potential difference, $V$, divided by resistance, $R$. 16:8
9. The path formed by a conductor for electrons is a circuit. 16:9
10. Electric power is the work done per unit of time. The unit of power is the watt (W). Electric energy can be measured in kilowatt hours. 16:10

# vocabulary

*Define each of the following words or terms.*

alternating current
ampere
circuit
conductor
direct current
electric current
electromagnet
insulators
kilowatt hours
ohms
parallel circuit
resistance
series circuit
static electricity
volts
watt

# study questions

**DO NOT WRITE IN THIS BOOK.**

## A. True or False

*Determine whether each of the following sentences is true or false. If the sentence is false, rewrite it to make it true.*

1. Static electricity is either positive or negative.
2. An object may gain or lose electrons.

3. A battery produces an electric current.
4. Electrons flow to the positive terminal.
5. A grounded lightning rod is less safe than one that is not grounded.
6. Electric resistance is measured in amperes.
7. A watt is a unit of power.
8. A kilowatt is equal to 100 watts.
9. A freely-swinging magnet points to the north.
10. A magnet has a magnetic field around it.

**B. Multiple Choice**

*Choose the word or phrase that completes correctly each of the following sentences.*

1. The resistance of a large diameter copper wire is *(more than, less than, the same as)* the resistance of a small diameter copper wire.
2. When a dry cell produces a current, the number of electrons inside the cell (*increases, decreases, remains the same*).
3. When the voltage in a circuit increases, the current (*increases, decreases, remains the same*).
4. If one lamp is removed from a series circuit, the current through the circuit (*increases, stops, continues*).
5. (*Iron, Copper, Lead, Calcium*) is used to make magnets.
6. A circuit breaker is often used instead of a(n) (*fuse, motor, bell, electromagnet*).
7. The fuse wire in an electric circuit will melt when the (*amperes, volts, ohms*) become too high.
8. The charge for electric service to a home is based on the total (*volts, amperes, kilowatt hours, watts*).
9. Electric power is measured in (*amperes, volts, watts*).
10. A magnetic north pole attracts a magnetic (*south, north*) pole.

**C. Completion**

*Complete each of the following sentences with a word or phrase that will make the sentence correct.*

1. A ______ cell and a ______ cell produce electric current.
2. The current produced by a battery is called ______.
3. An alternating current can be produced by pushing and pulling a magnet through ______.
4. A battery converts ______ energy to ______ energy.

5. When a piece of iron or steel is stroked with a(n) ______ the iron or steel becomes magnetized.
6. An electromagnet uses a coil of ______ and electricity to produce a magnetic field.
7. A gain of electrons produces ______ static electricity.
8. Two negatively charged objects ______ each other.
9. When lightning passes through the air, the rapid expansion of air produces a noise called ______.
10. A kilowatt hour is a unit of electric ______.

**D. How and Why**

1. What causes static electricity? Give two examples of static electricity.
2. How does a lightning rod work?
3. Is each of the following a conductor or an insulator: copper, glass, aluminum, silver, cork, zinc?
4. How does an alternating current differ from a direct current?
5. State Ohm's law. What is the resistance in ohms of a 12 volt circuit having 2 A of current?

## challenges

1. Obtain information from your local power company on ways to conserve electric energy. Plan a conservation program for home or school.
2. Test a number of different metals with a magnet. Make a list of those metals that are attracted by magnets and those that are not. From the classification tell which metals have unpaired electrons.
3. The transistor is a very important electronic invention. Prepare a library report on transistors.

## interesting reading

D'Ignazio, Fred, *Small Computers: Exploring Their Technology and Future.* New York: Franklin Watts, 1981.

Jacobsen, Karen, *Computers.* Chicago: Children's Press, 1982.

Sabin, Louis, *Thomas Alva Edison: Young Inventor.* Mahwah, NJ: Troll, 1983.

Stanley, Leon, *Easy to Make Electric Gadgets.* New York: Harvey, 1980.

# SIDE ROADS

## Studying Magnetic Fields

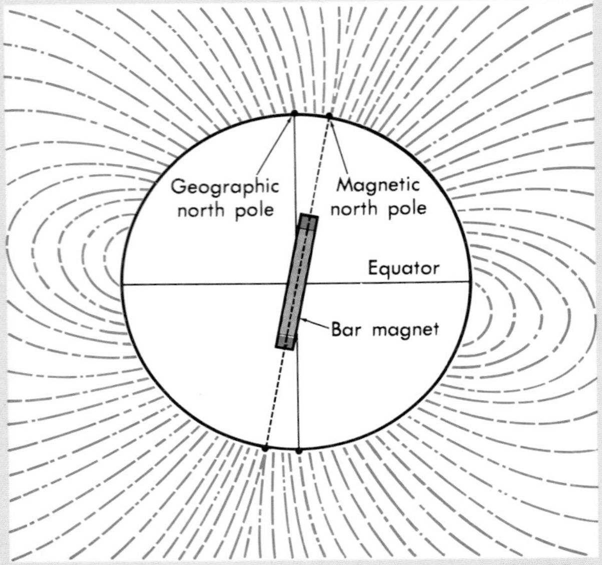


FIGURE A

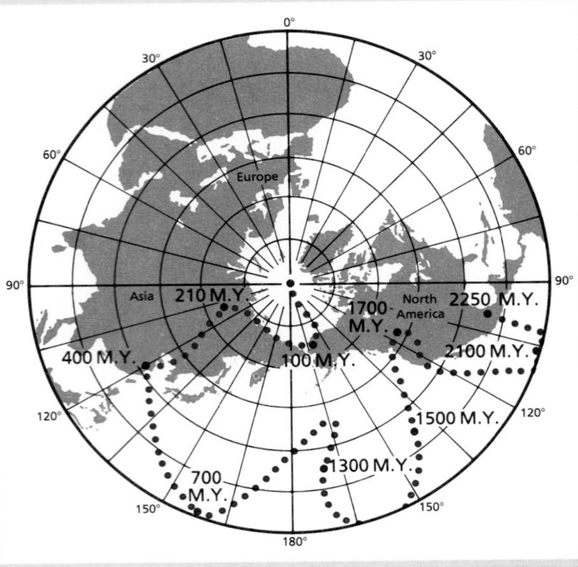


FIGURE B

*Earth has a magnetic field that shields it from much harmful radiation. The field is generated by the movement of Earth's fluid iron core. Heat in the core causes convective currents in the fluid iron. Electric currents are produced, and these currents create a magnetic field. This iron core acts like a large bar magnet at the center of the earth that is slightly inclined to the geographic north pole (Figure A).*

*Many rocks contain magnetic minerals. The most common magnetic mineral is magnetite. In rocks formed by volcanic eruptions, a magnetic field forms around each magnetite particle as the rock cools. The north end of each magnetite grain aligns with the north end of Earth's "bar magnet" and thus points to the magnetic north pole. Once the rock hardens, it becomes a permanent record of the position of the magnetic north pole at the time of the rock's formation. Scientists study the magnetic particles in rocks to learn about Earth's history.*

*Geologists have discovered that the magnetite grains in all rocks do not point to what is now Earth's magnetic north pole. The alignment of magnetite grains in rocks that have formed throughout Earth's history appear to indicate that the magnetic north pole has wandered about. The apparent position of the pole has been plotted on a map (Figure B). However, scientists believe that it is not the pole that has wandered, but the continents. By the continents moving to different positions throughout geologic time, the pole position stays constant. Thus, the alignment of magnetic particles has helped to support the theory of continental drifting, also known as plate tectonics.*

FIGURE C

*A second reason that magnetite grains do not all align with the current magnetic north pole is that Earth's magnetic field has reversed several times in the past. During a reversal in polarity, a compass needle would point south instead of north. Although it is not known why these reversals occurred, rocks indicate that they have occurred once or twice each million years. During a period of reversal, the magnetic field shielding Earth from harmful radiation weakens. Scientists have correllated the extinction of species thought to be sensitive to radiation with these reversals in polarity.*

*Magnetic field reversals also have become important in dating the seafloor. Scientists traveling back and forth across the Atlantic Ocean have detected variations in the magnetic field with a magnetometer. They have determined that as new ocean floor forms at the Mid-Atlantic Ridge, it becomes magnetized and imprinted with a distinct magnetic direction. A portion of the mid-ocean ridge is shown in Figure C. The variations observed when studying the sea floor are useful in determining the age of the underlying sea floor and the rate of seafloor spreading (Figure D).*

FIGURE D

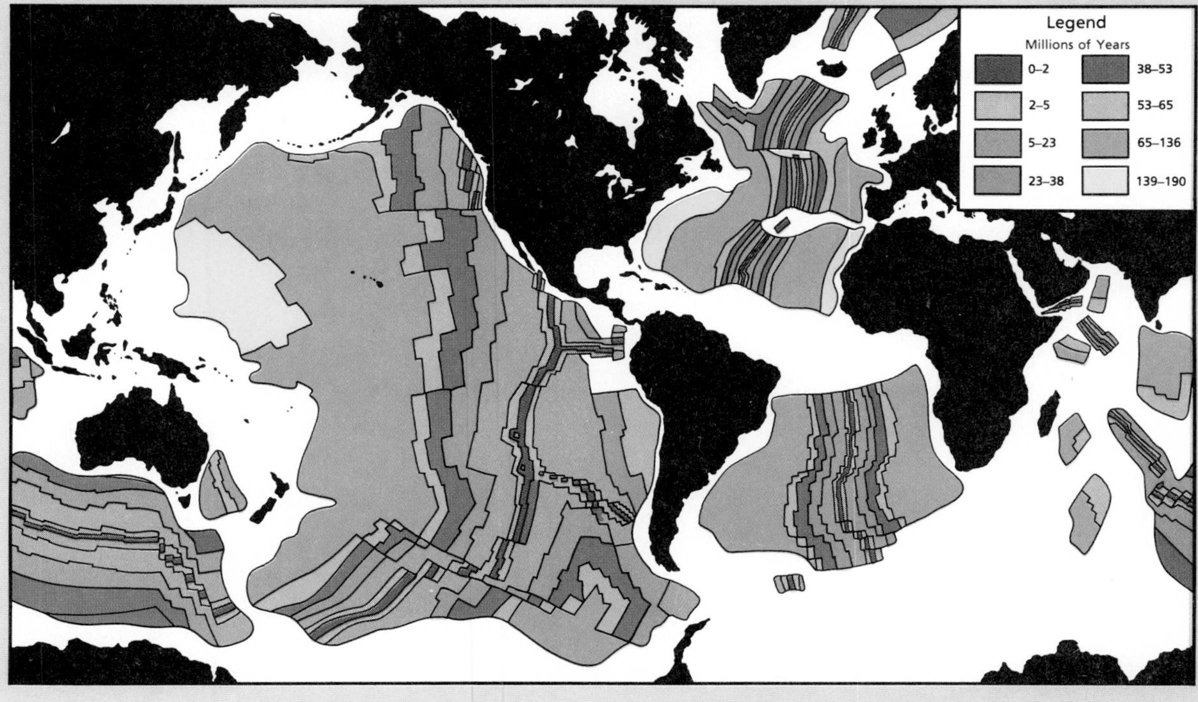

*This person's brain is being scanned by a PETT scanner. The PETT scanner measures chemical activity within the brain cells. The patient is given a shot of radioactive material. Then, the scanner traces the movement of this material through the brain. This procedure is helpful in diagnosing some diseases. What is radioactive material? What are other uses of radioactive material?*

Dan McCoy/Rainbow

# Nuclear Energy

# chapter 17

## 17:1 Radioactive Elements

GOAL: You will learn how nuclear energy is released from atoms, detected, and used.

Some naturally occurring elements and all elements with atomic numbers greater than 92 are radioactive elements. **Radioactive** means that the nuclei of these elements emit invisible, high-energy radiation. This radiation consists of particles and electromagnetic waves. As the radiation is released, the element may become another element. Radium, uranium, and polonium are naturally occurring radioactive elements.

Define radioactive and decay.

If the number of neutrons and protons in the nucleus is equal, the nucleus is stable. Stable nuclei are not radioactive. The more neutrons there are in a nucleus compared to the number of protons, the more likely a nucleus will decay. **Decay** is the process by which the nucleus of an atom emits radiation. All elements with atomic numbers above 83 are likely to decay. There are also some elements having less than 83 protons that can decay.

How does a radioactive element differ from a stable element?

Some elements have atoms that differ in atomic mass. For example, the most common form of hydrogen has an atomic mass of one. Other hydrogen atoms can have atomic masses of two or three. The atoms of the three forms of hydrogen are alike in that each has one proton in its nucleus. However, these three forms of hydrogen differ in

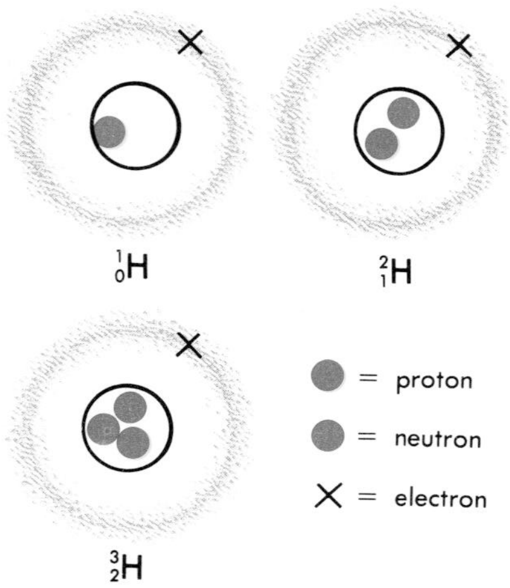


Figure 17-1. The three isotopes of hydrogen differ in atomic mass.

the number of neutrons there are in the nucleus. Hydrogen atoms with an atomic mass of one have no neutrons. Hydrogen atoms with an atomic mass of two have one neutron. Hydrogen atoms with an atomic mass of three have two neutrons each in their nuclei. Forms of the same element that differ in atomic mass are called **isotopes**. Isotopes of the same element differ in atomic mass, but they have the same chemical properties.

What is a nuclide?

Atoms of different elements and isotopes of the same element have a set number of protons and neutrons in their nuclei. An atom with its specific number of protons and neutrons is a **nuclide.** Hydrogen has three nuclides. They differ only in the number of neutrons found in their nuclei.

### making sure

1. How many neutrons are in each of the nuclides listed below?
   (a) $^{15}_{7}N$ (c) $^{4}_{2}He$
   (b) $^{16}_{6}C$ (d) $^{226}_{88}Ra$

## 17:2 Nuclear Radiation

Name three kinds of nuclear radiation.

When the nucleus of a radioactive atom decays, it emits radiation. Three kinds of nuclear radiation are, alpha (α), beta (β), and gamma (γ). Alpha, beta, and gamma are the first three letters in the Greek alphabet.

What is alpha radiation?

**Alpha radiation** consists of helium nuclei. Each helium nucleus contains two protons and two

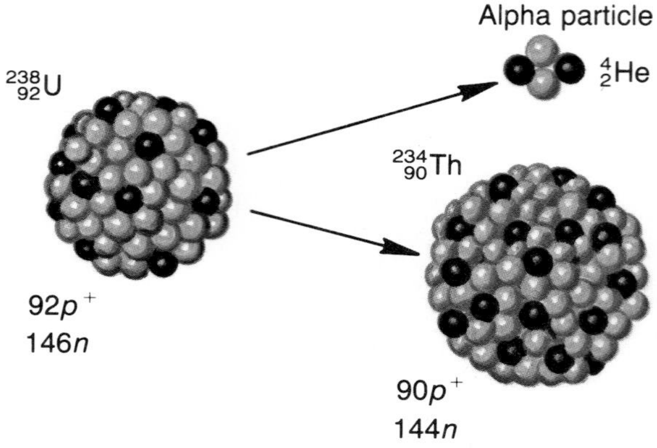


FIGURE 17-2. Uranium-238 decays to thorium-234 by emitting an alpha particle.

neutrons. ${}^{4}_{2}He$ is used as a symbol for an alpha particle. Alpha particles are positively charged. Alpha radiation does not have much penetrating power. It can be stopped by a thin sheet of paper.

Which of the three types of radiation can be stopped by a sheet of paper?

When a nucleus emits alpha radiation, the nucleus loses two protons. A new element forms. The changing of one element into another is called **transmutation** (trans myoo TAY shun). Radium is one element that emits alpha radiation. When radium undergoes alpha decay, it becomes radon. The equation for this transmutation is

$$ {}^{226}_{88}Ra \rightarrow {}^{222}_{86}Rn + {}^{4}_{2}He $$

What is beta radiation?

**Beta radiation** consists of electrons. These electrons are formed in the nucleus when a neutron changes. A neutron, n, changes to a proton, p. In this change, an electron, ${}^{0}_{-1}e$, and a neutrino (new TREE noh), $v$, are emitted. The equation for this change is

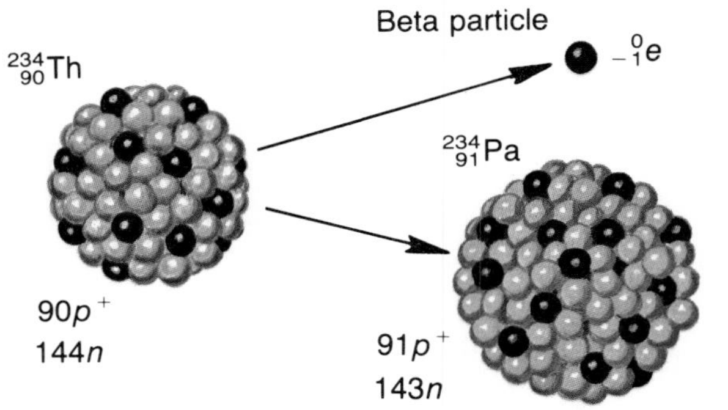


FIGURE 17-3. Thorium-234 decays to protactinium-234 by emitting a beta particle.

A neutrino has no mass and no charge. It travels at the speed of light and is very hard to detect. The proton remains in the nucleus and increases the atomic number by one, forming a new element. The electron emitted from the nucleus is the beta radiation. The nucleus of carbon 14 decays by beta emission. The equation for this transmutation is

$$ {}^{14}_{6}C \rightarrow {}^{14}_{7}N + {}^{0}_{-1}e + v $$

The penetrating power of beta radiation is 100 times that of alpha radiation. Beta radiation can pass through a piece of aluminum up to 6 mm thick.

What is gamma radiation?

Gamma decay does not result in the formation of a new element. Gamma radiation is emitted when a nucleus is rearranged during decay. **Gamma radiation** is a stream of very high-energy photons. A photon is a small packet of electromagnetic energy that travels in waves. Gamma radiation is called gamma rays. Gamma rays travel at the speed of light and have no charge. They can penetrate 30 cm of concrete and possess enough energy to damage or destroy living organisms.

### making sure

2. Make a table showing the symbol, mass, charge, and penetrating power of each form of nuclear radiation.

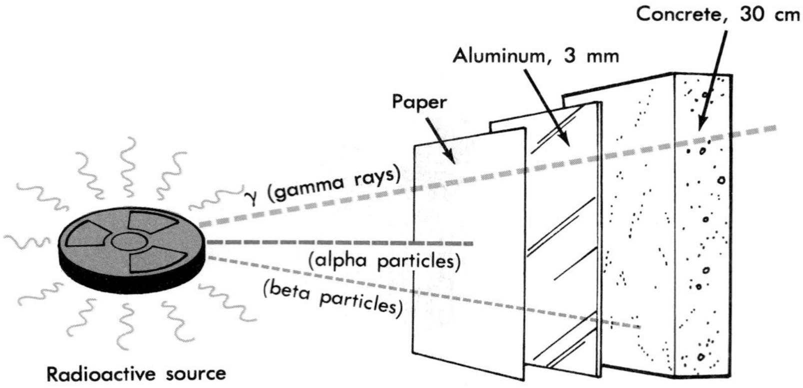


FIGURE 17-4. Alpha particles can be stopped by a sheet of paper. Beta particles can pass through a 3-mm thick piece of aluminum. Gamma rays can pass through 30 cm of concrete.

## 17:3 Half-Life and Decay Series

Radioactive nuclei of an element decay and release energy at a fixed rate. A fixed rate means that the rate of decay is constant over a period of time. Consider a quantity of popcorn in a hot skillet. Suppose there are 100 kernels of popcorn in the skillet. You know that the kernels will pop, but you do not know which kernels will pop first. As the kernels pop, you count them and find that one half the unpopped kernels pop every minute. This rate of one half the unpopped kernels popping per minute is a fixed rate. It is similar to the rate of decay of a radioactive element.

The time required for one half of a radioactive sample to decay is called **half-life**. For example, a rock sample contains 4 g of radium. The half-life of radium is 1620 years. In 1620 years, the mass of the radium remaining in the sample will be 2 g. The radium nuclei that decay will become radon and helium. After another 1620 years, 1 g of radium will remain. How much radium will be left after another 1620 years?

What is the half-life of an element?

The half-lives of known radioactive nuclides vary from a few milliseconds to billions of years. Table 17–1 lists the half-lives of some radioactive nuclides. The shorter the half-life, the more radioactive the nuclide.

Sometimes a radioactive nuclide decays to another element that is also radioactive. This new element then decays into a third element. This series of transmutations continues until a stable nucleus forms. When the decay proceeds through many steps it is called a **decay series**. Certain radioactive elements are found in nature as a result of the decay of other elements. Uranium 238 decays through a series of steps to form lead 206. Lead 206 is stable. Figure 17–5 shows the natural decay series for uranium 238. Note that the half-lives in the decay processes vary.

Describe the changes that occur in the uranium-238 decay series.

FIGURE 17-5. Uranium-238 decays through a series of steps to lead-206.

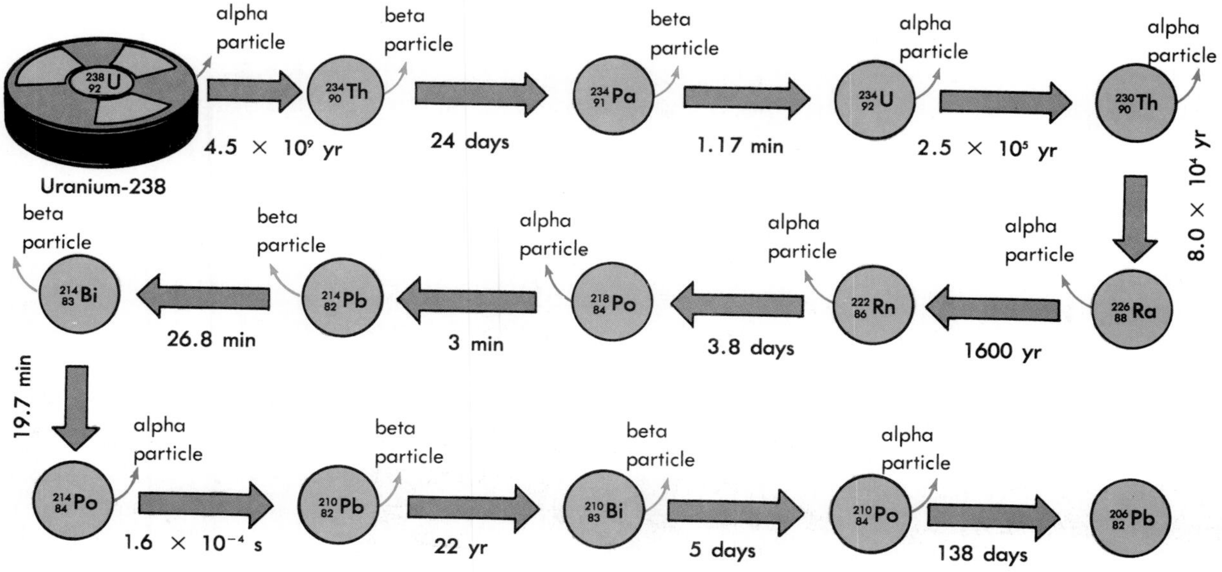

*Table 17–1.*
Half-lives of Some Radioactive Elements

| Atomic number | Element | Isotope | Half-life |
|---|---|---|---|
| 1 | Hydrogen | $^{3}_{1}H$ | 12.33 yr |
| 6 | Carbon | $^{14}_{6}C$ | 5730 yr |
| 7 | Nitrogen | $^{13}_{7}N$ | 9.96 min |
| 8 | Oxygen | $^{15}_{8}O$ | 122 s |
| 19 | Potassium | $^{40}_{19}K$ | 1.28 billion yr |
| 53 | Iodine | $^{131}_{53}I$ | 8.07 days |
| 84 | Polonium | $^{210}_{84}Po$ | 138.38 days |
| 92 | Uranium | $^{227}_{92}U$ | 1.3 min |
| 92 | Uranium | $^{238}_{92}U$ | 4.51 billion yr |
| 94 | Plutonium | $^{236}_{94}Pu$ | 2.85 yr |

What are some practical uses of radioactive nuclides?

The half-lives and decay patterns of some nuclides make them useful in practical applications. One application is determining the age of ancient materials. Radioactive dating using uranium-238 and other nuclides has shown the age of the oldest rocks on earth to be about four billion years. Another application is the use of carbon-14 to determine how much of the carbon dioxide in air is due to the burning of fuels.

Michael Collier

FIGURE 17–6. Radioactive nuclides can be used to find the age of an object.

## 17:4 Radiation Biology

We constantly receive radiation in small amounts. Radiation is part of our surroundings. This radiation is called background radiation. It comes from radioactive elements in the earth's crust and from cosmic rays from outer space.

What is background radiation and from where does it come?

The study of the effects of radiation on living tissue is called **radiation biology.** Radiation in large amounts can damage or destroy living cells. Radiation is used to treat cancer because it kills cancer cells. Usually gamma rays or X rays are used in radiation treatment. The radiation may be from a radioactive source, such as cobalt-60. Radiation is also used to sterilize bandages and surgical equipment because it kills most bacteria and viruses. Radiation can damage genes. Damage to genes results in mutation and birth defects. The effect of radiation on future generations is the cause of much concern.

How is radiation harmful?

Describe three uses for nuclear radiation.

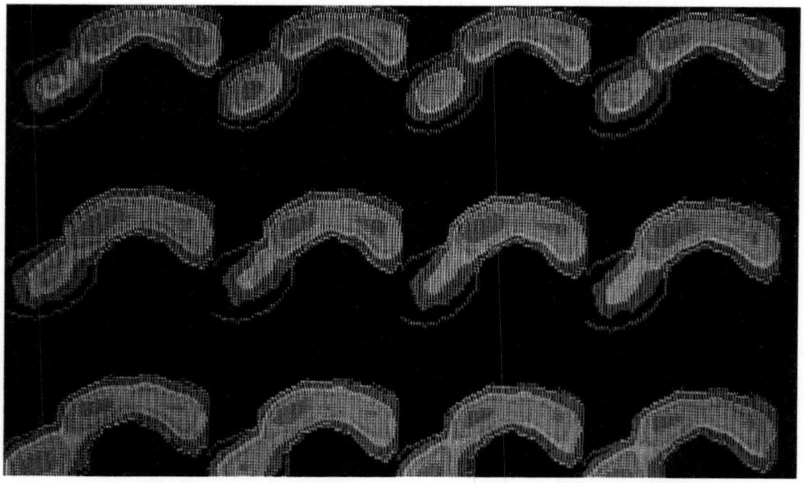

*Dan McCoy/Rainbow*

FIGURE 17–7. Radioactive nuclides can be used to diagnose diseases. The image of a heartbeat pulse provides information about the heart's efficiency.

Smaller amounts of radiation are used to diagnose disease and to trace the path of an element in plants and animals. Radioactive iodine is used to treat thyroid disorders. Phosphorus-32 is used to trace the movement of phosphorus in plants and to study the effect of phosphorus on plant growth. The path of food molecules through the digestive system can be traced with radioactive nuclides.

## 17:5 Detecting Radiation

Radiation from a radioactive nuclide gives the nuclide a tag. The tag allows the nuclide to be detected and measured. For this reason, radioactive nuclides are often called "tagged" atoms. Instruments have been built that can detect and measure the amount of radioactivity present in a sample.

How does a Geiger counter work?

A **Geiger** (GI gur) **counter** is an instrument that measures the amount of radiation present in the area of the counter. When the radiation passes through the Geiger counter, a tiny electric current is formed. The current is amplified and causes the instrument to produce either a click, a flash of light, or a reading on a dial. The number of clicks or flashes per second indicates the amount of radiation present.

Why is a cloud chamber important?

Other instruments have been developed that allow the path of a radiation particle to be seen. The most well-known of these devices is the cloud chamber. A **cloud chamber** contains a gas cooled to a very low temperature. The temperature is so low that the gas will condense when a nuclear particle passes through it. Nuclear particles passing through the chamber produce lines or trails of clouds (Figure 17–9).

From the study of cloud trails, much information has been gathered about radiation. Each kind of particle emitted from a nucleus produces its own type of cloud trail. The study of these trails helps scientists to understand what happens inside a radioactive nucleus.

FIGURE 17–8. Blood "tagged" with a nuclide is studied in a laboratory (a). Radiation level can be measured using a Geiger counter (b).

a

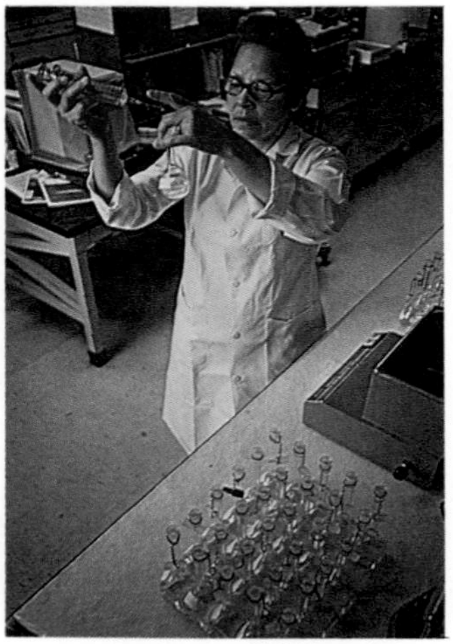

*U.S. Dept. of Energy*

b

*U.S. Dept. of Energy*

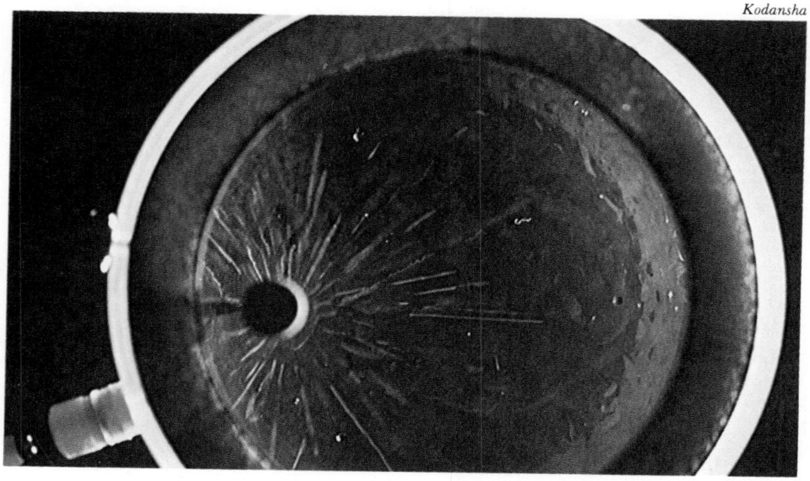
Kodansha

FIGURE 17-9. Particle tracks in a cloud chamber are recorded with the aid of cameras, lights, and mirrors. The film is then studied to identify the particles.

## activity MEASURING RADIATION

**(1)** Place a Geiger counter on the table and plug it into an electric outlet. Turn the counter on and record the number of clicks per minute. What is this radiation called? **(2)** Place a mantle from a camp lantern 15 cm from the counter tube. Record the number of clicks per minute. Is the rate different? Why? **(3)** Place a sheet of glass between the mantle and the Geiger counter. Record the number of clicks per minute. What happens to the number of clicks? Explain. **(4)** Place a piece of aluminum between the mantle and the counter. Record the number of clicks. What happens to the number of clicks? Explain. **(5)** Put a lead sheet in front of the mantle and count the clicks. What do you observe? Why are lead sheets used to provide protection against radiation?

## 17:6 Fission

A reaction occurs when a nucleus is struck by another nucleus or particle. The products of the reaction are different from the original materials. Two kinds of nuclear reactions are fission and fusion.

**Nuclear fission** is the splitting of one nucleus into two or more parts. The mass of the products is slightly less than the mass of the original materials.

What change occurs in nuclear fission?

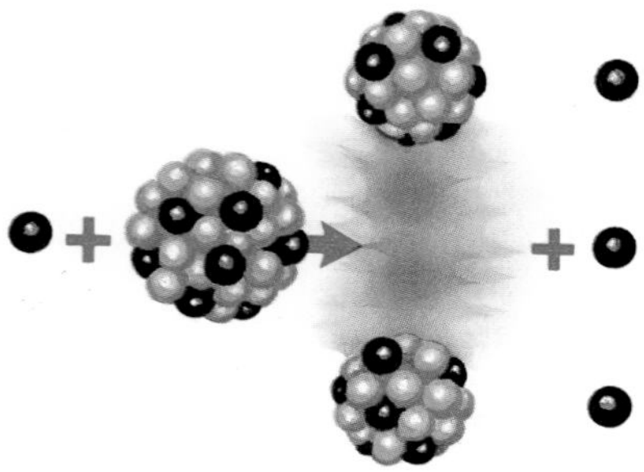

$^{1}_{0}n + ^{235}_{92}U \longrightarrow ^{143}_{54}Xe + ^{90}_{38}Sr + 3^{1}_{0}n$

FIGURE 17-10. A neutron striking a uranium-235 atom may cause the atom to undergo fission.

This mass difference is changed into energy in the form of radiation. Elements with atomic numbers greater than 90 can undergo fission. If a $^{235}_{92}U$ nucleus is hit by a neutron, its nucleus captures the neutron, forming $^{236}_{92}U$. $^{236}_{92}U$ is not stable and it splits into many products. In one reaction, $^{56}_{14}Ba$, $^{90}_{36}Kr$, and two neutrons are formed.

How does a nuclear chain reaction occur?

Fission in uranium atoms can result in a chain reaction. A **chain reaction** is a series of continuous, rapid nuclear fissions. In one type of chain reaction, a $^{235}_{92}U$ nucleus can be split by a neutron to release two neutrons. These two neutrons split two other $^{235}_{92}U$ nuclei. Each of these nuclei emit two neutrons. This reaction occurs many times. In a nuclear chain reaction, billions of fission reactions may occur per second.

Tremendous amounts of energy are released in nuclear fission. Energy equal to 25 000 kWh is released through the fission of 1 g of $^{235}_{92}U$. Fission produces radioactive nuclides as waste products. If these nuclides are not disposed of properly, they can cause mutations, cancer, and death. Some of the nuclides have very long half-lives. These radiation effects are the reason for banning the testing of nuclear weapons in the atmosphere.

## 17:7 Fusion

What change occurs in nuclear fusion?

Nuclear fusion is the opposite of nuclear fission. In **nuclear fusion**, two or more atomic nuclei combine to form one single nucleus. Two less massive elements combine to form a more massive element and release energy. The mass of the new element is slightly less than the combined masses of the original elements. This mass is changed to energy.

Define thermonuclear reaction.

For nuclear fusion to occur, the temperature must be very high—around 10 million°C. Because such a high temperature is needed, nuclear fusion is called a thermonuclear (thur moh NEW klee ur) reaction. Thermo means heat. At temperatures of 10 million°C and higher, atoms do not exist. All of the electrons have been stripped away from the nuclei. The matter

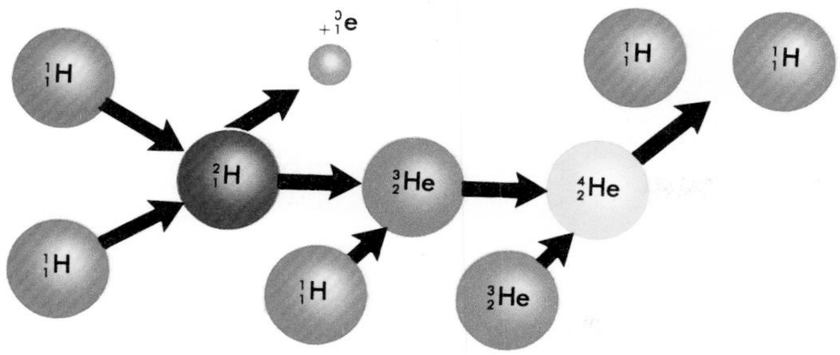


b

General Atomic Corporation

FIGURE 17–11. Hydrogen is converted to helium through fusion (a). The Tokamak Fusion Test Reactor, Princeton University, is the first machine to create fusion on a large scale (b).

Explain how hydrogen is changed to helium in a nuclear reaction.

consists of charged nuclei and free electrons. This matter is in the plasma state.

The conditions for fusion are found in the stars, including our sun. The sun's internal temperature is about 20 million°C. Deep within the sun, nuclides of hydrogen are fused to form helium. Part of the energy released is visible light.

There are two ways in which hydrogen can be converted to helium. The equations for one way, called the hydrogen cycle, are given below. This reaction occurs in stars whose internal temperature is about 15 million°C.

$$^{1}_{1}H + ^{1}_{1}H \rightarrow ^{2}_{1}H + ^{0}_{1}e$$

$$^{2}_{1}H + ^{1}_{1}H \rightarrow ^{3}_{2}He + \gamma$$

$$^{3}_{2}He + ^{3}_{2}He \rightarrow ^{4}_{2}He + ^{1}_{1}H + ^{1}_{1}H$$

Essentially, four hydrogen atoms are fused to form one helium atom and two hydrogen atoms. The four hydrogen atoms that fuse to form helium lose about 1 percent of their mass. This mass is converted to energy. The amount of energy released by fusion can be calculated using Einstein's equation, $E = mc^2$. The energy, E, released is equal to the mass, m, multiplied by the speed of light squared, $c^2$.

Nuclear fusion reactions are more efficient than fission reactions. Therefore, a controlled fusion reaction would be a more desirable way to produce energy. The fuel for the fusion reaction is the hydrogen nuclides found in seawater. Scientists believe there is an almost unlimited supply of hydrogen. However, there are still many problems to be solved before nuclear fusion can be controlled.

# PERSPECTIVES

## frontiers

# Radioactive Tracking

Radioactive elements emit radiation. Scientists have developed devices that detect the radiation. Thus, radioactive substances can be administered to an animal and the presence of that substance can be detected.

For many years, field biologists have studied animal behavior. Transmitters fitted to a collar have been used to track large animals. However, these devices are not usable on small animals such as tadpoles, turtles, or salamanders.

Biologists studying small animals may use radioactive substances to track the animal's movements. In South Carolina, biologists wanted to track a group of turtles. These turtles were common in the spring, but seemed to disappear in the warm summer months. Although it was known that the females left the ponds to lay eggs, the behavior of the males and the young turtles was a mystery. In order to track the turtles, scientists captured thirty turtles in the spring. Two small holes were drilled in the edge of each shell. Small radioactive pins were placed through the holes, and glue was placed over the pins to keep them in place. The turtles were also marked with a painted number for identification. The radioactive pins could be detected at distances up to 10 m. Thus, the scientists could follow the movements of the turtles. The movements of the turtles were monitored throughout the summer. At the end of the study, the scientists determined that the turtles generally moved a short distance, burrowed for about seven days, emerged, and moved about 10 m before burrowing again. The biologists believed that the turtles burrowed in order to avoid heat and predators. Similar techniques have been used with other animals. In some studies, radioactive wires have been placed under the skin of toads and salamanders so that their movements could be monitored.

*Steve Morreale/Savannah River*

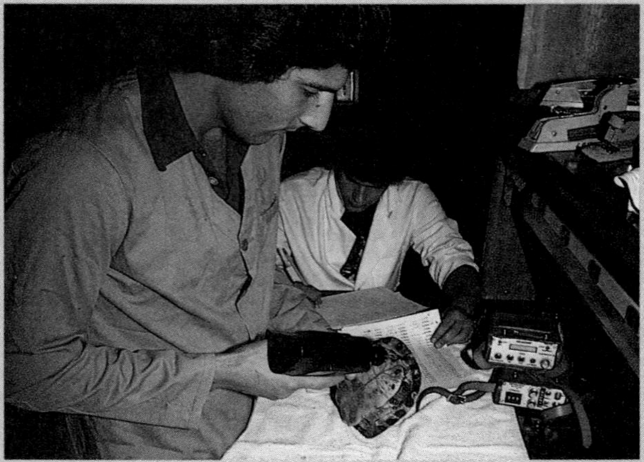

Often, biologists need to know the size of a population of animals in a certain region. Usually the animals are captured, marked and released. Later, the animals are recaptured and the number of marked individuals is compared to the number of unmarked ones. An estimate of the total population can then be determined. Large animals may be marked with a spot of paint, dye, or a neck band. However, it is often impossible to mark small animals this way. Radioactive substances are sometimes used in this situation. Tadpoles have been placed in a radioactive solution and allowed to swim for ninety minutes. They were then rinsed in water. When released, the marked ones could be detected for three to six days. After that time, the radioacive material decomposed.

If proper precautions are taken, these procedures do not harm the animal being monitored. Also, because an element with a short half-life is used, there is no danger of harm to the environment.

## main ideas

1. Radioactive atoms emit radiation from their nuclei. 17:1
2. Nuclei of atoms containing different numbers of neutrons are called nuclides. 17:1
3. Nuclear radiation can be alpha, beta, or gamma. Alpha radiation is a stream of helium nuclei. Beta radiation is a stream of electrons. Gamma radiation is a stream of high-energy photons. 17:2
4. The changing of one element into another element is called transmutation. 17:2
5. A radioactive nuclide decays at a fixed rate called half-life. 17:3
6. Radiation biology is the study of the effects of radiation on living organisms. Radioactive nuclides have many uses in medicine. 17:4
7. Nuclear radiation can be detected and measured. 17:5
8. Fission is a nuclear reaction in which the nucleus of an atom is split into two or more parts. A chain reaction is a series of continuous, rapid nuclear fissions. 17:6
9. Fusion is a nuclear reaction in which the nuclei of two atoms are combined to form one single nucleus. 17:7
10. Nuclear reactions release large amounts of energy. 17:6, 17:7

## vocabulary

*Define each of the following words or terms.*

alpha radiation
beta radiation
chain reaction
cloud chamber
decay
decay series
gamma radiation
Geiger counter
half-life
isotope
nuclear fission
nuclear fusion
nuclide
radiation biology
radioactive
transmutation

## study questions

**DO NOT WRITE IN THIS BOOK.**

### A. True of False

*Determine whether each of the following sentences is true or false. If the sentence is false, rewrite it to make it true.*

1. Trails of nuclear particles are detected inside a Geiger counter.

2. Radioactive elements emit radiation when they decay.
3. Beta radiation is a stream of high-energy photons.
4. Alpha radiation is a stream of electrons.
5. Fission is the combining of the nuclei of atoms.
6. Gamma radiation is a stream of high-energy helium nuclei.
7. Alpha radiation can damage or destroy living organisms.
8. In nuclear fission, atomic nuclei are split into two or more parts.
9. Elements with atomic numbers greater than 83 can undergo decay.
10. Nuclear reactions produce little energy.

## B. Multiple Choice

*Choose the word or phrase that completes correctly each of the following sentences.*

1. The best radiation shield is (*paper, aluminum, lead*).
2. Two nuclides of the same element differ in the number of (*protons, neutrons, electrons*) in their nuclei.
3. As time passes, the atoms of a radioactive element in a sample (*change to another element, remain the same, disappear*).
4. The time necessary for one half of a radioactive element in a sample to decay is called the element's (*critical mass, atomic number, half-life*).
5. A beta particle is a(n) (*photon, helium nucleus, electron*).
6. A nuclear chain reaction in uranium is caused by (*neutrons, protons, electrons*).
7. The process in which an atom emits nuclear radiation is called (*decay, radiation, transmutation*).
8. A helium nucleus is a(n) (*alpha particle, beta particle, gamma ray*).
9. A(n) (*alpha particle, beta particle, neutrino*) has no mass and no charge.
10. When a nucleus emits alpha radiation, the nucleus loses (*one, two, three*) protons and becomes a new element.

## C. Completion

*Complete each of the following sentences with a word or phrase that will make the sentence correct.*

1. The nucleus of an atom contains ______ and ______.

2. In fusion, two or more ______ unite to form a single, heavier nucleus.
3. In a nuclear reaction, mass is changed to ______.
4. In the sun, four hydrogen nuclei ______ to form one helium and two hydrogen nuclei.
5. The more radioactive a nuclide, the ______ its half-life.
6. Uranium-238 has more ______ than uranium-235.
7. All elements with atomic numbers greater than 92 are called ______ elements.
8. There are ______ neutrons in $^{15}_{7}N$.
9. ______ radiation and X rays are used to treat cancer.
10. In 1620 years (half-life of radium) ______ of a 4-g sample of radium will be unchanged.

**D. How and Why**

1. What are the properties of alpha, beta, and gamma radiation?
2. A radioactive element has a half-life of 30 days. How much of a 4-g sample will be unchanged after 90 days?
3. Do the electrons that are beta particles come from the electron cloud of an atom? Explain.
4. How is nuclear radiation detected?
5. How is nuclear fission different from nuclear fusion? How are they alike?

## challenges

1. Prepare a report on the harmful effects of exposure to large amounts of radiation.
2. Visit a local hospital and interview a person who works in nuclear medicine. Find out what the person does and what training is needed for the job. Report to your class.
3. Prepare a library report on the use of radiation in the treatment of disease.

## interesting reading

Brandt, Keith, *Marie Curie: Brave Scientist.* Mahaw, NJ: Troll, 1983

Lens, Sidney, *The Bomb.* New York: E. P. Dutton, 1982.

*What do you see when you observe the sky on a clear night? You may see space objects such as the moon, planets, and stars. Astronomers use special instruments to aid them in observing space objects. This image of interacting galaxies was made using an electronic camera. What other instruments do astronomers use in their observations?*

*Smithsonian Astrophysical Observatory*

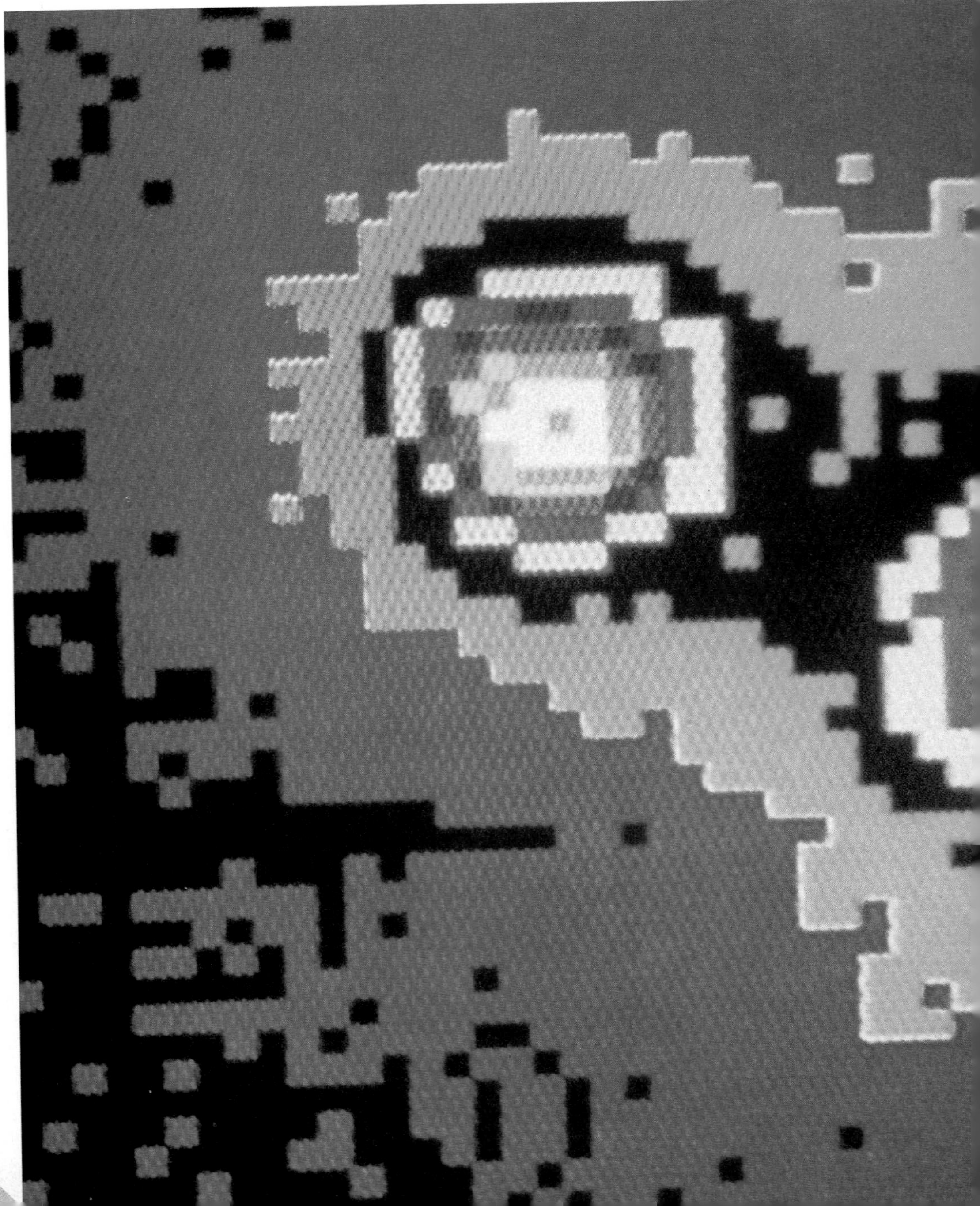

# Astronomy
## unit 5

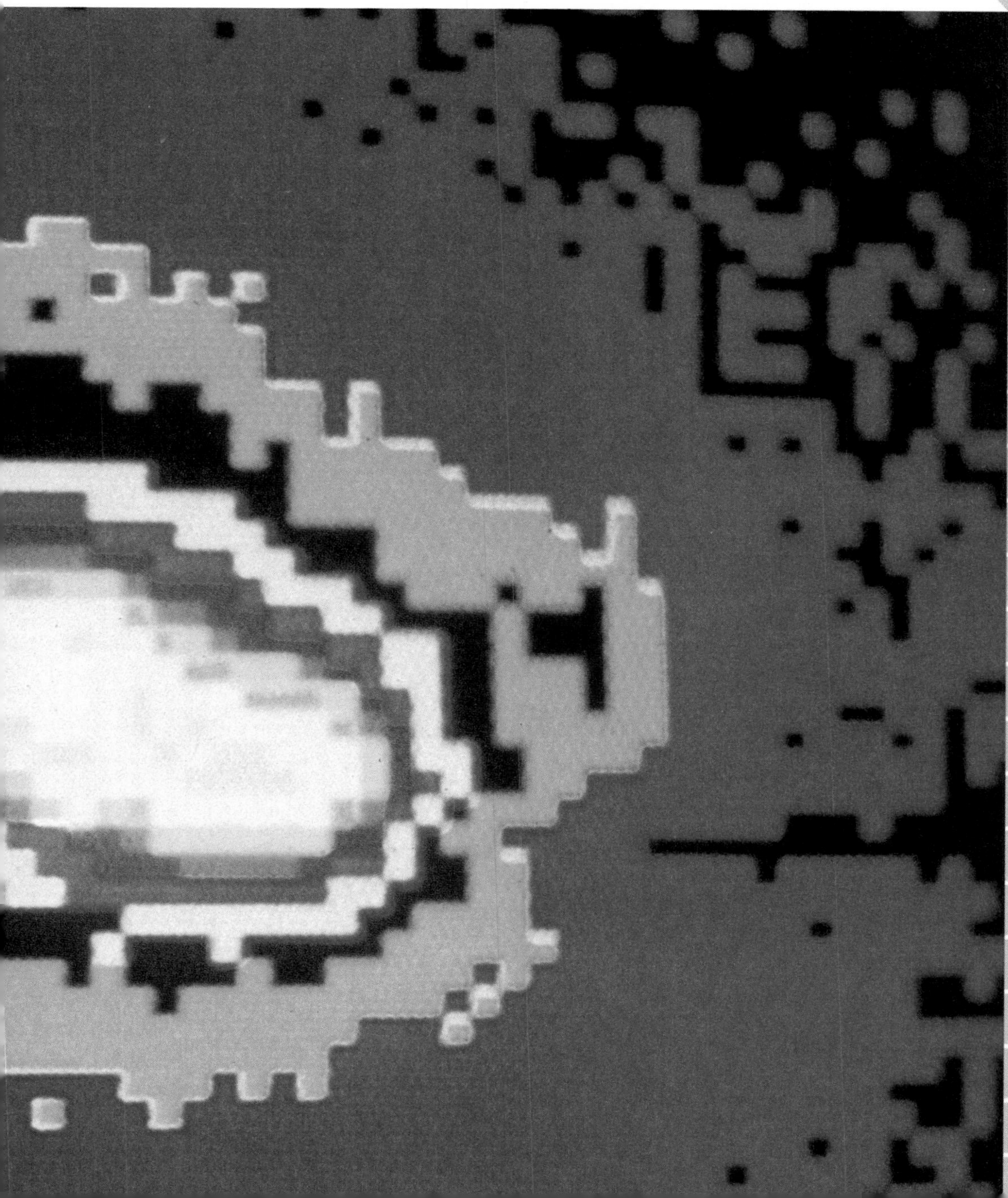

*People have always wondered about the universe. Centuries ago at Stonehenge, England, people built this observatory to keep track of the movements of the sun, moon, and stars. Today, astronomers use sophisticated instruments to study the universe. What types of instruments do astronomers use today? What have scientists learned about the moon and other space objects?*

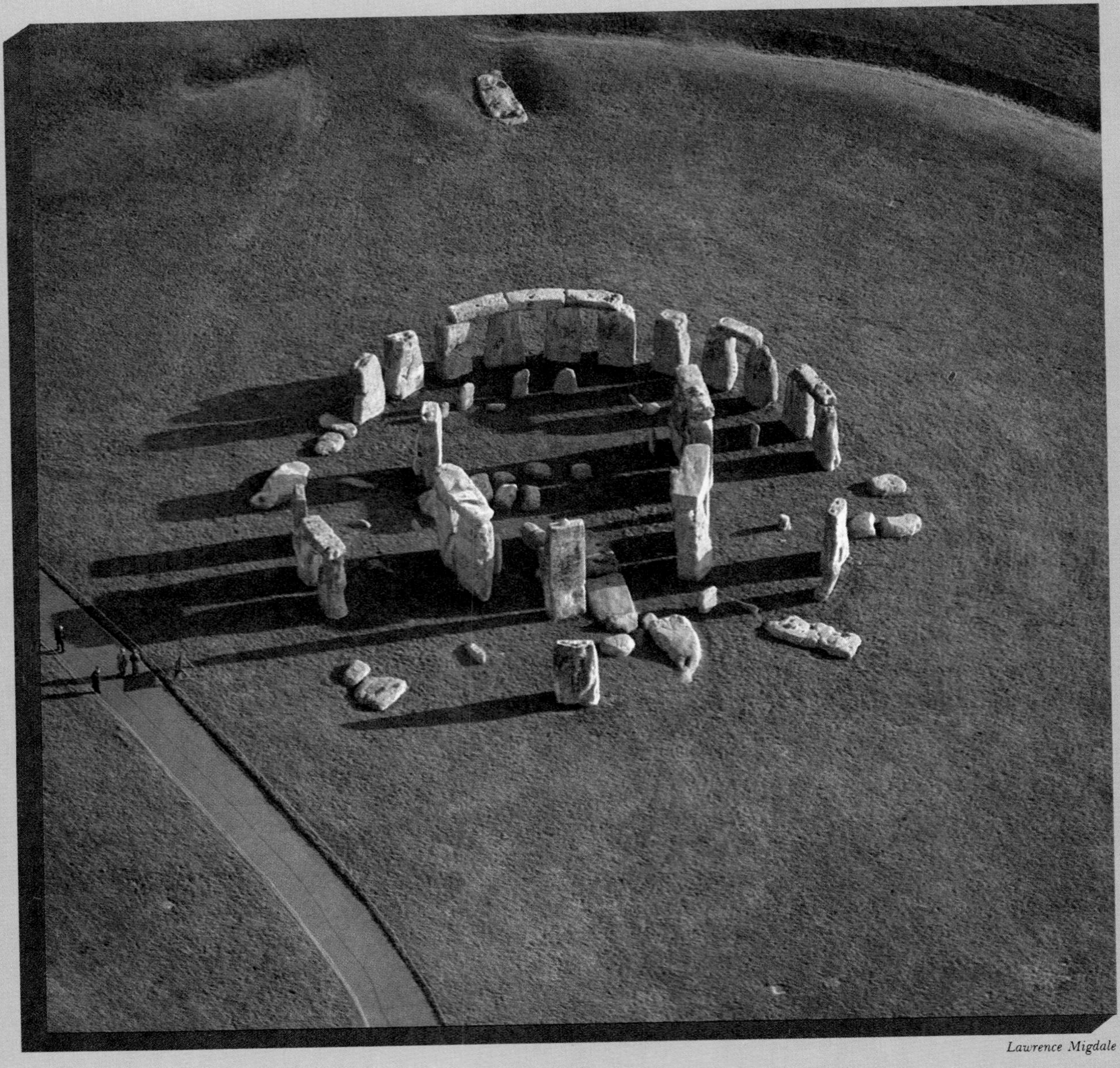

Lawrence Migdale

# Astronomy and the Moon

# chapter 18

## 18:1 Astronomy

GOAL: You will learn how astronomers study the skies and the features of Earth's moon.

**Astronomy** is the study of planets, stars, and all other objects in space. This study includes the motions, compositions, and origins of space objects. An astronomer is a scientist who specializes in astronomy. As early as 4000 B.C. people observed that the motions of the sun and moon followed a regular pattern. The Maya Indians of Central America developed a religion based on sky observations. The Chinese had a listing of over 800 stars as early as 350 B.C. They also kept records of other sky objects, such as comets, sunspots, meteorites, and novas.

What is astronomy?

Look at the sky on a clear night. It appears to be a bowl turned upside down over you. The Greeks called this view of the skies the celestial (suh LES chul) sphere. We use the celestial sphere to locate sky objects. The sphere has a north and a south celestial pole and an equator (Figure 18–1).

Describe the celestial sphere.

Greek astronomers kept careful maps of the locations of space objects on the celestial sphere. They found that some space objects remained in the same location on the celestial sphere. These objects were called stars. Other space objects appeared to move to different locations on the celestial sphere.

FIGURE 18-1. The celestial sphere can be used to locate objects in space.

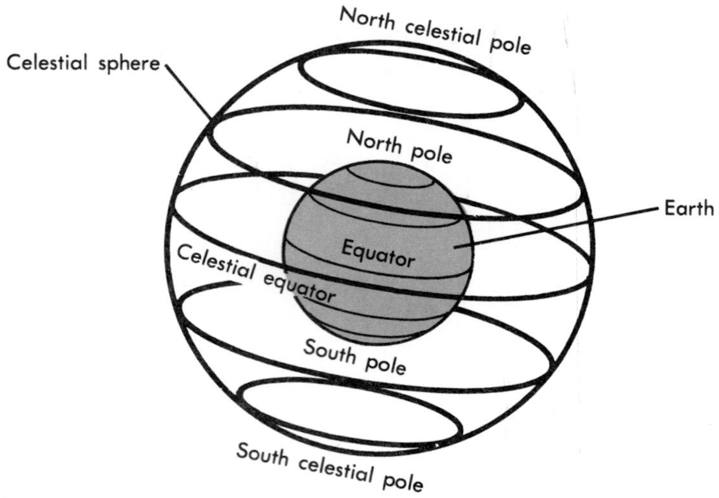


The Greeks named these wandering space objects planets. The word planet means wanderer.

What tools do astronomers use?

Greek and other ancient astronomers used only their eyes to make observations. Modern astronomers use many kinds of tools in their work. Powerful telescopes are used to see billions of kilometers into space. Special instruments are used to detect the colors of light produced by the sun and other stars. Pictures of space objects are taken with cameras. Scientists send spacecraft with television cameras into space to film space objects. Spacecraft also carry instruments to measure the temperature and amount of radiation in space. Much information has been gathered about space and space objects through special radio receivers that detect radio waves produced by objects in space.

### making sure

1. What kind of work does an astronomer do?
2. How are spacecraft used in astronomy?

## 18:2 Optical Telescopes

Optical (AHP tih kul) telescopes are used by astronomers to study planets, stars, and other objects in space. Optical means the telescopes use light to form an image. There are two main types of optical telescopes—refractor and reflector.

How is a refracting telescope different from a reflecting telescope?

The **refractor**, or refracting telescope, contains a convex lens mounted at one end of a closed tube (Figure 18–2a). The image is formed at the other end of the tube where it can be viewed through an eyepiece lens. The image can also be photographed. Galileo, an Italian astronomer, used such a telescope to make his astronomical observations of the planet Jupiter.

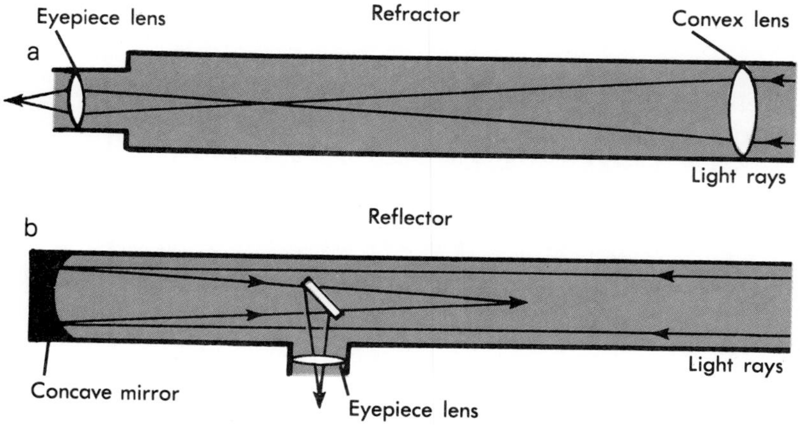


FIGURE 18-2. A refracting telescope uses a convex lens to form an image (a). A reflecting telescope uses a concave mirror to form an image (b).

A **reflector**, or reflecting telescope, consists of a concave mirror at the bottom of an open tube. The mirror reflects light back up the tube to form an image near the open end (Figure 18–2b). The eyepiece or camera must be placed on the tube where the image forms. The first reflector was built in 1668 by Isaac Newton.

Refractors and reflectors each have advantages and disadvantages. Refractors are excellent for making measurements of small angles in space and for determining exact positions of objects. The disadvantage of a refractor is that the size of the telescope is limited. The size of a telescope is given by the diameter of its lens or mirror. The world's largest refractor is the 102-cm telescope at the Yerkes Observatory in Wisconsin. The second largest refractor is the 91-cm telescope at Lick Observatory

FIGURE 18-3. The Yerkes Observatory telescope is a refracting telescope.

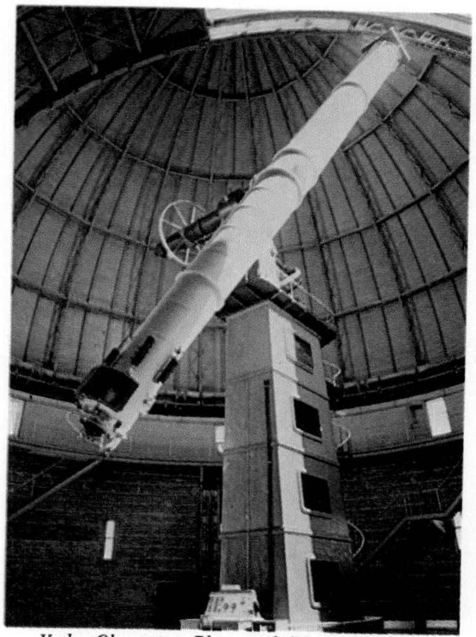

*Yerkes Observatory Photographs/University of Chicago*

Kitt Peak/Hansen Planetarium

FIGURE 18–4. The McMath solar telescope forms an image of the sun about one meter wide.

in California. A lens can be supported only on its edges. If a lens is made very large, its weight causes it to pull and sag out of shape. This distortion of the lens causes a fuzzy image.

Explain why the largest telescopes are reflectors.

Since reflectors use mirrors, they can be built in larger sizes than refractors. A mirror can be supported at points all along its back surface. The Hale telescope on Palomar Mountain in California has a 5.08-m mirror. There are larger reflectors but they are used for special purposes rather than general viewing. The disadvantage of the reflector is that it cannot be used to measure the small angles necessary to pinpoint locations.

A telescope is usually housed in a building covered by a dome. The dome has a window on one side that can be opened or closed. The telescope is movable. The dome is usually mounted on rails so it can be turned. The dome is insulated to maintain an even temperature. An even temperature helps prevent changes in the shape of the lens or mirror.

## activity MAKING A REFRACTING TELESCOPE

**(1)** Obtain two convex lenses with focal lengths of about 20 cm and 2.5 cm. Also obtain a piece of stiff cardboard and two mailing tubes. One tube should slide inside the other. The short focal length lens will be the eyepiece lens. The other lens will be the objective lens. **(2)** Cut two cardboard disks for each lens. The diameters of the disks should be the same as the inside diameters of the tubes. **(3)** Cut a circle in each disk with a diameter slightly smaller than the diameter of each lens. These rings will hold the lenses in place (Figure 18–5). **(4)** Apply a thin film of glue to each ring. Then glue the rings together around each lens. Avoid getting glue on the centers of the lenses. **(5)** Glue one disk in one end of each tube. **(6)** Slide the small tube inside the other. **(7)** Look at a distant object through the telescope. **CAUTION:** Never look at the sun with the unaided eye or with a telescope. Severe eye damage may result. To focus the telescope, slide the small tube in and out of the large tube. Is the image upright or inverted? What happens to the image as you slide the tube? Why?

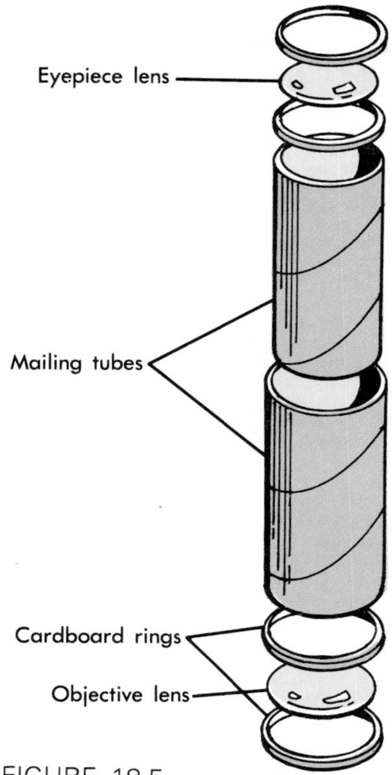

FIGURE 18-5.

### making sure

3. How are refractors and reflectors alike? Different?

## 18:3 Astronomical Observations

Why do astronomers use cameras and film?

Most astronomers use cameras and film to record the images they see through telescopes. There are several reasons for this method. Faint details not visible with other methods are revealed when the film is exposed for long periods of time. Film is not subject to fatigue as is the human eye. Photographs are also permanent records and can be kept for future study. Prints can be made for use by other astronomers.

Astronomers also take photographs of space objects that show a spectrum rather than an image of

FIGURE 18-6. A spectrograph is used to take pictures of the spectrums of stars.

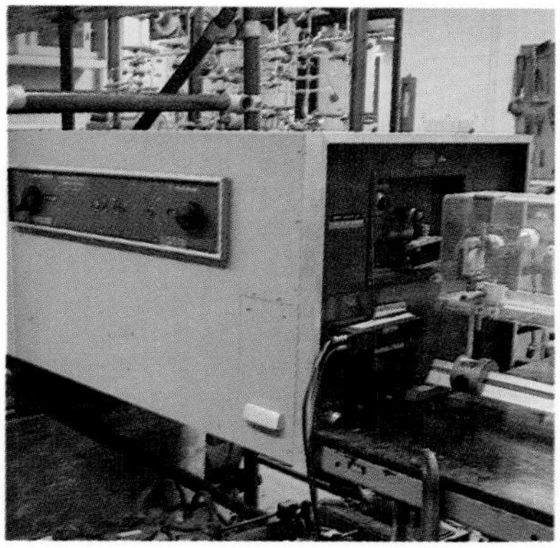

Doug Martin

Kodansha

a

Tersch Enterprises

b

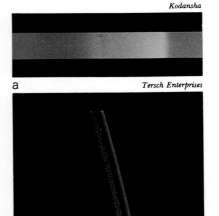

FIGURE 18-7. Comparing the spectrum of light from the sun (a) with the spectrum of light from the star Vega (b), scientists have learned that the sun and Vega are composed of the same elements.

the actual object. This method of photography is called **spectroscopy** (spek TRAHS kuh pee). A **spectrograph** (SPEK truh graf) is a camera that photographs the spectrum of light produced by a source. It can be used to study the light from a star. The spectrograph contains a diffraction (dif RAK shun) grating that produces a spectrum by separating white light into its colors. A diffraction grating is a piece of glass or transparent plastic marked with a series of fine, parallel lines. There are thousands of lines per centimeter.

The spectrum of a star's light can be used to determine the composition of the star. Each element has its own characteristic lines of color in its spectrum (Figure 18–8). Scientists have discovered that the elements that make up the stars are also found here on Earth.

Kodansha

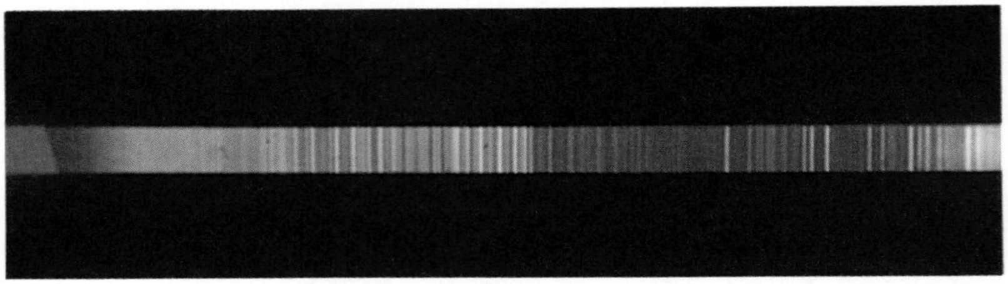

FIGURE 18-8. The spectrum of iron is different from the spectra of all the other elements.

Why is the Earth's atmosphere a major problem in astronomy?

A problem for an astronomer who observes the sky is Earth's atmosphere. The atmosphere limits the usefulness of all optical telescopes. Optical telescopes cannot be used if it is cloudy or rainy. Why? Also, the atmosphere filters out some light and thereby dims the visible light from outer space. In daylight, air molecules scatter sunlight, making the sky appear blue. The blue sky hides all objects except the sun, the moon, and Venus. Charged particles hitting the atmosphere from space cause the air to glow and produce colored light. The glowing air is called an aurora. Auroras interfere with spectroscopy. Also, when the air is unsteady due to winds, the images of the stars are blurred. Changes in the density of the upper air cause light waves to bend (Section 15:8). The bending of the light waves causes stars to "twinkle."

## 18:4 Radio Astronomy and Satellites

Some of the limitations of optical telescopes are overcome by the use of radio telescopes. **Radio telescopes** detect radio waves that come from space instead of light. Radio waves are a form of electromagnetic radiation. Radio waves are not scattered or blocked by the atmosphere. The use of radio waves to study space objects is called **radio astronomy**.

What are the advantages in using a radio telescope?

What is radio astronomy?

The radio waves detected by radio telescopes have frequencies that are different from the frequencies used by radio stations. Because different frequencies are used, astronomers know the radio waves come from space.

A radio telescope is actually a radio antenna and a receiver. One type of radio telescope also has a curved dish, or reflector. This type of telescope is a reflecting radio telescope. The antenna is mounted above the center of the dish. Radio waves strike the dish and reflect back to the antenna. The radio waves cause an electric current in the antenna. The current, called a signal, is amplified by the receiver. A computer processes the signal and produces an image astronomers can study. The entire telescope is mounted on movable supports. In this way, it can be directed toward any point in the sky. Two of the best known radio telescopes are the 76 m dish at Jodrell Bank, in England, and the 91 m dish at Greenbank, West Virginia.

What is a radio telescope?

*National Radio Astronomy Observatory*

FIGURE 18-9. A radio telescope uses radio waves to study objects in space. Some radio telescopes can be aimed at any part of the sky.

FIGURE 18-10. The reflector of the radio telescope at Arecibo lines a hollow in the ground. The receiver is suspended over the reflecting dish.

Some radio telescopes are "bowls" carved in the earth and lined with metal. These radio telescopes cannot be aimed at different points in the sky. Instead, they detect radio waves from sources that pass overhead. One radio telescope of this type is the 305-m dish at Arecibo, Puerto Rico.

Rockets, satellites, and other spacecraft are used to carry instruments into space above Earth's atmosphere. These instruments are used to detect and measure radiation from outer space. The main advantage of these instruments is that they are above Earth's atmosphere. The blanket of air that surrounds Earth filters out certain kinds of radiation before they reach the surface. For example, X rays are filtered. Only a fraction of this radiation entering the atmosphere actually reaches Earth's surface. Using satellites to detect X rays has led to the discovery of new stars. Detection of gamma radiation enables astronomers to explore the farthest reaches of space.

FIGURE 18-11. Satellites are used to observe space objects without interference from the atmosphere.

*NASA*

## making sure

**4.** How does a radio telescope overcome the limitations of optical telescopes?

**5.** How are satellites useful in astronomy?

NASA

FIGURE 18-12. The moon is Earth's nearest neighbor.

## 18:5 The Moon

What have astronomers learned from their study of the skies? Let us begin with our closest neighbor, the moon. The moon has been the most observed space object for a long time. Romans called the moon Luna, which means shining.

List the major features of the moon.

The moon is a large spherical body. Its diameter is 3476 km. The moon's average distance from Earth is 384 400 km. The actual distance from the moon to Earth varies. At its farthest point from Earth, the moon is 406 699 km away. At its nearest point, the moon is 356 399 km away. The force of gravity on the moon is $\frac{1}{6}$ that of gravity on Earth. A rock that weighs 90 N on Earth would weigh 15 N on the moon.

How far are the moon's farthest and nearest points from the Earth?

The moon has two main types of motions. The moon moves around Earth in a motion called **revolution.** One complete revolution takes about $27\frac{1}{3}$ Earth days. The moon also turns slowly on its axis in

How is the rotation of the moon different from its revolution?

| *Table 18–1.* Important Facts about the Moon | |
|---|---|
| Age | More than 4 450 000 000 (4.45 billion) yr |
| Distance from Earth | 356 399 km Shortest<br>406 699 km Greatest<br>384 400 km Average |
| Diameter | 3476 km |
| Volume | 1/50 that of Earth |
| Mass | $7.35 \times 10^{22}$ kg |
| Density | 3.3 g/cm$^3$ |
| Gravity | 1/6 that of Earth |
| Temperature | 130°C Noon<br>−170°C Midnight |
| Rotation Period | 27 days, 7 hours, 43 minutes |
| Revolution Period | 27 days, 7 hours, 43 minutes |

a motion called **rotation**. It rotates once in each revolution around Earth. One complete rotation of the moon takes about 27⅓ days, the same time as one revolution. For this reason, the same side of the moon always faces Earth. One moon day is equal to 27⅓ earth days. A moon day is the time it takes the moon to make one complete rotation.

FIGURE 18-13.

## activity THE DISTANCE TO THE MOON

**(1)** Go outside with a pencil and a meter stick on a night when there is a full moon (complete circle). **(2)** Hold the meter stick just below one eye and close your other eye. **(3)** Sight along the meter stick toward the moon. **(4)** Hold the pencil beside the meter stick and move it until its width just blocks your view of the moon. **(5)** Record the distance in millimeters from your eye to the pencil. **(6)** Measure the width of the pencil in millimeters and record it. Determine the distance to the moon using the equation

$$\frac{\text{diameter of moon (km)}}{\text{diameter of pencil (mm)}} = \frac{\text{distance to moon (km)}}{\text{distance to pencil (mm)}}$$

How close is your answer to the distance given in the text?

## making sure

6. What is the difference between rotation and revolution?
7. Why do we see only one side of the moon?
8. Does the same side of the moon always face the sun? Why?
9. In earth days, how long is one moon day?

## 18:6 Moon Phases

The same side of the moon faces Earth at all times. Also, one half of the moon is always illuminated by sunlight while the other half is dark. From Earth, the lighted part of the moon appears to change from a small slice to a full circle and back again. The apparent shape of the moon depends on how much of its lighted side we see. The different shapes we see are called **moon phases.** The major phases are named new moon, crescent, first quarter, full moon, and third quarter.

What causes the different phases of the moon?

During new moon, the moon is between the sun and Earth. The moon's lighted side faces the sun and its dark side faces Earth (Figure 18–14). Thus, the moon is not seen from Earth. Within 24 h, a slim, curved slice of the lighted side of the moon becomes visible. This phase is a crescent. More and more of the lighted side of the moon becomes visible as the moon revolves around Earth.

Describe the phases of the moon.

FIGURE 18-14. The phases of the moon are caused by the moon revolving around Earth. Through most of its revolution, we see only a portion of the lighted side of the moon.

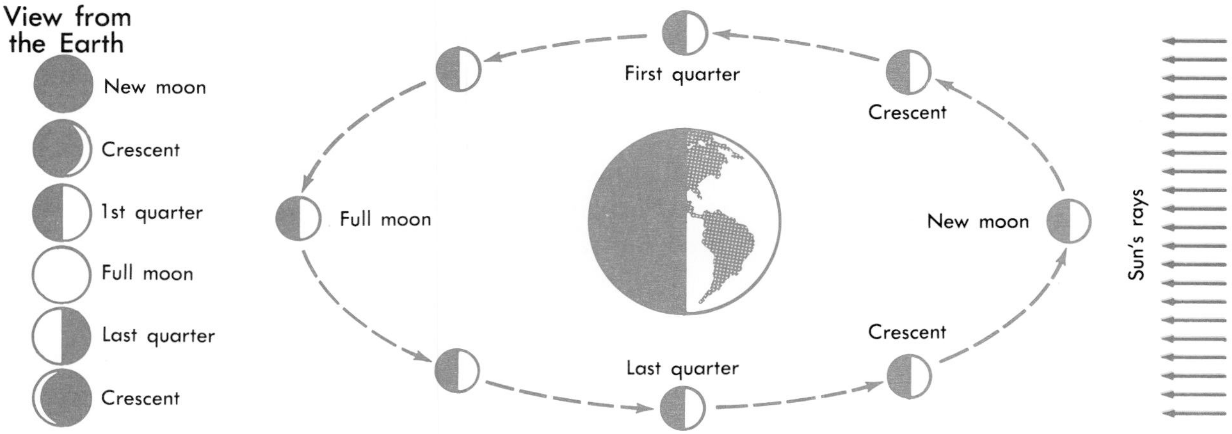

Seven days after new moon, the moon looks like a half-circle. This phase is called first quarter. The moon has now completed ¼ of its revolution around Earth. Full moon, the second quarter, occurs a week later. Now, Earth is between the sun and the moon. The moon's lighted side faces Earth (Figure 18–14). After full moon, the amount of the lighted side of the moon that we see decreases. One week after full moon, we see the third quarter phase. Finally we see the crescent moon again. The next night there will be another new moon phase.

FIGURE 18-15. The cresent phase (a) occurs just before and just after the new moon. The first quarter phase occurs a few days after a cresent moon (b).

a *PHOTRI*

b *PHOTRI*

In the evening, the moon appears to rise in the east. If you watch it for some time it will appear to travel across the sky to the west. This apparent motion from east to west is caused by the rotation of the earth. It is not a true motion of the moon. You are actually moving with the earth.

During the moon's revolution, its true motion is from west to east. The moon's position in the sky changes about 13° each day. The movement causes a change in the time of moonrise. Each night the moon rises an average of 50 min later than the night before.

activity

## MOON WATCH

**Objective:** To record the positions and shapes of the moon

### Materials

almanac
(see daily newspaper)
paper, 100 cm × 80 cm
pencil

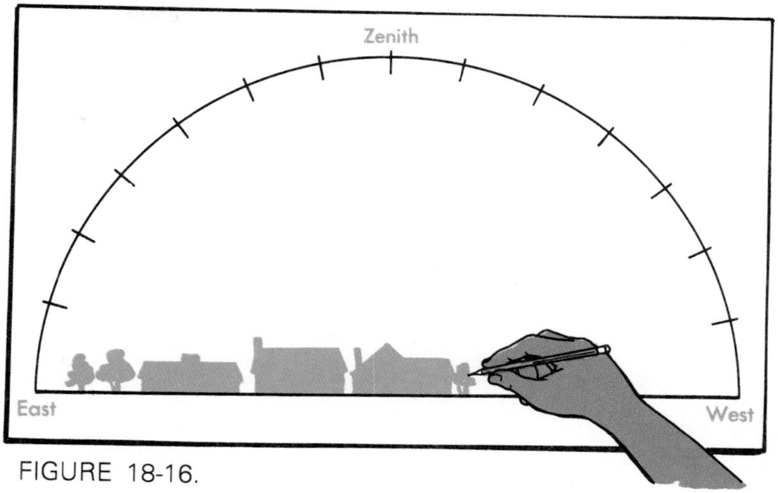

FIGURE 18-16.

### Procedure

1. Draw a large half-circle on the paper. Divide the half-circle into 14 equal parts (Figure 18–16). Label east and west at opposite ends of the half-circle.
2. Take the diagram outside and look south. Draw some landmarks, such as trees and buildings, on the bottom of the half-circle.
3. Two days after new moon, begin observing the moon. Sketch the exact position and shape of the moon on your diagram. Date the sketch.
4. On the same day, begin to record the moonrise and moonset times. Use the almanac for moonset times.
5. Sketch the position and shape of the moon every night for two weeks at about the same time each day. Date each sketch. Leave a dated space on your diagram if you cannot see the moon.
6. Record the moonrise and moonset times every day for two weeks.

### Observations and Data

| Date | Moonrise time | Moonset time |
|---|---|---|
| | | |
| | | |
| | | |

### Questions and Conclusions

1. According to your diagram, in what direction did the moon travel?
2. Where is the moon on your diagram after two weeks?
3. What was the moon's shape?
4. How much later was moonrise each night?
5. If the moon rose at 6:00 P.M. on Monday, at what time would it rise the following Sunday?

## 18:7 Eclipses

The earth and the moon cast long cone-shaped shadows into space. When one of these two objects moves into the shadow cast by the other one, an eclipse (ih KLIHPS) occurs. Each shadow has two parts—the total shadow called the **umbra** (UM bruh) and the partial shadow called the **penumbra** (puh NUM bruh).

What causes a lunar eclipse?

A **lunar eclipse** occurs when the moon moves into Earth's shadow. When the moon moves into Earth's umbra, a total lunar eclipse occurs. A lunar eclipse can occur only during a full moon. Earth blocks sunlight from reaching the moon. During a lunar eclipse, the moon is usually not in total darkness. The moon is seen as a copper-red disk. This color is caused by the bending of sunlight by Earth's atmosphere. Some of the red part of the light bounces off the moon back to Earth.

How are partial and total eclipses of the moon different?

A lunar eclipse does not occur every time there is a full moon. The moon must be in a direct line with Earth and the sun. Most of the time, the moon passes above or below Earth's shadow. When the moon passes through Earth's penumbra, a partial lunar eclipse occurs.

FIGURE 18–17. A lunar eclipse occurs when the moon moves into Earth's shadow (a). A total solar eclipse occurs when Earth moves into the moon's umbra (b).

a

Dennis diCicco

b

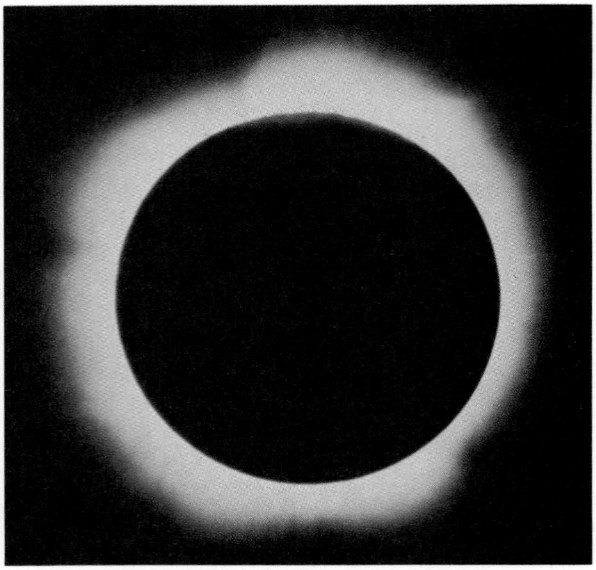

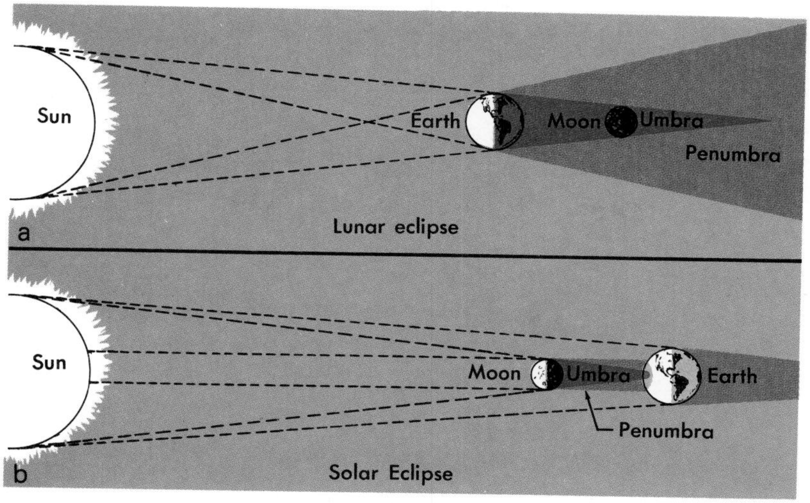


FIGURE 18-18. During a lunar eclipse, Earth is between the sun and the moon (a). In a solar eclipse, the moon is between Earth and the sun (b).

What causes a solar eclipse?

A **solar eclipse** occurs when Earth moves into the moon's shadow. If Earth moves into the moon's umbra, a total solar eclipse occurs. A solar eclipse can occur only during a new moon. The umbra of the moon is about 270 km in diameter. Thus, a total solar eclipse is visible from only a small part of the earth. The longest solar eclipses are visible at the equator, where they can last as long as 7½ minutes. Table 18-2 lists the dates and locations for total solar eclipses from 1987 to 2000.

***Table 18–2.***
Total Solar Eclipses

| Date | Time of Totality (min) | Location |
|---|---|---|
| 1987 Mar. 29 | 0.3 | Central America |
| 1988 Mar. 18 | 4.0 | Phillipines, Indonesia |
| 1990 July 22 | 2.6 | Finland, Arctic |
| 1991 July 11 | 7.1 | Hawaii, Brazil, Central America |
| 1992 June 30 | 5.4 | South Atlantic |
| 1994 Nov. 3 | 4.6 | South America |
| 1995 Oct. 24 | 2.4 | Southern Asia |
| 1997 Mar. 9 | 2.8 | Siberia, Arctic |
| 1998 Feb. 26 | 4.4 | Central America |
| 1999 Aug. 11 | 2.6 | Central Europe, Central Asia |

During a total solar eclipse, partial darkness slowly covers Earth's surface. Just before the sun is covered, a string of bright lights appears briefly along the edge of the moon's disk. These lights are called Bailey's beads. They are caused by sunlight shining through the deep valleys among the moon's mountains.

Which are seen more often—partial or total solar eclipses? Why?

Partial solar eclipses are much more common than total eclipses. They can be viewed over a larger part of Earth. Partial eclipses are seen in areas on either side of the narrow total solar eclipse path. They are also seen when only the moon's penumbra reaches the earth. (Never look at the sun directly without special equipment. Serious eye damage can result. If you use a telescope, be sure it has a special sun lens and that the lens is on the telescope.)

The sun is about 400 times larger than the moon. How can the small disk of the moon block light from the sun? Besides being 400 times larger than the moon, the sun is 400 times farther from Earth than is the moon. Thus, both appear to be the same size when viewed from Earth. Therefore, when Earth moves directly into the moon's umbra, sunlight is blocked.

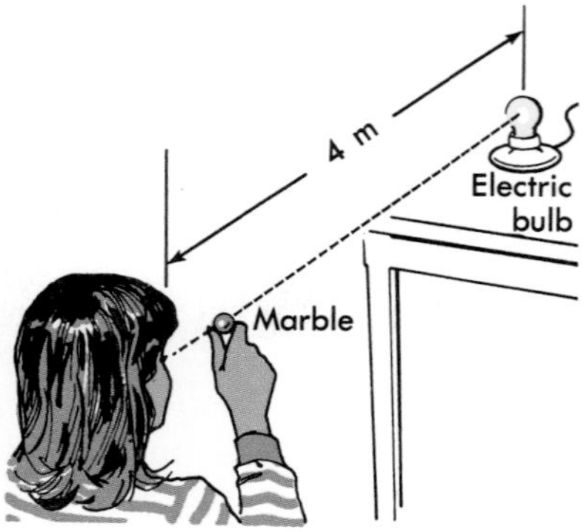

FIGURE 18-19.

**activity**

**SOLAR ECLIPSE**

Place a bare, lighted electric bulb at a distance of 4 m from you. Close one eye and hold a marble at arm's length in front of you. Line up the marble with the bare bulb. Move the marble closer to your eye. What happens? How is this activity similar to a solar eclipse? What does the marble represent? What does the bare light bulb represent?

## 18:8 Lunar Surface and Composition

Describe the moon's surface.

The moon's surface is solid rock covered with dust. The layer of dust varies from thin to very deep. Rocks and boulders dot the landscape. There are no plants or animals on the moon. The moon does not have an atmosphere or water. Temperatures reach

130°C on the lighted side and drop to −170°C on the moon's dark side.

How were the craters on the moon formed?

After the moon formed, its crust melted to a depth of several hundred kilometers. Then the crust slowly cooled and hardened. Pieces of rock from space bombarded the surface and formed craters. A crater is a bowl-shaped hole. One huge crater, named Copernicus, is 91 km from rim to rim. Some craters have central peaks and mountain walls as high as 6 km. More than 30 000 craters have been observed on the moon and named.

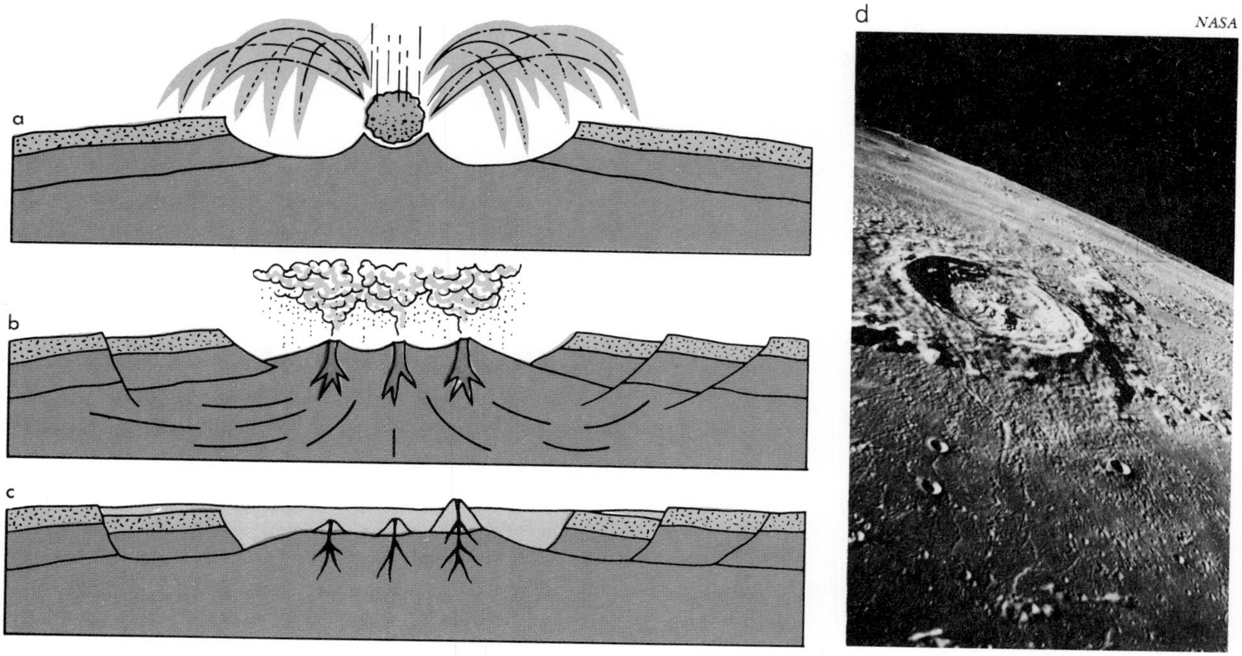


FIGURE 18–20. Maria may have formed when the impact of large objects (a) caused cracks in the moon's surface through which melted rock could flow (b). The melted rock then hardened to form the smooth maria (c). Moon craters were formed by rocks from space bombarding the surface (d).

The moon has plains called maria (MAR ee uh). Early astronomers thought the plains were seas, so they named them maria, which is Latin for sea. These plains do not contain water. Their surfaces are covered by a layer of hardened lava. Scientists believe that this lava pushed up through the floors of the plains many years ago. The lava is rich in iron, magnesium, and silicon. It is like basalt found on Earth. Some lunar seas are quite large. The largest, Mare Imbrium (MAR ay • IHM bree um), is 1000 km in diameter. The side of the moon that faces away from Earth has few maria.

NASA

NASA

a b

FIGURE 18–21. The surface of the moon is rock and dust (a). Samples of the lunar surface were collected by the Apollo astronauts (b).

Lunar mountains, such as the Apennines (AP uh ninez), are found on the edges of the plains. The peaks may be as high as 5 km. These mountains were probably formed when huge chunks of rock from space struck the moon's surface.

How are moon rocks similar to and different from Earth rocks?

Apollo astronauts brought moon rocks back to Earth. Analyses of these rocks show the moon to be composed of the same elements as Earth. However, the elements on the moon are in different proportions. The most abundant element on the moon is oxygen. Oxygen on the moon is not in the gaseous state. It is in mineral compounds and accounts for 58 percent of the moon's crust. Silicon

NASA

NASA

FIGURE 18-22. Lunar rock samples brought to Earth by the Apollo astronauts show that the moon is composed of the same substances as Earth.

accounts for 20 percent. Aluminum, calcium, iron, and magnesium are also present. Some lunar samples consist of pieces of rock and dust squeezed together by heat and pressure. Moon dust is composed of natural glass (silicon dioxide) and ground rock.

### making sure

**10.** How were the craters on the surface of the moon formed?

**11.** How were lunar mountains, such as the Apennines, probably formed?

**12.** What is the most abundant element on the moon?

## 18:9 Origin of the Moon

Scientists have used special methods to determine the age of moon rocks. These tests show most moon rocks to be about 3.8 billion years old. A few rocks were found to be 4.45 billion years old, which is about the same age scientists have calculated for the Earth. No signs of life, past or present, have been discovered in lunar samples.

How and where did the moon form? Scientific theories have been proposed to answer these questions. One theory states that Earth and the moon were formed from the same gas and dust cloud that produced the solar system. Earth and moon formed separately from two parts of the gas–dust mass.

State two theories that explain the origin of the moon.

Another theory is that the moon was a small planet. It moved close enough to Earth to be captured by Earth's gravity. Once captured, the planet orbited Earth, becoming the moon.

Perhaps someday we will know the true origin of the moon. Until then, scientists will debate and discuss these theories. More exploration is needed before the mystery is solved.

### making sure

**13.** What is one theory of the moon's origin?

# PERSPECTIVES

## frontiers

# Exploring Space with Liquid Telescopes

Most of the optical telescopes in use today use a glass mirror or lens to form an image of a distant object in space. Building a glass mirror or lens for the larger scopes, such as the refractor at Yerkes Observatory or the Hale reflector, is a difficult and expensive task. The glass must be cut and ground to a perfect shape, or it will not be useful in making astronomical observations.

In 1909, R. W. Wood constructed a telescope that did not use a glass lens. He poured liquid mercury into a bowl and found that as he spun the bowl, the mercury swirled higher at the edges than in the center, forming a lens. Because liquid mercury is a metal with high luster, it makes an excellent reflecting surface. However, some problems occurred that Wood was not able to solve.

Recently, Ermanno Borra, an astrophysicist at Laval University in Quebec, built a telescope similar to R. W. Wood's. Using modern instruments, he has overcome some of the problems Wood encountered. Because a bowl of liquid mercury cannot be tilted it can be focused on only one point in the sky. Such a small photo is of little value to an astronomer. Borra proposed that each night's photograph be stored in a computer, and eventually combined to form one large photo of an area in space.

Liquid mercury telescopes have an advantage over conventional telescopes in that they are lighter, stronger, and less expensive to build. For example, a five meter mercury lens would cost approximately $300 000.00, whereas a glass mirror telescope of that size would cost millions of dollars. There are some disadvantages, however. Liquid mercury is very toxic and escapes quickly into the atmosphere.

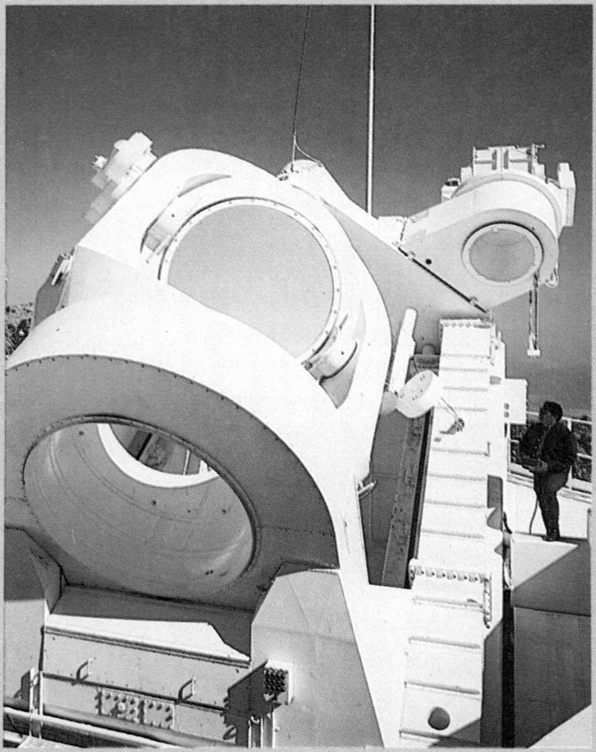

*Kitt Peak/Cerro Tololo Observatories*

Any hazard to humans could be prevented by using a thin layer of clear liquid, such as glycerine, to prevent evaporation along with exhaust fans to remove any fumes that escape.

So far the largest model made and tested by Borra is about one meter in diameter. His idea of a liquid telescope with a 30 meter lens is possible with today's technology. When all the problems of a larger telescope can be overcome, astronomers will be able to gather new data from space and better understand our universe.

# main ideas — Chapter Review

1. Astronomy is the study of the planets, stars, and all other objects in space. 18:1
2. Optical telescopes are classified as refractors or reflectors. 18:2
3. Astronomers study the spectra of light from the stars. 18:3
4. Radio telescopes are used to detect radio waves coming from space. They are not affected by weather and sunlight. 18:4
5. One complete revolution of the moon requires about 27⅓ days. One rotation of the moon occurs in the same amount of time. 18:5
6. Moon phases are the result of the moon's revolution around Earth. 18:6
7. A lunar eclipse occurs during a full moon when the moon moves into Earth's shadow. 18:7
8. A solar eclipse occurs during a new moon when Earth moves into the moon's shadow. 18:7
9. The moon's surface features include craters, plains, and mountains. 18:8
10. Different scientific theories have been proposed to explain the moon's origin. 18:9

## vocabulary

*Define each of the following words or terms.*

astronomy
lunar eclipse
moon phases
penumbra
radio astronomy
radio telescopes
reflector
refractor
revolution
rotation
solar eclipse
spectrograph
spectroscopy
umbra

## study questions

**DO NOT WRITE IN THIS BOOK.**

**A. True or False**

*Determine whether each of the following sentences is true or false. If the sentence is false, rewrite it to make it true.*

1. Astronomers use telescopes to make observations of the skies.
2. As the moon rotates, the same side always faces Earth.
3. A refracting telescope contains convex lenses.

4. Stars can be located using radio telescopes.
5. During a full moon, the lighted side of the moon faces Earth.
6. No signs of life have been found on the moon.
7. Maria is the name given to the moon's plains.
8. A crater can be formed by the collision of the moon with a rock from space.
9. One moon day and one moon year are about the same length of time.
10. Few maria exist on the side of the moon that faces away from Earth.

**B. Multiple Choice**

*Choose the word or phrase that completes correctly each of the following sentences.*

1. The moon revolves from (*west to east, east to west, north to south*).
2. Each time the moon makes one revolution, it completes (*one, two, three*) rotation(s).
3. The moon appears to rise in the (*west, east*).
4. The darkest part of Earth's shadow is called the (*penumbra, umbra, orbit*).
5. A lunar eclipse can occur only during (*new moon, full moon, first quarter moon*).
6. A (*solar, lunar*) eclipse occurs when the moon blocks the sun.
7. Earth moves into the moon's (*penumbra, umbra, orbit*) during a total solar eclipse.
8. Scientists believe the moon is (*older than, younger than, the same age as*) Earth.
9. Every element has (*its own, the same, a similar*) spectrum.
10. A total solar eclipse can occur only during (*new, full, first quarter*) moon.

**C. Completion**

*Complete each of the following sentences with a word or phrase that will make the sentence correct.*

1. Two types of optical telescopes are the ______ and the ______.
2. A(n) ______ telescope contains a concave mirror.
3. The size of a telescope is given by the ______ of its lens or mirror.

4. A(n) ______ telescope does not use light to detect objects in space.
5. The gravity of the moon is ______ that of Earth.
6. Bailey's beads are caused by sunlight shining through deep valleys on the ______.
7. Moon lava rock is similar to ______ found on Earth.
8. The most abundant element on the moon is ______.
9. Some scientists believe that most moon rocks are about ______ years old.
10. Moon maria are actually ______.

**D. How and Why**

1. Describe the lunar surface.
2. Why do we see only one side of the moon?
3. How does a lunar eclipse occur?
4. How does a solar eclipse occur?
5. Draw a diagram showing the orbit of the moon around Earth. Draw the sun at the top of your paper. Show the position of the moon in the new, full, first quarter, and last quarter phases.

## challenges

1. Locate *Astronomy* magazine in a library. Prepare a report on how this magazine is helpful to students interested in astronomy as a hobby.
2. Locate a map of the moon. Observe the moon with binoculars or a telescope and identify as many features as you can.
3. Obtain a topographic map of the moon. Use modeling clay to build a model of part of the lunar surface. Label the features and display the model in your classroom.

## interesting reading

Herbst, Judith, *Sky Above and Worlds Beyond.* New York: Atheneum. 1982.

Provenzo, Eugene F., Jr. and Asterie Provenzo, *Rediscovering Astronomy.* LaJolla, CA: Oak Tree, 1980.

*Haley's Comet is a regular visitor to our solar system. While comets are visitors to our solar system, other space objects are permanent members of it. What are the members of our solar system? What are the unique characteristics of these members? How much do we really know about our solar system?*

*Association of Universities for Research in Astronomy, The Kitt Peak National Observatory*

# Our Solar System

chapter 19

## 19:1 Motion of the Planets

GOAL: You will learn the features and relationships among the members of our solar system.

Our solar system is the sun and the objects that travel around the sun. Nine major planets revolve around the sun. These planets are Mercury, Venus, Earth, Mars, Jupiter, Saturn, Uranus, Neptune, and Pluto (Table 19–3, page 390). Neptune and Pluto are the only planets not visible with the unaided eye. Most planets have moons. Two planets (Mercury and Venus) do not have moons. The solar system also includes the solar wind, asteroids, meteoroids, comets, and dust. Most of the solar system is empty space.

Name the nine planets.

People tried to determine the structure of the solar system many years before the telescope was invented. Ptolemy (TAHL uh mee), a Greek astronomer, believed that Earth stood motionless in space. He believed that the other parts of the solar system revolved around Earth. Ptolemy's idea was published in 150 A.D. and accepted for more than 1400 years.

How was Copernicus' theory different from Ptolemy's idea?

In the middle of the 16th century, Nicholas Copernicus (koh PUR nih kus), a Polish astronomer, stated a different theory. He proclaimed that the

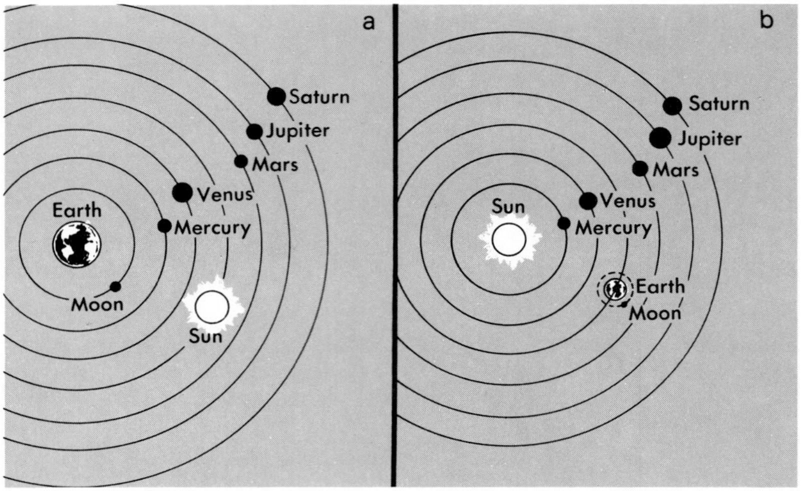


FIGURE 19-1. According to Ptolemy's theory, Earth was at the center of the solar system (a). Copernicus' theory said that Earth and the rest of the planets orbited the sun (b).

What do Kepler's laws describe?

What points in a planet's orbit are the perihelion and aphelion?

sun, not Earth, was the center of the solar system. He also stated that Earth and the other planets revolve around the sun in perfect circles. However, Copernicus could not predict the positions of the planets. This problem was solved early in the 17th century by Johannes Kepler, a German astronomer. Kepler published three mathematical relationships for planetary motion based on many years of observation. These relationships are called Kepler's laws.

Kepler's first law states that the shape of a planet's orbit is an ellipse with the sun at one focus. An **ellipse** is the path a point makes so that the sum of its distances from two fixed points is constant (Figure 19–2a). A planet traveling in an elliptical (ih LIHP tih kul) orbit will not be the same distance from the sun at all times. The point in the orbit closest to the sun is called the **perihelion** (per uh HEEL yun). The point in the orbit farthest from the sun is called the **aphelion** (a FEEL yun).

Kepler's second law states that a planet moves along its orbit so that a line from the planet to the sun sweeps across equal areas in equal times (Figure 19–2b). This means that a planet does not always move at the same speed. A planet travels faster as it moves toward perihelion. The planet travels slower as it moves toward aphelion.

FIGURE 19-2. The shape of a planet's orbit is an ellipse with the sun at one focus (a). The time it takes a planet to go from A to B is equal to the time it takes to go from C to D (b).

a

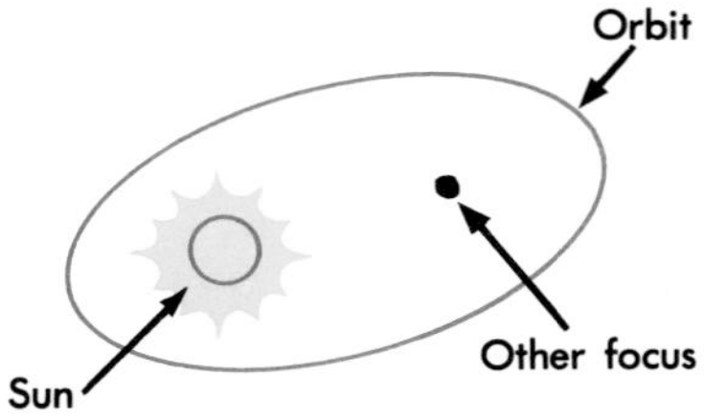


b

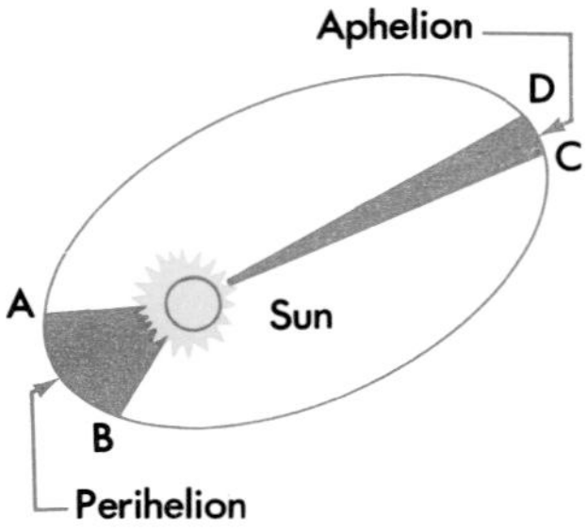

Kepler's third law states that the time a planet takes to make one complete revolution around the sun depends upon the distance of the planet's orbit from the sun. A planet farther from the sun takes longer to complete a revolution than a closer planet.

Inertia and the force of gravity keep the planets in orbits. Inertia is the tendency of an object to keep moving in a straight line. Gravity is the force that matter exerts on other matter. The sun's gravity pulls the planets toward it. However, the sun's gravity is not strong enough to overcome the inertia of the planets. Because of inertia, a planet tends to move away from the sun. Because the force of gravity and inertia balance, a planet orbits the sun.

## activity
### AN ELLIPSE

**(1)** Stick two thumbtacks 14 cm apart into a piece of stiff cardboard. **(2)** Tie the ends of a 40-cm piece of string together to form a loop. **(3)** Place the loop around the tacks and place your pencil inside the loop. **(4)** Draw a figure keeping the string tight at all times. Describe the figure you draw. This figure is called an ellipse. **(5)** Move the tacks closer together and draw another ellipse. How does this figure compare to the first one? **(6)** Remove one tack and draw a third figure. How is it different from the other two?

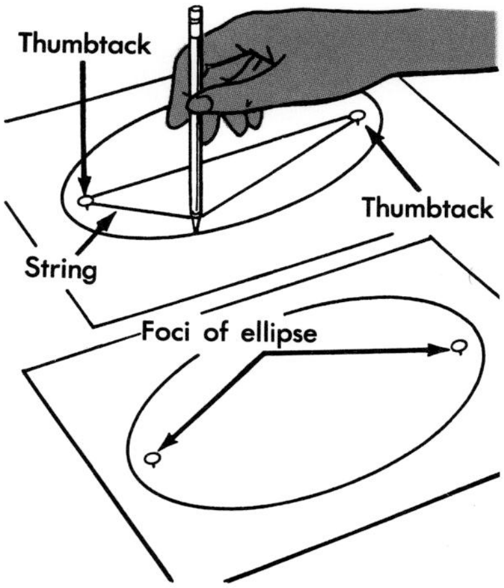

FIGURE 19-3.

### making sure

1. Which planet revolves around the sun fastest? Slowest? Explain your answers.
2. Where in an orbit is a planet's perihelion?

## 19:2 The Sun

The sun is a star, a sphere of hot, glowing gases. It is the center of our solar system. It contains 99 percent of the matter in the solar system. The sun is about 150 000 000 km from Earth. The sun rotates on its axis.

Describe the sun.

| Table 19–1. Some Facts about the Sun | |
|---|---|
| Average distance from Earth | 149.6 million km |
| Average length of time for light to reach Earth | 8 min 20 s |
| Diameter | 1 392 000 km |
| Temperature | Surface, about 6000°C<br>Interior, about 15 000 000°C |
| Age | About 4.6 billion years |

The sun is composed of several different regions (Figure 19–4b). Only the outer three regions are visible. These regions make up the sun's atmosphere.

Describe the sun's atmosphere.

The **photosphere** (FOHT uh sfihr) is the innermost layer of the atmosphere. It is the layer you see when you look at the sun. Most of the light that reaches Earth comes from this layer.

The **chromosphere** (KROH muh sfihr) is the middle layer of the atmosphere. It is a red layer of gas about 2500 km thick. The chromosphere is visible during a total solar eclipse.

The outermost layer of the atmosphere, the **corona** (kuh ROH nuh), is visible during a total eclipse. The corona extends from about 2500 km

FIGURE 19-4. The sun's corona is visible during a solar eclipse (a). The sun is made up of several layers with different temperatures and brightnesses (b). The deepest visible layer is the photosphere.

a

NASA

b

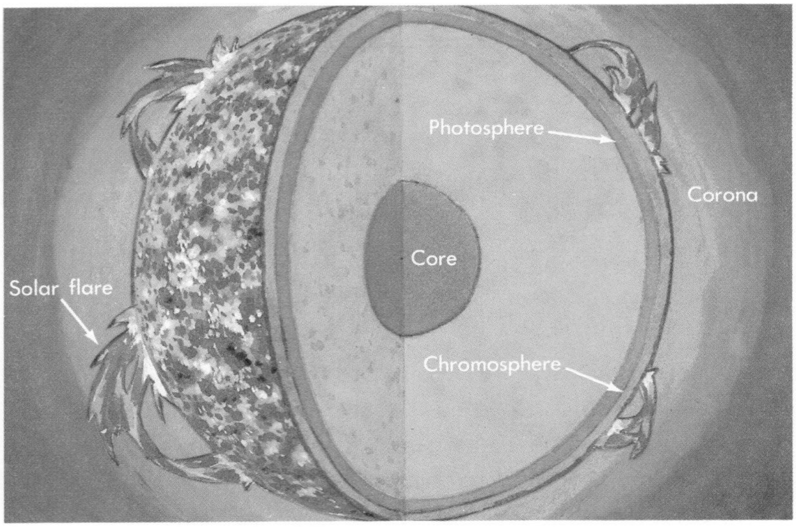

above the photosphere to beyond Earth's orbit. It is a huge cloud of gas. Photographs of the corona show that it has a fan shape extending beyond both poles of the sun. This pattern is evidence of the sun's strong magnetic field.

Between the photosphere and the core are regions where energy is moved to the sun's atmosphere. These regions do not have specific names. The actual method of energy transfer is not known.

Nuclear fusion reactions occur in the core of the sun. Temperatures in the core rise to 15 million°C. The energy produced in the fusion reactions moves out of the core by radiation and convection.

What reaction produces the sun's energy?

**making sure**

3. From which layer of the sun does the light that reaches Earth come?
4. How is energy produced in the sun?
5. How much of the matter in the solar system is contained in the sun?

## 19:3 Sunspots, Solar Flares, and Solar Wind

There are features in the photosphere that can be observed and studied. One of these features is sunspots. **Sunspots** are cooler, dark areas on the sun's surface. Galileo studied sunspots with his telescope in 1612. He observed some dark spots on a projected sun image. He noted that the spots moved across the sun's surface.

Scientists believe that sunspots are the result of magnetic storms in the sun because sunspots have a strong magnetic field. This magnetic field keeps some of the sun's energy from reaching the surface. Thus, sunspots are cooler and darker than the surrounding surface of the sun.

What are sunspots and what is the sunspot cycle?

Sunspots vary in diameter from 1500 km to 50 000 km. They can occur in groups of two to twenty. Most sunspots disappear within a day, but some last a week or longer.

FIGURE 19–5. Sunspots are the result of magnetic storms within the sun (a). A solar prominence appears as a column of gas arching above the sun's surface (b).

Tersch Enterprises

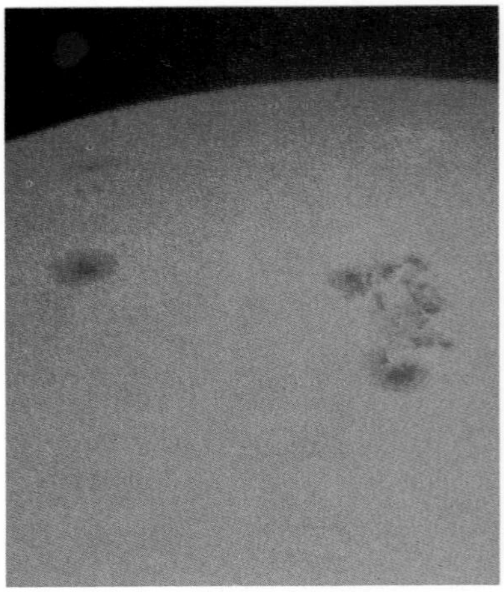

a

NASA

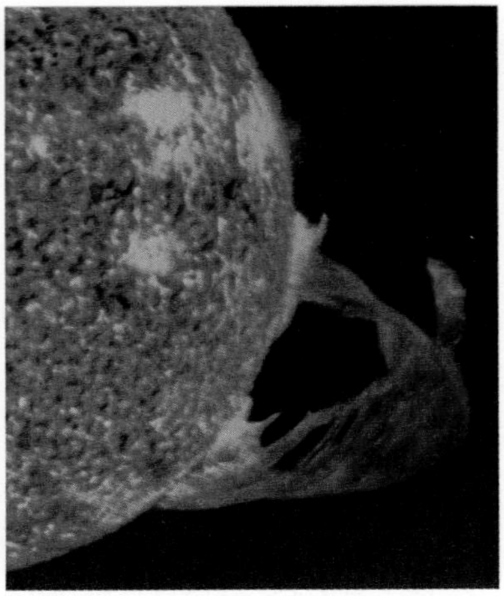

b

Since Galileo's time, scientists have observed and recorded sunspot activity. The number of sunspots increases and decreases in a cycle of about 11 years. We say the sun is active when there are many sunspots. It is termed inactive when there are few sunspots. Scientists are also studying the effects of sunspots on Earth's climate. They have observed that glaciers retreat when the sun is active. From 1645 to 1710, the sun was very inactive. During this time, Earth's temperatures were unusually cold.

How do sunspots affect the Earth?

Scientists have observed that sunspots are related to other features of the sun such as prominences (PRAHM nunts uz) and flares. **Prominences** are glowing clouds of dust that form arches or plumes in the chromosphere. Matter falls from the corona back to the photosphere in most prominences. In a few prominences, matter is ejected from the sun's surface.

Define prominence and solar flare.

**Solar flares** are bright flashes of light that appear near sunspots. Solar flares usually last less than an hour. Flares eject electrons and electromagnetic radiation from the sun. Solar flares can affect Earth. Two days after a solar flare, electrically charged particles from the sun strike Earth's upper atmosphere. These particles cause a magnetic storm on Earth. Auroras, or lights, are seen and shortwave radio communications are disrupted. The earth's

How do solar flares affect the Earth?

Dennis diCicco

a

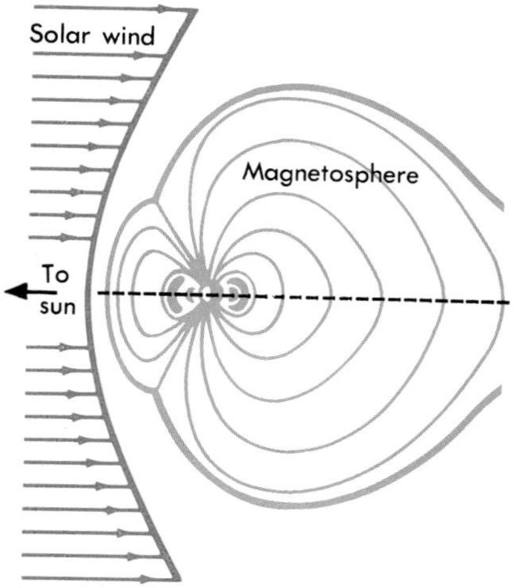


b

FIGURE 19–6. Auroras, also called the northern and southern lights, are the result of solar flares (a). A "gust" in the solar wind distorts a planet's magnetosphere (b).

What is solar wind?

magnetic field is disturbed. Compass needles sometimes swing away from the magnetic poles.

Electrically charged particles are carried to Earth and beyond in the **solar wind**. The solar wind travels outward from the sun's corona to beyond Jupiter. As it passes a planet with a magnetic field, the solar wind distorts the field into a shape like a cage. This cage is the planet's **magnetosphere** (mag NEET uh sfihr). When a solar flare occurs, there is a "gust" in the solar wind. The magnetosphere of a planet protects the planet from this gust.

### making sure

**6.** How does the sun's magnetic field affect Earth?

## 19:4 Mercury

Since 1962, spacecraft have aided scientists in their observations of the solar system. Table 19–2 lists some of these spacecraft and the planet(s) visited. Much has been learned about the planets from these flights.

List the main features of Mercury.

**Table 19–2.**
United States Planetary Spacecraft

| Launch year | Spacecraft | Planet(s) studied |
|---|---|---|
| 1962 | Mariner 2 | Venus |
| 1964 | Mariner 4 | Mars |
| 1967 | Mariner 5 | Venus |
| 1969 | Mariner 6 | Mars |
| 1969 | Mariner 7 | Mars |
| 1971 | Mariner 9 | Mars |
| 1972 | Pioneer 10 | Jupiter |
| 1973 | Pioneer 11 | Jupiter, Saturn |
| 1973 | Mariner 10 | Mercury, Venus |
| 1975 | Viking 1 and 2 | Mars |
| 1976 | Voyager 1 & 2 | Jupiter, Saturn |
| 1978 | Pioneer-Venus | Venus |

Mercury is the planet closest to the sun. It has a diameter of 4880 km. Mercury revolves around the sun faster than any other planet. One Mercury year is equal to 88 Earth days. One Mercury day is equal to 59 Earth days. Mercury has no moons.

Mercury has a surface similar to that of Earth's moon. It is a bleak, barren desert with mountains and craters. At the equator of Mercury, the temperature ranges from −183°C during a Mercury

FIGURE 19-7. Images of Mercury taken by the Mariner 10 spacecraft show that Mercury's surface is heavily cratered. It appears to be very similar to Earth's moon.

NASA

NASA

night to 330°C at noon on a Mercury day. This temperature is hot enough to melt lead or tin.

Mercury has an iron core. This iron core makes Mercury almost as dense as Earth even though it has only 1/18 Earth's mass. Mercury's magnetic field may be strong enough to hold a thin veil of gases. The veil is not dense enough to call it an atmosphere.

Sometimes, Mercury is visible just after sunset. At other times, it is visible just before sunrise. Although Mercury is visible, its image is indistinct. Astronomers did not have pictures of its surface until Mariner 10 relayed images to Earth.

## activity

### PERIOD OF REVOLUTION

**(1)** Obtain a one-hole stopper and a 1.5-m piece of string. **(2)** Tie the string securely to the stopper. **(3)** Hold the string at a distance of 50 cm from the stopper and twirl the stopper in an orbit around your head. Twirl the stopper just fast enough to keep it level. **CAUTION:** Do not hit anyone or anything with the stopper. **(4)** Have a partner time how long it takes for the stopper to make 10 revolutions around your head. Divide the time by 10 to find the time of one revolution. What in space does your head represent? The stopper? **(5)** Hold the string 75 cm from the stopper and repeat Steps 3 and 4. How does the time of one revolution in this trial compare to the previous trial? **(6)** Hold the string 100 cm from the stopper and repeat Steps 3 and 4. How does this time compare to the other two? How does this activity demonstrate Kepler's third law? How does this activity provide evidence that Mercury has the shortest period of revolution for the planets?

FIGURE 19-8.

## making sure

**7.** In Earth days, how long is Mercury's year?

**8.** How is the surface of Mercury similar to that of Earth's moon?

**9.** What would happen to a tin can if it were on Mercury in the middle of the day?

*Table 19–3.*
Our Solar System

| Object | Type of Object | Average distance to sun (millions of km) | Diameter (km) | Rotation period (Earth time) | Revolution period (Earth time) |
|---|---|---|---|---|---|
| Sun | Star | — | 1 392 000 | 25.4 d | — |
| Mercury | Planet | 57.9 | 4 880 | 59 d | 88 d |
| Venus | Planet | 108.2 | 12 100 | 243 d | 224.7 d |
| Earth | Planet | 149.6 | 12 756 | 23 h 56 min | 365 d |
| Moon | Moon of Earth | — | 3 475 | 27 ⅓ d | |
| Mars | Planet | 227.9 | 6 794 | 24 h 37 min | 687 d |
| Jupiter | Planet | 778.3 | 143 200 | 9 h 55 min | 11.86 yr |
| Io | Moon of Jupiter | — | 3 630 | — | — |
| Europa | Moon of Jupiter | — | 3 130 | — | — |
| Callisto | Moon of Jupiter | — | 4 820 | — | — |
| Ganymede | Moon of Jupiter | — | 5 275 | — | — |
| Saturn | Planet | 1 427 | 120 000 | 10 h 40 min | 29.46 yr |
| Titan | Moon of Saturn | — | 5 150 | — | — |
| Uranus | Planet | 2 870 | 51 800 | 13-24 h | 84 yr |
| Neptune | Planet | 4 497 | 49 500 | 18 h 30 min | 165 yr |
| Pluto | Planet | 5 900 | 3 000 | 6 d 9 h | 248 yr |
| Charon | Moon of Pluto | — | 1 300 | — | — |

## 19:5 Venus

Venus appears as a bright object in the morning or evening sky. It is visible without a telescope. Sometimes you can see Venus during the day. Venus has a diameter of 12 100 km. It orbits the sun at an average distance of 108 million km. This distance places Venus's orbit closer to Earth's orbit than that of Mars. Because the orbits are close, Venus is said to be our nearest planetary neighbor.

Venus rotates from east to west. This direction of rotation is opposite that of Earth. On Venus, the sun rises in the west and sets in the east. A Venus day is 243 Earth days, and a Venus year is 225 Earth days. Venus has no moons.

How is Venus different from Earth?

NASA

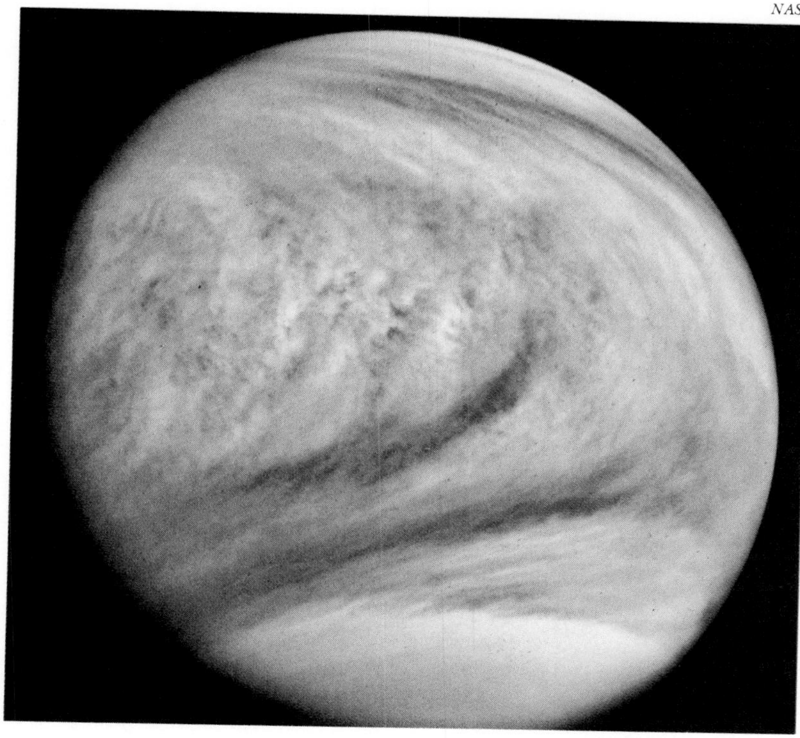

FIGURE 19-9. Venus has an atmosphere of carbon dioxide and sulfuric acid clouds.

The atmosphere of Venus has three layers of clouds. These clouds are not like Earth clouds. The clouds are composed of drops of sulfuric acid and give Venus its yellowish color. The top layer of clouds moves at speeds of 360 km/h.

Below the cloud layers, the atmosphere of Venus is mainly carbon dioxide. The clouds and the atmosphere trap solar radiation and prevent it from escaping. As a result, Venus is very hot. The surface temperature averages 460°C. The pressure of the atmosphere is almost 100 times that of Earth. There is no water on Venus and no life has been detected.

Details of Venus's surface were relayed to Earth from the Pioneer-Venus spacecraft. The photographs show a cratered surface. Some of the craters are filled with liquid rock. Venus has a mountain chain of inactive volcanoes, a plateau the size of the United States, and a vast canyon. This canyon is four times as long as Earth's Grand Canyon and twice as deep. The canyon may have been formed by quakes in the planet's solid surface.

## making sure

**10.** Of what chemical are Venus's cloud layers composed?

**11.** How does the carbon dioxide atmosphere keep Venus's surface temperature high?

## 19:6 Earth

Viewed from space, Earth looks like a blue sphere with white streaks. The blue is caused by light reflecting from the oceans and the white is clouds.

How is Earth unique among the planets?

Earth is unique among the planets in that it supports life. The atmosphere contains nitrogen and oxygen. Oxygen is vital to life as we know it. Nitrogen is part of every living organism. The average temperature of Earth is 14°C. Over 70 percent of Earth's surface is covered by water. Plants and animals are found almost everywhere on Earth.

Earth's surface has mountains, canyons, deserts, basins, and even a few craters. Earth is constantly changing. Mountains are uplifted and worn away,

FIGURE 19-10. From the moon, Earth looks like a blue ball with clouds forming white streaks and patches.

lakes are formed and dry up, volcanoes erupt and become inactive.

Like all planets, Earth revolves around the sun. Earth makes one complete revolution of the sun in about 365.25 Earth days. Earth rotates once on its axis every 24 hours. The diameter of Earth is 12 756 km. Earth has one natural satellite, the moon.

### making sure

**12.** How is Earth unique among the planets in the solar system?

## 19:7 Mars

Describe the major features of Mars.

Mars is visible from Earth without a telescope. Mars has a diameter of 6794 km. The length of its day is 24 h, 37 min Earth time. Its year is 687 Earth days. Mars has two moons, Phobos (FOH bus) and Deimos (DI mos). Phobos has a diameter of 27 km, and Deimos has a diameter of 15 km. Phobos and Deimos are not round.

A year on Mars has seasonal changes. Astronomers have observed ice caps at the poles. These ice caps change in size. As one ice cap expands, the other cap retreats. The south ice cap seems to be frozen carbon dioxide. The north ice cap is frozen water.

On July 20, 1976, Viking I landed on Mars and sent back pictures of the surface. Soil samples were also collected and analyzed. The soil and rocks of Mars contain the same elements as Earth. The material is mostly silicon and oxygen combined with metals. The soil is coated with iron oxide, which gives the soil a red color. No life has been detected on Mars.

The surface of Mars is covered with craters. A huge dome, 5000 km in diameter, rises more than 7 km above the surrounding plain near the equator. Four giant volcanoes are found on this plain. They are all inactive. The largest volcano, Olympus Mons, is three times as tall as Earth's Mt. Everest. It is 550 km across its base. Along the eastern side of the dome is a series of canyons. These canyons are four

Tersch enterprises NASA

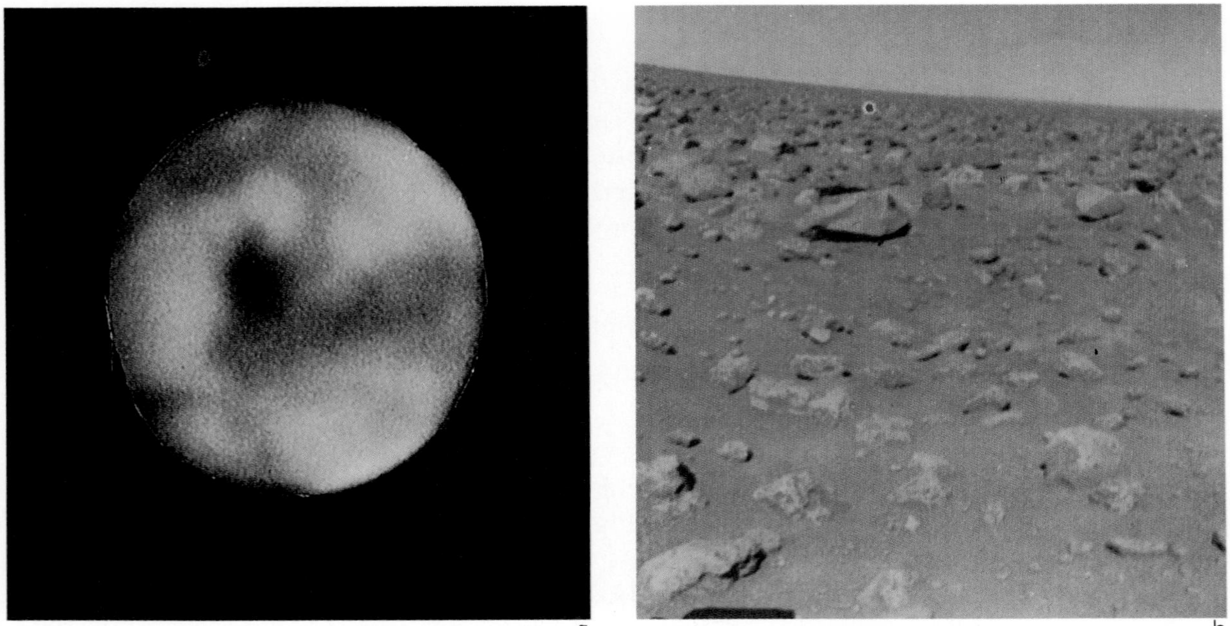


FIGURE 19-11. Mars is known as the red planet (a). Its soil is coated with iron oxide, giving it the red color (b).

times deeper than the Grand Canyon. Their length would stretch completely across the United States. Scientists believe these canyons were formed by quakes and then eroded by landslides and wind.

Temperatures on Mars range from about room temperature, 21°C to −100°C. The thin atmosphere is mainly carbon dioxide. Winds near the surface can blow enough dust into the air to make the planet's surface invisible for months.

### making sure

**13.** How long would it take to drive across the base of Olympus Mons if you traveled at a speed of 88 km/h?

## 19:8 Asteroids and Meteors

What are asteroids?

Where in the solar system are asteroids located?

**Asteroids** (AS tuh roydz) are minor planets that orbit the sun. Most asteroids make one complete revolution every five Earth years. Most asteroids are in a band between the orbits of Mars and Jupiter. Scientists do not know exactly how many asteroids there are. Hundreds are discovered each year. The diameters of the asteroids range from less than 16 km to more than 160 km. The average distance between two asteroids is probably about 6 million km.

Why do so many asteroids exist? Their origin is not known, but there are three scientific theories for their formation. One theory states that asteroids may be pieces of what was once a single planet. When its orbit carried the planet close to Jupiter, the planet shattered. A second theory states that asteroids are pieces of two planets that collided and smashed into fragments. A third theory states that asteroids are bits of matter that did not fuse to form a planet.

If you can get away from the glare of city lights, you can see between 10 and 20 "falling stars" on a clear night. These objects are not really falling stars. They are pieces of rock or metal. When in space, these objects are called **meteoroids** (MEET ee uh roydz). Most meteoroids come from the asteroid belt.

When a meteoroid enters Earth's atmosphere, it begins to glow. A glowing meteoroid is called a **meteor** (MEET ee ur). Sometimes a large meteor may be bright enough to be seen during the day. Its brilliant light gives it the name "fireball." Most meteors burn completely above Earth's surface. If a meteor reaches Earth's surface, it is called a **meteorite** (MEET ee uh rite). A meteorite found in Africa weighed nearly 580 000 N. A meteorite that struck Earth in Arizona created a crater 1200 m in diameter and 180 m deep. This crater is called Barringer Crater.

Millions of meteoroids approach Earth each day. Why do few of these reach the ground? The atmosphere provides a protective blanket. Most meteoroids burn completely 50 to 100 km above Earth's surface.

Tersch Enterprises

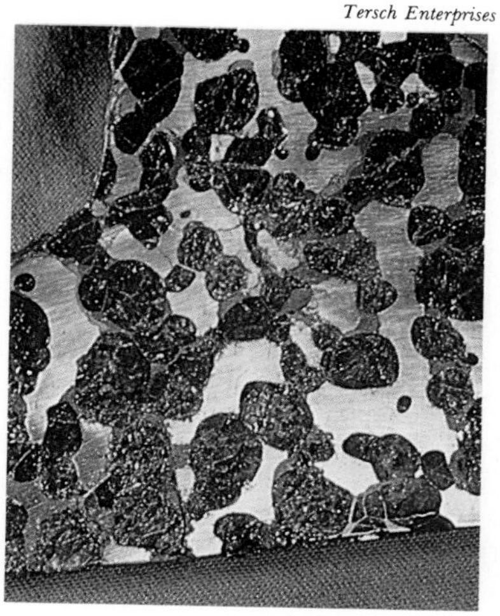

FIGURE 19-12. Some meteorites contain iron and nickel.

Describe three theories that explain the origin of asteroids.

Define meteoroid, meteor, and meteorite.

## making sure

**14.** What are asteroids?

**15.** Explain the difference between meteoroids and meteorites.

NASA

a

NASA

b

FIGURE 19-13. Jupiter (a) is the largest planet in the solar system. It appears banded because of very fast winds in its atmosphere (b).

Why is the gravity on Jupiter about 2½ times that on Earth?

List the major features of Jupiter.

## 19:9 Jupiter

Jupiter is the largest of the planets. Its diameter, 143 200 km, is eleven times that of Earth. Jupiter's mass is second only to that of the sun. Because of its great mass, Jupiter has 2½ times the gravity of Earth. Jupiter rotates faster than any other planet. One day on Jupiter is 9 h 55 min. This high speed of rotation causes Jupiter to bulge like a flattened orange. A year on Jupiter equals 11.9 Earth years. Jupiter has 16 moons and a thin, transparent ring.

The atmosphere of Jupiter accounts for most of Jupiter's volume. Jupiter's atmosphere is composed of several layers. The top layer consists of frozen ammonia. The bottom layer is mainly hydrogen and helium gases.

The "surface" of Jupiter may be liquid hydrogen. About 20 000 km beneath this layer, there may be a dense layer of hydrogen that acts like a metal. Jupiter's core may be iron and silicon.

Jupiter emits twice as much energy as it receives from the sun. Astronomers believe that Jupiter began as an enormous gas sphere that contracted and heated. Jupiter's mass was too small for the core temperatures to become high enough to start nuclear fusion. Therefore, Jupiter did not become a star. It is still cooling and emitting energy.

The most noticeable feature of Jupiter is the Great Red Spot. The diameter of the Great Red Spot is more than three times the diameter of Earth. The temperature of the Great Red Spot is lower than that of the surrounding gas. The most widely accepted theory of the Great Red Spot is that it is a swirling mass of gas like a giant hurricane.

What is Jupiter's Red Spot?

The four largest moons of Jupiter can be seen with a small telescope. The largest moon is Ganymede with a diameter of 5275 km. It is the closest of the four moons to Jupiter. Outward from Ganymede is Callisto, 4820 km in diameter. Callisto has a huge group of rings probably formed after a meteoroid struck the surface and compressed the frozen crust.

Describe Jupiter's four largest moons.

Europa, 3130 km in diameter, is covered with lines many kilometers long. These lines crisscross the moon, giving it a cracked-egg appearance. Europa may have an active volcano on its surface.

Io (ɪ oh), the most distant of the four moons from Jupiter, has a diameter of 3630 km. Io has eleven active volcanoes that erupt and eject material. Besides the sun, Io is the most active object in the solar system.

## 19:10 Saturn

What material makes up Saturn's rings?

Saturn, with a diameter of 120 000 km, is the second largest planet. It has 95 times the mass and 9.4 times the diameter of Earth. A series of rings revolve around the planet. The rings are composed of billions of chunks of frozen material ranging in size from tiny marbles to nine-meter wide globes. Viewed from Earth, the rings appear smooth and wide. Photographs taken by the Voyager probes show that there are hundreds of narrow rings. The diameter of the outermost ring is 275 000 km. Saturn has at least 17 moons.

FIGURE 19-14. Saturn's ring system makes it a curious and interesting planet.

*Tersch Enterprises*

Saturn is a gas planet like Jupiter. The layers of Saturn's atmosphere are the same as are found on Jupiter. Because it is mostly gas, Saturn is less dense than water. The gravity of Saturn is about the same as that of Earth.

Saturn rotates rapidly. One day on Saturn is 10 h, 40 min long. Saturn revolves around the sun in

29.46 Earth years. Because of Saturn's rapid rotation, it bulges in the middle. Saturn is the most flattened of the planets.

Titan, Saturn's largest moon, has a diameter of 5800 km. It is larger than Mercury or Pluto. Titan is the only moon in the solar system that is known to have an atmosphere. The atmosphere is composed of methane. Scientists do not believe that life exists on Titan.

### making sure

**16.** Why is Saturn's moon, Titan, unique?

## 19:11 Uranus, Neptune, and Pluto

List the main features of Uranus, Neptune, and Pluto.

Uranus (YOOR uh nus) is barely visible without a telescope. It was not discovered until the 18th century. Uranus has a diameter of 51 800 km. It is considered to be a gas planet like Jupiter and Saturn. Uranus's blue-green color is probably caused by the methane in its atmosphere. Most of Uranus is composed of light gases and ice. Its surface gravity is a little more than that of Earth.

FIGURE 19-15. Uranus (a) has five moons, three can be seen here. Neptune (b) has two moons. The visible moon is 20 times larger than the other one.

a

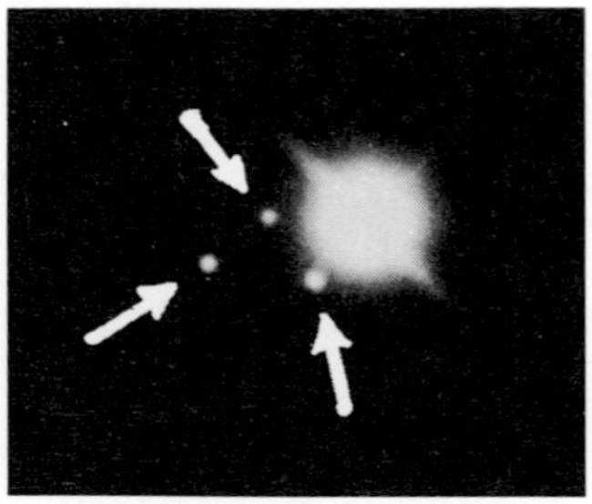

*Lick Observatory*

b

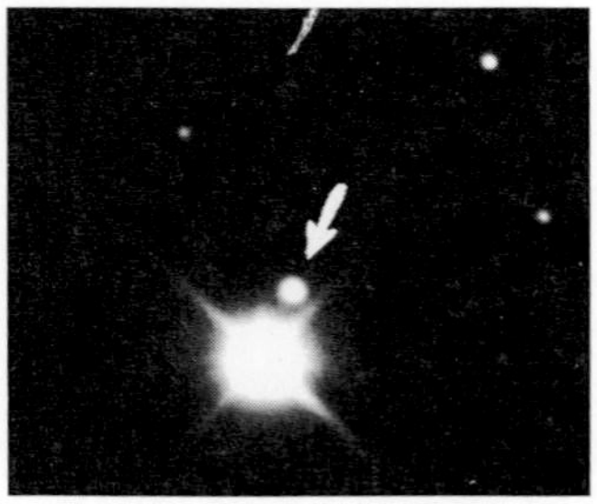

*Lick Observatory*

A unique feature of Uranus is its rotational position. Uranus is tipped almost on its side. Uranus also rotates from east to west. The length of one day on Uranus is not known for certain. Scientists estimate that it is between 13 and 24 hours. Uranus makes one complete revolution of the sun in 84 Earth years.

Uranus has five known moons and nine rings. These rings appear as black loops around the planet. They may be debris from a moon that is being torn apart by Saturn's gravity. Scientists may find answers to some of the questions about this planet from data obtained by Voyager 2.

Neptune, the last of the "gas" planets, appears pale blue. Neptune has a diameter of about 49 500 km. One day on Neptune is thought to be 18 h, 30 min. One year on Neptune equals 165 Earth years. The planet has two known moons. The atmosphere of

Neptune is mostly hydrogen and helium. Neptune's surface gravity is a little greater than that of Earth.

Scientists do not know if Neptune has rings. It is very difficult to detect features on Neptune. Photographs of the planet show some cloud movements, so Neptune must have weather. Most answers to questions about Neptune are yet to be discovered.

Pluto, the last known planet, is located near the edge of the solar system. Occasionally, Neptune is farther from the sun because Pluto's orbit is more elliptical than the orbits of the other planets. Neptune will be farther from the sun than Pluto from 1979 through 1999. Pluto's diameter may be no larger than 3000 km. Pluto has one moon, Charon (KER un), that is almost as large as Pluto itself. Because of the sizes of Pluto and Charon and their closeness, 20 000 km, some astronomers classify the system as a double planet. Pluto has a day equal to 6 days, 9 h Earth time. Its year is equal to 248 Earth years.

There are several scientific theories about the formation and origin of Pluto. One theory states that Pluto is a moon that escaped from Neptune. Another theory states that Pluto and Charon are leftover material from the formation of the solar system.

### making sure

**17.** What is the difference between the rotational position of Uranus and the rotational positions of other planets?

**18.** How are Neptune and Uranus similar?

**19.** Why do some astronomers consider Pluto and Charon a double planet system?

## 19:12 Comets

**Comets** are space objects made of minerals, dust, gases, and ice particles that orbit the sun. They look like fuzzy stars. Comet is a Latin word meaning long-haired. A comet consists of a head and a tail.

What is a comet?

Describe the structure of a comet.

Tersch Enterprises

FIGURE 19-16. A comet's head contains most of the comet's matter. Its tail is dust and gases.

The head contains most of the matter of the comet. A comet's long tail of dust and gases extends into space for million of kilometers. The tail reflects sunlight and is visible. As a comet approaches the sun, its tail points away from the sun. As the comet moves away from the sun, the tail still points away from the sun. The solar wind and sunlight keep a comet's tail always pointed away from the sun.

Long ago, people believed that the appearance of a comet happened by chance. However, in 1758, Edmund Halley, a British astronomer, predicted the appearance of a comet. He had observed that the path of a comet seen at regular intervals in the past was always the same. This comet, named for Halley, appears once every 76 years. Since Halley's time, the orbits of many comets have been calculated and the periods of time that they will be visible from Earth determined.

From where do comets come? Comets seem to come from the outer edges of the solar system. This region contains a large cloud of dust and gas. The cloud may be leftover from the time of the solar system's formation.

How might comets have formed?

There are at least two scientific theories concerning the origin of comets. Most astronomers believe comets were formed in the large cloud of gas and dust at the edge of the solar system. However, some astronomers believe comets are pieces of planets or moons that were flung into orbits. The actual origin of comets is not known.

Comets are the most distant objects in the solar system. Beyond the cloud of gas and dust where they seem to form lies the vastness of outer space.

### making sure

**20.** Halley's comet was visible in 1910. When will it be visible again?

**21.** Why does a comet's tail point away from the sun?

## 19:13 Origin of the Solar System

State two theories that explain the origin of the solar system.

How did the solar system form? Astronomers do not have enough facts to completely answer this question. There are several scientific theories. One idea is the exploding star theory. This explanation states that the planets were formed from an explosion of a companion star of our sun. The matter from this exploding star contracted to form the planets. Support for this theory is the existence of pairs of stars in space. Many of these stars are known to revolve around each other.

The most widely accepted theory today is the dust cloud theory. This explanation states that the sun and planets formed at the same time from a large cloud of dust and gas. As the cloud revolved in space, parts of it began to contract and form the planets and the sun. Because the cloud revolved, the planets revolved. The sun contracted and began to heat. This heat blew much of the cloud that had not condensed into planets to the outer edges of the solar system. By this time, the planets were large enough to remain in orbit. The entire process may have taken 100 million years. This theory is supported by the existence of clouds of gas and dust in outer space.

If the dust cloud theory is correct, it is likely that there are other solar systems similar to ours. Among the billions of stars in outer space, there may be many planets much like our own. Some of these planets may support some form of life.

# Predictable Extinctions?

Sixty-five million years ago, the last remaining dinosaurs died. At the same time, most of the oceanic plankton died, as did many other major groups of animals. The cause of these extinctions has been debated, and many hypotheses have been proposed. It has been suggested that the earth's average temperature rose, causing mass extinctions. Some scientists suggested that volcanic activity on the moon showered the earth with dust, killing many groups of organisms. Others have suggested that the amount of oxygen in the oceans changed, that some groups of organisms could not compete with others, or that diseases swept through populations. Some hypotheses are supported by evidence, others are not.

Recently, it was observed that extinctions occur in a 28 million year cycle. Then two scientists found a large amount of iridium in layers of rock 65 million years old. Usually, this element is very rare in nature and occurs abundantly only in space objects. The scientists proposed that 65 million years ago, a space object, such as an asteroid or meterorite, struck the earth, producing a cloud of dust that blocked the sunlight and caused many organisms to die. Their hypothesis received much criticism until a second cosmic event was proposed that also occurs in a 28 million year cycle.

At the edge of our solar system is a cloud of millions of comets. Scientists propose that every 28 million years, a companion star to our sun passes through the cloud. Astronomers predict that the gravitational pull of the star would send millions of comets towards the sun. Most would miss Earth, but several dozen would strike Earth, filling the atmosphere with dust and changing Earth's climate. Scientists have found that the ages of the seven largest impact craters from comets and meteorites coincide with the estimated dates of mass extinctions.

The impact hypothesis does not answer all of the questions scientists have about mass extinctions, but it is supported by the discovery of the iridium dust and the ages of the craters. Scientists are now studying star sightings to determine if the companion star exists. They also are waiting for information from space probes to determine if comets have a rocky center capable of producing the clouds of dust on impact.

*Jet Propulsion Labs*

# main ideas — Chapter Review

1. Our solar system contains the sun, nine major planets, moons, asteroids, meteoroids, comets, and dust. 19:1
2. The sun is the center of our solar system and contains 99 percent of the matter in the solar system. 19:2
3. Sunspots are magnetic storms on the surface of the sun. 19:3
4. Mercury is the closest planet to the sun. Venus is the second planet from the sun. Venus's atmosphere is carbon dioxide. 19:4, 19:5
5. Earth is the only planet that has life. 19:6
6. Mars has a thin atmosphere of carbon dioxide. 19:7
7. Most asteroids are found between Mars and Jupiter. 19:8
8. Jupiter, Saturn, Uranus, and Neptune are gas planets. Jupiter is the largest planet. 19:9–19:11
9. Comets are composed of minerals, dust, gases, and ice particles. 19:12
10. The dust cloud theory is the most widely accepted theory of the origin of the solar system. 19:13

# vocabulary

*Define each of the following words or terms.*

aphelion
asteroids
chromosphere
comets
corona
ellipse
magnetosphere
meteor
meteorite
meteoroids
perihelion
photosphere
prominences
solar flares
solar wind
sunspots

# study questions

**DO NOT WRITE IN THIS BOOK.**

**A. True or False**

*Determine whether each of the following sentences is true or false. If the sentence is false, rewrite it to make it true.*

1. The orbit of a planet around the sun is a circle.
2. The Copernican theory places Earth at the center of the solar system.

3. The sun contains 99 percent of the matter in the solar system.
4. Kepler's laws describe the motions of the planets in their orbits.
5. Most of the light that reaches Earth comes from the sun's chromosphere.
6. Jupiter is the largest planet.
7. Gravity and inertia keep the planets in orbit around the sun.
8. Pluto is the planet closest to the sun.
9. Venus and Uranus rotate from west to east.
10. Earth does not have any craters.

## B. Multiple Choice

*Choose the word or phrase that completes correctly each of the following sentences.*

1. An asteroid is most like a *(star, planet, comet).*
2. A "falling star" is a *(meteor, meteoroid, meteorite).*
3. Energy is produced in the sun's *(corona, core, chromosphere).*
4. The tail of a comet always points *(toward, away from, at right angles to)* the sun.
5. The most massive planet in the solar system is *(Jupiter, Mars, Earth).*
6. Mercury is the planet *(closest to, farthest from, mid-way from)* the sun.
7. The metal most likely to be found in a meteorite is *(gold, copper, iron).*
8. The region of the sun that we see is the *(corona, chromosphere, photosphere).*
9. Titan, a moon of Saturn, has a(n) *(atmosphere, active volcano, ocean).*
10. *(Gravity, The atmosphere, The magnetosphere)* protects Earth from the solar wind.

## C. Completion

*Complete each of the following sentences with a word or phrase that will make the sentence correct.*

1. The ______ theory states that the solar system formed from a cloud of dust and gas.

2. Most asteroids are found in orbits between the planets of Mars and ______.
3. If a planet were discovered beyond Pluto, its period of revolution would be ______ than Pluto's.
4. Uranus and ______ rotate from east to west.
5. ______ and Mercury have no moons.
6. Saturn, Jupiter, and ______ have known rings.
7. The atmosphere of Venus is mainly ______.
8. Pluto and ______ may be a double planet.
9. ______ is tilted so it lies almost on its side.
10. ______ has the shortest period of revolution.

**D. How and Why**

1. How is an ellipse different from a circle?
2. How is the Copernican theory of the solar system different from Ptolemy's theory?
3. Why do most meteoroids burn up in Earth's atmosphere?
4. How do meteoroids, meteorites, and meteors differ?
5. How is a comet different from a planet?

## challenges

1. Obtain information on the development and use of the NASA space telescope. Prepare a presentation for your class.
2. Prepare a report on a famous meteorite. What information did scientists learn from it?
3. Prepare a report on the relationship between sunspots and Earth's climate. Explain the changes that occurred in the climate during the Little Ice Age.

## interesting reading

Berger, Melvin, *Comets, Meteors, and Asteroids.* New York: Putnam, 1981.

Jabor, William, *Exploring the Sun.* New York: Messner, 1980.

Snowden, Sheila, *The Young Astronomer.* Tulsa, OK: Educational Development Corp., 1983.

# SIDE ROADS

## Voyager

Jet Propulsion Labs

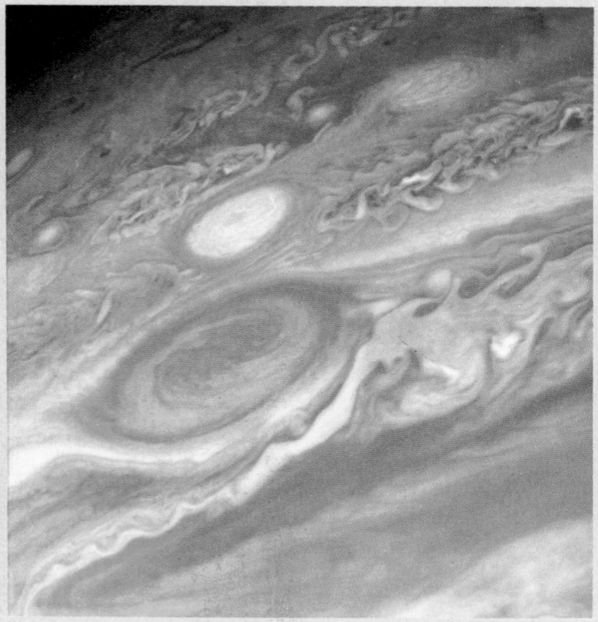
Jet Propulsion Labs

*Galileo Galilei made many discoveries with his telescope. He discovered four moons circling Jupiter and that Saturn had an unusual shape. A few years later, Christian Huygens found the reason for Saturn's unusual shape—the rings. These discoveries marked the beginning of modern astronomy.*

*Since the early 1600s, scientists have used telescopes to learn about objects in space. But these telescopes have limits. For example, they cannot provide a close-up view of Jupiter. They cannot give the speed of the wind on Saturn. To gain this information, scientists use robot space probes.*

*On August 20, 1977, Voyager 2 was launched. Sixteen days later, on September 5, Voyager 1 was launched. Both spacecraft had the same targets—Jupiter and Saturn. Voyager 2 was launched first because it would travel a longer distance, reaching Jupiter four months after Voyager 1.*

*Each spacecraft is nuclear powered and has a variety of equipment. Photographs can be taken with televisionlike cameras. The cameras can be pointed in almost any direction. In addition to visible light, each craft has sensors to detect radio waves. Infrared and ultraviolet radiation, charged particles, and magnetic fields can also be detected. The information from these sensors is converted to numbers by the computer on the craft. The information is then radioed to Earth. Here the information is reconstructed by computer.*

Voyager 1 began observing Jupiter on January 4, 1979. Its closest approach occurred on March 5. One surprising discovery was evidence of a narrow ring around the planet. As a result of this discovery, Voyager 2 was reprogrammed to investigate the ring system. Voyager 2 made its closest approach on July 8 and 9. As photographed by Voyager 2, the ring system is seen as two light orange lines.

Other surprises included a plasma cloud that circles the planet. The orbit of the moon, Io, seems to be within the cloud. Auroras fill the sky but are much stronger than expected. The Great Red Spot was also investigated.

To reach Saturn, the Voyager spacecraft used Jupiter's gravity to increase their speeds. Jupiter's gravity was accelerating them as they approached the planet. By approaching at the proper angle, they did not go into orbit. Instead, they curved and left the planet in a new direction. Because of their acceleration, their speeds were increased. Using this method, very little fuel was burned to accelerate the spacecraft.

*Jet Propulsion Labs*

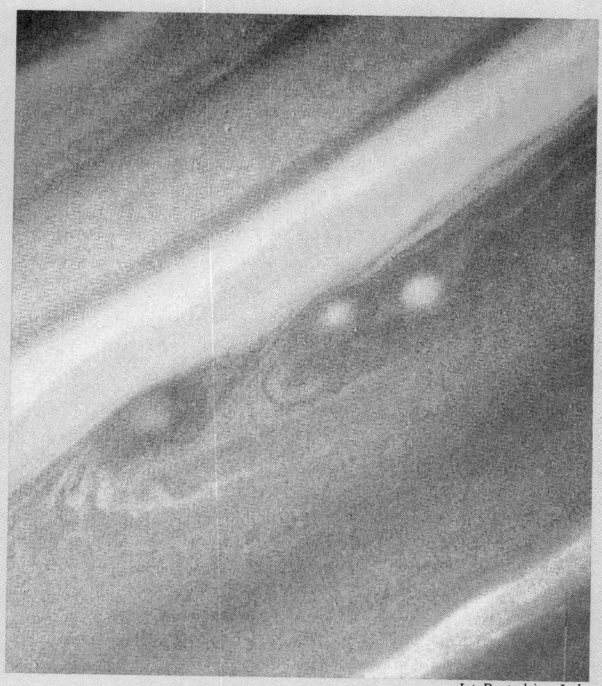

*Jet Propulsion Labs*

Voyager 1 reached Saturn in November, 1980, followed by Voyager 2 in August, 1981. Seven major rings were observed. The rings appear bright because they reflect light. The rings have unusual spokes and braids. Some scientists think the braids in the outer ring are due to two small satellites.

Cloud belts were observed in Saturn's atmosphere. Unlike Jupiter's atmosphere, wind direction changes do not occur at the borders of these belts. Saturn's equatorial winds are three times faster than hurricane-force winds on Earth.

Upon leaving Saturn, Voyager 1 proceeded out of the solar system. It's mission is to provide data on the conditions above the orbital plane of the planets. Voyager 2 continued on to the planets Uranus and Neptune.

*Andromeda is a large spiral galaxy that is 2.2 million light-years away. Andromeda is shaped like our galaxy, the Milky Way. There are many other galaxies of differing sizes and shapes within the universe. What is a galaxy? How are stars related to galaxies? What other material exists within the universe?*

U.S. Naval Observatory

# Stars and Galaxies

# chapter 20

## 20:1 Stars and Stellar Distances

GOAL: You will learn the properties of stars and galaxies.

What is a star?

Ancient Greek astronomers believed the stars were burning objects. Today, we know that stars are composed of very hot gases. Stars produce energy by nuclear fusion. If you observe the sky on a clear night, you can see as many as 2000 stars.

Some stars in the night sky are brighter than others. However, the brightest points of light in the night sky may not be stars. Some planets—Venus, Mars, Jupiter, and Saturn—may be brighter at times than most stars. A planet usually appears as a point of light with a steady glow. Stars usually twinkle. Twinkling is caused by the refraction of the starlight as it passes through Earth's atmosphere (Section 15:8).

A star's apparent brightness depends on its size, type, and distance from Earth. A large, hot star produces more light than a small, cool star. Thus, the large star would be brighter than the small star if both were at the same distance.

Suppose a light is held near you and then moved slowly away. You would observe that the light

FIGURE 20-1. Many stars can be seen through a telescope. Each star's apparent brightness depends on distance, size, and type.

Kitt Peak National Observatory

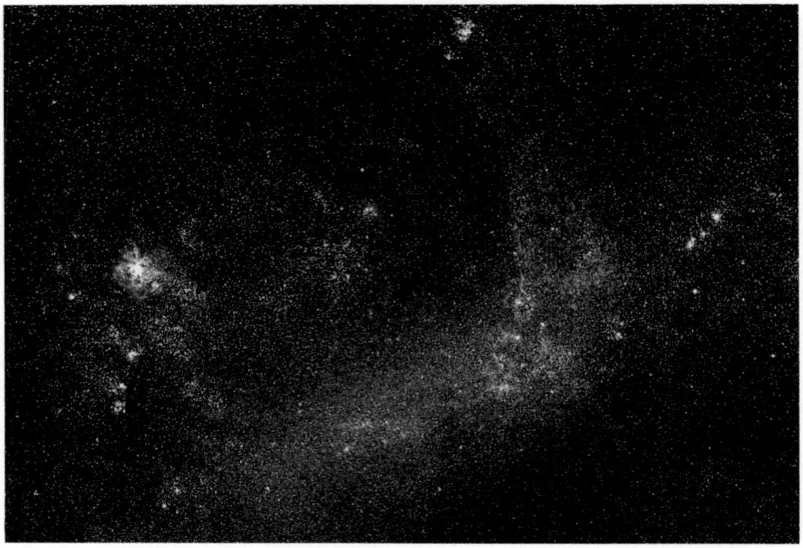

decreases in brightness as its distance increases. The brightness of stars depends on distance much like the brightness of the light does. A large, hot star that is a great distance from Earth is dimmer than a star of the same type nearer Earth.

Because apparent brightness depends on size, type, and distance, stars may appear to produce less light than they actually produce. A very bright star far from Earth appears less bright than a dim star close to Earth.

The actual brightness of a star can be used to indicate the amount of light produced by a star. To compare the actual brightness of stars, astronomers calculate what their brightnesses would be if the stars were at the same distance. Using this method, brightness can also be used to indicate a star's distance from Earth.

Define parallax.

How is parallax used in measuring the distance to a star?

Stellar distances can be measured by parallax (PER uh laks). **Parallax** is the apparent change in position of an object caused by the actual change in position of the observer. As shown in Figure 20–2, a nearby star will appear to change position relative to a background star as the earth revolves around the sun. Using the distance between Earth's first and second positions and the parallax, astronomers can compute the distance to the star.

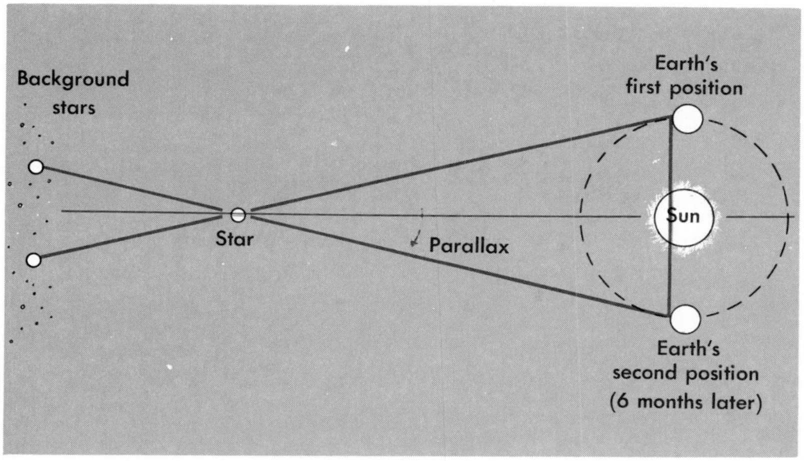


FIGURE 20-2. The parallax method can be used to measure the distances to nearby stars.

The parallax method works only for stars that are relatively close to Earth. Parallax decreases as distance increases. When a star is very far from Earth, no parallax is observed. About 1000 stars are close enough to use parallax.

Why can parallax be used only to determine the distance to relatively near stars?

Astronomers work with very large numbers. The star closest to Earth is about 38 000 000 000 000 km (38 trillion km) away. Astronomers measure distance with a unit called the light-year. A **light-year**, the distance light travels in one year, is 9.5 trillion kilometers. Alpha Centauri, the nearest star, is about 4 light-years away.

How far is a light-year?

About 40 stars in the sky are within 16 light-years of Earth. The brightest star, Sirius, is 9 light-years away. Betelgeuse, one of the largest known stars, is 520 light-years away. Stars more than 5 billion light-years away have been identified. This distance is impossible to grasp. Yet the universe extends at least this far in every direction.

How large is the universe?

## activity
### LIGHT AND DISTANCE

Mount a 25-watt bulb at the end of a meter stick. In a totally dark room, light the 25-watt bulb and hold a photographic light meter at various distances from it. Record both the distances and the light meter readings. Can you discover the mathematical relationship between distance and amount of light?

FIGURE 20-3.

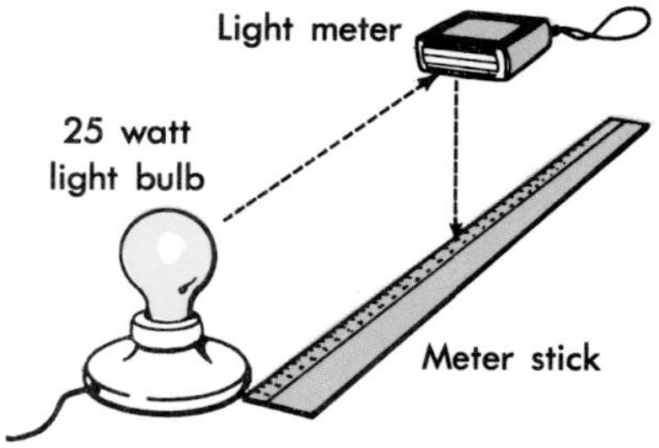

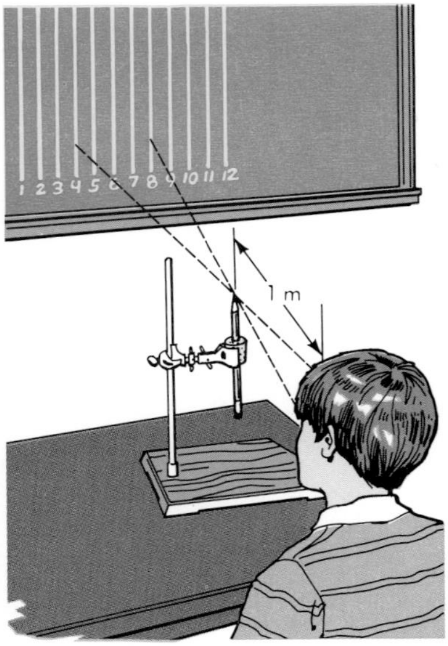


FIGURE 20-4.

## activity PARALLAX

**(1)** Put a series of vertical lines, 10 cm apart, on the chalkboard. Number them in order (Figure 20–4). **(2)** Clamp a pencil to a ring stand and place it between you and the chalkboard. **(3)** Stand 1 m from the pencil. Use your left eye to observe the pencil's position against the lines on the chalkboard. **(4)** Without moving, repeat the observation with your right eye. The apparent change in position of the pencil is the parallax. For example, if the pencil is aligned with line 8 on the chalkboard when seen with your right eye and aligned with line 4 when seen with your left eye, the parallax is 4 (8 − 4 = 4). **(5)** Repeat Steps 3 and 4 at 2 m, 3 m, and 4 m from the pencil. Record the amount of parallax in each case. What is the relationship between the amount of parallax and your distance from the pencil?

### making sure

1. How does a star's apparent brightness depend on its distance from Earth?
2. What is parallax and how is it used by astronomers?
3. What is a light-year?

## 20:2 Classifying the Stars

Most of the information we have about stars comes from studying starlight. Stars of different temperatures radiate different colors of light. Stars that appear blue or blue-white are the hottest stars. Other stars are yellow, orange, or red. Red stars are the coolest. The amount of energy a star releases is related to its color. A blue star radiates more energy than a red star of the same size.

FIGURE 20-5. The line spectrum of the sun (a star) can be used to determine the composition of the sun.

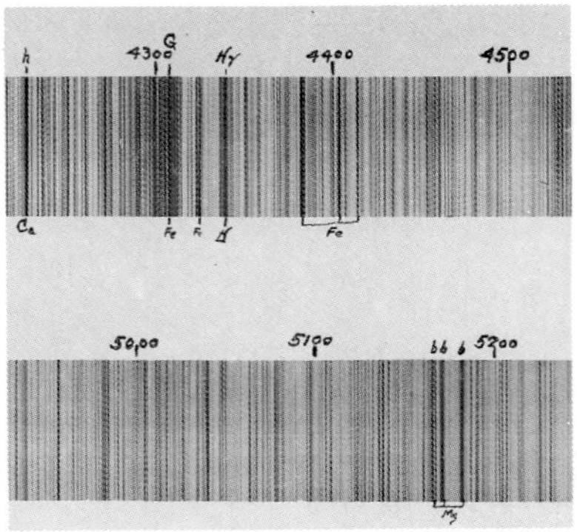


*Mount Wilson and Palomar Observatories*

Starlight is studied by passing it through a spectroscope to produce a spectrum (Section 18:3). The spectrum produced contains sharp, dark lines (Figure 20–5). These lines indicate that some of the light is absorbed as it passes through the star's outer

**Table 20–1.**
**Spectral Classification of Stars**

| Class | Color | Surface Temperature* (°C) |
|---|---|---|
| O | Blue | above 25 000 |
| B | Blue | 11 000–25 000 |
| A | Blue | 7 500–11 000 |
| F | Blue-white | 6 000–7 500 |
| G | White to yellow | 5 000–6 000 |
| K | Orange to red | 3 500–5 000 |
| M | Red | below 3 500 |

*Surface temperature is the temperature in the middle of a star's photosphere.

How is the color of a star used to classify it?

regions. Studying a star's spectrum enables astronomers to determine the elements present in the star, the temperature of the star, and the size of its magnetic field. Using the data obtained through spectroscopy, stars are grouped into seven or more spectral types. These types can be plotted against brightness of the stars. When graphed in this manner, stars fall into several groups. Most stars fall into a diagonal band called the main sequence (Figure 20–6). Stars that do not fit in the main sequence are classified as giants, supergiants, and white dwarfs.

How is the light from a star studied?

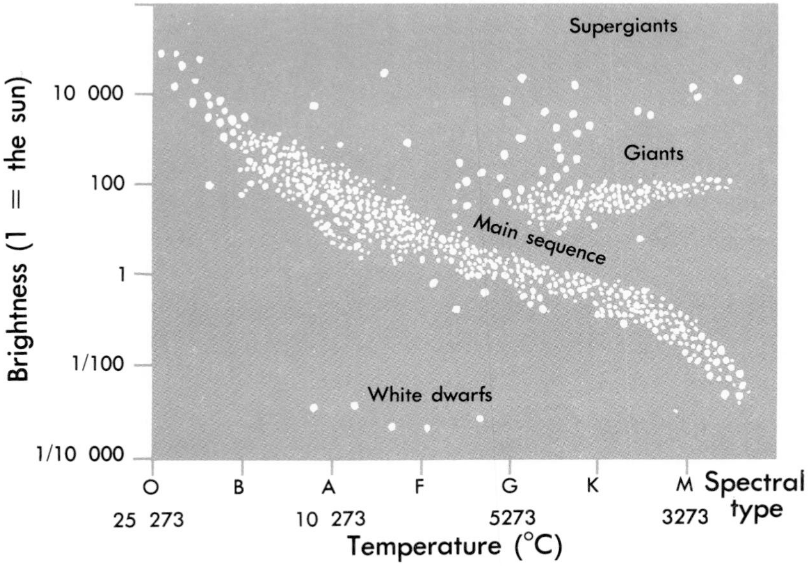


FIGURE 20-6. When star classes are graphed with star brightness, the result is a band called the main sequence. Most stars are part of the main sequence.

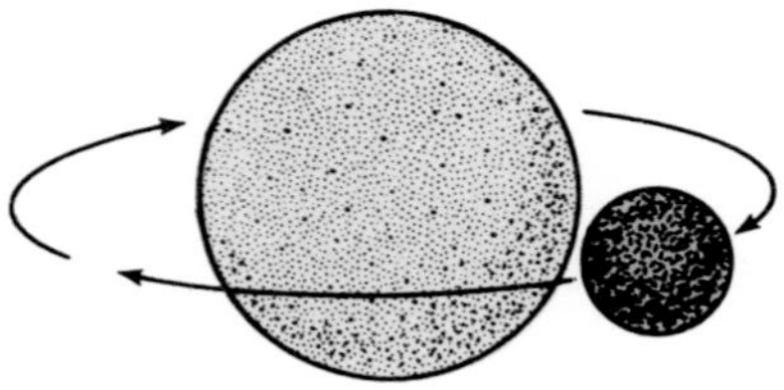

FIGURE 20-7. Two stars revolve around each other in a binary star system.

Most stars shine with constant light. Some stars do not. These stars are called **variable stars**. Cepheids (SEE fee udz) are variable stars whose brightness changes in regular cycles. Polaris, our North Star, is a cepheid. It changes from bright to dim and back to bright in a cycle of four days. Some stars change size as well as brightness. These stars are called pulsating variable stars.

What are binary stars?

Most of the stars we can observe are in pairs or in groups of three or more. The stars revolve around each other. Two stars revolving around each other form a binary system. In a binary system, one star is usually brighter than the other one. Sometimes stars in a binary system appear to change in brightness because the stars eclipse each other. These stars are called eclipsing variable stars. They are not really variable, but the name is still used.

### making sure

**4.** How is a spectroscope used to classify stars?

**5.** What is a variable star? Name two types of variable stars.

## 20:3 Early Stages of a Star

A star is formed in a cloud of hydrogen gas and dust in space. The most widely accepted theory indicates that a star forms in several stages.

How is a star formed?

A star begins when matter in a region of space is pulled together by gravity into a spinning cloud. At first, matter collapses toward one area very slowly. The particles of matter release heat when they hit each other. The star glows a dull red and some energy is released. Pressure in the center of the star increases as more matter is added. The density in this central region becomes very high. Eventually, the pressure becomes large enough that matter cannot fall into the central region. This region becomes the core of the star. This first stage in star formation occurs in a few thousand years.

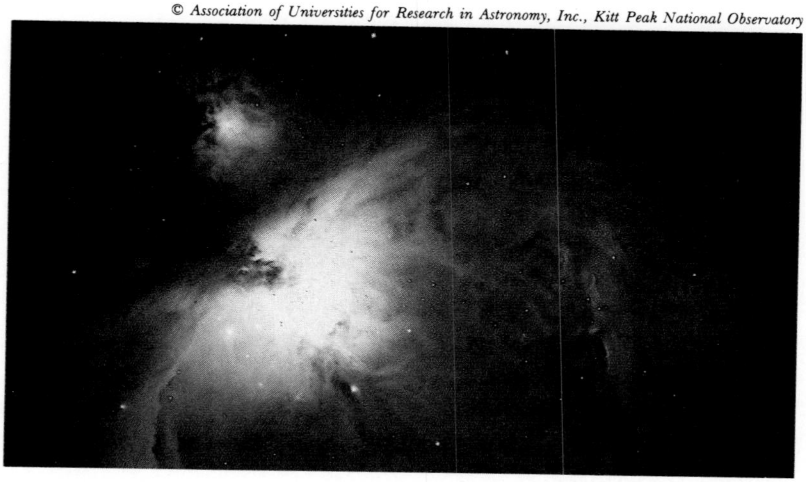

FIGURE 20-8. Clouds of dust and gas, such as the Great Nebula in Orion, are the birthplace of stars.

During the second stage, matter is added to the outer layers of the star. This addition is a relatively slow process. Millions of years may pass until the energy released by the matter raises the core's temperature to the fusion point—about 10 000 000°C. Once fusion begins, no additional matter is gained.

The star is now formed and shining brightly. It is a main sequence star. A **main sequence star** produces almost all of its energy by nuclear fusion. The star shines brightly most of its life. The lifetime of a main sequence star varies depending on its mass. Very massive stars may shine only millions of years. Less massive stars may shine for billions of years.

How does a main sequence star produce its energy?

When all of the hydrogen in the core has been changed to helium, the next stage of a star begins. The core of the star contracts while the outer regions expand. During this period, a star may alternately contract and expand. The amount of light produced changes. Sometimes the star appears very bright; at other times it is barely visible. The outer regions cool and the star becomes red. Now the star is a **red giant**. The red giant stage in a star's life is relatively short.

What is a red giant?

## making sure

**6.** Where does a star form?

**7.** How high must the core temperature of a star rise before fusion reactions occur?

## 20:4 Final Stages of a Star

What is a white dwarf star?

A star collapses once all of its nuclear fuel is used. The star becomes a very dense ball of matter. The star still produces light but eventually it will stop shining. A very long time is needed before a star stops shining completely. Even then, the star may still emit X rays. A collapsed star is called a **white dwarf**. Most of the old stars in the universe seem to be white dwarfs.

Define nova and supernova.

Some stars, such as our sun, will collapse quietly and become white dwarfs. Other stars must eject some mass before they become white dwarfs. A star that ejects matter into space is called an eruptive variable star. The most well-known type of eruptive variable star is called a nova. A **nova** is a star that suddenly appears much brighter than normal. The star may be tens of thousands of times brighter. After a few days or weeks, the star suddenly becomes very faint. Ancient Chinese astronomers called novas "guest stars" because they came and went. When a nova occurs, scientists believe that part of the star is being ejected into space.

A more spectacular variable star is called a supernova. A **supernova** is an exploding star. A supernova may increase in brightness up to hundreds of millions of times its normal brightness. Three supernovas have been observed in the last ten centuries. A large fraction of the mass of a star may be ejected during a supernova explosion. An example of the remains of a supernova explosion is

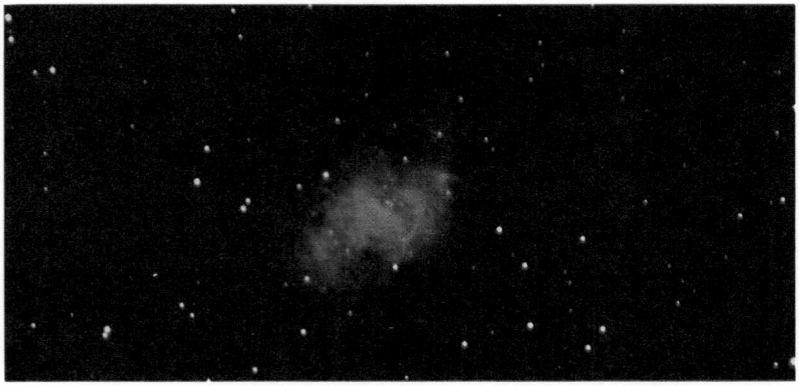

PHOTRI

FIGURE 20-9. The Crab Nebula is the remains of a super nova. The source of radiation in the Crab Nebula is a neutron star.

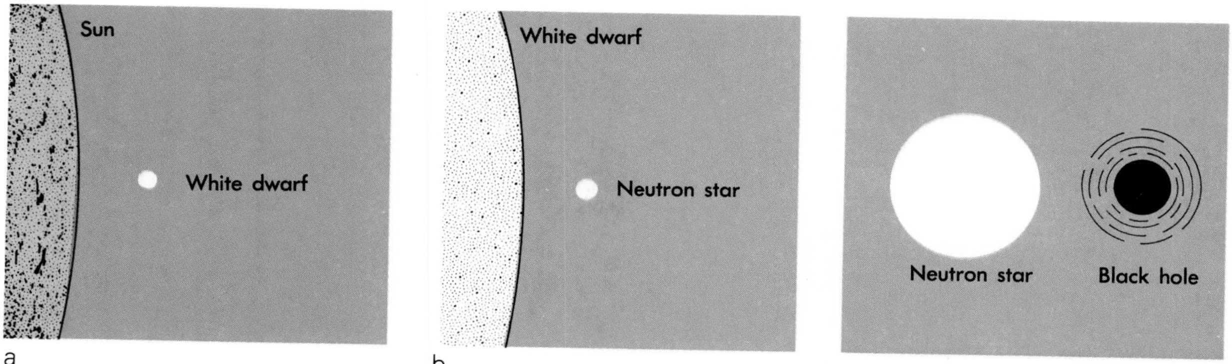


FIGURE 20-10. Our sun's diameter is 230 times the diameter of a white dwarf (a). The diameter of a neutron star may be 600 times smaller than that of a white dwarf (b). A black hole may have ⅓ the diameter of a neutron star (c).

the Crab Nebula. The Crab Nebula is a cloud of gas and dust that is a strong source of X rays, gamma rays, radio waves, infrared waves, and light.

What is a neutron star?

A neutron star may be formed in a supernova explosion. A **neutron star** is one in which all the electrons in the star have been forced into the atomic nuclei. The electrons combine with protons to form neutrons. All matter in the star becomes neutrons. A neutron star is very small. A neutron star with the same mass as our sun would have a diameter of about 10 km. Neutron stars spin very rapidly. As they spin, they release energy. This energy is detected as radio pulses. Spinning neutron stars are called **pulsars**. Pulsars eventually slow down and stop releasing energy.

What is a black hole and how is it formed?

A star may become a black hole. A **black hole** is an area in space that has a gravity field so strong that even light cannot escape. Astronomers believe that a black hole is formed when a neutron star continues to contract until it disappears within itself. Once a black hole is formed, the matter continues to contract until a point remains. How are black holes detected if no energy can escape them? Any matter pulled into a black hole appears to be heated to very high temperatures. Before this matter disappears, it releases large bursts of X rays. Thus, X rays are used to detect black holes.

## making sure

**8.** What happens when a star runs out of nuclear fuel?

**9.** What is a pulsar?

## *Table 20–2.*
## Types of Stars

| Type of star | Features |
|---|---|
| Main sequence stars | Largest group of stars; stars in a stable state |
| Blue stars | Hottest and most massive |
| White stars | Cooler than blue stars |
| Yellow stars | Cooler than white stars |
| Red stars | Coolest and least massive |
| Giants and Supergiants | Very massive and bright; collapsed cores |
| Red or yellow | Giants |
| White, blue, yellow, or red | Supergiants |
| White Dwarfs | Light is faint; matter packed tightly together; high density |
| Variable stars | |
| Pulsating (Cepheids) | Outer layer alternately expands and contracts; becomes brighter during contractions and dimmer during expansions |
| Eclipsing (binary) | Two stars that appear to change in brightness because they revolve around each other |
| Eruptive (nova and supernova) | Stars that are in a state of collapse; one or more periods of brightness and then they dim; may disappear or explode at the end of their life cycle |

FIGURE 20-11. An average star is born in a cloud of gas. Eventually, it becomes a Red Giant; then it fades into a white dwarf.

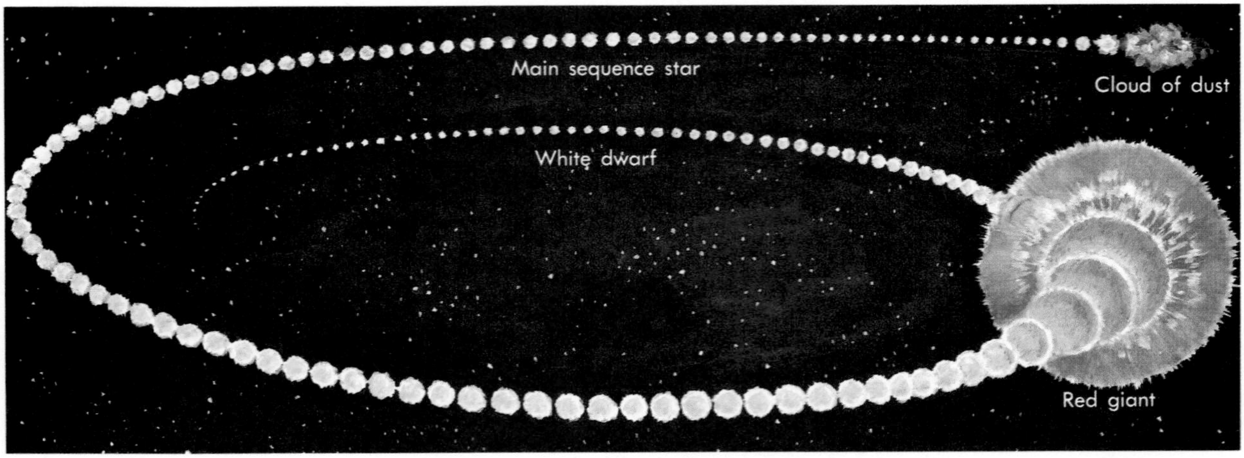

## 20:5 Life Cycle of Our Sun

Our sun is a main sequence yellow star. Scientists estimate that by the end of the next five billion years most of the hydrogen in the sun's core will be gone. The core will be about 98 percent helium. At that time, the sun will be about 1000 times brighter than it is now. It will also increase greatly in size and its light will be reddish in color. It will be a red giant. The sun will engulf Mercury. The temperature on Earth will be too hot to support life. From this point, the sun will slowly cool and collapse, becoming a white dwarf star.

What is the future of our sun?

## 20:6 Interstellar Space

Most people think space is empty except for planets, stars, and other objects. However, there are molecules of matter in space between stars. Sometimes the molecules form clouds. Clouds of gas and dust are called **nebulas** (NEB yuh luhz). Table 20–3 lists some of the molecules discovered in space.

What is a nebula?

***Table 20–3.***
Some Molecules Found in Interstellar Space

| | | | |
|---|---|---|---|
| $H_2$ | hydrogen | $NH_3$ | ammonia |
| CO | carbon monoxide | HCOOH | formic acid |
| HCN | hydrogen cyanide | $H_2CO$ | formaldehyde |
| $H_2O$ | water | $CH_3OH$ | methanol |

Most of the gases in space are hydrogen and helium. The gas is only visible when it surrounds very hot, bright stars. Intense ultraviolet light from the stars heats the gas making it glow. Glowing gas can be observed with a large telescope.

What kinds of matter are present in interstellar space?

How is dust detected in space? Stars seen in certain regions are always much redder in color than would be normal for a star. Scientists believe these stars are in areas where there are high concentrations of dust particles. The dust particles are very small. They are about the size of a light

Hale Observatories

FIGURE 20-12. The dark patches in the Trifid Nebula are caused by dust and gas between the Nebula and Earth.

What does reddened by the dust mean?

wave. These tiny particles scatter blue light more than they do red light. The light from a white star passing through the dust particles appears yellow or red. Scientists say that the white star has been "reddened by the dust."

Large amounts of dust particles around a star may absorb almost all the radiation given off by the star. This radiant energy heats the dust around the star. The particles become warm enough to emit infrared light. This infrared light is not visible, but it can be detected with infrared-sensing instruments. The star appears very dim in an area of the sky in which infrared radiation is apparent.

### making sure

**10.** How is the color of light used to detect nebulas in space?

## 20:7 Galaxies

What is a galaxy?

Have you ever looked into the night sky and observed a broad band of brightness across the entire sky? This band of stars is called the Milky Way. It contains over 100 billion stars, including our sun. When you look at the Milky Way, you are looking into the plane of a galaxy. A **galaxy** is a vast collection of billions of stars, planets, dust, and gas.

PHOTRI

FIGURE 20-13. Seen from Earth, the Milky Way is a band across the night sky.

At the center of a galaxy is the galactic nucleus. Around the nucleus is the galactic disk containing stars of all ages and sizes.

What is the shape of the Milky Way galaxy?

Our solar system belongs to a galaxy called the Milky Way. The Milky Way is spiral-shaped, something like a pinwheel (Figure 20–14). All of the objects in the galaxy revolve around the galactic nucleus. Our sun takes 230 million Earth years to complete one revolution. This period of time is called a galactic year.

The Milky Way is just one of millions of galaxies. Only sixteen galaxies are within 3 000 000 light-years of Earth. One of these galaxies is the spiral-shaped Andromeda (an DRAHM ud uh) (Figure 20–15). This galaxy is 2 000 000 light-years away. It is about twice the size of the Milky Way.

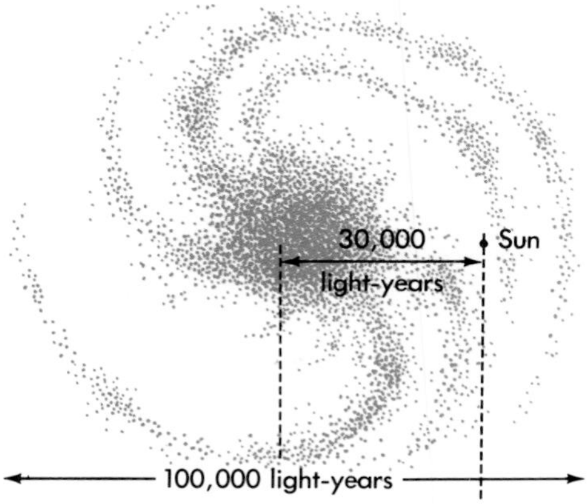


FIGURE 20-14. The Milky Way is a spiral galaxy about 100 000 light-years across.

FIGURE 20-15. Andromeda galaxy is a large, spiral galaxy about 2 million light-years from Earth.

List the main types of galaxies.

There are different types of galaxies. Spiral galaxies have arms. Irregular galaxies like the Large Magellanic (maj uh LAN ihk) Cloud have no special shape (Figure 20–16). Elliptical galaxies are shaped like a football or a slightly flattened sphere (Figure 20–16). Peculiar galaxies have some special feature, such as an exploding center.

Most galaxies are in groups called clusters. Our Galaxy has two companion galaxies, the Large and Small Magellanic Clouds. These galaxies are visible in the southern hemisphere. Our cluster of galaxies contains 21 galaxies.

FIGURE 20-16. The major types of galaxies are irregular, spiral, and elliptical.

Scientists believe that all galaxies are moving away from each other at high speeds. Support for this theory comes from a study of light spectra. When a shining object is moving away, the lines seen in its light spectrum are shifted from the positions of the lines observed in a laboratory. The lines shift toward the red end of the spectrum. This change is called a **redshift**. It is an example of the Doppler effect (Section 15:4).

Why do scientists believe that galaxies are moving away from each other?

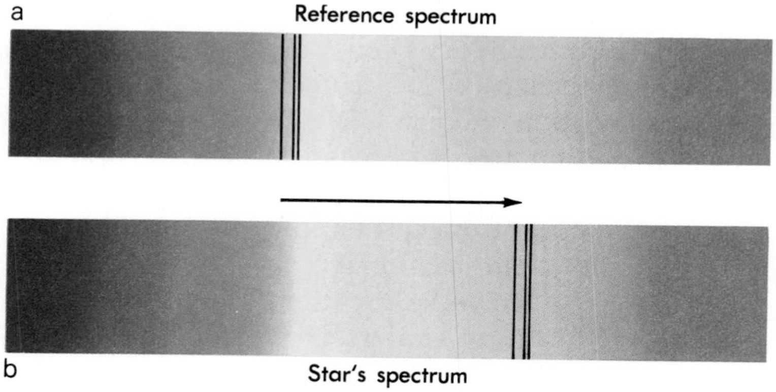


FIGURE 20-17. The red shift of a star is determined by comparing a reference line spectrum (a) with the star's line spectrum (b).

A redshift has been observed in the spectra produced by the stars in all galaxies. This observation indicates that the distant galaxies we view from Earth are moving away from us. Their speeds are estimated at over 48 000 km/s. Some astronomers believe that this indicates that the universe is expanding.

### making sure

**11.** What is a galaxy?
**12.** Describe the three types of galaxies.
**13.** What type of galaxy is the Milky Way?
**14.** How does the Doppler effect indicate that the galaxies are moving away from each other?

## 20:8 Origin of the Universe

All galaxies, including the Milky Way, make up what is called the universe. How did the universe begin? At present, there are three scientific theories.

The "big-bang" or explosion theory is the most widely accepted theory. None of these theories has been proven.

What is the Big Bang theory?

The big-bang theory is that all matter now in the galaxies was once packed tightly into a small space. This stage occurred between 16 and 24 billion years ago. Somehow, the huge mass of matter was torn apart in a giant explosion. The explosion caused the formation of the galaxies. This explosion accounts for the movements of galaxies away from each other.

The steady state theory is that the universe has always been as it is today. This idea is also called the continuous creation theory. Continuous creation means that new matter is constantly being produced. From this new matter, new galaxies are formed. The new galaxies take the place of those that move away from each other. The total effect, according to the theory, keeps the universe in a steady, expanding state. There is no total change from year to year.

Another theory is that the universe expands and contracts. According to this idea, the galaxies move outward, as they are doing now, until the universe reaches a certain size. Then the universe shrinks to a smaller size. The process reverses again and the universe expands. Expansion and contraction are repeated. Eventually, expansion would stop as energy is used up.

FIGURE 20-18. According to the big-bang theory, the universe began as a huge mass of matter (a). It exploded and the galaxies formed, all moving away from each other (b).

a

b

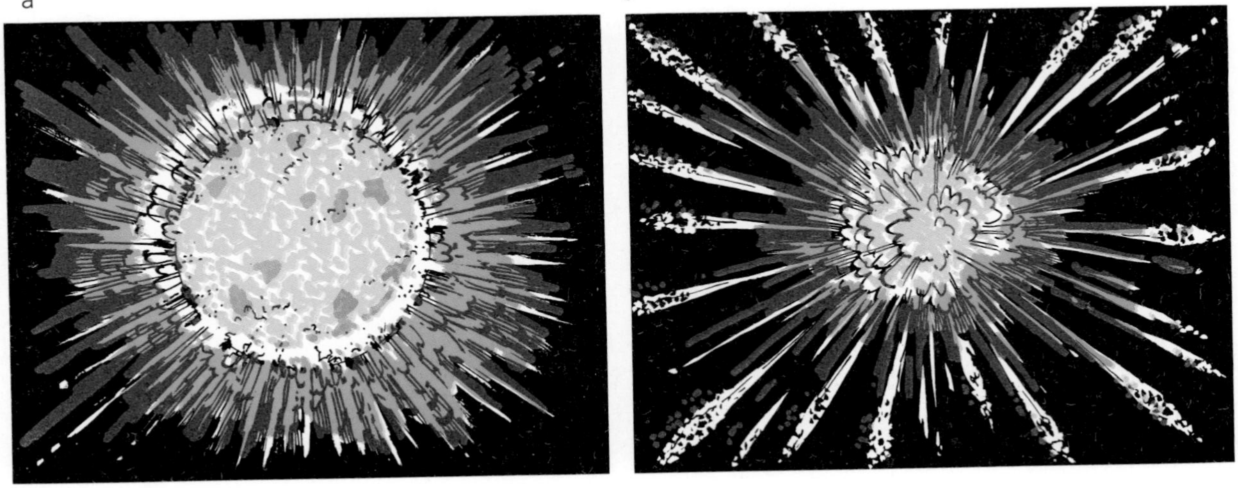

## main ideas

1. A star is a huge mass of gas in which energy is produced by nuclear fusion reactions. 20:1
2. Distance in space can be measured in light-years. 20:1
3. The spectrum of a star's light is used to determine the elements in the star and its temperature. Stars are grouped according to their temperatures and color. 20:2
4. The lifetime of a main sequence star depends on its mass. 20:3
5. Stars collapse when all of their nuclear fuel is used. They collapse to form white dwarfs. Eruptive variable stars lose mass to become white dwarfs. 20:4
6. X rays may indicate the presence of black holes. 20:4
7. The sun is a main sequence, yellow star that will become a white dwarf. 20:5
8. Space contains clouds of dust and molecules between stars. New stars form in these clouds. 20:6
9. The Galaxy, or the Milky Way, is one of millions of galaxies. 20:7
10. The big-bang theory is the most widely accepted theory of the origin of the universe. 20:8

## vocabulary

*Define each of the following words or terms.*

black hole
galaxy
light-year
main sequence star
nebulas
neutron star
nova
parallax
pulsars
red giant
redshift
supernova
variable stars
white dwarf

## study questions

**DO NOT WRITE IN THIS BOOK.**

**A. True or False**

*Determine whether each of the following sentences is true or false. If the sentence is false, rewrite it to make it true.*

1. The sun is a white dwarf.
2. Stars contain hydrogen and helium.

3. White stars are the coolest of all stars.
4. The sun is the most massive of all stars.
5. Most stars are individual objects in space.
6. The North Star is a pulsar.
7. Most stars are within one light-year from Earth.
8. There are three stars in a binary system.
9. A star's spectrum contains information about the chemical composition of the star.
10. Stars are formed from heavy metals such as iron.

**B. Multiple Choice**

*Choose the word or phrase that completes correctly each of the following sentences.*

1. Energy in a star is produced by (*nuclear fission, nuclear fusion, oxidation*).
2. A (*blue, yellow, orange, red*) star is the hottest.
3. Polaris is a(n) (*eclipsing, pulsating, erupting*) variable star.
4. (*Binary stars, Supernovas, Supergiant stars*) are twin stars that revolve around each other.
5. As the sun reaches the end of its life cycle, its color will become (*blue, white, red*).
6. A supernova has a(n) (*very short, very long, average*) lifetime.
7. Our sun will become a (*nova, white dwarf, cepheid variable*).
8. The Milky Way is a (*white star, supernova, galaxy*).
9. The galaxies in space are (*moving away from each other, moving toward each other, not moving*).
10. The density of matter in a black hole is (*greater than, less than, the same as*) the density of matter in a star.

**C. Completion**

*Complete each of the following sentences with a word or phrase that will make the sentence correct.*

1. Astronomers study the spectrum of a star's light to determine the ______ in the star.
2. Main sequence stars produce their energy by nuclear ______.
3. Stars form in clouds in space called ______.
4. A blue star radiates ______ energy than a red star of the same size.

5. Parallax decreases as the distance ______.
6. A collapsed star that produces some light is called a ______.
7. As a star ages, its energy supply ______.
8. A(n) ______ is a spectacular outburst of radiation and matter from a star.
9. Astronomers use ______ to try to detect black holes.
10. According to the ______ theory, a huge explosion of matter caused the formation of the galaxies.

**D. How and Why**

1. How is parallax used to measure distances to some stars?
2. How is a star formed?
3. How does a main sequence star change during its lifetime?
4. What factors determine the apparent brightness of a star?
5. Why do astronomers study a star's spectrum?

## challenges

1. Cut out pictures of galaxies from old astronomy magazines. Use the pictures to make a poster for your classroom. Explain the type of galaxy each picture represents.
2. On a clear night, count the number of red, white, blue, and yellow stars you can see. Compare the number of stars of each color.
3. Use a star map and see if you can locate the stars Arcturus, Polaris, and Vega on a clear night.

## interesting reading

Adler, Irving, *The Stars: Decoding Their Messages.* New York: Crowell, 1980.

DeCerto, Joseph, *Star Voyage.* New York: Messner, 1981.

Kals, W. S., *The Stargazer's Bible.* New York: Doubleday, 1980.

Levitt, I. M., and Roy K. Marshall, *Star Maps for Beginners.* New York: Simon and Schuster, 1983.

Simon, Seymour, *Look to the Night Sky: An Introduction to Star Watching.* New York: Penguin, 1983.

*The space shuttle is a reusable craft designed to transport astronauts, materials, and satellites to and from space. Astronauts manipulate the robot arm to lift payloads into space and to recover satellites. What type of information is gathered by scientists aboard the space shuttle? Why do scientists feel that it is important to explore the universe? What are some benefits of space exploration?*

NASA

# Space Exploration chapter 21

## 21:1 Gravity and Space Flight

GOAL: You will learn how rockets, satellites, and spacecraft are used to explore space.

Every object in the universe is attracted to every other object. This force of attraction is called the gravitational force. On a planet or satellite, the weight of an object is due to the force of gravity. On Earth, the weight of a 1 kg mass is 9.8 N. If that same mass were moved to Jupiter, it would weigh 25 N. On the moon, the mass would weigh 1.6 N. Thus, the force of gravity varies with the mass of the planet. The more massive the planet, the greater the force of gravity.

What is escape velocity?

Overcoming Earth's gravity is a problem in exploring space. A spacecraft must achieve a speed of 11.2 km/s to escape Earth's gravity. This speed is called **escape velocity.** Escape velocities vary for the moon and the planets. The larger the gravitational force of a planet, the higher the escape velocity needed.

NASA

a

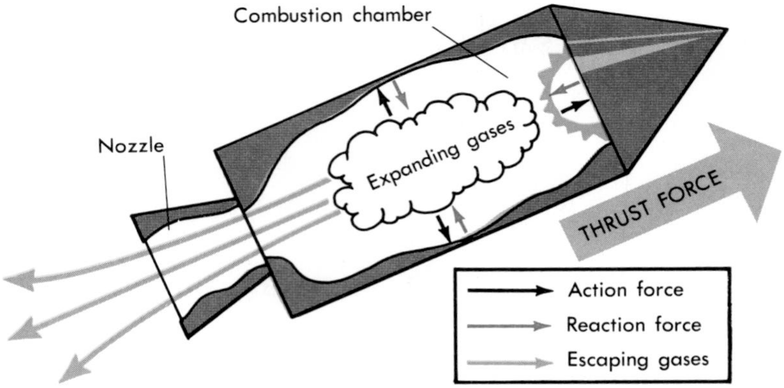


b

FIGURE 21–1. Rockets are used to produce the thrust needed for a spacecraft to reach escape velocity (a). The thrust force in a rocket builds up at the end of the combustion chamber opposite the nozzle (b).

How does a spacecraft overcome Earth's gravity?

What is thrust?

Rockets are used to lift satellites and spacecraft off Earth into space. Rockets burn fuel very rapidly and produce enough power to overcome Earth's gravity and reach escape velocity. When a rocket fuel burns, gases expand and create a force that propels the rocket forward. Modern rockets often use liquid hydrogen as fuel.

Rockets are an application of Newton's third law—for every force there is an equal and opposite force. Forces always come in pairs—action force and reaction force. Rocket fuel burns in a combustion (kum BUS chun) chamber that has a nozzle at one end. The expanding hot gases exert an action force on all surfaces of the combustion chamber. The chamber pushes back with a reaction force on all surfaces except at the nozzle, where hot gases escape. A thrust force builds up at the end of the chamber opposite the nozzle. **Thrust** is the force that propels the rocket forward. The thrust produced by a rocket must be greater than its weight. The Saturn V rocket that launched the Apollo flights to the moon had a thrust to weight ratio of more than 12:1.

## activity ACTION–REACTION

Blow up a balloon and release it quickly. What happens? How is a rocket similar to a balloon? Would the balloon move faster, slower, or at the same speed if room air pressure were decreased? Explain.

FIGURE 21-2.

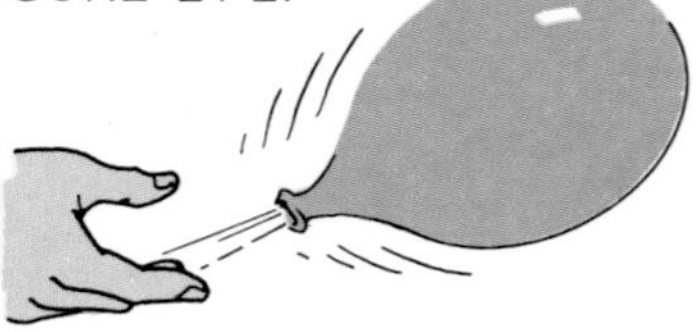

## activity ROCKET THRUST

(1) Obtain a narrow-neck bottle, a cork, a piece of tissue, 50 g baking soda, and 20 mL vinegar. You also need two round pencils. (2) Add vinegar to the bottle. (3) Wrap the baking soda in the tissue. Place it in the bottle in the vinegar. (4) Place the cork in the bottle firmly but not too tightly. CAUTION: Be certain the cork end is not pointed toward any person. (5) Set the two pencils on a table or desktop 5 cm apart. Tip the bottle sideways and lay it on the pencils. How is thrust produced inside the bottle? Compare the action of the bottle to a rocket.

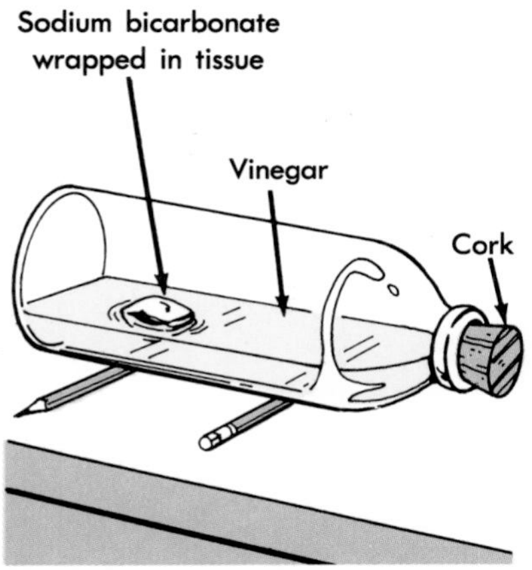


FIGURE 21-3.

### making sure

1. Why is escape velocity on Jupiter greater than on Earth?
2. Why is escape velocity on the moon less than on Earth?
3. Explain how a rocket can operate in space.

## 21:2 Types of Rocket Engines

Describe a solid-fuel rocket.

Rocket engines may burn solid or liquid fuels. In solid-fuel rockets, a solid oxidizer (AHK suh di zur) is mixed with the fuel. An **oxidizer** supplies the oxygen necessary for burning the fuel. The solid fuel mixture is molded to fit the inner walls of the combustion chamber. After ignition, the fuel burns directly in the chamber. The hot gases that are produced are forced out the exhaust nozzles and the rocket lifts off.

Solid-fuel rockets have some advantages. The fuel can be stored easily and safely for long periods of time. Solid-fuel rockets can be ignited readily and launched in a short time. One disadvantage is that solid-fuel rockets do not develop enough thrust to carry large spacecraft into orbit. Also, they cannot be stopped once they are ignited.

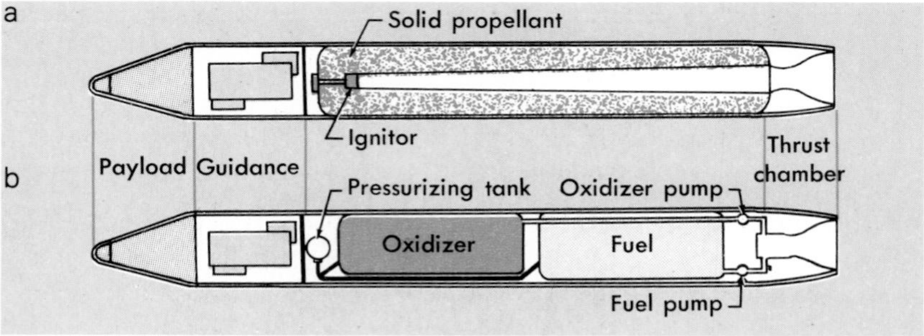


FIGURE 21-4. The construction of a solid-fuel rocket (a) is simpler than the construction of a liquid-fuel rocket (b). Solid-fuel rockets do not need a system for mixing the oxidizer and fuel. Liquid-fuel rockets produce more thrust than solid-fuel rockets.

How does a liquid-fuel rocket work?

Most rockets used to launch spacecraft have liquid-fuel engines. The fuel and the oxidizer are stored in separate tanks. They are fed separately into the combustion chamber. Liquid hydrogen is often the fuel and liquid oxygen (LOX) is the oxidizer.

The rocket engines we use today rely on chemicals to produce hot gases for propulsion. However, these rockets are not suitable for long space journeys. They cannot carry enough fuel and oxidizer. Two types of rocket engines are being tested for long space journeys. One engine is called a nuclear rocket. Liquid hydrogen is heated by a nuclear reactor. It changes into a gas and expands. The hot, expanding gas provides the thrust.

What fuel is used in a nuclear rocket?

Ion engines have also been tested. In an ion engine, the fuel is ionized (stripped of its electrons) and accelerated by an electric field. The high speed ions produce the thrust. Ion engines produce low thrust but can maintain the thrust for long periods of time. They could serve as engines on long journeys. The electricity needed to operate the ion engines could come from solar cells.

What is an ion engine?

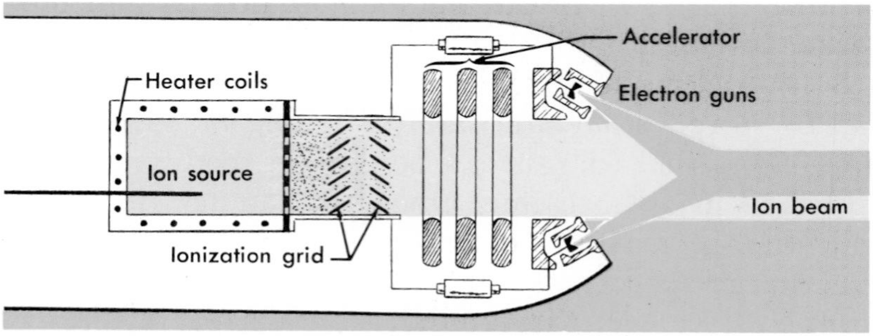


FIGURE 21-5. Designed to operate only in space, ion engines produce a small thrust over a long period of time.

## making sure

4. Why are liquid-fuel rockets used to launch most spacecraft?
5. Why are liquid-fuel rockets unsuitable for long space journeys?

## 21:3 Rocket Guidance Systems

To hit a distant target with an arrow or a bullet is a difficult task. An accurate guidance system is needed. For example, an arrow has feathers on one end to keep it in a straight path. Feathers keep the arrow balanced and keep it from wobbling. A bullet is made to spin by the rifling (spiral grooves) inside the gun barrel. A spinning bullet is less likely to veer from a straight path. The motion of the spin keeps the bullet in a straight path.

How is the path of a rocket controlled?

The method used to guide rockets is called **inertial** (ihn UR shul) **guidance**. Inertial guidance does not rely on reference points or radio signals. Inertial guidance depends on gyroscopes (JI ruh skohps) and accelerometers (ak sel uh RAHM ut urz). A **gyroscope** is a mounted spinning wheel that can be used to indicate direction. **Accelerometers** are devices that measure changes in speed and direction.

What is a gyroscope?

NASA

FIGURE 21-6. The guidance system for a spacecraft undergoes extensive tests before it is actually used.

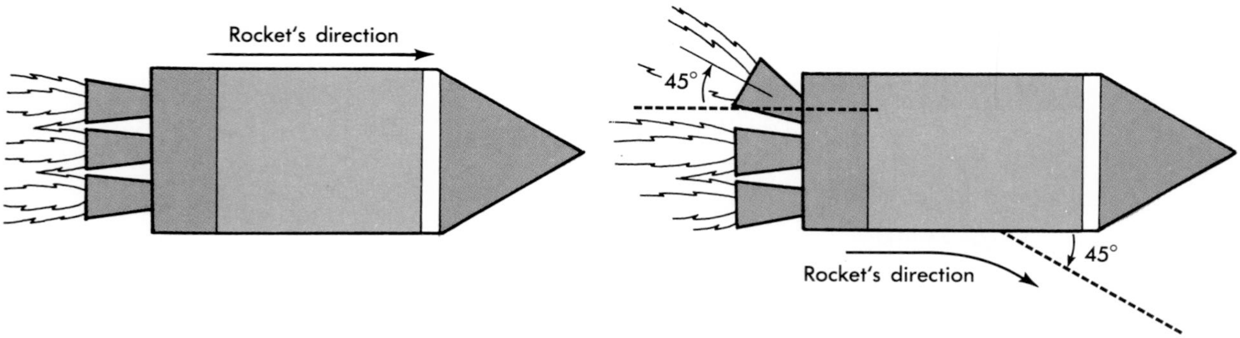


FIGURE 21-7. Some rockets change direction by adjusting the direction of the thrust.

The inertial guidance system measures how far a vehicle has traveled from a vertical line. The axis of the gyroscope can be set to point constantly in one direction. The gyroscope is mounted so that the vertical line of its axis never changes. The accelerometers detect changes in the rocket's motion in reference to the gyroscope's line.

A rocket moves in a path directly opposite to the path of its exhaust gases. Thus, it can be guided by changing the direction in which gases leave its engine. The tail of the rocket may contain a cluster of engine nozzles. The outer nozzles in the cluster may be rotated by remote control from a computer. The computer uses information provided by the gyroscopes and accelerometers to calculate the rocket's position. It then uses electric motors to move the engine's exhaust nozzles. By changing the positions of these nozzles, the direction of the engine's exhaust is changed. Changing the path of the exhaust changes the path of the rocket.

## activity A GYROSCOPE

Obtain a gyroscope and start it spinning. Hold it in your hand and try to twist it in different directions. What happens? Hold a string taut between your two hands. Have someone place the spinning gyroscope on the string. Raise and lower your right hand so that the gyroscope slides back and forth. What did you observe when the gyroscope slid back and forth on the string? How does the speed at which a gyroscope turns affect its behavior?

FIGURE 21-8.

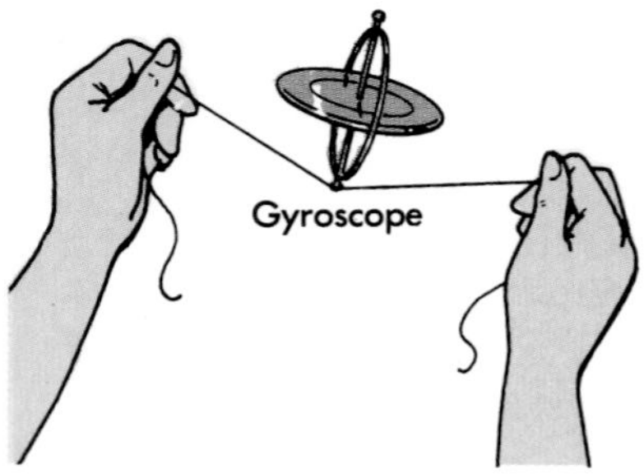

## 21:4 Satellites

The Space Age began on October 4, 1957 when the Soviet Union launched the first artificial satellite, Sputnik I. It was about the size of a large grapefruit. Sputnik sent radio signals back to Earth from space. A satellite is any object that orbits a larger object. The moon is a natural satellite of Earth. **Artificial satellites** are devices that people have placed in orbits.

What is an artificial satellite?

Satellites carry radio transmitters that send radio signals to Earth. These signals are used to track the satellites. Other radio transmitters relay information gathered by instruments to Earth.

Many satellites now orbit Earth. They can be classified into five general types—communication, scientific, navigational, weather, and military. Table 21–2 lists some satellites and their functions.

Once satellites were successfully launched, work began to put people into space. On April 12, 1961 the first human flew in space. A Soviet cosmonaut,

What are four types of satellites and their functions?

***Table 21–2.***
Some Satellites and Their Functions

| Type of Satellite | Name | Function |
|---|---|---|
| Communication | Score, Telstar, Syncom, Relay Intelsat, Marisat | Receive, store, amplify, and transmit radio signals |
| Scientific | HEAO, OSO, LandSat, ATS, Explorers, Skylab | Study sun, stars, galaxies, and radiation; experiment with laser communications; photograph crops, geologic structures; monitor water pollution, soil types; measure magnetic field of Earth |
| Navigation | Transit, NAVSTAR | Continuous broadcast of the satellite's position enables ships and planes to calculate their own locations |
| Weather | Vanguard, TIROS, Nimbus, SMS, GOES | Photograph cloud cover world-wide and record atmospheric conditions of temperature, moisture, and air movement; photographs entire Earth once a day |

Courtesy of Bell Laboratories

PHOTRI

a

b

FIGURE 21-9. Satellites, such as Telestar II, are used for communications (a). Nimbus B is used to observe weather patterns on Earth (b).

Yuri A. Gagarin, made one complete orbit of Earth in Vostok I. He flew at an altitude of 320 km.

The first American in space was Alan B. Shepard on May 5, 1961. His space flight was designed to send him into space and to return. Shepard did not go into orbit. John Glenn, Jr. was the first American to orbit Earth. He made three complete orbits of Earth on February 20, 1962. These two spaceflights led the way to putting people on the moon.

At present, more than 1000 satellites orbit Earth. A satellite can orbit over the poles, parallel to the equator, or at any angle in between. However, the

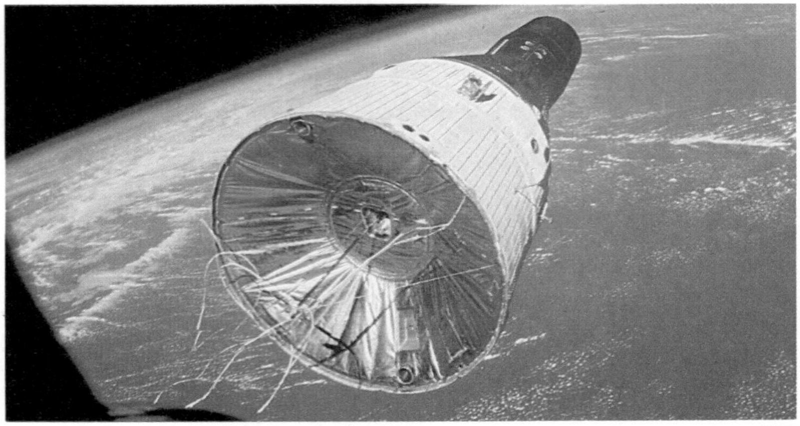

NASA

FIGURE 21-10. In the Gemini program, two astronauts were carried into Earth orbit with each launch. The information gained in these flights was used in designing the Apollo capsules and in designing improved life-support systems for space suits.

path of the satellite must take it over Earth's center of gravity.

Explain how a satellite stays in orbit.

Gravity and inertia keep a satellite in orbit. Gravity pulls a satellite toward Earth. The inertia of the moving satellite keeps it from falling to Earth. Without gravity, a satellite would fly away from Earth in a straight path. Without a high orbiting speed, a satellite would fall to Earth.

The speed a satellite must have to stay in orbit depends upon its altitude. At an altitude of 480 km, a satellite must have a speed of 29 000 km/h. At an altitude of 35 400 km, it must have a speed of 11 000 km/h to stay in orbit. Gravity decreases as altitude increases so less speed is needed at higher altitudes.

What is the ideal orbit for a satellite?

The ideal path for an orbit is a circle. In a circular orbit, the speed is the same at every point. However, most satellites have elliptical orbits. The point in an elliptical orbit farthest from Earth is called the **apogee** (AP uh jee). The closest point is called the **perigee** (PER uh jee).

Air particles slow a satellite. After many orbits, the satellite may slow enough for gravity to overcome inertia. Then the satellite falls toward Earth. Usually, it burns up in the lower atmosphere. Small satellites in high orbits remain in orbit the longest time.

### making sure

**6.** A satellite orbits in the same direction that Earth rotates. It orbits Earth once every 24 h. Would the satellite appear in a different part of the sky each night? Explain.

## 21:5 The Apollo Program

The **Apollo Program** began in 1961 and resulted in six moon landings between 1969 and 1972. To reach the moon requires more power than to orbit Earth. A spacecraft must reach a speed of 39 110 km/h. The Apollo spacecraft used in each mission was launched by a Saturn V rocket. Saturn V is a

NASA

a

NASA

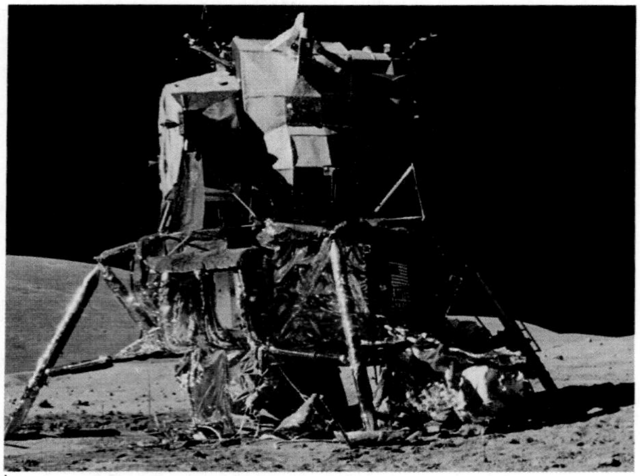

b

FIGURE 21-11. During the Apollo moon missions, the command and service modules remained in orbit (a) while the lunar module landed on the moon (b).

Identify the main parts of the Apollo spacecraft.

What scientific experiments were part of the Apollo project?

FIGURE 21-12. The Apollo missions were launched using Saturn V rockets.

NASA

three-stage, liquid-fuel rocket. The first stage has a cluster of five engines and uses kerosene for fuel. The second and third stage rocket engines use liquid hydrogen for fuel. Liquid oxygen is the oxidizer in all three stages.

Each Apollo spacecraft had three parts—a command module, a service module, and a lunar module. The command module served as the control center and living quarters for the crew of three astronauts. The main propulsion system for the spacecraft was the service module. Most of the supplies used during the mission, such as oxygen and water, were stored in the service module. The lunar module was used to land on the moon.

Astronauts who traveled to the moon on the Apollo missions brought back samples of moon rocks for study and analysis. They also set up instruments on the moon to detect moonquake vibrations. An aluminum foil screen was erected to detect particles of the solar wind. A laser reflector was set up. This reflector and a laser beam from Earth were used to accurately measure the distance to the moon.

The mission in the Apollo Program that first landed men on the moon was Apollo 11. Apollo 11 was launched from Kennedy Space Center in Florida on July 16, 1969. About 2 min 30 s after lift-off, the first stage of the Saturn V rocket separated. The

Apollo 11 spacecraft was then traveling at 9980 km/h and was 66 km above Earth. The engine in the second stage pushed the vehicle to an altitude of 187 km and to a speed of 24 780 km/h before separating.

Next, the engine in the third stage fired and put the spacecraft into Earth orbit. At this time, the astronauts checked to be sure the spacecraft was operating properly. The third stage engine was fired again and the spacecraft headed for the moon. The third stage rocket burned for about 5 min 30 s and pushed the spacecraft to a speed of about 39 000 km/h. Later, the third stage separated.

When the Apollo 11 spacecraft reached the moon, it went into a lunar orbit. Two astronauts left the command module and entered the lunar module. The lunar module then separated from the command module and descended to the surface of the moon. Michael Collins remained in the command module while it continued to orbit the moon.

The Apollo 11 lunar module landed on the moon on July 20, 1969. Astronauts Neil Armstrong and Edwin Aldrin, Jr. were the first people to walk on the moon. They explored the area near their spacecraft for about 2 h. Each astronaut carried a special backpack containing life support systems, including an oxygen supply.

When did people first walk on the moon?

NASA

FIGURE 21-13. The first manned moon landing occurred on July 20, 1969.

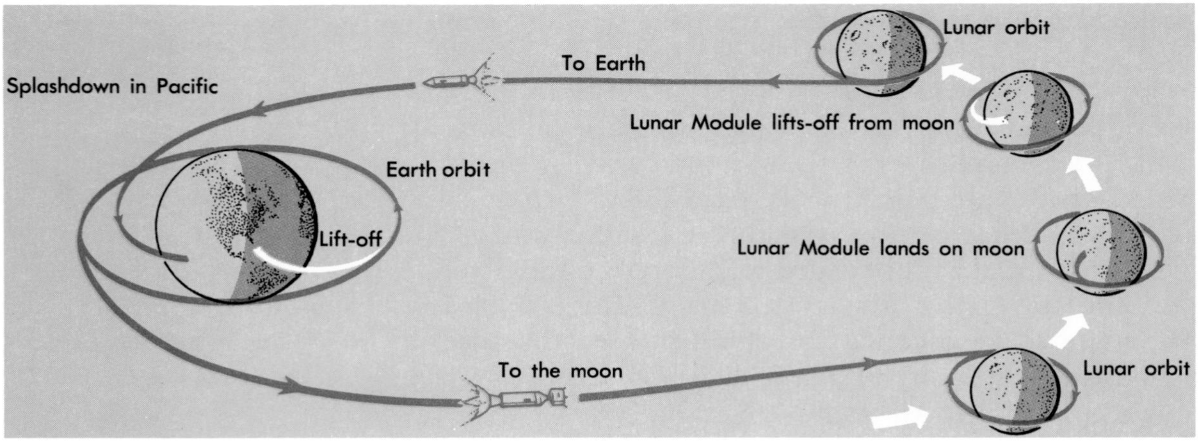


FIGURE 21-14. All of the Apollo moon missions followed the same basic flight path.

After completing their moon exploration, the astronauts returned to the lunar module. The lunar module engine fired and propelled the spacecraft into a lunar orbit on July 21. The lunar module was guided into the same orbit as the command module and then docked with the command module. After the astronauts returned to the command module, the lunar module was disconnected. Later, the engine of the service module was started. The spacecraft left lunar orbit and headed for Earth.

What happens as a spacecraft reenters the Earth's atmosphere?

Before the Apollo spacecraft entered Earth's atmosphere, the service module was disconnected. The command module was turned so its blunt end entered the atmosphere first. As it streaked down through the atmosphere, air friction caused the temperature of the heat shield on the command module to rise to more than 2000°C. However, the temperature inside the command module stayed about 27°C. At about 7100 m above the Earth, special parachutes were released to slow the spacecraft. The main parachutes were released at an altitude of about 3200 m. These large parachutes slowed the spacecraft to about 35 km/h. The spacecraft landed in the Pacific Ocean on July 24. The astronauts and the command module were removed from the ocean by helicopters and taken to a nearby ship. During their eight-day journey, the astronauts had flown more than 800 000 km.

NASA

FIGURE 21-15. When the Apollo capsule splashed down, a special flotation collar was used to keep it afloat until a ship could pick it up.

**making sure**

**7.** How many Apollo moon landings were made?
**8.** What were the three Apollo spacecraft modules?
**9.** Why does the outside temperature of a spacecraft increase when it enters the Earth's atmosphere?

## 21:6 Space Stations

As the Apollo missions came to an end, people began working on a further step in space exploration. Spacecraft so far were very small and crowded. The next step was an orbiting station where people could live and work. The Soviet Union launched such a station in April, 1971. Additional stations were launched in 1973 and 1974.

**Skylab**, the United States space station, was launched in May, 1973. Skylab was 36 m long and provided working space for three astronauts. Three crews visited Skylab for periods of 28, 59, and 84 days.

What did astronauts study while in Skylab?

The astronauts conducted experiments in three fields—Earth resources, medicine, and solar astronomy. The astronauts studied the effects of weightlessness on the human body. Intensive study of the sun added a lot of information about the ultraviolet and X-ray regions of the spectrum. Skylab astronauts also investigated the behavior of liquid metals, the growth of crystals, and welding in space.

NASA

FIGURE 21-16. The gold sheet covering part of Skylab is the sunshade that was used to prevent overheating.

Over 40 000 photographs of Earth and much data about Earth's surface were obtained and relayed to Earth. Some experiments performed by the astronauts were designed by American students.

Skylab suffered extensive damage during its launch. One of the solar panels that was to supply the space station with electricity was torn away. The other solar panel was jammed. The crew of Skylab 1 fixed a sunshade to protect the station from overheating. Skylab fell into the atmosphere and burned in 1979.

## 21:7 Space Shuttle

What is a Space Shuttle?

The next stage in the development of a space station began with the successful flight of the space shuttle *Columbia* in 1981. A **space shuttle** is a ship that can make repeated trips into space and return to Earth. It is a rocket, spaceship, and aircraft combined. The rocket engines of the space shuttle launch it into Earth orbit. While in orbit, it is a spaceship containing everything necessary for the life of its crew and passengers. Upon returning to Earth, the space shuttle flies through the atmosphere and lands like an aircraft. Then, the space shuttle is serviced and readied to fly again.

Describe the structure of the Space Shuttle *Columbia.*

America's first space shuttle, *Columbia,* contained three main sections. The forward or flight section

NASA

FIGURE 21-17. For lift-off, the Space Shuttle fires both solid-fuel rocket boosters and the main liquid-fuel engines.

contained instruments and controls. It had seating for four crew members and additional passengers. The middle section was a large cargo area. It held the payload, which is the material and equipment being carried into space. In the rear section were the main rocket engines. After five missions, the *Columbia* was overhauled and the *Challenger* launched.

At lift-off, a shuttle stands vertically alongside its launch tower. Attached to the space shuttle is a large liquid-fuel tank. Solid-fuel engines are attached to the liquid-fuel tank. These rockets provide extra power at lift-off and during the early minutes of flight.

All engines are fired with full power to push the vehicle into orbit. After about 2 min of flight, the solid-fuel rockets burn out and detach. Parachutes in the rockets lower them to the ocean. They are picked up by a recovery ship and used again. After 8 min the main engines are shut down. The liquid-fuel tank is released and falls to Earth. It is not used again. After 10 min of flight, the Space

FIGURE 21-18. Once in orbit, the cargo bay doors are opened. They allow cargo to be moved out of the Shuttle and experiments to be operated. The doors are also used to prevent overheating.

NASA

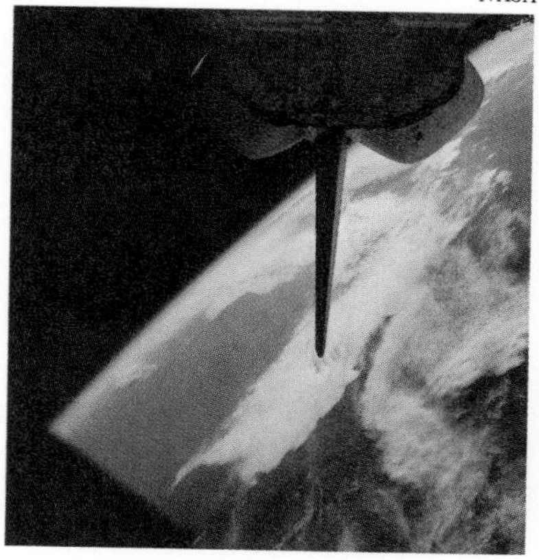

FIGURE 21–19. Crew members on the Space Shuttle conduct many scientific experiments in space.

NASA

Shuttle is in Earth orbit. It completes one Earth orbit in about 2 h.

Name three uses for a Space Shuttle.

One function of the Space Shuttle is to carry satellites and place them in orbit. Crew members can leave the Shuttle and work outside to repair satellites. Many experiments can be conducted in the laboratory on the Shuttle. Cameras can take pictures of Earth in a search for minerals and other resources and can check for pollution. Also, the Shuttle can carry telescopes to study the stars and galaxies. Since there is no atmosphere in space, observations made with these telescopes are clearer and more distinct.

**making sure**

**10.** What is the value of a spacecraft that can be used many times?

**11.** When does the Space Shuttle fly like an aircraft?

## 21:8 Space Training and Survival

Astronauts traveling in spacecraft must be protected from large gravitational forces, or g-forces. Tests show that most people can tolerate a force of five g-forces for several minutes. Astronauts may encounter g-forces as high as twelve when their spacecraft is launched into space and when it returns to Earth. The position of the body helps to overcome the effect of the g-force. If an astronaut were sitting

Why is the position of the body important in toleration of g-forces?

straight up at launch, the g-force would cause the blood to drain from the brain. A force of three to four can cause an astronaut to faint. However, if the body is positioned at an angle to the g-force, fainting does not occur as easily. Astronauts usually recline at a 45° angle during launch.

A problem in space for an astronaut is weightlessness. An astronaut in orbit around Earth is said to be in a state of **weightlessness**, also called zero gravity. Weightlessness does not mean that gravity is not present. It means that the weightless object is being acted upon by another force that is equal and opposite to gravity.

Define weightlessness.

When does an object become weightless?

Being weightless for long periods of time can cause weakened muscles and loss of bone minerals. Other effects are still not known. It is known that humans differ widely in their reactions to being weightless. Some people find it pleasant, while others develop a "space sickness" feeling.

How do g forces and weightlessness affect astronauts?

Many simple tasks present special problems under conditions of weightlessness. Liquids float around inside a spacecraft if they are not kept in sealed containers. Walking is impossible because the body cannot push against any surface. Space travelers use magnetic shoes or small gas jets to propel themselves. Special sleeping bags keep astronauts from floating while asleep.

*NASA*

FIGURE 21-20. In orbit, astronauts experience weightlessness.

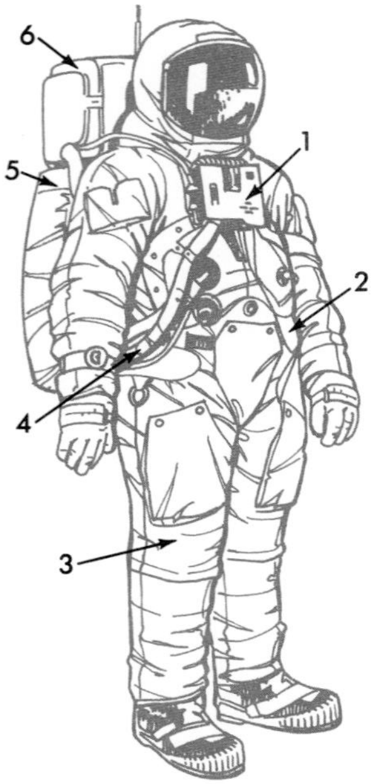


1. Life-support system control box
2. Communication, ventilation, and liquid cooling tubes
3. Pressure suit with heat and meteoroid protection
4. Emergency oxygen tube
5. Life-support system (cooling and oxygen)
6. Emergency oxygen system

FIGURE 21-21. A space suit must be designed to provide complete life support for an astronaut.

Why are humans unsuited for space?

Why may food made from algae become a future diet of astronauts?

Humans are unsuited for space. For people to survive during space travel, a spacecraft must have an environment similar to that of Earth. Since oxygen is not present in space, it must be supplied inside a spacecraft. Also, people must be protected from heat, cold, radiation, meteroids, and weightlessness. Proper air pressure and humidity must be maintained. A supply of food and water must be available and there must be a method for disposing of human wastes. The Skylab mission solved many of these problems. Special exercises were developed to keep astronauts fit. Further studies will be done to find answers to these problems for a long space journey.

For long space flights, the use of nature's oxygen–carbon dioxide cycle may be a good idea. Plants, such as algae, may be carried in the spacecraft. They will help in keeping a balance between oxygen and carbon dioxide.

Algae are green, one-celled, living organisms. They can produce oxygen and food for space travelers. During photosynthesis, algae take in carbon dioxide and release oxygen. Algae grow very rapidly when enough light is provided. In some cases, they double their mass in two hours. Foods made from algae may be in the future diet of astronauts.

## making sure

**12.** The oxygen–carbon dioxide cycle goes on in an aquarium.
- (a) What living things in an aquarium use oxygen?
- (b) What living things in an aquarium produce oxygen?
- (c) How is food for the fish supplied by the plants?
- (d) How is oxygen supplied by the plants for the fish?

**13.** Answer Question 12 again. This time change the word aquarium to spacecraft and fish to people.

## 21:9 Space Colonies

How could a space colony be built?

A possible space venture is building a space city or a moon colony. NASA scientists and engineers have designed a space city. The materials needed to build this city would be carried by space shuttles. The city is a giant circular tube, about 2 km in diameter. The tube is called a torus (TOR us) and is designed to hold 10 000 people. People would work in shops, factories, and offices in the hub of the space city. They would live in houses in the torus. Trees and food crops would be grown in soilless racks. The torus would spin at a rate of once a minute. This rate would produce normal Earth gravity at the rim of the torus.

The people would breathe an Earth-like atmosphere provided by the plants. Electricity to operate homes and shops would be generated by solar cells. Space Shuttles would transport people and products back and forth between Earth and the space city. Imagine taking a vacation to Earth!

Space cities and space colonies are for the future. Their design and construction face many problems. However, through the application of science, a space city may one day be a reality.

NASA

FIGURE 21-22. A future space colony may be a giant torus attached to a central hub.

# Space Sickness

Have you ever ridden on a plane, boat, or roller coaster and felt sick? Although these situations are common, the general population was surprised when the astronauts reported similar incidences during space flight. Approximately half of the astronauts have had space sickness problems, including those who had considerable experience in flying planes. At first, the astronauts were reluctant to discuss the problem. However, NASA officials considered it important enough that research was increased on the subject and a doctor was included on the crew of the eighth shuttle mission.

Motion sickness studies had been made prior to space flights. It was known that liquids and special sacs filled with small crystals in the inner ear sense body movements. The liquid and the crystals shift when a person moves, and nerves transmit the information to the brain. Doctors believe that under some conditions, the two detection systems contradict each other, resulting in motion sickness.

NASA

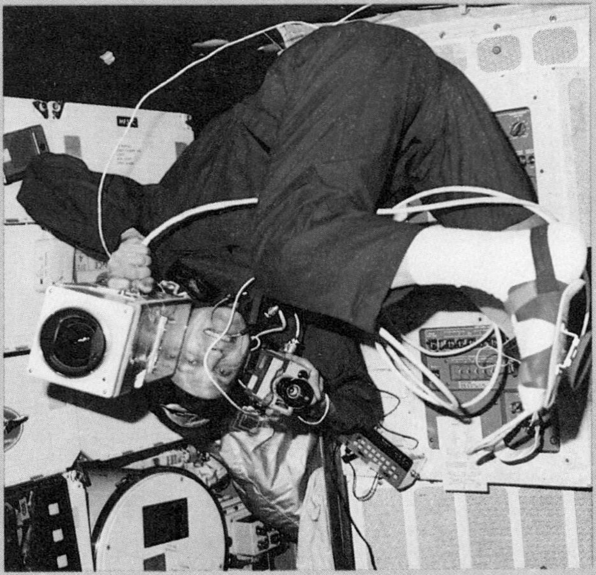

William Thornton is the astronaut-physician who participated in the shuttle flight. During the flight, Thornton kept track of his own body functioning using electrodes taped to his eyes and skin. He found that normal motion sickness symptoms—cold sweating, paleness, and nausea preceding vomiting—were not present in most astronauts. Instead, vomiting came on suddenly with no warning signals. He also confirmed the findings of an earlier astronaut that the digestive tract of affected astronauts was quiet. Normally, the digestive tract makes noise as food moves through it. Thornton was prepared with a drug that sets the digestive tract in motion. This drug relieved the nausea, eliminated vomiting, and increased the appetite.

Other treatments for space sickness have been used. A drug called scopolamine has been partially successful, although it does have side effects such as drowsiness. For astronauts, this drug has been mixed with a stimulant to counter the drowsiness. Andrew Weil, a Harvard botanist, has found that the leaves of the coca plant provide relief from motion sickness without causing drowsiness. The coca plant seems to contain a stimulant that aids a person in staying alert.

NASA has plans for continuing research on the problem of space sickness. Dr. Thornton is planning more tests on his digestive drug on future shuttle missions, and is hoping to find a cure that will allow all the astronauts to function at peak capacity.

## main ideas — Chapter Review

1. A rocket is needed to produce the power required to send a satellite or spacecraft into space. 21:1
2. Rockets use chemicals to produce hot gases for propulsion. 21:2
3. Rockets are guided by an inertial guidance system. 21:3
4. Artificial satellites can receive and send radio signals. 21:4
5. Early space missions led to the Apollo Program which landed men on the moon. 21:4, 21:5
6. Experiments on Skylab produced much information in the fields of medicine, astronomy, and Earth resources. 21:6
7. The Space Shuttle is a rocket, spaceship, and aircraft combined into one. It can be used over and over to carry people and equipment back and forth between earth and space. 21:7
8. Objects and people in space may become weightless. 21:8
9. Life support systems, including an oxygen supply, are needed for space travelers. 21:8
10. The exploration of space presents many problems which are solved through the applications of science and technology. 21:9

## vocabulary

*Define each of the following words or terms.*

accelerometers
apogee
Apollo Program
artificial satellites
escape velocity
gyroscope
inertial guidance
oxidizer
perigee
rockets
Skylab
space shuttle
thrust
weightlessness

## study questions

**DO NOT WRITE IN THIS BOOK.**

### A. True or False

*Determine whether each of the following sentences is true or false. If the sentence is false, rewrite it to make it true.*

1. Airplanes can escape Earth's gravity.
2. The escape velocity on the moon is greater than on Earth.

3. A thrust is a force.
4. Some rocket engines burn liquid hydrogen.
5. Liquid oxygen is an oxidizer.
6. Gyroscopes are used in the guidance system of a spacecraft.
7. A parachute was used to lower the Apollo lunar module to the moon.
8. The moon is an artificial satellite.
9. Large satellites in low orbits stay up the longest.
10. Apollo 11 was the first artificial satellite.

### B. Multiple Choice

*Choose the word or phrase that completes correctly each of the following sentences.*

1. Escape velocity for a rocket would be greatest on *(the moon, Earth, Jupiter).*
2. Gravity on Jupiter is *(less than, greater than, the same as)* gravity on Mercury.
3. Liquid *(nitrogen, hydrogen, oxygen)* is the oxidizer used in most rocket engines.
4. The Apollo 11 *(command module, service module, lunar module)* landed on the moon.
5. Astronauts first landed and walked on the moon in the year *(1964, 1969, 1973).*
6. A lunar orbit is an orbit around *(Earth, the moon, an artificial satellite).*
7. *(Electricity, Burning, Air friction)* causes the heat shield of a spacecraft to heat up when it enters Earth's atmosphere.
8. The space shuttle is designed to make *(one, ten, many)* trips into space.
9. After *(lift-off, reentry into the atmosphere, going into orbit)* the space shuttle flies like an aircraft.
10. People traveling in space need a supply of *(oxygen, carbon dioxide, nitrogen).*

### C. Completion

*Complete each of the following sentences with a word or phrase that will make the sentence correct.*

1. ______ are one-celled green plants which may be used in space travel to produce food and oxygen.

2. A rocket's ______ must be greater than its weight.
3. For every action force there is an equal and opposite ______ force.
4. The thrust of a rocket is produced by hot, expanding ______.
5. A(n) ______ satellite is used to send television pictures long distances.
6. The orbits of most satellites are ______ in shape.
7. Apollo 11 landed astronauts on the ______.
8. The Apollo 11 spacecraft landed in the ______ when it returned to Earth.
9. Space shuttle *Columbia* has ______ main sections.
10. ______ engines could possibly be the type of rocket engine used for long journeys.

**D. How and Why**

1. How is the thrust of a rocket produced?
2. How is a satellite placed in orbit?
3. How is the space shuttle different from the Apollo 11 spacecraft?
4. What are some important uses of the space shuttle?
5. What special problems exist for people in a space environment?

## challenges

1. Locate information in a library that explains the design of a nuclear-powered rocket or an ion engine. Design a model of a nuclear-powered rocket or an ion engine rocket.
2. Prepare a report on the Space Shuttle. Obtain the latest information on its use in America's space program.
3. Make a time line chart showing major space missions and the year in which each took place.

## interesting reading

Dwiggins, Don, *Flying the Frontiers of Space.* New York: Dodd, Mead, 1982.

Hawkes, Nigel, *Space Shuttle.* New York: Glouster Press, 1983.

Lambert, Mark, *50 Facts About Space.* New York: Warwick, 1983.

Lampton, Christopher, *Space Science.* New York: F. Watts, 1983.

*An increasing world population increases the demand for food. Through the use of science and technology, many areas that were considered unfit for farming, such as the desert below, are now producing food. What are some other human ecology problems? How are science and technology being used to solve these problems?*

Photri

# Human Ecology

# unit 6

*The* Solar Challenger *is a small, light-weight aircraft that is powered by energy from the sun. It uses special devices to convert sunlight to electricity. In what other ways can humans use solar energy? What are some other energy resources? How can energy resources such as the wind and tides be utilized?*

*Jim Collison/Black Star*

# People and Resources

chapter 22

## 22:1 People

GOAL: You will learn the major resources of the earth and their uses.

Scientists estimate that there were probably 5 million people on Earth around 10 000 years ago. In 1980 there were over 4.2 billion people. Four babies are born every second. This birth rate increases the world's population by 122 million people each year.

How is the size of the world's population changing?

The large increase in population began with the Industrial Revolution. Until that time Earth's population had been doubling every 1500 years. In 1650, the population was 500 million. However, by 1850, the population was 1 billion. In another 80 years, the population doubled to 2 billion. By 1975, the population doubled to about 4 billion.

The rate of increase in population has recently begun to slow down. However, the effects of the population growth are visible. Pollution, overcrowding, and famine are all caused by the pressure of more and more people.

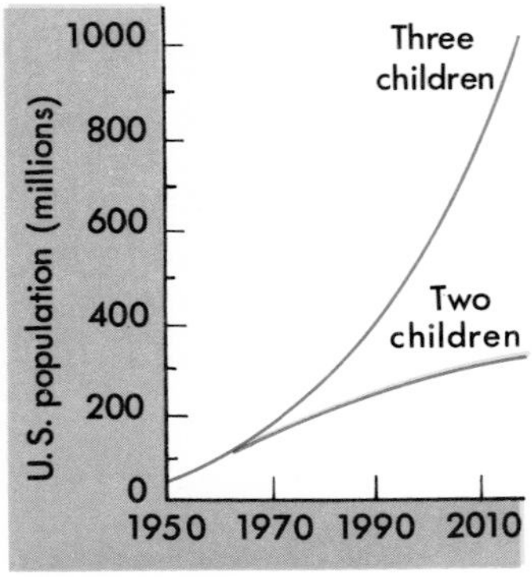


FIGURE 22-1.

## activity THE DIFFERENCE ONE CHILD MAKES

Figure 22–1 shows United States population growth based on an average of two or three children per family. How will a difference of one child per family affect the size of the United States population in the year 2010? In the year 2050? What effect would this difference have on food needs in these years?

### making sure

1. People are our most important resource. Do you agree or disagree? Give reasons for your opinion.
2. Can Earth's population keep doubling forever? What might slow the present population growth rate?

## 22:2 Resources

What are two groups of resources?

What is a resource? A resource is something people use to make the things they need. For example, trees are used to make paper. Sand is used to make glass. Resources can be divided into two groups. One group is living resources. It includes all

Susan Rhoades

FIGURE 22-2. Living resources are plants, animals, and people.

Larry Hamill

FIGURE 22-3. Salts removed from seawater are valuable nonliving resources.

plants, animals, and other organisms used to provide things such as food, clothing, and shelter. Nonliving resources include minerals, air, and water.

Resources also can be divided into renewable and nonrenewable. A **renewable resource** is one that can be replaced within a person's lifetime. Garden plants are renewable resources. After you pick the first crop of lettuce, you can plant more lettuce and harvest it.

How do renewable and nonrenewable resources differ?

Some resources can be renewed over a period of time. Forests and fish stocks are examples of these resources. After a forest is cut for lumber, new trees can be planted. These young trees will grow to produce a new forest. The time it takes for forest renewal depends on the type of trees and the environment. It takes about 25 years for pine trees to mature and about 50 years for oak trees to mature.

A resource such as coal that has taken millions of years to form cannot be renewed as it is used. Once coal is burned, it is gone forever. A **nonrenewable resource** is one that cannot be replenished in one's lifetime. Although some nonrenewable resources such as iron and aluminum can be recycled, once a deposit of these minerals is used it cannot be replaced.

## activity
RESOURCES

Cut pictures of renewable resources from old magazines. Glue them to a large piece of cardboard. Label each resource. Explain why each one is considered a renewable resource. Do the same thing for nonrenewable resources. How is each renewable resource renewed?

### making sure

3. Why is the water you drink a renewable resource?
4. What type of resource is iron? Explain.

## 22:3 Food

According to the United Nations Food and Agricultural Organization (FAO), enough food can be produced to feed all of the people in the world. Yet, every day thousands of people in the world die of hunger or related diseases.

Estimates of food requirements indicate that each person needs about 250 kg of grain per year to remain healthy. In the past few years, an average of 1.2 billion metric tons of grain have been produced each year. One metric ton is 1000 kg. The

J.C. Allen & Son

FIGURE 22-4. Corn produces the highest energy yield of the cereal grains.

M. Stefan for Transworld Feature Syndicate

FIGURE 22-5. In Asia, rice is the major source of food energy.

industrialized, or developed, nations used half this total amount of grain. These nations have only 25 percent of the world's population.

Why is grain an important food?

Cereal grains supply most of the food energy needs for people and farm animals. In the United States, 20 percent of our food energy comes from cereal grains. For more than half the world's population, cereal grains supply 66 percent of the total food energy.

Wheat, rice, and corn are examples of cereal grains. Of the cereal grains, wheat is the most common plant in the world. The seed of cereal grains is the part of the plants that is eaten. Corn produces the highest energy yield of the cereals. As much as 3.2 million Calories of energy per acre can be obtained with a corn crop. Cereal grains can be stored for months and years. No freezing, canning, or food preservative is needed. Flour made by grinding cereals can also be stored for long periods of time.

How much food does a person need to be healthy?

The amount of food people need to maintain good health varies. The amount depends on age, sex, amount of physical activity, and climate. Estimates of food needs for a person are between 2300 and 2500 Calories per day. Also, about 38 to 40 g of protein are needed per person per day. Meat, fish, eggs, milk, and cheese are foods high in protein. Many plants such`as soybeans are also high in protein. An

Sharon Kurgis

FIGURE 22-6. Land that cannot grow crops can be used for grazing. Thus, poor land can also be used to produce food.

adult can eat only plants and remain healthy. However, care must be taken to eat the correct balance of plants.

What percent of the world's farmland is good only for animal grazing?

About 60 percent of the world's farmland is good only for animal grazing. Animals are the only way to use this land for food production. Cows, sheep, and other grazing animals increase the food supply by changing grass and other plants into meat. Grass cannot be digested and used by humans. Yet it is an excellent food for grazing animals. Animals convert the grass into meat that can be eaten by people.

## activity

### FOOD PRICE COMPARISON

Obtain a full-page newspaper advertisement for a local supermarket. Compare the prices of fruits and vegetables with the prices of fish and meat. Compare the prices of bread and packaged cereals. How many factors can you name that affect the price of food? Which factor do you think is the most important?

## making sure

**5.** Why do cattle fed on grass increase the food supply for people more than cattle fed on grain?

## 22:4 Increasing Food Production

Many countries have increased their crop yields. The increase in crop production is called a "green revolution." Wheat yields in Mexico for example, increased from eleven to more than forty bushels per acre. Yields of corn more than doubled and potato yields tripled. Mexico no longer has to import wheat to feed its people. Enough wheat is now grown so that it can be exported to feed hungry people in other nations.

What is the "green revolution"?

The increase in crop yields is due in part to genetic breeding of plants. Hybrid plants can be grown that produce good yields in many different parts of the world. A **hybrid** plant is one that contains the combined traits of two or more strains or varieties. One strain of rice, named IR8, doubles rice yields per acre.

Name methods used to increase crop yields.

High-yielding hybrid plants require large amounts of nutrients. **Fertilizer** is a mixture of substances that contains the nutrients plants need. Manure from farm animals is one kind of fertilizer. Manure improves the water-holding ability of soil, but it is low in mineral nutrients.

How is fertilizer important in producing food?

How does chemical fertilizer differ from organic fertilizer?

Chemical fertilizer contains chemical compounds rich in minerals. It contains little or no organic matter. Over 40 million metric tons of commercial

*Kevin Fitzsimons*

FIGURE 22-7. One way to increase food production is to develop hybrid plants.

Larry Hamill

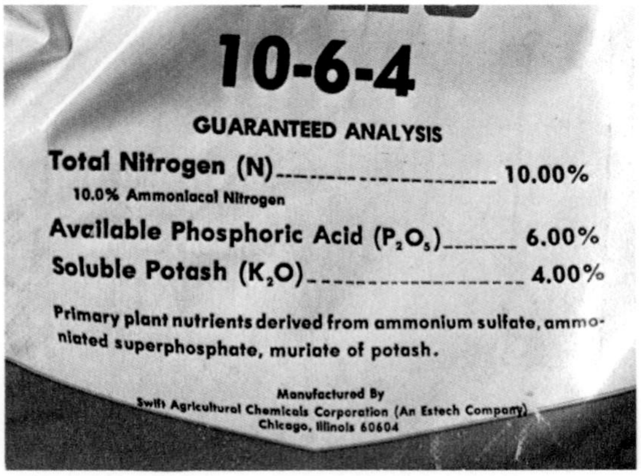
10-6-4
GUARANTEED ANALYSIS
Total Nitrogen (N) 10.00%
10.0% Ammoniacal Nitrogen
Available Phosphoric Acid ($P_2O_5$) 6.00%
Soluble Potash ($K_2O$) 4.00%
Primary plant nutrients derived from ammonium sulfate, ammoniated superphosphate, muriate of potash.
Manufactured By
Swift Agricultural Chemicals Corporation (An Estech Company)
Chicago, Illinois 60604

a

Grant Heilman Photography

b

FIGURE 22-8. Fertilizers supply minerals lacking in some soils (a). Corn does not grow well in soil that is low in phosphorus (b).

fertilizer are produced each year. About one fourth of a crop yield may be due to the addition of chemical fertilizer. Fertilizer is labeled with the content of the three main minerals—nitrogen, phosphorus, and potassium. For example, a 20–10–5 fertilizer contains 20 percent nitrogen, 10 percent phosphorus, and 5 percent potassium.

How does irrigation increase our food supply?

For crops to grow and produce high yields, water is needed. In some areas, rain provides enough water for growing crops. In other areas where there is not enough rain, water for crops can be supplied by irrigation. **Irrigation** means supplying water to fields from wells, rivers, lakes, and reservoirs. Often the water is carried to the fields over long distances. Adding water to a field may mean the difference between no crops and a good harvest. About one third of the crops grown in the United States come from irrigated land.

How does drip irrigation conserve water?

When fields are irrigated by open trenches, water is lost to the air by evaporation. One solution to this problem is drip irrigation. In drip irrigation, a series of rubber water hoses is connected to valves. The valves allow water to drip out of the hoses directly into the soil. Very little water is on the soil surface where it can evaporate. Each valve is set so the amount that drips is just enough to meet a plant's needs. Thus, there is little water lost by evaporation. Drip irrigation can also be used to fertilize plants. Liquid fertilizer is added directly to the irrigation water that passes through the system. Some scientists

Grant Heilman Photography

a

John Colwell for Grant Heilman Photography

b

FIGURE 22-9. Many desert areas have become productive through the use of irrigation (a). In drip irrigation, little water is lost through evaporation (b).

believe irrigation could add 200 million acres to the world's productive farmland.

To receive full benefit from the crops, plant diseases and pests must be controlled. Because plant diseases and insects can cause a decrease in yield, pesticides and herbicides are used by many farmers. These chemicals help control crop damage by pests.

Seeds, fertilizers, and farm machinery cost money. A farmer must pay for these investments. Many small-scale farmers cannot afford modern farming methods. Thus, their food production does not increase. One solution to the cost factor may be a farming cooperative. In a cooperative, several farmers may share the cost and use of machinery.

## activity

### LOSS OF WATER BY EVAPORATION

Add 10 mL of water to each of three small beakers. Place two beakers on a window sill where they will be in the sun. Cover one of these two beakers with a piece of cotton cloth. Place the third beaker in the shade. Observe the three beakers each day until all the water has evaporated from one of them. In which beaker does the water evaporate fastest? Why is evaporation slower in the other two beakers? How could your observations be applied to reduce the amount of irrigation water lost by evaporation?

FIGURE 22-10.

## making sure

6. A fertilizer for house plants is labeled 5–10–5. What do these numbers tell you about the fertilizer?
7. Why does drip irrigation reduce the amount of water needed to irrigate a crop?

Define mineral resource.

## 22:5 Minerals

**Mineral resources** are nonliving materials taken from the earth. Iron, copper, salt, coal, uranium, and limestone are all mineral resources. Mineral resources are nonrenewable. Once the supply of a mineral resource is used, it cannot be replaced. Many mineral resources can be recycled.

Name three metallic minerals.

Mineral resources can be divided into metallic resources and nonmetallic resources. An important metallic resource is iron. Iron is the main mineral in steel. Iron accounts for 95 percent of the metal mined, refined, and used today. Iron can be alloyed with other metals, can be recycled, and is very strong. Other important metallic resources are copper, zinc, lead, tin, and aluminum. Metals are used to make cars, buildings, wires, jewelry, and many other products.

*Camerique*

FIGURE 22-11. When iron is separated from its ore, it is in the liquid state. Liquid, or molten, iron can be poured into molds or further refined to make metal objects.

a

b

Paul Schrock    Susan Rhoades

FIGURE 22-12. Many buildings are made using nonmetallic minerals (a). Nonmetallic minerals are used to make concrete blocks (b).

Nonmetallic mineral resources are used in the construction industry. These resources include sand, gravel, clay, cement, gypsum, and stones like marble, granite, and limestone. Sand and gravel are used to make bricks. Gypsum is used to make wallboard for houses. Cut granite, marble, and limestone are used to build office buildings and monuments.

Name some nonmetallic mineral resources.

The chemical industry uses large amounts of nonmetallic mineral resources. One of the most important of these resources is sulfur. Many processes in the chemical industry require sulfuric acid. Phosphorus is an important mineral in the production of fertilizers. Fluorite is the chief source of hydrogen fluoride used to produce hydrofluoric acid. Hydrofluoric acid is used to clean stone, purify filter paper, dissolve ores, and etch glass. Ammonia is a very important product of the chemical industry. Ammonia is used to make fertilizer. Many nonmetallic resources are found as solids in Earth's crust.

Many useful organic compounds are made from petroleum and natural gas. Plastics and synthetic fibers are examples of these products.

Major sources of mineral resources in the future may be the oceans, asteroids, and other planets. Scientists and engineers search the oceans for mineral deposits and seek ways to mine these minerals. Large deposits of manganese in the form

What are possible future sources of minerals?

of small round nodules have been discovered on the ocean floor at great depths. Other minerals have been discovered near the vents of ocean floor volcanoes. Asteroids, the moon, and planets have mineral deposits. Someday, robot miners or space colonists may live on these space objects and mine the minerals.

### activity
MINERAL RESOURCES

Look around your classroom. List 15 different objects you see. How many objects on your list are made from mineral resources? How many are made from living resources?

### making sure

8. Why are minerals important natural resources?
9. Obtaining mineral resources requires large amounts of energy. Why?

Define energy and name four energy sources.

## 22:6 Electric Energy

FIGURE 22-13. Chemical energy is often used to operate electric generators. The generators convert the energy to electricity.

Roger K. Burnard

Energy is the ability to do work. Energy can have different forms. Electric energy is vital to modern life. Think of all the ways people use electricity. Electric motors are used in household appliances and in industry. Radio, television, and telephone communication use electrical energy. Calculators and computers are electronic devices that operate on electricity.

Electricity is produced from other sources. Most of the electricity we use comes from electric generators powered by steam turbines. The steam is produced by burning coal, oil, or natural gas. Steam also may be produced in a nuclear reactor. Of the coal, oil, and gas burned in the United States, 35 percent is converted to electrical energy. Some of the remaining 65 percent is used to heat buildings.

## 22:7 Fossil Fuels

Coal, petroleum, and natural gas are fossil fuels. **Fossil fuels** are energy sources that come from the remains of once-living plants and animals. Petroleum and natural gas account for nearly 75 percent of the energy used in the world. They are our chief sources of gasoline and fuel oil.

The largest use of petroleum fuels is for transportation—moving people and objects. Most cars, buses, trucks, and airplanes and many trains run on either gasoline or fuel oil. Without them, our world would come to a halt. Fuel oil is also used to heat buildings and generate electricity. It is a major source of heat for industry.

An important energy resource of the future is oil shale. Oil shale is a layered, sedimentary rock. Oil is spread throughout the shale layers. About one-half barrel of oil can be removed from one ton of a good quality shale deposit. Major oil shale deposits are located in Colorado, Utah, and Wyoming. As much as 600 billion barrels of oil may be available in these areas. This amount is about seventeen times the known United States petroleum reserves.

Coal ranks third behind petroleum and natural gas in supplying energy needs. Both in the United States

*Hickson-Bender Photography*

FIGURE 22-14. A large portion of the energy produced from fossil fuels is used for transportation.

What are fossil fuels?

Why is petroleum an important fuel source?

Why is coal an important fuel source?

*U.S. Department of Energy*

FIGURE 22-15. Strip mining can be used to obtain surface deposits of coal.

and worldwide, coal is available in huge amounts. About 93 percent of all fossil fuel reserves is coal. About 70 percent of the coal produced is used to generate electricity. When burned, coal releases two and one-half times as much energy as wood. Ever increasing demands for energy indicate that the use of coal will increase in the future.

Why will the use of coal probably increase?

The supplies of fossil fuels are limited. Once the supplies are used, they cannot be replaced. Some scientists estimate that oil and natural gas supplies will be gone by the year 2025. Coal supplies will last much longer. Much research is being done to find new sources of fossil fuels.

Also, scientists are seeking replacements for fossil fuels. Coal can be changed into a fuel gas. The process of changing coal into gas is called **gasification** (gas uh fuh KAY shun). The basic reaction is to combine carbon (coal) and water to form methane ($CH_4$) and carbon monoxide (CO). This reaction requires the heating of coal in the absence of air inside a reaction chamber.

State briefly how coal is gasified.

Liquid fuels can be produced from coal by controlled heating in the absence of air. This process is similar to the fractional distillation of petroleum (Section 13:3).

## making sure

**10.** What are three major types of fossil fuels?

**11.** Which fossil fuel is most abundant?

American Gas Assoc., Inc.

FIGURE 22-16. Coal is changed to methane at coal gasification plants.

United Nations

FIGURE 22-17. The kinetic energy of water falling over a dam can be used to produce electricity.

## 22:8 Hydroelectricity and Geothermal Energy

How is hydroelectricity produced?

Electricity generated by moving water is called **hydroelectricity** (hi droh ih lek TRIHS ut ee). One common method for producing hydroelectricity is to build a dam across a river. The water trapped in a lake behind the dam is allowed to fall through a vertical shaft. At the bottom of the shaft, the blades of a turbine rotate rapidly as falling water strikes them. Connected to the water turbine is an electric generator. Rotation of the water turbine turns an electric generator.

Hydroelectricity supplies about four percent of the total United States energy supply. There is little chance of increasing this percentage. Most of the good hydroelectric sites in the United States have been developed and are now producing electricity. Many remaining sites will not be used because it would harm the environment. However, worldwide, there are many good places left for generating hydroelectricity. Less than one tenth of the world's potential hydroelectric power has been tapped and put to use.

What is geothermal energy?

**Geothermal** (jee oh THUR mul) **energy** refers to heat within the earth's crust. Evidence of this heat is found in the form of volcanoes, geysers, and hot

FIGURE 22-18. Hot springs and underground "hot spots" can provide energy to heat buildings or generate electricity.

U.S. Department of Energy

springs. In some areas, geothermal energy can be used to heat buildings or to supply other energy needs. For instance, about 500 homes and offices in Klamath Falls, Oregon are heated by hot water from a hot spring.

Why can geothermal energy be used only in certain areas?

In some areas, hot igneous rocks are found close to the surface. Geothermal energy in the form of steam or hot water may be tapped from these areas. A well may be drilled into the reservoir and the steam brought to the surface. In some areas, water is pumped down a hole near the hot rocks to be heated. The hot water or steam can be used to generate electricity. In Geysers Valley, California, steam from geothermal wells is used to turn turbines. These generators produce a total of 500 000 kW of electrical energy. This is enough electricity to supply half of the needs of San Francisco.

### making sure

**12.** How is water used to generate electricity?

**13.** How can geothermal energy be used?

## 22:9 Nuclear Energy

Many nuclear power plants are operating in the United States today. These power plants supply more than 10 percent of the electricity generated in this country. At present, all of the power generated by

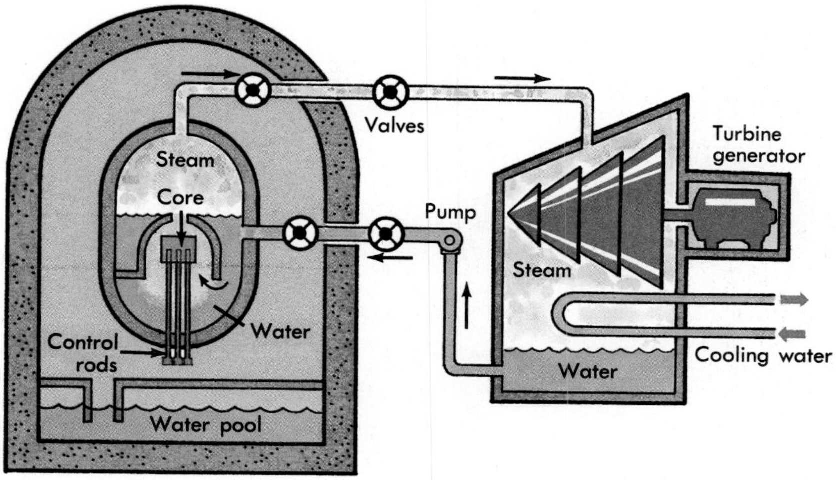


FIGURE 22-19. In a nuclear power plant, nuclear fission produces heat, which makes steam. The steam is used to operate generators.

nuclear power plants is obtained through nuclear fission. Fission is the splitting of the nucleus of an atom.

In a nuclear power plant, nuclear fission takes place inside a reactor. Nuclear fission produces heat that makes steam. The steam drives a turbine that turns an electric generator. The reactor shown in Figure 22–19 is a boiling water reactor. The nuclear fuel is uranium oxide pellets held in zirconium alloy tubes in the core. Water is pumped through the core where it boils and produces steam. The steam is piped to the turbine where it generates electricity. Other nuclear reactors heat molten metal which in turn heats water to produce steam.

How is nuclear energy used to generate electricity?

### making sure

**14.** How is nuclear energy used to produce electricity?

## 22:10 Energy from Tides, Waves, and Wind

Two features of the ocean, waves and tides, may provide significant energy in the future. Scientists are working to harness the energy of tides and winds. Tidal power has been used in France since 1966 when the first tidal power plant was opened at Rance. Rance is an ideal tidal power site. It is a

How are tides, waves, and wind used to obtain energy?

ERDA

FIGURE 22-20. In some areas, wind can be used to produce electricity.

narrow channel in which the water level changes over a depth of about 12 m. Beyond the dam, the channel widens into a large basin where water can be stored at high tide and released at low tide. The number of sites for tidal power is limited. The Bay of Fundy in eastern Canada and the Pacific coast of Alaska are promising regions.

The potential energy in waves is ten times that of the tides. Great Britain is involved in a large-scale research program to harness this energy. One wave power device is called the Salter duck. A Salter duck rocks back and forth in the waves. This motion captures 90 percent of the potential energy of the waves. This energy could be used to pump oil in the ducks to drive generators to produce electricity.

Wind has been used to pump water for many years. Today, huge windmills are used to turn turbines that generate electricity. In the United States, scientists estimate that wind power systems could meet 10 percent of the electricity needs in the year 2000. One difficulty with wind power is storing the energy for use on windless days.

## 22:11 Solar Energy

The sun is the world's largest energy resource. Energy from the sun is called **solar energy**. The solar energy that reaches Earth is more than the current energy needs. However, it cannot supply all our energy needs because it is scattered and not always available. The problems in tapping this resource range from how to collect and store solar energy to how to use it.

What are the problems of using solar energy?

*Doug Martin*

FIGURE 22-21. The sun is the energy source for plant and animal growth. It is also the energy source for wind.

Solar energy is used for heating space, heating water, and producing electricity. Someday solar energy may be developed to the point that it supplies power for industry and transportation. Space stations of the future will use solar energy to run machinery and supply other energy needs.

State three ways solar energy is used.

One use of solar energy is to convert it to heat for homes and other buildings. A **solar collector** is one device for converting solar energy to heat. In a solar collector, a series of water pipes is attached to a flat piece of wood. Both the pipes and the wood are painted dull black to absorb as much energy as possible. A few centimeters above the pipes are glass panes or clear plastic sheets. The glass or plastic

How is solar energy used for heating?

FIGURE 22-22. In a solar collector panel, a liquid such as water is circulated through pipes. The pipes are on a black surface to absorb heat from the sun. The warmed liquid then circulates through the building, providing heat.

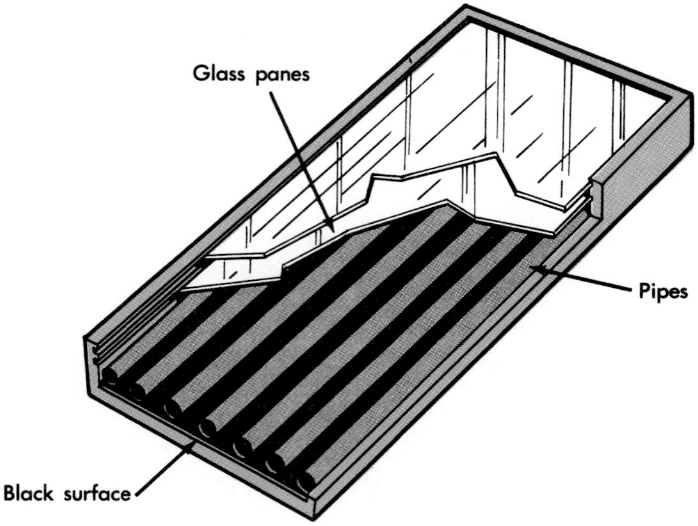


prevents loss of trapped heat. A solar collector is usually put on a roof so it faces south. Under ideal conditions 80 to 90 percent of the solar energy striking the collector is absorbed. The energy heats the water in the pipes. The heated water is then circulated inside the building for space heating. A solar collector can also be used as a hot water heater for use in a building. Solar space and water heating has been used in many homes for over 20 years.

*U.S. Department of Energy*

FIGURE 22-23. Using groups of solar collectors, an entire building may be heated.

What is a photovoltaic cell?

Solar energy can be converted to electric energy by means of a **photovoltaic** (foht oh vohl TAY ihk) **cell.** One type of photovoltaic cell contains silicon. When sunlight shines on it, the energy knocks electrons out of the silicon. These electrons form an electric current.

Camerique

FIGURE 22-24. A bank of photovoltaic cells converts solar energy directly into electricity to operate this air sampler. The air sampler monitors air pollution levels.

Use of photovoltaic cells to collect solar energy is costly because the cells are expensive to make. New methods of producing less expensive cells will bring down the cost. Someday the price may drop to the point where electric energy from photovoltaic cells competes with other energy resources.

It may someday be possible to collect solar energy with photovoltaic cells on a satellite. The energy would be beamed down to a receiving antenna on Earth. This process may prove to be a more efficient way of collecting solar energy. Because a satellite is above the atmosphere, it could constantly collect energy. The satellite would always be in the sunlight. The light would never be blocked by clouds or the horizon.

## making sure

**15.** How can a solar collector be used for space heating?

**16.** What is a photovoltaic cell?

**17.** What are the possible uses of solar energy?

# PERSPECTIVES

## people

# Acid Rain at Close Range

Humans pollute the air in a number of ways. Acid rain is one type of air pollution that is suspected of causing environmental damage. Plant pathologist Carolyn McQuattie works for the U. S. Forest Service and studies the effects of acid rain and other air pollutants on plants, both in the laboratory and in the field.

McQuattie is currently experimenting with a combination of ozone and acid rain mist on plant seedlings. She has found that after six weeks of the treatment, clean air seedlings grew better than those subjected to air pollutants. Despite the fact that acid rain damages plants in the laboratory, McQuattie cautions against making hasty conclusions about the effects of the rain in the field. She believes that a real forest is a complex system, and that acid rain may be only one contributing factor to plant damage. Also, two factors may work together to cause an effect that neither could cause alone.

A second area of McQuattie's research involves the symbiotic relationship of plants and fungi. Symbiosis is a relationship in which two organisms live in close association and both benefit from the relationship. The fungi she studies live on or in the roots of about 97% of the world's plants. They aid the roots in absorbing nutrients. In turn, the fungi benefit from food produced by the plant. McQuattie is trying to determine if acid rain has a negative effect on the fungi, resulting in damage to the plants.

A third problem that Ms. McQuattie is investigating is the effect of aluminum on spruce trees. Detailed examinations have revealed that root growth is stunted in trees subjected to aluminum. Air pollutants known as particulates, along with water and soil pollutants, can contaminate healthy plants with metals such as aluminum.

All of McQuattie's research involves using electron microscopes that magnify up to 360 000 times, as well as light microscopes. Each type of scope gives a biologist different information, which then must be combined to form a hypothesis.

Carolyn McQuattie is fascinated by her work. She says that looking at images through the electron microscope is like looking at scenery. Like many scientists, she enjoys the continual challenge of observing the results of experiments and then having the opportunity of trying to explain those results.

*Image Workshop*

## main ideas

1. The increase in the world's population causes an increase in the need for resources. 22:1
2. Some resources are renewable and others are nonrenewable. 22:2
3. Cereals provide most of the food energy needs of people. 22:3
4. New, higher-yielding varieties of plants and animals can increase the world's supply of food. 22:4
5. Mineral resources are nonrenewable. 22:5
6. Many energy sources are used to generate electricity. 22:6
7. Fossil fuels provide 75 percent of the energy used in the world. 22:7
8. Hydroelectricity is generated by moving water. Geothermal energy comes from within Earth's crust. 22:8
9. The power generated by nuclear energy is obtained through nuclear fission. 22:9
10. Tides, waves, and wind are sources of energy. 22:10
11. Solar energy can be converted to electric energy by means of a photovoltaic cell. 22:11

## vocabulary

*Define each of the following words or terms.*

fertilizer
fossil fuels
gasification
geothermal energy
hybrid
hydroelectricity
irrigation
mineral resources
nonrenewable resource
photovoltaic cell
renewable resource
solar collector
solar energy

## study questions

**DO NOT WRITE IN THIS BOOK.**

**A. True or False**

*Determine whether each of the following sentences is true or false. If the sentence is false, rewrite it to make it true.*

1. Petroleum is a fossil fuel.
2. Oil can be obtained from shale.
3. The largest use of petroleum is for home heating.

4. Very little coal is left to be mined in the United States.
5. Geothermal energy refers to heat within the earth's crust.
6. Coal is a renewable resource.
7. Cereals such as wheat supply most of the energy needs for people and farm animals.
8. Electrical energy is used to do work.
9. Most crops require large amounts of nitrogen.
10. Most mineral resources are taken from the earth by mining.

**B. Multiple Choice**

*Choose the word or phrase that completes correctly each of the following sentences.*

1. There is a (*geothermal, wave, tidal*) power plant at Rance, France.
2. (*Coal, Oil, Natural gas*) is the most abundant fossil fuel.
3. (*Hydrogen, Uranium, Methane*) may be made by heating coal.
4. Electricity generated in a nuclear power plant is obtained through nuclear (*fusion, fission, decay*).
5. Mineral resources are (*renewable, nonrenewable, living*) resources.
6. A photovoltaic cell uses (*solar, geothermal, fossil fuel*) energy.
7. Geothermal energy comes from (*rocks in the earth, synthetic fuels, burning hydrogen*).
8. As the number of people in the world increases, the need for resources (*increases, decreases, remains the same*).
9. Living organisms are (*renewable, nonrenewable, mineral*) resources.
10. (*Meat, Water, Fruit*) is a source of high quality protein.

**C. Completion**

*Complete each of the following sentences with a word or phrase that will make the sentence correct.*

1. ______ are a good source of high quality plant protein.
2. A solar ______ converts solar energy to heat.
3. The ______ revolution refers to the increase in food production in many countries.
4. ______ fertilizer contains compounds rich in nitrogen, phosphorus, and potassium.
5. ______ irrigation is a method used to decrease water loss by evaporation.

6. ______ resources are nonliving, nonrenewable resources taken from the earth.
7. An energy source that comes from buried plants and animals is called a(n) ______ fuel.
8. The world's largest energy source is the ______.
9. Most of the energy in coal, oil, and gas is used for ______.
10. Hydroelectricity is generated by the force of falling ______.

**D. How and Why**

1. How can the world's food production be increased?
2. Why are fossil fuels important?
3. List the advantages and disadvantages of wind power.
4. How is solar energy collected and used?
5. Explain the differences between renewable and nonrenewable resources.

## challenges

1. Petroleum engineering provides jobs for many people. Obtain information on a career in this field. Make a brief report to your class.
2. Obtain a library book on nuclear power. Make a model of a nuclear fission reactor.
3. Obtain information on solar energy. Find out how you can build a solar collector for heating water.
4. Prepare a report on the pros and cons of nuclear power. Include your own conclusions based on library research on this topic. If possible, arrange to visit a nuclear power plant to obtain information for inclusion in this report.

## interesting reading

Asimov, Isaac, *How Did We Find Out About Solar Power?* New York: Walker, 1981.

Goldin, Augusta, *Geothermal Energy: A Hot Perspective.* New York: Harcourt, 1981.

Polking, Kirk, *Oceans of the World: Our Essential Resource.* New York: Philomel, 1983.

*Your environment is all of your surroundings. Some of the setting in this photograph is natural. However, people have changed the natural environment to suit their needs. By changing the natural setting, people are creating variety within the environment. What are some of these changes? Are all these changes helpful?*

*Steve Lissau*

# People and Their Environment chapter 23

## 23:1 Environment

Earth is the environment for all people. However, the local environment for any one person depends on the country, state, city, town, or area in which the person lives. Weather and climate are part of your environment. Your environment includes air, buildings, noise, sunlight, people, streets, cars, plants, and many other things. **Environment** is the sum total of your surroundings. Your environment supplies your needs for living and growing.

GOAL: You will learn how people influence their environments.

What is your environment?

People need clean air to breathe and pure water to drink. They also need food, clothing, and homes. When people use resources to produce the things they need, wastes are also produced. These wastes affect the quality of the environment. When wastes enter the air, soil, or water, pollution results. The wastes that cause pollution are called **pollutants** (puh LEWT unts).

What are pollutants?

FIGURE 23-1. The ash from the Mount St. Helens eruption polluted the air and water around the mountain.

## 23:2 Air Pollution

What are natural causes of air pollution?

On May 18, 1980, Mt. St. Helens in Washington erupted. A huge cloud of gas, smoke, and ash entered the air. The eruption of Mt. St. Helens polluted the air. Volcanoes are one of many natural sources of pollutants. Forest fires, dust storms, and some biological processes are other sources of natural pollution.

What are the five types of air pollutants?

There are five types of air pollutants. They are carbon oxides, hydrocarbons, sulfur oxides, nitrogen oxides, and particles. The most abundant air pollutant is carbon dioxide. Carbon dioxide is a product of the respiration of all plants and animals. The amount of carbon dioxide in the atmosphere has increased because of the burning of fossil fuels and wood. Carbon monoxide is also a by-product of burning and is an air pollutant.

Hydrocarbons are emitted by industrial plants and produced by the burning of fuels in cars. Hydrocarbons often produce a blue haze over dense forests and over cities. Methane, or marsh gas, and sulfur dioxide are produced by rotting plants. Sulfur dioxide is also produced by the burning of coal. Nitrogen oxides are also produced when oil and gasoline are burned. Particles in the air come from many sources such as the burning of trash, fossil fuels, and wood.

Under certain conditions some air pollutants will form smog. **Smog** is air pollution caused by chemical reactions among hydrocarbons, nitrogen oxides, and other pollutants exposed to sunlight. Smog irritates the eyes and causes coughing and headaches. In high concentrations, smog may cause death. Smog causes the breakdown of rubber, fabrics, and building materials. Smog also damages trees and other organisms.

A steady increase in the carbon dioxide level may have a long-term "greenhouse" effect. Carbon dioxide acts as a blanket in reducing the escape of heat from Earth. An increase in the amount of carbon dioxide could cause the Earth to warm. The heating effect could result in changes in climate and cause glaciers to begin melting.

Rain and snow wash pollutants from the air. If the air contains oxides of nitrogen and sulfur, they may dissolve in the precipitation, forming nitric and sulfuric acids, or **acid rain.** Acid rain can cause a

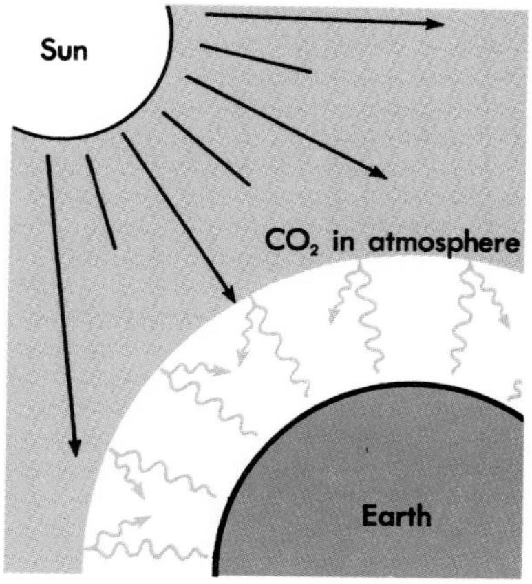


FIGURE 23-2. In the greenhouse effect, sunlight passes through the atmosphere and heats Earth's surface. The atmosphere prevents the escape of heat into space. Thus, Earth's surface temperature rises.

How is air pollution harmful?

FIGURE 23–3. Changing atmospheric conditions can cause air quality to differ from day to day.

*Gordon Anderson*

*Gordon Anderson*

decrease in the number of fish in lakes and streams. It also increases the wearing away of buildings made of materials such as limestone and concrete. Metals corrode faster than normal when exposed to acid rain.

Name two ways air pollution can be controlled.

What is being done to combat air pollution? Changing the design of an engine so that it burns gasoline more completely reduces some types of air pollution. The use of a catalytic (kat uh LIHT ihk) converter on a car exhaust pipe reduces the amount of carbon monoxide and unburned hydrocarbons. One method of reducing pollution from smokestacks is the use of precipitators (prih SIHP uh tayt urz). A **precipitator** collects the particles of smoke within a smokestack. Thus, solid pollutants do not enter the atmosphere.

FIGURE 23-4. A smoke stack without a precipitator (a) emits much more solid pollution into the air than the same stack with a precipitator (b).

a

b

FIGURE 23-5.

## activity ACID WATER

(1) Add drops of bromothymol blue to 5 mL of water in a test tube until the water becomes light blue. (2) Set a small candle in a glass jar. Light the candle and place a glass plate over the jar. (3) After the candle goes out, add the water in the test tube to the jar. Replace the glass cover and shake the jar vigorously. What change occurs in the water? What gas caused the water to turn acid? Name two other gases that make water acid when they dissolve.

## making sure

1. How can an increase in the use of energy resources increase air pollution?
2. What substances produce acid rain?

## 23:3 Water Pollution

What causes water pollution?

Water quality was among the first environmental problems studied by scientists. One type of water pollution is caused by sediments. Sediments are solid particles of soil that settle to the bottom of a body of water. Sediments come from mining, land development, highway construction, and farm fields. Sediments can clog streams, rivers, and lakes.

Water can be polluted by microorganisms from sewage disposal, by wastes from industry, and by brine from oil wells. Mine wastes and fertilizers used to grow crops can also cause pollution.

How is water pollution harmful?

Polluted water can be the source of diseases such as dysentery (DIHS un ter ee), typhoid fever, cholera (KAHL uh ruh), and infectious hepatitis. Chemicals used to control weeds and kill insects may be washed by runoff water into lakes and streams. These chemicals enter a food chain when absorbed by algae and other organisms. The algae and other organisms

Allan Roberts

FIGURE 23-6. One fork of this river has been polluted by silt from a gravel pit.

Tracy Borland

FIGURE 23-7. Cooling towers are used to reduce the thermal pollution of rivers and streams.

are eaten by aquatic animals. In this way, chemicals move up the food chain and become more concentrated. The highest concentrations are found in predators at the tops of food chains. Some chemicals can upset the reproduction of certain species of animals. The chemicals are also harmful to human health.

How is thermal pollution caused?

What are the results of thermal pollution?

How can the problem of thermal pollution be solved?

Some industries pollute waterways with hot water. Water is used by certain industries and power plants for cooling. The water becomes heated and is piped into a nearby waterway. The increase in temperature of the waterway is called **thermal pollution.** Thermal pollution causes the rapid growth of algae. As the algae die and decay, the oxygen content of the water decreases, resulting in fish kills.

Cooling towers can prevent thermal pollution. In a cooling tower, hot water is pumped through long pipes where it cools to air temperature. Then the cooled water is released into a lake or river without any harmful effects.

Pollution from sewage can be prevented by treating the sewage at a modern sewage treatment plant (Section 13:7). Sediment pollution can be decreased through the use of contour plowing and other land-use techniques.

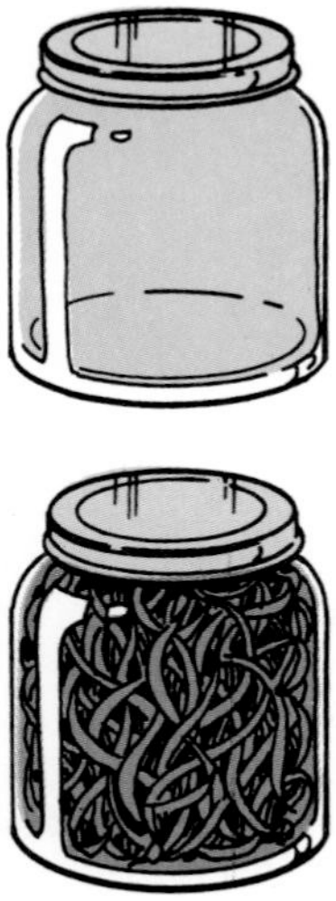

FIGURE 23-8.

## activity DECAY AND OXYGEN

(1) Obtain two small jars with caps that screw on tight. Fill each jar half full of water. Add drops of bromothymol blue to each jar until the water turns light blue. (2) Add some dried grass to one jar. (3) Completely fill each jar with water and screw the caps on tight. Make certain the jars are completely full of water and that there is no air in the tops. (4) Let the jars stand for 5 days. Observe the jars each day and record any changes you see. A change in the color of the blue indicator shows that oxygen is being used. How does decay change the oxygen content of the water? Which jar is the control?

**making sure**

3. Why might it be unsafe to drink water in a country stream?
4. What kinds of wastes cause water pollution?

## 23:4 Noise Pollution

What is noise pollution?

Loud, unpleasant, or unwanted sounds cause noise pollution. People disagree about whether some sounds are noise or not. A radio may produce noise for one person and enjoyment for another. Ringing telephones can be noise to office workers. However, the ring of a telephone when you know it is a friend calling may be very pleasant. Most people do agree that very loud sounds such as those made by airplanes and traffic are noise pollution.

What damage can sound do?

Sounds can cause damage. The vibration of a high-pitched sound can cause crystal to break. Loud sounds such as sonic booms can crack plaster and break windows. Even a continual soft sound such as water dripping from a faucet can be damaging to a person's peace of mind.

R. Church/Tom Stack & Associates

FIGURE 23-9. Some people live in areas with much noise pollution.

FIGURE 23-10. People who work near loud machines may wear ear plugs to protect their eardrums from the noise.

What are some effects of too much noise?

Noise can affect different parts of the body. Very loud sounds can cause temporary hearing loss. If exposure to loud sounds continues over a long time, the hearing loss can become permanent. In response to noise, heart rate, breathing rate, and blood pressure may rise. Digestion may be affected. People may get headaches, become grouchy, or even lose their appetites when around too much noise. Because of these effects, people should wear protective ear covering when they are going to be around loud noises.

What can you do to decrease noise pollution?

What can be done to decrease noise pollution and its effects? Lowering the volume of stereos and televisions decreases noise pollution and show consideration for others. Keeping good mufflers on motor vehicles reduces the noise they produce. Manufacturers are now producing appliances that run more quietly. New jet engines produce less noise than older models. Keeping machinery well lubricated and replacing parts that are worn out cuts down on noise pollution.

Local governments can pass laws limiting noise levels in their communities. They can require that airplanes take off and land over water or open spaces whenever possible. Insulation and sound absorbant material can be required in the construction of new buildings. Trees can be planted near busy highways to absorb sound and reduce the noise level of the traffic.

## 23:5 Radiation Pollution

Radiation is a natural part of your environment. Sunlight contains visible radiation as well as ultraviolet and other radiation. Radioactive elements in Earth's crust emit some nuclear radiation. Cosmic rays from deep space are another source. The natural level of radiation in the environment is not dangerous.

Name four kinds of natural radiation.

Radio waves and microwaves are other kinds of radiation that are part of the environment. Radios, televisions, and long distance telephone transmitters emit radiation. Radiation is also added to the environment by radar transmitters and communication satellites. Low-level radiation is produced by garage door openers, microwave ovens, and some burglar alarms. It is not known how dangerous these levels of radiation are. However, exposure to high levels of radiation is dangerous.

What are some radiation sources that are not natural?

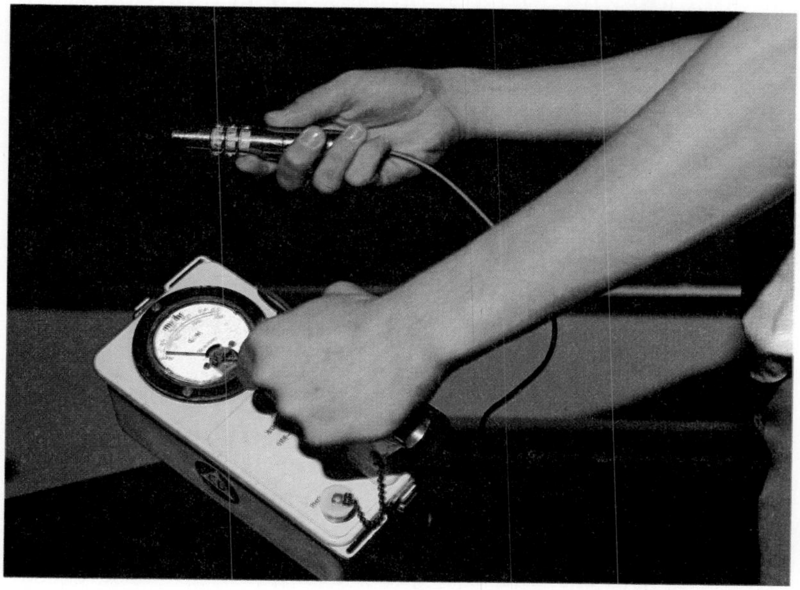

*Allan Roberts*

FIGURE 23-11. The natural, or background, radiation level is not harmful.

Janet Adams

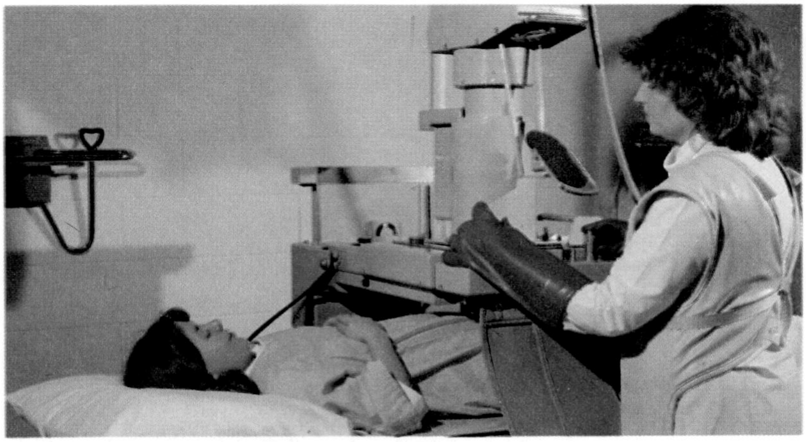

FIGURE 23-12. Without adequate protection, a person working in an X-ray laboratory could be exposed to high levels of radiation.

High-level radiation could come from a variety of sources. People working with radioactive isotopes in industry or medicine can be exposed to nuclear radiation. People can be exposed to high levels of ultraviolet radiation through sunbathing. Each time you have an X ray taken of your mouth or other part of your body, you are exposed to X rays.

How is radiation harmful?

Radiation can be harmful to living tissue. Continuous exposure to low levels of radiation can cause leukemia and cancer of the lungs, skin, or thyroid gland. The period of time between exposure to radiation and the diagnosis of cancer can be from 5 to 20 years. Exposure to low-level radiation over a long period of time can accelerate the aging process and shorten a person's life. Birth defects in children can be caused by overexposure to one or both parents to X rays or nuclear radiation. The level of radiation inside a nuclear reactor can cause death. Death may also result from the radiation received from exposure to radioactive wastes from a nuclear reactor.

When a person's body absorbs radiowaves or microwaves, heat is produced inside the body. As a result, blood circulation increases to remove this heat from the internal organs. However, should the internal organs become overheated, permanent damage could be done. Organs that are very sensitive to heat are the eyes, gall bladder, digestive tract, urinary bladder, and the testes. Very high levels of radio wave and microwave radiation can cause cancer, nervous disorders, eye cataracts, and heart disease.

### making sure

5. What radiation is a natural part of the environment?
6. Why is it important that the door of a microwave oven be sealed properly?

## 23:6 Pesticides: Benefits and Risks

About half the world's food production is consumed or destroyed by insects, rats, and mice. A **pesticide** (PES tuh side) is a chemical used to kill these pests. Pesticides reduce the damage done by pests to crops and stored food supplies. Also, they aid in disease prevention by killing organisms that carry and spread disease.

What is a pesticide?

How are pesticides helpful?

Pesticides may kill helpful insects, too. Honey bees are helpful because they pollinate crops such as apples, cherries, and strawberries. Honey bees can be killed by pesticides. Pesticides may also kill natural predators that prey on pests. Ladybug beetles eat harmful plant lice. Ladybugs are killed by some pesticides. Another risk in the use of a pesticide is

In what ways are pesticides harmful?

*Grant Heilman Photography*

FIGURE 23-13. Pesticides are used to reduce crop damage from insects.

that it can enter food chains. Animals may be harmed as the pesticide concentration builds up inside their bodies. Several species have become endangered because of the use of pesticides.

What happens when insect populations become resistant to pesticides?

A growing concern about the use of pesticides is the increase in the number of pests that are resistant to them. How do certain species of pests become resistant? Here is one example that will help you understand what happens. Suppose a chemical is used to kill flies. Most, but not all, of the flies will die when they are sprayed. The flies that do not die have an inborn resistance to the pesticide. When these resistant flies reproduce, their resistance is inherited by their offspring. The offspring flies go on to produce even more flies that have the inherited resistance. Larger concentrations of the pesticide must be used to kill the flies. Sometimes, different chemicals must be used. Many years of heavy pesticide use can cause the breeding of super-resistant pests. As a result, it becomes more and more difficult to control harmful pests.

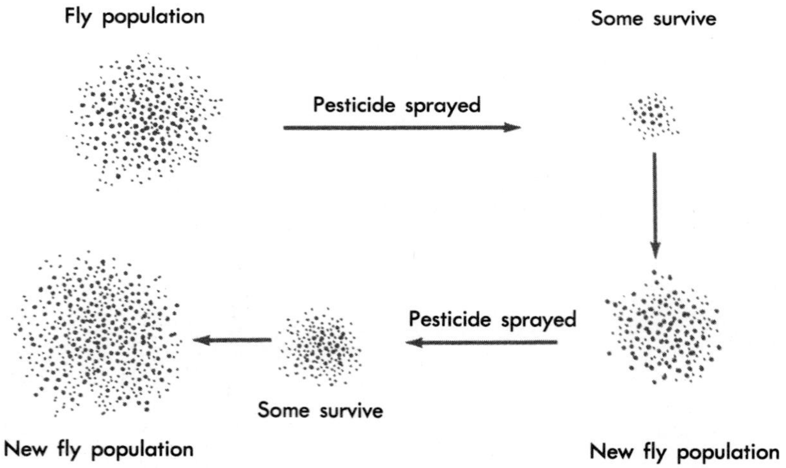


FIGURE 23-14. Insect pests can become resistant to a particular pesticide in a very short time.

## making sure

7. How do pesticides help prevent disease?
8. How might the killing of natural predators cause an increase in the number of insects?

## 23:7 Solid Wastes

Every time you use something and throw it away it becomes a solid waste. Old newspapers, food cans, plastic milk cartons, and soft drink containers are common solid wastes. Solid wastes are also produced when things wear out. Shoes, furniture, tires, batteries, and clothing wear out and must be discarded. Usually these articles go into the trash and are taken to a dump.

Name five examples of solid wastes.

*Kevin Fitzsimons*

FIGURE 23-15. People produce a large amount of solid waste.

Solid wastes are produced in industry when products are manufactured. Mining and the refining of mineral ores produce solid wastes such as mill tailings, slag, and fly ash. The production of one metric ton of copper generates more than 500 metric tons of solid waste. Raising plants and animals on

*Kevin Fitzsimons*

FIGURE 23-16. Industry produces millions of metric tons of solid waste each year.

farms produces more than two billion metric tons of solid waste each year. Three fourths of this waste is animal manure and plant wastes left after crops are harvested and processed for food.

Define biodegradable and list two examples.

Solid wastes may be classified in two groups. **Biodegradable wastes** are wastes that can be broken down by the action of microbes such as bacteria, yeast, and molds. Wastes from animals and plants are mostly biodegradable.

The second group of wastes includes all materials that are not biodegradable. These wastes cannot be broken down by microbes. Most mining and mineral wastes are not biodegradable. Solid wastes from people's homes are a mixture of biodegradable and not biodegradable materials.

What is an incinerator plant?

A major problem in protecting the environment is the disposal of solid wastes. Burning is one way to get rid of many solid wastes. Farmers may burn off the remaining plant material after a crop such as rice is harvested. However, burning causes air pollution. Many cities collect their solid waste and burn it in large incinerators (ihn SIHN uh rayt urz). These incinerators are equipped with air pollution control devices. The heat generated may be used to produce electricity. About ten to twenty percent of the waste is left after burning. This remaining waste is then taken to a landfill.

Eric Hoffhines

FIGURE 23-17. Some cities use solid wastes to produce electricity.

Kevin Fitzsimons

FIGURE 23-18. Solid wastes in a sanitary landfill are covered with soil.

What is a sanitary landfill?

A **sanitary landfill** is another method used to dispose of solid wastes. At a sanitary landfill, a trench is dug with a bulldozer and solid wastes are spread into the trench. Each day the waste is covered with a layer of soil. When the trench is full, another one is dug and the procedure is repeated.

Some landfills are in small canyons and valleys. The solid waste is repeatedly dumped into the canyon or valley and covered with soil until the area is full. A completely filled landfill can be put to good use. It may become a site for a park, baseball field, small airport, or a place to grow crops. One hazard with landfills is that rainwater seeping through the wastes can pollute underground water supplies.

What are toxic wastes?

Some solid wastes are poisonous, or toxic (TAHK sihk). These wastes are a threat to human health. Examples of toxic wastes are radioactive wastes and metals such as lead and zinc. Many chemicals produced as wastes in the manufacture of

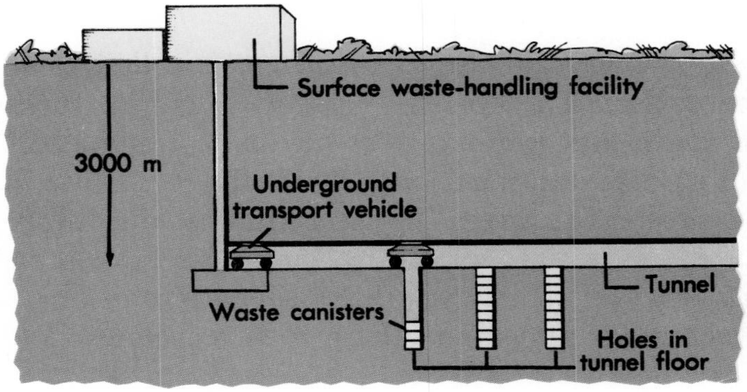


FIGURE 23-19. Radioactive wastes may be stored in underground chambers.

pesticides, fertilizers, and other products are toxic. Special toxic waste disposal sites have been prepared for these toxic wastes. Here the wastes may be stored in steel drums or other secure containers so they do not contaminate the soil, air, and groundwater.

Describe toxic waste disposal.

## activity ANALYSIS OF TRASH

Obtain permission to observe the disposal of trash into a cafeteria trash container. Stand by the trash container and observe the objects students throw away. Keep a record of the number of objects that are (a) paper, (b) metal, (c) plastic, and (d) food. When you have counted 100 objects, total the number in each group. Calculate the percent of objects for each group. Repeat this procedure by keeping track of the objects thrown into a home trash container during a single day. How are the contents of the two trash containers alike and different?

## making sure

9. What is a solid waste?
10. How is a biodegradable waste different from one that is not biodegradable?
11. How is the sanitary landfill trash disposal method different from a trash incinerator?
12. What are the hazards in toxic waste disposal? How can they be reduced?

## 23:8 Conservation

Wise and careful use of resources is called **conservation**. To conserve resources such as forests, fossil fuels, and mineral ores means to not waste them. Conservation of resources helps guarantee that there will be resources for all people in the future.

Why is conservation important?

Have you ever taken newspapers to school for a paper drive? Perhaps you have saved aluminum beverage cans and taken them to a recycling center.

Larry Hamill

a

United Nations

b

FIGURE 23-20. Metals can be collected (a) and taken to a recycling center. There they are separated by type and shredded (b) so they can be used to make new products.

**Recycling** means to use a resource again after it has been used. About one-third of all new paper is made from waste paper. Recycling paper reduces the number of new trees that must be cut down each year to make new paper.

Items made of rubber, glass, and metal can be separated from trash and reused. Every time something is reused it reduces the amount of natural resources needed to make new products. In the United States, the recycling of wastes is a multibillion dollar a year business. Much of this business comes from the recovery of scrap metal from the more than eight million cars junked each year.

How can recycling save resources and energy?

FIGURE 23-21. Millions of cars are junked each year creating eyesores (a). Recycling these cars as scrap metal is one way to reduce energy use and conserve metals (b).

a

United Nations

b

Paul C. Brown

Eric Hoffhines

FIGURE 23-22. A small, economy car (25 mpg) is more fuel efficient than a larger car (17 mpg). Fuel economy labels (insets) indicate average miles per gallon.

Conservation of energy means to not waste energy. Recycling saves energy because less energy is needed to recycle many products than to make new ones. Recycled aluminum requires less than five percent of the energy needed to produce aluminum from ore.

List ways to conserve energy in transportation.

Next to industry, transportation accounts for the largest use of energy. Most of this energy is used by cars. Cars that are light in weight and have small engines burn less gasoline than large cars. Diesel engines help conserve energy because they burn less fuel than gasoline engines. The use of a diesel engine in a car increases fuel efficiency. Car pools and the use of buses to transport people also saves energy.

PHOTRI

FIGURE 23-23. Mass transit systems conserve fuel by transporting many people in a single vehicle.

John Swartz Paul Brown Gerard Photography

a b c

FIGURE 23-24. Energy can be conserved in houses by weatherstripping doors and windows (a), adding insulation to attics (b), and setting the thermostat at 21°C in winter and 26°C in summer (c).

List ways to conserve energy at home.

Houses and apartments use about 20 percent of all energy. More than half of this energy is for space heating and air conditioning. Energy waste can be prevented by conservation at home. Adding insulation to attics and outside walls decreases the heat loss in winter. Putting weather stripping around doors and windows keeps out cold air. Setting thermostats so rooms are not overheated during winter and overcooled in the summer saves energy. A room temperature of 21°C in winter and 26°C in summer is comfortable for many people.

## making sure

**13.** How can the recycling of a resource save energy?

**14.** How can the use of car pools and buses save energy?

# The Invasion Continues. . .

In 1869, a biologist in Medford, Massachusetts imported several gypsy moths, which he hoped would produce a better silkworm. By accident, several of these moths escaped. Twenty years later, Medford was overrun with caterpillars. Campaigns were launched to destroy the caterpillars, and thousands were picked up with shovels and burned. However, not all the caterpillars were destroyed. Moving at the rate of five to fifteen miles a year, the gypsy moth has spread to other states while feeding on the leaves of trees, especially oaks.

In the fall, one gypsy moth female lays from 500 to 1000 eggs. The eggs that survive the winter hatch in late spring. The small caterpillars are capable of ballooning, or spinning a long fiber of silk that is picked up by the wind, carrying the caterpillar with it. Thus, the caterpillar can travel long distances. As the caterpillar grows, it consumes the leaves of trees for food. By July, the caterpillars are five to ten centimeters long. They spin cocoons, and several weeks later, the moth emerges to mate and lay eggs.

In 1956, a massive spraying effort was launched to try to eliminate the gypsy moth. The insecticide DDT was used, and it seemed that the moth would be eliminated. But DDT was banned because of the effects it has on organisms other than the target pest. Several years after the spraying, the gypsy moth population exploded. Scientists believed that the pesticides killed the organisms that preyed on the moths.

The Department of Agriculture is now investigating an integrated pest management plan for controlling the moths. Besides spraying with chemicals, researchers are trying to find parasites that attack the moth caterpillars. Developing techniques that interfere with the insect's reproduction and/or growth is also being tried. Some biologists are working on synthesizing the substance that the female moths use to attract the males. If sprayed over a large area, the scent confuses the male moths and prevents them from mating.

At the present time, no satisfactory method has been found for containing the moths. The gypsy moth continues to expand its range, and is expected to invade the south and southwest within the next few years.

*William Griffin/Animals, Animals*

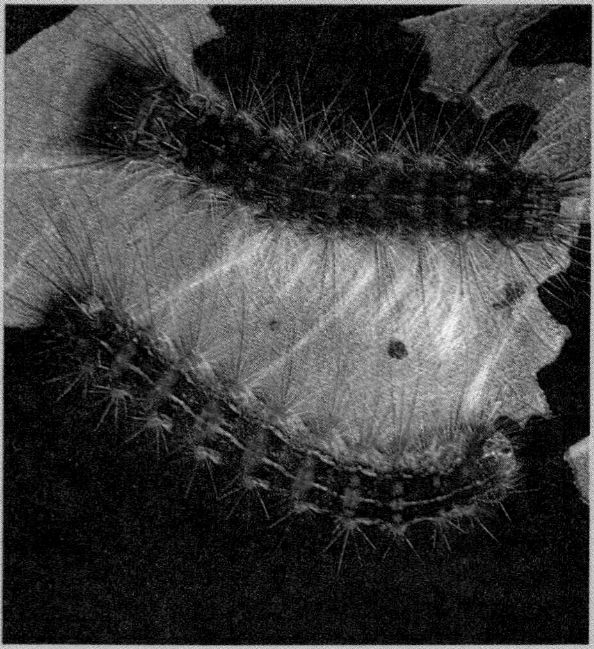

Adapted from "Gypsy Moths, Well Named, Are Showing Wanderlust," which originally appeared in the May, 1984 issue of *Smithsonian* © Donald Dale Jackson.

## main ideas

1. A person's environment is everything around the person. 23:1
2. Burning fossil fuels produces air pollution. Air pollution can cause rainwater to become acid. 23:2
3. Polluted water can be a source of disease. 23:3
4. Radiation is harmful to living tissue and can cause birth defects. 23:5
5. Use of pesticides has both benefits and risks. 23:6
6. Solid wastes can be buried in a landfill or burned. 23:7
7. Some solid wastes are toxic and therefore a threat to human health. 23:7
8. Recycling reduces the waste of energy and natural resources. 23:8
9. Everyone can be involved in the conservation of resources and energy. 23:8

## vocabulary

*Define each of the following words or terms.*

| | | |
|---|---|---|
| acid rain | pesticide | sanitary landfill |
| biodegradable wastes | pollutants | smog |
| conservation | precipitator | thermal pollution |
| environment | recycling | |

## study questions

**DO NOT WRITE IN THIS BOOK.**

**A. True or False**

*Determine whether each of the following sentences is true or false. If the sentence is false, rewrite it to make it true.*

1. The environment is the sum total of your surroundings.
2. Living organisms are part of the environment.
3. Pesticides kill only harmful pests.
4. Automobile exhaust does not contain pollutants.
5. To recycle means to use a resource over again.
6. Biodegradable wastes cannot be broken down by microbes.

7. Sediments are solid particles in water.
8. A precipitator can reduce the pollution from a smokestack.
9. Acid rain contains dissolved pollutants.
10. All radiation comes from devices made by humans.

**B. Multiple Choice**

*Choose the word or phrase that completes correctly each of the following sentences.*

1. (*Oxygen, Nitrogen, Carbon monoxide*) is a pollutant in air.
2. Acid rain is produced when (*oxygen, nitrogen, sulfur dioxide*) is dissolved in rainwater.
3. A microwave oven is an example of a (*natural, low-level, high-level*) radiation source.
4. A(n) (*incinerator, precipitator, pesticide*) is used to kill harmful insects.
5. Lack of (*oxygen, hydrogen, carbon dioxide*) in lake water can cause the death of fish.
6. (*Carbon dioxide, Sulfur dioxide, Heat*) causes thermal pollution.
7. (*Energy, Air, Water*) can be conserved by lowering a home thermostat in winter.
8. An example of biodegradable waste is (*manure, aluminum, iron*).
9. A sanitary landfill is used mostly to store (*solid, liquid, gaseous*) wastes.
10. A toxic waste is (*very dense, always biodegradable, poisonous, harmless*).

**C. Completion**

*Complete each of the following sentences with a word or phrase that will make the sentence correct.*

1. Wise and careful use of resources is called ______.
2. ______ engines use less fuel than gasoline engines.
3. A(n) ______ is used to cool hot water from an industry.
4. ______ wastes are stored in steel drums.
5. Cosmic rays are an example of ______ radiation.
6. Hydrocarbons and nitrogen ______ react to form smog.
7. An insect that is not ______ by a pesticide is said to be resistant.

8. An increase in the ______ in the atmosphere causes a "greenhouse" effect.
9. High-level radiation is present in a(n) ______ reactor.
10. Wastes that cause pollution are called ______.

**D. How and Why**

1. How can air pollution be reduced?
2. Why is radiation hazardous?
3. What are the benefits and risks in using pesticides?
4. What is recycling and how does it help in the conservation of natural resources?
5. List three examples of ways in which the quality of the environment is being improved.

## challenges

1. Obtain information from a library on the history of DDT. Prepare a short report for your class that includes the main facts about DDT and its use.
2. Investigate the use of pesticides in your area. Find out what kinds are sold in local stores. Find out the kinds used by local parks and the highway department. Obtain information about different pesticides from a school or community library. Prepare a large chart listing your findings.
3. Plan a field trip to a recycling center. Learn how solid wastes are separated and recycled.

## interesting reading

Epstein, Samuel S., Lester O. Brown, and Carl Pope, *Hazardous Wastes in America.* San Francisco: Sierra, 1982.

Goldin, Augusta, *Oceans of Energy: Reservoir of Power for the Future.* New York: Harcourt Brace Javonovich, Inc., 1980.

Purcell, Arthur H., *The Waste Watchers: A Citizen's Handbook for Conserving Energy and Resources.* Garden City, NY: Anchor/Doubleday, 1980.

# SIDE ROADS

## And Then There Were None

David M. Dennis

Townsend Dickinson/Photo Researchers

*The population of humans is rising. As it increases, the demand for resources, both living and nonliving, also increases. A larger human population requires more space in which to live, more food, and more consumable goods. Humans have not always exercised caution or sensitivity to the environment while exploiting the Earth's resources. As a result, other organisms have suffered.*

*During the years of the westward expansion, travelers reported seeing prairie dog towns that extended for hundreds of miles across the plains. When ranchers began using these areas for grazing, horses and cattle often broke their legs when they stepped into the prairie dog burrows. The prairie dogs also ate plants on which the other animals could graze. Thus, the prairie dogs were poisoned and their large towns reduced. The reduction in the number of prairie dogs affected other animals as well. One animal that fed on prairie dogs was the black-footed ferret, a relative of the mink and weasel. By the 1970s, some biologists feared that the removal of the prairie dogs had caused the ferret's extinction. However, in 1981, a dog in Wyoming killed a ferret. Biologists immediately began searching for more, and eventually twenty-two were found. Biologists are hopeful that this population can be monitored and protected.*

*In some Florida marshes there is a hawk, called the snail kite, which is not found anywhere else in the world. It's most unique feature is a special curved beak that is adapted for removing snails from their shells. Biologists estimate that the snail kite consumes about 50 snails each day. As humans have developed Florida, low wet areas have been drained, destroying the bird's habitat. By the mid 1950s, only about 20 snail kites remained. However, efforts made by conservation groups to restore the bird's habitat has enabled the population to grow to an estimated 430 individuals.*

*Another bird whose habitat is being destroyed is the dusky seaside sparrow. Found only in Florida, these birds feed on salt marsh plants. Because these salt marshes are also the breeding ground for mosquitoes, many of them have been impounded and flooded with fresh water. The flooding has changed the type of plant that grows in these areas, and introduced more sparrow predators to the environment. These conditions have reduced the sparrow population to only six individuals, all male.*

*Paul W. Sykes, Jr./ National Fish & Wildlife*

*Animals, Animals/M. Austerman*

*The California condor is the largest vulture found in the United States with an average wingspan of 290 cm. Their original range has shrunk to a two county area in California. Vultures are ecologically important because they minimize the chance that diseases from dead animals can be passed to living organisms. It is estimated that only 27 condors are living. The exact cause of the condor's decline is not known, but many scientists believe that the birds have been poisoned by pesticides. In a desperate attempt to save the condors, eggs have been removed from nests in the wild and hatched in captivity. The success of these efforts will not be known until the captive hatched birds are released and observed.*

*These examples demonstrate that many factors may work together to cause an animal population to decline. It is important for scienists to learn as much as possible about the habitats of organisms and the results that our actions will have if many species are to survive.*

# Appendix A

## Science Classroom Safety

The science classroom is a safe place in which to perform activities if you are careful. You must assume responsibility for the safety of yourself and your classmates. Here are some safety rules to help guide you in protecting yourself and others from injury.

1. Do not perform activities that are unauthorized. Always obtain your teacher's permission.
2. Study your assignment. If you are in doubt about a procedure, ask your teacher for help.
3. Use the safety equipment provided for you. Know the location of the fire extinguisher, safety shower, fire blanket, and first aid kit.
4. Safety glasses and safety apron should be worn when any activity calls for heating, pouring, or mixing of chemicals.
5. Report any accident, injury, or incorrect procedure to your teacher at once.
6. Smother fires with a towel. If clothing should catch fire, smother it with a blanket or coat or quench it under a safety shower. **NEVER RUN.**
7. Handle chemicals and bend glassware only under the direction of your teacher. If you spill acid or another corrosive chemical, wash it off immediately with water. Never taste any chemical substance or draw poisonous materials into a glass tube with your mouth. Never inhale chemicals. Keep combustible materials away from open flames.
8. Place broken glass and solid substances in designated containers. Keep insoluble waste material out of the sink.
9. When your activity is completed, be sure to turn off the water and gas and disconnect electrical connections. Clean your work area. Return all materials and apparatus to their proper places.

## First Aid

1. Report all accidents or injuries to your teacher at once.
2. Know where and how to report an accident or injury. Know the location of the phone and fire alarm, and where to locate the nurse.
3. All cuts and bruises should be treated as directed by the instructions included in your first aid kit and should then be reported to a nurse or physician.
4. In case of severe bleeding, apply pressure or a compress directly to the wound. **GET MEDICAL ATTENTION IMMEDIATELY.**
5. If any substance is spilled or gets into your eyes, wash them with plenty of water and notify your teacher for additional aid.
6. Minor burns should be immersed in cold water immediately. In cases of severe burns, **NOTIFY YOUR TEACHER AT ONCE.**
7. In case of fainting or collapse, give the person fresh air and recline him/her so that the head is lower than the body. **NOTIFY YOUR TEACHER AT ONCE.** Mouth-to-mouth resuscitation may be necessary. Call a nurse or physician.
8. In case of poisoning, **NOTIFY YOUR TEACHER WHO WILL CALL A PHYSICIAN AT ONCE.** Note the suspected poisoning agent.
9. If any solution, acid, or base is spilled on you or your desk, wash the area with plenty of water at once. Baking soda (sodium bicarbonate) may be used on acid burns and boric acid on base burns. **NOTIFY YOUR TEACHER AT ONCE.**

# Appendix B Measurement

## SI Base Units

| Measurement | Unit | Symbol |
|---|---|---|
| Length | Meter | m |
| Mass | Kilogram | kg |
| Time | Second | s |
| Temperature | Kelvin | K |
| Electric current | Ampere | A |

## Common SI Prefixes

| Prefix | Symbol | Multiplier | Prefix | Symbol | Multiplier |
|---|---|---|---|---|---|
| | Greater than 1 | | | Less than 1 | |
| Mega- | M | 1 000 000 | Deci- | d | 0.1 |
| Kilo- | k | 1 000 | Centi- | c | 0.01 |
| Hecto- | h | 100 | Milli- | m | 0.001 |
| Deka- | da | 10 | Micro- | μ | 0.000 001 |

## Derived SI Units

| Measurement | Unit | Symbol | Expressed in Base Units |
|---|---|---|---|
| Energy (work) | Joule | J | $kg{\cdot}m^2/s^2$ |
| Force (weight) | Newton | N | $kg{\cdot}m/s^2$ |
| Power | Watt | W | $kg{\cdot}m^2/s^3$ (J/s) |
| Pressure | Pascal | Pa | $kg/m{\cdot}s^2$ ($N/m^2$) |
| Frequency | Hertz | Hz | 1/s |
| Electric potential difference | Volt | V | $kg{\cdot}m^2/s^3{\cdot}A$ ($J/A{\cdot}s$) |
| Electric resistance | Ohm | Ω | $kg{\cdot}m^2/s^3{\cdot}A^2$ (V/A) |
| Area | Square meter | $m^2$ | |
| Volume | Cubic decimeter | $dm^3$ | |

## Common Laboratory Units

| Measurement | Standard SI Unit | Common Unit | Equivalency to SI Standard |
|---|---|---|---|
| Length | Meter (m) | Millimeter (mm) | 1 mm = 0.001 m |
| | | Centimeter (cm) | 1 cm = 0.01 m |
| | | Hectometer (hm) | 1 hm = 100 m |
| | | Kilometer (km) | 1 km = 1000 m |
| Mass | Kilogram (kg) | Milligram (mg) | 1 mg = 0.000 001 kg<br>1 mg = 0.001 g |
| | | Gram (g) | 1 g = 0.001 kg |
| Volume | Cubic meter ($m^3$) | Cubic decimeter ($dm^3$) | 1 $dm^3$ = 0.001 $m^3$ |
| | | Cubic centimeter ($cm^3$) | 1 $cm^3$ = 0.001 $dm^3$ |
| | | Milliliter (mL) | 1 mL = 1 $cm^3$ |
| | | Liter (L) | 1 L = 1000 mL = 1 $dm^3$ |
| Time | Second (s) | Millisecond (ms) | 1 ms = 0.001 s |
| Temperature | Kelvin | Degree Celsius (°C) | °C = K − 273 |

# Appendix C

## Calorie Chart for Some Common Foods

| | Amount | Calories |
|---|---|---|
| **Dairy Foods** | | |
| Cheese: | | |
| American | 28 g | 105 |
| American spread | 28 g | 82 |
| Blue | 28 g | 100 |
| Cheddar | 28 g | 115 |
| Cottage (1% fat) | 120 mL | 82 |
| Cottage (2% fat) | 120 mL | 102 |
| Cottage (4% fat) | 120 mL | 117 |
| Cream | 30 mL | 100 |
| Mozzarella | 28 g | 90 |
| Parmesan (grated) | 30 mL | 100 |
| Ricotta | 28 g | 71 |
| Romano | 28 g | 110 |
| Swiss | 28 g | 105 |
| Eggnog | 240 mL | 340 |
| Ice cream: | | |
| Regular (11% fat) | 240 mL | 270 |
| Rich (16% fat) | 240 mL | 350 |
| Soft | 240 mL | 375 |
| Milk: | | |
| Buttermilk | 240 mL | 100 |
| Chocolate | 240 mL | 210 |
| Dried (skim) | 240 mL | 82 |
| Fresh (skim) | 240 mL | 85 |
| Fresh (lowfat, 2%) | 240 mL | 120 |
| Fresh (whole) | 240 mL | 150 |
| Malted | 240 mL | 235 |
| Shake (chocolate) | 355 mL | 391 |
| Sherbet | 240 mL | 270 |
| Sour cream | 15 mL | 25 |
| Whipped cream topping | 30 mL | 19 |
| Yogurt: | | |
| Low-fat (fruit-flavored) | 240 mL | 230 |
| Low-fat (plain) | 240 mL | 145 |
| Nonfat | 240 mL | 125 |
| Whole-milk | 240 mL | 140 |
| **Meat, Fish, Poultry** | | |
| Beef: | | |
| Corned-beef (canned) | 85 g | 185 |
| Corned-beef hash (canned) | 240 mL | 400 |
| Hamburger (21% fat) | 85 g | 235 |
| Liver (fried) | 85 g | 195 |
| Roast | 85 g | 165 |
| Steak | 85 g | 330 |

| | Amount | Calories |
|---|---|---|
| Chicken: | | |
| Broiled | ½ chicken | 240 |
| Fried | ½ breast | 160 |
| Fish: | | |
| Bluefish (baked in butter) | 85 g | 135 |
| Fish sticks (breaded) | 3 sticks | 150 |
| Haddock (breaded, fried) | 85 g | 140 |
| Ocean perch (breaded, fried) | 85 g | 195 |
| Sardines (canned) | 85 g | 175 |
| Tuna (canned in oil) | 85 g | 170 |
| Tuna salad | 85 g | 175 |
| Lamb: | | |
| Chop (broiled) | 57 g | 120 |
| Leg (roasted) | 85 g | 235 |
| Pork: | | |
| Bacon (2 slices, crisp) | 15 g | 92 |
| Chop (broiled) | 85 g | 305 |
| Ham (baked) | 85 g | 179 |
| Sausage links (2) | 28 g | 135 |
| Luncheon meats: | | |
| Bologna (2 slices) | 56 g | 172 |
| Frankfurter | 57 g | 172 |
| Shellfish: | | |
| Clams (fresh) | 85 g | 65 |
| Scallops (breaded, fried) | 85 g | 165 |
| Shrimp (breaded, fried) | 85 g | 190 |
| Oysters (fresh) | 1 doz. | 160 |
| Turkey (roasted): | | |
| Dark meat | 85 g | 175 |
| White meat | 85 g | 150 |
| Veal: | | |
| Cutlet | 85 g | 135 |
| Rib | 85 g | 230 |
| Eggs: | | |
| Fried in butter | 1 | 85 |
| Hard-boiled | 1 | 80 |
| Raw (large) | 1 | 80 |
| **Fruits** | | |
| Apple (fresh) | 1 | 80 |
| Apple juice | 240 mL | 120 |
| Applesauce (sweetened) | 120 mL | 115 |
| Apricots: | | |
| Dried (4 halves, uncooked) | 15 g | 39 |
| Fresh | 3 | 100 |
| Banana | 1 | 100 |

| | Amount | Calories |
|---|---|---|
| Blueberries (fresh) | 120 mL | 45 |
| Cantaloupe | ½ melon | 80 |
| Cherries: | | |
| Canned in water (sour) | 120 mL | 53 |
| Fresh (sweet) | 10 | 45 |
| Cranberry juice cocktail | 240 mL | 165 |
| Cranberry sauce | 60 mL | 101 |
| Dates (fresh) | 10 | 220 |
| Fruit cocktail (canned in heavy syrup) | 120 mL | 98 |
| Grapefruit (fresh) | ½ | 50 |
| Grapes (fresh) | 10 | 40 |
| Honeydew melon | ⅕ melon | 100 |
| Lemon | 1 | 20 |
| Lemon juice | 240 mL | 55 |
| Orange | 1 | 65 |
| Orange juice (frozen) | 240 mL | 120 |
| Peaches: | | |
| Canned in heavy syrup | 120 mL | 100 |
| Fresh | 1 | 40 |
| Pears: | | |
| Canned in heavy syrup | 120 mL | 98 |
| Fresh | 1 | 100 |
| Pineapple: | | |
| Canned in heavy syrup | 240 mL | 95 |
| Fresh | 120 mL | 40 |
| Plum | 1 | 30 |
| Prunes (unsweetened, cooked) | 120 mL | 128 |
| Raisins | 43 g | 123 |
| Raspberries (fresh) | 120 mL | 35 |
| Strawberries: | | |
| Fresh | 120 mL | 28 |
| Frozen (sweetened) | 120 mL | 124 |
| Tangerine | 1 | 40 |
| Watermelon | 1 large slice | 110 |
| **Vegetables** | | |
| Broccoli | 120 mL | 20 |
| Brussell sprouts | 120 mL | 28 |
| Cabbage (raw) | 120 mL | 15 |
| Carrots | 120 mL | 25 |
| Cauliflower | 120 mL | 15 |
| Celery | 120 mL | 10 |
| Corn | 1 small ear | 70 |
| Green beans | 120 mL | 15 |
| Lettuce | 2 leaves | 5 |
| Potatoes: | | |
| French fries | 10 | 110 |
| Baked | 1 | 145 |
| Mashed | 120 mL | 98 |
| Potato salad | 120 mL | 125 |

| | Amount | Calories |
|---|---|---|
| **Cereals and Grains** | | |
| Bagel | 1 | 165 |
| Biscuit | 1 | 90 |
| Bread: | | |
| Pumpernickel | 1 slice | 80 |
| Rye | 1 slice | 60 |
| White | 1 slice | 70 |
| Whole wheat | 1 slice | 65 |
| Cereals: | | |
| Bran flakes | 240 mL | 105 |
| Corn flakes | 240 mL | 95 |
| Oatmeal | 240 mL | 130 |
| Puffed rice | 240 mL | 60 |
| Cornmeal | 240 mL | 120 |
| Crackers: | | |
| Graham | 2 | 55 |
| Saltines | 4 | 50 |
| Muffins: | | |
| Bran | 1 | 105 |
| Plain | 1 | 120 |
| Waffle | 1 | 210 |
| Pancake | 1 | 60 |
| Macaroni (soft) | 240 mL | 155 |
| Noodles | 240 mL | 200 |
| Rice: | | |
| Instant | 240 mL | 180 |
| Long-grained | 240 mL | 225 |
| **Desserts and Snacks** | | |
| Brownie (with nuts) | 1 | 85 |
| Cakes: | | |
| Angel food | 57 g | 140 |
| Coffee cake | 57 g | 175 |
| Devil's food (chocolate icing) | 57 g | 175 |
| Gingerbread | 57 g | 150 |
| Poundcake | 28 g | 165 |
| Candy: | | |
| Carmels | 28 g | 115 |
| Chocolate | 28 g | 145 |
| Fudge | 28 g | 115 |
| Gum drops | 28 g | 100 |
| Hard | 28 g | 110 |
| Cookies: | | |
| Chocolate chip | 4 | 200 |
| Fig bars | 4 | 200 |
| Oatmeal (with raisins) | 4 | 235 |
| Sandwich | 4 | 200 |
| Vanilla wafers | 10 | 185 |

| | Amount | Calories |
|---|---|---|
| Doughnuts: | | |
| Glazed (leavened) | 1 | 205 |
| Plain (cake type) | 1 | 100 |
| Nuts: | | |
| Almonds | 60 mL | 194 |
| Peanut butter | 15 mL | 95 |
| Peanuts (roasted in oil, salted) | 60 mL | 210 |
| Pecans | 60 mL | 203 |
| Sunflower seeds | 28 g | 101 |
| Pies: | | |
| Apple | 140 g | 345 |
| Blueberry | 140 g | 325 |
| Custard | 140 g | 285 |
| Pecan | 140 g | 550 |
| Pumpkin | 140 g | 275 |
| Popcorn: | | |
| Plain | 240 mL | 25 |
| With oil and salt | 240 mL | 40 |
| Potato chips | 10 | 115 |
| Pretzels (thin) | 10 | 235 |
| **Beverages** | | |
| Coffee (with milk and sugar) | 240 mL | 55 |
| Cola drinks | 360 mL | 145 |
| Fruit sodas | 360 mL | 170 |
| Ginger ale | 360 mL | 115 |
| Tea (with sugar) | 240 mL | 30 |
| **Selected Main Dishes** | | |
| Chicken a la king | 240 mL | 470 |
| Chicken pot pie | 230 g | 545 |
| Chili con carne (with beans, canned) | 240 mL | 235 |
| Macaroni and cheese: | | |
| canned | 240 mL | 230 |
| homemade | 240 mL | 430 |
| Pizza | 1 slice | 145 |
| Soups: | | |
| Canned consomme | 240 mL | 30 |
| Cream of chicken (diluted with milk) | 240 mL | 191 |
| Cream of mushroom (diluted with water) | 240 mL | 129 |
| Split pea with ham (diluted with water) | 240 mL | 189 |
| Tomato (diluted with water) | 240 mL | 86 |
| Vegetarian vegetable | 240 mL | 80 |
| Spaghetti and meatballs: | | |
| Canned | 240 mL | 260 |
| Homemade | 240 mL | 330 |
| Stew with vegetables | 240 mL | 230 |
| **Other** | | |
| Butter (salted) | 2 pats | 70 |
| Corn oil | 15 mL | 120 |
| Margarine | 2 pats | 70 |
| Mayonnaise | 15 mL | 65 |
| Honey | 15 mL | 65 |
| Jams, jellies, or preserves | 15 mL | 55 |
| Sugar: | | |
| Brown | 240 mL | 820 |
| White, granulated | 15 mL | 45 |
| Tomato catsup | 15 mL | 15 |
| Vegetable shortening | 15 mL | 110 |

# Appendix D

## International Atomic Masses

| Element | Symbol | Atomic number | Atomic mass |
|---|---|---|---|
| Actinium | Ac | 89 | 227.02779* |
| Aluminum | Al | 13 | 26.98154 |
| Americium | Am | 95 | 243.06139* |
| Antimony | Sb | 51 | 121.75 |
| Argon | Ar | 18 | 39.948 |
| Arsenic | As | 33 | 74.9216 |
| Astatine | At | 85 | 209.98704* |
| Barium | Ba | 56 | 137.33 |
| Berkelium | Bk | 97 | 247.07032* |
| Beryllium | Be | 4 | 9.01218 |
| Bismuth | Bi | 83 | 208.9808 |
| Boron | B | 5 | 10.81 |
| Bromine | Br | 35 | 79.904 |
| Cadmium | Cd | 48 | 112.41 |
| Calcium | Ca | 20 | 40.08 |
| Californium | Cf | 98 | 251.07961* |
| Carbon | C | 6 | 12.011 |
| Cerium | Ce | 58 | 140.12 |
| Cesium | Cs | 55 | 132.9054 |
| Chlorine | Cl | 17 | 35.453 |
| Chromium | Cr | 24 | 51.996 |
| Cobalt | Co | 27 | 58.9332 |
| Copper | Cu | 29 | 63.546 |
| Curium | Cm | 96 | 247.07038* |
| Dysprosium | Dy | 66 | 162.50 |
| Einsteinium | Es | 99 | 254.08805* |
| Erbium | Er | 68 | 167.26 |
| Europium | Eu | 63 | 151.96 |
| Fermium | Fm | 100 | 257.09515* |
| Fluorine | F | 9 | 18.998403 |
| Francium | Fr | 87 | 223.01976* |
| Gadolinium | Gd | 64 | 157.25 |
| Gallium | Ga | 31 | 69.737 |
| Germanium | Ge | 32 | 72.59 |
| Gold | Au | 79 | 196.9665 |
| Hafnium | Hf | 72 | 178.49 |
| Helium | He | 2 | 4.00260 |
| Holmium | Ho | 67 | 164.9304 |
| Hydrogen | H | 1 | 1.0079 |
| Indium | In | 49 | 114.82 |
| Iodine | I | 53 | 126.9045 |
| Iridium | Ir | 77 | 192.22 |
| Iron | Fe | 26 | 55.847 |
| Krypton | Kr | 36 | 83.80 |
| Lanthanum | La | 57 | 138.9055 |
| Lawrencium | Lr | 103 | 256.099* |
| Lead | Pb | 82 | 207.2 |
| Lithium | Li | 3 | 6.941 |
| Lutetium | Lu | 71 | 174.967 |
| Magnesium | Mg | 12 | 24.305 |
| Manganese | Mn | 25 | 54.9380 |
| Mendelevium | Md | 101 | 258* |
| Mercury | Hg | 80 | 200.59 |
| Molybdenum | Mo | 42 | 95.94 |
| Neodymium | Nd | 60 | 144.24 |
| Neon | Ne | 10 | 20.179 |
| Neptunium | Np | 93 | 237.0482 |
| Nickel | Ni | 28 | 58.71 |
| Niobium | Nb | 41 | 92.9064 |
| Nitrogen | N | 7 | 14.0067 |
| Nobelium | No | 102 | 255.093* |
| Osmium | Os | 76 | 190.2 |
| Oxygen | O | 8 | 15.9994 |
| Palladium | Pd | 46 | 106.4 |
| Phosphorus | P | 15 | 30.97376 |
| Platinum | Pt | 78 | 195.09 |
| Plutonium | Pu | 94 | 244.06424* |
| Polonium | Po | 84 | 208.98244* |
| Potassium | K | 19 | 39.0983 |
| Praseodymium | Pr | 59 | 140.9077 |
| Promethium | Pm | 61 | 144.91279* |
| Protactinium | Pa | 91 | 231.0359* |
| Radium | Ra | 88 | 226.0254 |
| Radon | Rn | 86 | 222* |
| Rhenium | Re | 75 | 186.2 |
| Rhodium | Rh | 45 | 102.9055 |
| Rubidium | Rb | 37 | 85.4678 |
| Ruthenium | Ru | 44 | 101.07 |
| Samarium | Sm | 62 | 150.4 |
| Scandium | Sc | 21 | 44.9559 |
| Selenium | Se | 34 | 78.96 |
| Silicon | Si | 14 | 28.0855 |
| Silver | Ag | 47 | 107.868 |
| Sodium | Na | 11 | 22.9898 |
| Strontium | Sr | 38 | 87.62 |
| Sulfur | S | 16 | 32.06 |
| Tantalum | Ta | 73 | 180.9479 |
| Technetium | Tc | 43 | 96.9062* |
| Tellurium | Te | 52 | 127.60 |
| Terbium | Tb | 65 | 158.9254 |
| Thallium | Tl | 81 | 204.37 |
| Thorium | Th | 90 | 232.0381 |
| Thulium | Tm | 69 | 168.9342 |
| Tin | Sn | 50 | 118.69 |
| Titanium | Ti | 22 | 47.90 |
| Tungsten | W | 74 | 183.85 |
| Uranium | U | 92 | 238.029 |
| Vanadium | V | 23 | 50.9415 |
| Xenon | Xe | 54 | 131.30 |
| Ytterbium | Yb | 70 | 173.04 |
| Yttrium | Y | 39 | 88.9059 |
| Zinc | Zn | 30 | 65.38 |
| Zirconium | Zr | 40 | 91.22 |
| Element 104† | | 104 | 257* |
| Element 105† | | 105 | 260* |
| Element 106† | | 106 | 263* |
| Element 107† | | 107 | 258* |
| Element 108† | | 108 | 256* |
| Element 109† | | 109 | 266* |

*The mass of the isotope with the longest known half-life.

†Names for elements 104–109 have not yet been approved by the IUPAC. The USSR has proposed Kurchatovium (Ku) for element 104, and Bohrium (Bh) for element 105. The United States has proposed Rutherfordium (Rf) for element 104, and Hahnium (Ha) for element 105.

# Appendix E

## Physical Properties of Some Elements

| Element | Symbol | Melting point (°C) | Boiling point (°C) | Density ($g/cm^3$) |
|---|---|---|---|---|
| Barium | Ba | 725 | 1640 | 3.5 |
| Beryllium | Be | 1278 | 2970 | 1.8477 |
| Calcium | Ca | 839 | 1484 | 1.55 |
| Cesium | Cs | 28.4 | 678 | 1.873 |
| Chromium | Cr | 1857 | 2672 | 7.18 |
| Cobalt | Co | 1495 | 2870 | 8.92 |
| Copper | Cu | 1083 | 2567 | 8.96 |
| Francium | Fr | 27 | 677 | —— |
| Gold | Au | 1064 | 2807 | 19.3 |
| Iron | Fe | 1535 | 2750 | 7.874 |
| Lithium | Li | 180.54 | 1347 | 0.534 |
| Magnesium | Mg | 649 | 1090 | 1.738 |
| Manganese | Mn | 1244 | 1962 | 7.32 |
| Nickel | Ni | 1453 | 2732 | 8.90 |
| Potassium | K | 63.7 | 774 | 0.862 |
| Radium | Ra | 700 | 1140 | 5.5 |
| Rubidium | Rb | 39 | 688 | 1.532 |
| Silver | Ag | 961.9 | 2212 | 10.50 |
| Sodium | Na | 97.81 | 882.9 | 0.971 |
| Strontium | Sr | 769 | 1384 | 2.54 |
| Zinc | Zn | 419.6 | 907 | 7.13 |

# Appendix F

## Apollo and Skylab Missions

| Mission | Launch | Astronauts | Mission Objective |
|---|---|---|---|
| Apollo 1 | | Chaffee, Grissom, White | To be the first manned Apollo flight: astronauts killed in a fire in the spacecraft January 27, 1967. |
| Apollo 4 | Nov. 9, 1967 | Unmanned | Testing the Saturn rocket. |
| Apollo 5 | Jan. 22, 1968 | Unmanned | Testing the design and operation of the Lunar Module systems. |
| Apollo 6 | April 4, 1968 | Unmanned | Final testing of Saturn rocket and Apollo spacecraft. |
| Apollo 7 | Oct. 11, 1968 | Cunningham, Eisele, Schirra | First manned flight, 10 days, live TV coverage from space, 260 h. |
| Apollo 8 | Dec. 21, 1968 | Anders, Borman, Lovell | First manned flight to escape Earth's gravity, first manned flight to moon, 147 h. |
| Apollo 9 | March 3, 1969 | McDivitt, Scott, Schweickart | First Apollo extra vehicular activity (EVA), first Lunar Module (LM) docking, 241 h. |
| Apollo 10 | May 18, 1969 | Cernan, Young, Stafford | Separation and docking of LM in lunar orbit, visual look at landing sites, 192 h. |
| Apollo 11 | July 16, 1969 | Aldrin, Armstrong, Collins | First lunar landing, first lunar surface EVA, first lunar soil samples returned to Earth, 195 h. |
| Apollo 12 | Nov. 14, 1969 | Bean, Conrad, Gordon | Set up scientific instruments on the moon, 244 h. |
| Apollo 13 | April 11, 1970 | Haise, Lovell, Swigert | Successful return to Earth after an explosion damaged spacecraft, LM used as emergency lifeboat, 143 h. |
| Apollo 14 | Jan. 31, 1971 | Mitchell, Roosa, Shepard | 3rd lunar landing, extensive lunar surface EVA, 216 h. |
| Apollo 15 | July 26, 1971 | Irwin, Scott, Worden | 4th landing, extensive exploration of Hadley Apennine region by Lunar Rover, 295 h. |
| Apollo 16 | April 16, 1972 | Duke, Young, Mattingly | Explored lunar highlands, used moon as an astronomical observatory, 265 h. |
| Apollo 17 | Dec. 7, 1972 | Cernan, Evans, Schmitt | Longest mission, longest total EVA time, first use of scientist-astronaut on space mission, 302 h. |
| *Skylab 1 | May 25, 1973 | Conrad, Kerwin, Weitz | A modified Saturn V rocket which astronauts entered from an Apollo craft that had docked with it, scientific experiments conducted, 673 h. |
| Skylab 2 | July 28, 1973 | Bean, Garriott, Lousma | Scientific experiments conducted, 1427 h. |
| Skylab 3 | Nov. 16, 1973 | Carr, Gibson, Pogue | Scientific experiments conducted, 2017 h. |

*Skylab disintegrated when it reentered Earth's atmosphere in 1979.

# Appendix G

## The Microscope and Its Use

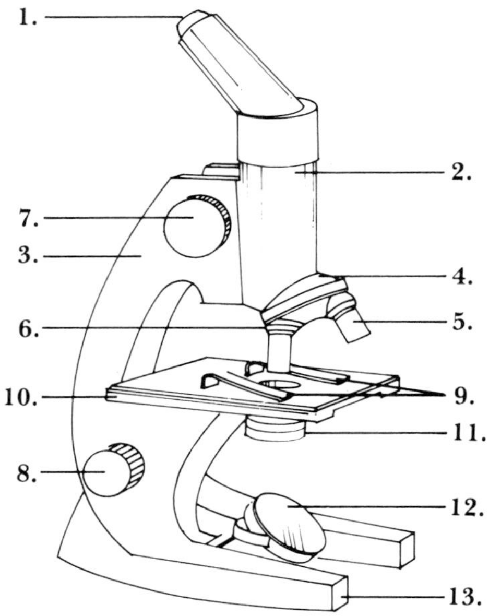


1. Eyepiece
2. Body tube
3. Arm
4. Revolving nosepiece
5. Low power objective lens
6. High power objective lens
7. Coarse adjustment lens
8. Fine adjustment knob
9. Stage clips
10. Stage
11. Diaphragm
12. Mirror
13. Base

These procedures should always be followed when using the microscope.

1. Always carry the microscope with both hands. Hold the arm with one hand. Place the other hand beneath the base.
2. Place the microscope on the table gently with the arm toward you and the stage facing a light source. The top of the table should be cleared of other objects.
3. Look through the eyepiece and adjust the diaphragm so that the greatest amount of light comes through the opening in the stage. The circle of light is called the field of view.
4. Turn the nosepiece so that the low power objective lens (10×) clicks into place.
5. Always focus first with the coarse adjustment and the low power objective lens. Raise the body tube by turning the coarse adjustment knob.
6. Turn the nosepiece until the high power objective lens clicks into place. Use only the fine adjustment with this lens. There will be less light coming through the opening in the stage.
7. Be sure to keep your fingers from touching the lenses.
8. Use only special lens paper to clean the lenses.
9. Before putting the microscope away, always turn the low power objective into place over the stage.
10. Raise the body tube until the low power objective is about two or three centimeters from the stage.

# Appendix H

## Scientific Notation

Scientific notation greatly simplifies the handling of large and small numbers. They are shortened by expressing decimal places as powers of ten. A power of ten is the number of times a number is multiplied by ten. The number 6 000 is written as $6 \times 10^3$ or $6 \times 10 \times 10 \times 10$.

A number is written in scientific notation by moving the decimal point until a single digit is to the left of the decimal point. The number of places the decimal point moved is the exponent of the power of ten. For a number larger than one, the decimal point is moved left, and the exponent is positive. For a number smaller than one, the decimal point is moved right, and the exponent is negative. The number 0.002 is written $2 \times 10^{-3}$ or 2 multiplied by $1/10$ three times—$2 \times 1/10 \times 1/10 \times 1/10$.

Example:

The estimated volume of water in the Pacific Ocean is 700 000 000 000 $m^3$. What is the volume written in scientific notation?

Solution

*Step 1:* Write the number and the unit.

700 000 000 000 $m^3$

*Step 2:* Move the decimal point until a single digit is to the left of it.

7.00 000 000 000 $m^3$

*Step 3:* Count the number of places you moved the decimal point. Use that number as the exponent.

700 000 000 000 $m^3 = 7.0 \times 10^{11}$ $m^3$

The volume of water $= 7 \times 10^{11}$ $m^3$

Example:

One second is 0.000 011 5 day. How is it written in scientific notation?

Solution

*Step 1:* Write the number and unit.

0.000 011 5 day

*Step 2:* Move the decimal point until a single digit is to the left of it.

0 000 01.1 5 day

*Step 3:* Count the number of places you moved the decimal point and use that number as the exponent.

0.000 011 5 day $= 1.15 \times 10^{-5}$ day

1 s $= 1.15 \times 10^{-5}$ day

# Glossary

The glossary contains all of the major science terms of the text and their definitions. Below is a pronunciation key to help you use these terms. The word or term will be given in boldface type. If necessary, the pronunciation will follow the term in parenthesis.

**PRONUNCIATION GUIDE**

a . . . back (BAK)
er . . . care, fair (KER, FER)
ay . . . day (DAY)
ah . . . father (FAHTH ur)
ar . . . car (KAR)
ow . . . flower, loud (FLOW ur, LOWD)
e . . . less (LES)
ee . . . leaf (LEEF)
ih . . . trip (TRIHP)
i(i + con + e) . . . idea, life (i DEE uh, LIFE)
oh . . . go (GOH)
aw . . . soft (SAWFT)
or . . . orbit (OR but)
oy . . . coin (KOYN)
oo . . . foot (FOOT)
yoo . . . pure (PYOOR)
ew . . . food (FEWD)
yew . . . few (FYEW)
uh(u + con) . . . comma, mother (KAHM uh, MUTH ur)
sh . . . shelf (SHELF)
ch . . . nature (NAY chur)
g . . . gift (GIHFT)
j . . . gem, edge (JEM, EJ)
ing . . . sing (SING)
zh . . . vision (VIHZH un)
k . . . cake (KAYK)
s . . . seed, cent (SEED, SENT)
z . . . zone, raise (ZOHN, RAYZ)

## A

**accelerometers** (ak sel uh RAHM ut urz): devices that measure change in speed and direction; used to guide rockets

**acid:** substance that has a sour taste, reacts with metals, and produces hydronium ions when dissolved in water

**acid rain:** rain and snow that contain nitric and sulfuric acids; forms as the pollutants are washed from the air

**addiction:** a physical need for a drug

**aeration** (er AY shun): process in which water is sprayed into the air to add oxygen to aid bacteria in breaking down biodegradable substances

**alkali** (AL kuh li) **metals:** elements of Group IA (with the exception of hydrogen); have one electron in their outer energy level and are the most chemically active of all metals

**alkaline** (AL kuh lun) **earth metals:** elements of Group IIA; have two electrons in their outer energy level; slightly less chemically active than the alkali metals

**allergy:** overreaction of the body's immune system to a foreign antigen

**alpha radiation:** a type of nuclear radiation that consists of positively-charged particles with little penetrating power; consists of helium nuclei

**alternating current (AC):** electron flow in which electrons reverse directions many times each second

**alveoli** (al VEE uh li): spongy air-filled sacs lined with moist membranes, found in the lungs

**amino acids:** the building blocks of proteins; acidic compounds containing carbon, hydrogen, oxygen, and nitrogen

**amniocentesis** (am nee oh sen TEE sus): a process in which some of the fluid surrounding the fetus in the mother's uterus is removed; used to determine the genetic state of the fetus

**ampere** (AM pihr) **(A):** unit used to measure electric current

**amplitude** (AM pluh tewd): distance a wave rises or falls from its rest position

**antibiotic:** a chemical produced by an organism that slows or stops the growth of microbes

**antigen** (ANT ih jun): protein foreign to the body

**aorta** (ay ORT uh): the largest artery in the body; connects the heart to smaller arteries

**aphelion** (a FEEL yun): the point in a planet's orbit farthest from the sun

**apogee** (AP uh jee): the point in an elliptical orbit of a satellite farthest from Earth

**Apollo Program:** a series of United States moon missions that began in 1961 and resulted in six moon landings between 1969 and 1972

**arteries:** vessels that carry blood away from the heart

**artificial satellites:** devices that people have placed into space orbits

**asteroids:** (AS tuh roydz): minor planets that orbit the sun; most are between the orbits of Mars and Jupiter

**astronomy:** study of planets, stars, and all other objects in space

**atom:** the smallest piece of an element that has the properties of that element

**atomic number:** number of protons in the nucleus of an atom

**autoimmune** (awt oh ihm YEWN) **disease:** disease in which the immune system responds to the body's own protein and produces antibodies that attack the person's own tissues

**autonomic nervous system:** part of the peripheral nervous system that controls involuntary functions of the body; the system is automatic

# B

**base:** a substance that tastes bitter, feels slippery, and dissolves fats and oils; releases hydroxide ions when dissolved

**behavior:** the ability of an organism to react to its internal and external environments

**beta radiation:** a type of nuclear radiation that consists of electrons; results in the formation of a new element with a higher atomic number

**binary** (BI nuh ree) **compounds:** compounds containing two elements

**biodegradable** (bi oh dih GRAYD uh bul): substance that can be broken down by bacteria

**biodegradable waste:** waste that can be broken down by the action of microbes

**black hole:** an area in space that has a gravity field so strong that even light cannot escape; formed by the contraction and disappearance of a neutron star

**bronchial** (BRAHN kee ul) **tubes:** two air passages that branch from the trachea and lead to the lungs

# C

**Calorie:** amount of heat needed to raise the temperature of 1 kg of water 1°C

**calorimeter** (kal uh RIHM ut ur): a device used to measure heat changes

**cancer:** a disease in which there is abnormal cell division and a rapid increase in certain body cells

**capillaries:** blood vessels that connect arteries to veins

**carbohydrates:** compounds containing carbon, hydrogen, and oxygen that are changed to the sugar glucose when digested; food substances converted to glucose and used by body cells to produce energy

**carcinogen** (kar SIHN uh jun): a cancer-causing substance

**carrier:** a person who carries a gene for a recessive trait without showing the trait

**cartilage** (KART uh lihj): bluish-white, rubbery tissue present in most joints; serves as a cushion between bones; present in nose and in outer ear

**cell:** the basic unit of structure and function in all living organisms

**Celsius** (SEL see us): basic unit of temperature in SI

**cerebellum** (ser uh BEL um): the smaller part of the brain that controls muscular activity and maintains balance

**cerebrum** (suh REE brum): Largest part of the human brain; controls thought, memory, learning, some voluntary movements, and the five senses

**chain reaction:** series of continuous, rapid nuclear fissions

**chemical change:** a change in which new substances with different properties are formed

**chemical properties:** properties of a substance that depend upon the behavior of that substance in the presence of other substances

**chemistry:** the study of the properties of matter, the changes that matter can undergo, and the laws that describe these changes

**chromosphere** (KROH muh sfihr): the middle layer of the sun's atmosphere; a red layer of gas about 2500 km in thickness

**circuit** (SUR kut): path formed by the conductors for electrons

**cloud chamber:** a device used to observe the path of a radiation particle; contains a gas cooled to a very low temperature

**colloid** (KAHL oyd): a mixture in which substances mix but do not dissolve; differs from a suspension in smaller particle size and the inability to be filtered

**comets:** space objects made of minerals, dust, gases, and ice particles that orbit the sun

**compound:** a substance formed when two or more elements are chemically joined

**conditioned reflex:** reflex in which a new stimulus takes the place of the original stimulus

**conduction:** transfer of heat energy through collisions that occur between particles

**conductor** (kun DUK tur): substance through which electricity flows easily; metals are excellent conductors

**convection** (kun VEK shun): transfer of heat by the movement of large numbers of particles from one place to another

**corona** (kuh ROH nuh): the outermost layer of the sun's atmosphere; a huge cloud of gas that extends above the photosphere to beyond Earth's orbit

**coronary circulation:** movement of blood through the tissues of the heart

**covalent bond:** bond between atoms in which electrons are shared

**cubic meter ($m^3$):** basic unit of volume in SI

**cytoplasm** (SITE uh plaz um): the living, jellylike material found inside human cells

# D

**data:** recorded observations

**decay:** the process by which the nucleus of an atom emits radiation

**decay series:** nuclide decay through many steps

**depressant:** a substance that relieves pain, tension, and anxiety and causes muscle relaxation; may produce a sense of well-being and contentment

**detergent:** a synthetic soap that breaks particles of grease or oil into smaller particles

**diaphragm** (DI uh fram): a sheet of muscle stretched across the bottom of the chest cavity that aids in breathing

**diffusion** (dihf YEW zhun): movement of particles of a material from regions of higher concentration to regions of lower concentration of that material

**digestion:** chemical and physical process in which foods are changed to a form that can be taken into the cells

**direct current (DC):** electron flow that occurs in one direction

**disease:** the abnormal functioning of any part of the body

**distillation:** process of obtaining a liquid by evaporation and condensation

**dominant:** the gene that is expressed

**drug:** any substance entering the body that changes the functioning of body systems

# E

**effectors:** structures that respond when nerve impulses are received; muscles are effectors that contract when they receive nerve impulses

**egg:** female sex cell; ovum

**electric current:** the flow of electrons; rate of flow of electric charge

**electromagnet** (ih lek troh MAG net): a piece of metal (usually iron or steel) surrounded by a coil of wire that acts like a magnet when electricity is passed through the wire

**electromagnetic** (ih lek troh mag NET ihk) **waves:** waves that transfer energy without matter

**electron:** a negatively charged particle that makes up part of the atom; has a very small mass and is located outside the nucleus

**electron cloud model:** modern model of the atom in which electrons do not remain in fixed orbits but instead occupy certain regions outside the nucleus based on their energy

**element:** a substance that cannot be broken down into simpler substances by a chemical change

**ellipse:** the shape of a planet's orbit around the sun; the path a point makes so that the sum of its distances from two fixed points is constant

**endocrine** (EN duh krun) **system:** system of ductless glands that produce hormones to control body functions

**endothermic** (en duh THUR mihk): a chemical reaction in which energy must be added

**energy:** the capacity to do work

**environment:** the sum total of your surroundings

**enzyme:** a substance that can speed a chemical reaction in the body

**epiglottis** (ep uh GLAHT us): flap of cartilage that prevents food from entering the upper end of the trachea

**escape velocity:** the speed a moving body must achieve to free itself from the force of gravity

**excretion:** the removal of wastes from the body

**exothermic** (ek soh THUR mihk): a chemical reaction in which energy is released

## F

**families:** 18 columns of the periodic table; also called groups

**fats:** compounds containing carbon, hydrogen, and oxygen; rich in energy; solids at room temperature

**fertilizer:** a mixture of substances that contains the nutrients plants need to grow

**fetus** (FEET us): embryo that has the shape and form of a human

**focal point:** point where light waves meet after leaving a lens

**food:** any substance that provides energy for the body to build and repair tissues and nutrients to carry on life processes

**fossil fuels:** energy sources that come from the remains of once-living plants and animals; coal, oil, and natural gas are fossil fuels

**fractional distillation:** process used to separate the hydrocarbons in petroleum by heating it slowly and collecting each fraction as it changes to a gas

**fracture:** a break in a bone

**frequency** (FREE kwun see): the number of waves that pass a given point in a second

## G

**galaxy:** a vast collection of billions of stars, planets, dust, and gas

**gamma radiation:** a type of nuclear radiation in which high energy photons are emitted when a nucleus is rearranged during decay

**gasification** (gas uh fuh KAY shun): the process of changing coal into gas

**Geiger** (GI gur) **counter:** an instrument that measures the amount of radiation present in a given area

**gene:** the unit of inheritance that is passed from parents to children

**geothermal** (jee oh THUR mul) **energy:** energy that is generated from heat within the earth's crust

**groups:** 18 columns of the periodic table; also called families

**gyroscope** (JI ruh skohp): a mounted spinning wheel that is used to indicate direction; used to guide rockets

## H

**habit:** a learned pattern of behavior, done without thinking about how to do it

**half-life:** the time required for one-half of a radioactive sample to decay

**hallucination** (huh lews un AY shun): what a person sees that does not exist

**hallucinogen:** a substance that causes illusions and hallucinations; may act as either a stimulant or a depressant

**halogens:** the most chemically active nonmetals; Group VIIA in the periodic table

**heat:** the total internal energy of a substance

**heat of fusion** (FYEW shun): the energy needed to change a solid to a liquid

**heat of vaporization** (vay pur uh ZAY shun): the energy needed to change a liquid to a gas

**hemoglobin** (HEE muh gloh bun): blood protein that contains iron

**heredity:** the passing of characteristics from parents to offspring

**hormone:** a chemical that controls certain body functions; produced by endocrine glands and released directly into the blood

**hybrid:** a plant that contains the combined traits of two or more strains or varieties

**hydrocarbons:** compounds that contain only the elements hydrogen and carbon

**hydroelectricity** (hy droh ih lek TRIHS ut ee): electricity that is generated by moving water

# I

**illusion:** what a person sees that is a distortion or change from what really is

**image:** visual likeness of an object

**immunity:** having a special defense against a disease

**impulse:** nerve "message" that moves rapidly from one end of a neuron to the other

**inertial guidance:** the method used to guide rockets; depends on gyroscopes and accelerometers

**insulation** (ihn sul LAY shun): any substance that slows or controls the movement of heat energy

**insulators** (IHN suh layt urz): substances that do not conduct electricity well

**ion:** an atom that has gained or lost one or more electrons, thereby acquiring a charge

**ionic** (i AHN ihk) **bonding:** the transfer of electrons between atoms; bonding that occurs between ions

**irrigation:** a method of supplying water to fields from wells, rivers, lakes, and reservoirs

**isotopes** (I suh tohps): forms of the same element that differ in atomic mass

# J

**joule** (JEWL): metric unit used to measure work and energy

# K

**kidneys:** two bean-shaped organs that remove wastes from the blood and excrete them from the body

**kilogram (kg):** basic unit of mass in SI

**kilowatt hour (kWh):** energy of 1000 W delivered constantly for one hour

# L

**larynx** (LER ingks): boxlike structure made of cartilage that contains the vocal cords

**lens:** any transparent substance that refracts light so that it is focused

**ligaments** (LIHG uh munts): strands of tough tissue that hold bones together

**light-year:** the distance light travels in one year; equal to 9.5 trillion km

**lunar eclipse** (ih KLIHPS): movement of the full moon into the earth's shadow

**lymph:** colorless liquid that moves out of blood carrying food to the cells and removing wastes

**lymphocytes** (LIHM fuh sites): white blood cells; part of the immune system

# M

**magnetosphere** (mag NEET uh sfihr): a "cage" around a planet formed by the distortion of the magnetic field caused by the solar wind

**main sequence star:** one of a group of stars that forms a diagonal band across a graph of star temperature and brightness

**marijuana:** a nonnarcotic drug derived from the dried leaves and flowers of Indian hemp, *Cannabis sativa*

**marrow** (MER oh): soft tissue in the center of many bones that produces blood cells

**mass:** the amount of matter in an object

**matter:** anything that has mass and occupies space

**measurement:** the dimensions, capacity, or amount of something expressed in units

**mechanical waves:** waves that transfer energy as they travel through matter

**medulla** (muh DUL uh): smallest part of the brain; controls breathing, heartbeat, muscular action of the digestive tract, and secretion by some glands; located below the cerebellum at the base of the skull

**menstrual cycle:** cycle of events occurring within the human female reproductive system that includes development and release of eggs and preparation of uterus for possible pregnancy

**metabolism:** the sum of all the activities inside your body that keeps you alive

**metals:** elements usually having three or less electrons in their outer energy level; characterized by their luster, conductivity, mallèability, and ductility

**metalloids** (MET ul oydz): elements that have properties of both metals and nonmetals

**meteor** (MEET ee ur): a glowing meteoroid; a meteoroid as it enters Earth's atmosphere

**meteorite** (MEET ee uh rite): a meteor that reaches Earth's surface

**meteoroids** (MEET ee uh roydz): pieces of rock or metal in space

**meter (m):** basic unit of length in SI

**microbe:** a living organism so small that it can be seen only with a microscope

**minerals:** chemical substances needed by the body; usually found in the form of compounds that contain elements such as calcium, sodium, iron, and iodine

**mineral resources:** nonliving substances taken from the earth and used to make things

**mirror:** smooth, shiny surface that reflects light waves in a regular pattern

**mixture:** two or more substances that are physically mixed but not chemically joined

**molecule:** particle formed by a covalent bond

**moon phases:** the different shapes of the moon as viewed from Earth

**muscle:** a tissue that moves the parts of your body

# N

**nebulas** (NEB yuh luhz): clouds of gas and dust in space; remains of a supernova explosion

**neurons** (NOO rahnz): cells that make up the nervous system; cells that carry nerve impulses

**neutralization** (noo truh luh ZAY shun): a chemical reaction that occurs between an acid and a base in which a salt and water are produced

**neutron:** an atomic particle having no charge and about the same mass as a proton; located in the nucleus of an atom

**neutron star:** a star in which all the electrons have been forced into the atomic nuclei

**nicotine:** a chemical compound in tobacco that acts as a stimulant on the body

**noble gases:** Group VIIIA of the periodic table; elements with complete outer energy levels

**nonmetals:** elements having five or more electrons in their outer energy levels; generally have dull surfaces, are solids, brittle, and poor conductors

**nonrenewable resources:** resources that cannot be replaced as they are used; cannot be replaced in one's lifetime

**nova:** a star that explodes, appears brighter than normal and then becomes faint after a few days; a type of eruptive variable star

**nuclear fission:** the process of splitting an atomic nucleus into two or more parts

**nuclear fusion:** the process of combining two or more light atomic nuclei to form one single nucleus

**nucleus:** control center of a cell; central part of an atom containing protons and neutrons

**nuclide:** an atom that has a specific number of protons and neutrons in its nucleus

**nutrients:** materials required by cells to carry on life processes

**nutrition:** the study of nutrients and their use by the body

# O

**observation:** noting or recognizing something that has occurred

**ohms (Ω):** unit used to measure resistance

**oils:** compounds containing carbon, hydrogen, and oxygen that are rich in energy; liquids at room temperature

**organ:** several different tissues working together to perform a function

**organic compounds:** compounds that contain carbon

**osmosis** (ahs MOH sus): diffusion of water through a membrane

**ovaries:** structures that produce the female sex cells

**oxidation number:** the number of electrons an atom transfers or shares in forming compounds

**oxidizer** (AHK suh di zur): the source of oxygen that is necessary for burning the fuel in rocket engines

# P

**parallax** (PER uh laks): the apparent change in position of an object caused by the motion of the observer

**parallel circuit:** a circuit that has two or more paths for electrons to travel

**pathogen:** a microbe that causes disease

**penumbra** (puh NUM bruh): the partial shadow cast by the Earth or the moon into space

**perigee** (PER uh jee): the point in an elliptical orbit of a satellite closest to Earth

**perihelion** (per un HEEL yun): the point in a planet's orbit closest to the sun

**periodic table:** classification system of elements based on atomic number and chemical properties

**periods:** seven rows of the periodic table

**periosteum** (per ee AHS tee um): outer covering of a bone

**pesticide** (PES tuh side): a chemical used to kill insects, rats, and mice

**petroleum:** liquid mixture of hydrocarbons obtained from deep wells; crude oil

**photosphere** (FOHT uh sfihr): the innermost layer of the sun's atmosphere

**photovoltaic** (foht oh vohl TAY ihk) **cell:** a device used to convert solar energy into electric energy

**pH scale:** the scale used by scientists to measure the relative strengths of acids and bases; scale that measures the number of hydronium ions in an acid or base solution

**physical change:** a change in the size, shape, color, or physical state of a substance; does not effect the chemical composition or properties

**physical properties:** characteristics of a substance that can be observed and measured; include mass, volume, color, density, melting point, and freezing point

**pitch:** highness or lowness of sound determined by the frequency of sound waves

**plastics:** polymers made from petroleum compounds

**platelets** (PLAYT lutz): small cell-like structures found in blood that produce clots when bleeding occurs; produced in bone marrow

**polarized light:** light that vibrates in only one plane

**pollutants** (puh LEWT unts): waste material that causes pollution

**polyatomic** (pahl ee uh TAHM ihk) **ion:** a group of atoms that acts as one ion

**polymers** (PAHL uh murz): carbon compounds that exist as long molecular chains or rings

**precipitator:** a device used to collect pollutants as they pass through a smokestack

**pregnancy:** condition resulting after an egg is fertilized by a sperm

**prism:** solid triangular piece of transparent material that refracts light

**products:** substances formed in a chemical reaction; usually found on the right side of the arrow in a chemical equation

**prominences** (PRAHM nunts uz): glowing clouds of dust that form arches or plumes in the chromosphere

**protein:** a compound made of amino acids

**proton:** a positively charged particle that makes up part of the atom; located in the nucleus of an atom

**pulmonary** (PUL muh ner ee) **circulation:** pathway of blood from the heart to the lungs and back to the heart

**pulsars:** spinning neutron stars that give off energy as radio pulses

# Q

**quarantine** (KWOR un teen): to isolate an infected person or animal for a certain length of time until they can no longer carry or transmit disease

# R

**radiation:** transfer of energy such as heat without the presence of matter

**radiation biology:** the study of the effects of radiation on living tissue

**radioactive:** nuclei of elements that emit invisible, high-energy radiation

**radio astronomy:** the use of radio waves to study space objects

**radio telescope:** a telescope that detects radio waves from space; consists of a radio antenna and a receiver

**reactants:** substances involved in a chemical reaction; usually found on the left side of the arrow in a chemical equation

**real image:** image formed by light rays passing through; may be projected onto a screen

**receptors:** specialized structures of the nervous system that detect changes in the environment

**recessive:** the unexpressed gene; gene masked by the dominant form

**recycling:** using a resource again after it has been used once

**red blood cells:** most numerous of blood cells; blood cell that contains hemoglobin, carries oxygen to body cells and carbon dioxide to the lungs; produced in bone marrow

**red giant:** a relatively short stage in a star's life when the outer regions cool and the star becomes red

**redshift:** a shift of colors in the light spectrum toward the red end of the spectrum that occurs when a shining body is moving away from the observer; an example of the Doppler effect

**reflection** (rih FLEK shun): bouncing of waves from an object

**reflector:** a reflecting optical telescope containing a concave mirror

**reflex:** reaction in which the response to a stimulus occurs without the person being aware of it

**reflex arc:** path an impulse follows in a reflex

**refraction** (rih FRAK shun): bending of waves

**refractor:** a refracting optical telescope containing a convex lens

**refrigeration:** process of removing heat energy from a substance

**renewable resources:** resources that can be replaced as they are used

**resistance** (rih ZIHS tunts): measure of how difficult it is to move electrons through a conductor

**respiration:** the process through which cells receive oxygen, obtain energy, and release carbon dioxide

**response:** how an organism reacts to a stimulus

**revolution:** movement of a body in a circular path around a central point

**rockets:** devices used to lift satellites and spacecraft off Earth into space; produces power to overcome gravity by burning solid or liquid fuels

**rotation:** turning motion of a body on its axis

# S

**salts:** compounds that contain at least one metal and one nonmetal

**sanitary landfill:** a method of disposing of solid wastes; waste dumped into a trench or valley and covered with a layer of soil

**science:** facts collected and ideas developed by scientists as well as methods used in collecting information

**series circuit:** a circuit in which there is only one path for electrons to travel

**settling:** process of water purification in which aluminum sulfate is added to water to remove suspended solids

**sex-linked trait:** trait controlled by genes on the chromosomes that determine the sex of a person

**SI (International System of Units):** a decimal measurement system based on 10 and multiples of 10

**Skylab:** the United States space station launched in 1973 with room for astronauts to conduct experiments in space

**small intestine:** a coiled tubelike organ in which most of the digestive processes occur

**smog:** a chemical reaction of nitrogen oxides and hydrocarbons in the presence of sunlight; a product of air pollution

**soap:** long chain of carbon and hydrogen atoms with either sodium or potassium bonded to one end

**sodium zeolite:** a chemical used in water softeners to absorb iron, magnesium, and calcium ions

**solar collector:** a device that converts solar energy into heat

**solar eclipse:** movement of Earth into the moon's shadow

**solar energy:** energy from the sun

**solar flares:** bright flashes of light that appear near sunspots

**solar system:** the sun and the objects that travel around the sun

**solar wind:** the flow of electrically charged particles from the sun outward through the solar system

**solute** (SAHL yewt): the substance dissolved in a solution

**solution:** a mixture composed of two or more substances; a solute is dissolved in a solvent

**solvent** (SAHL vunt): the substance that dissolved the solute in a solution

**space shuttle:** a ship that can make repeated trips into space and return to Earth; a rocket, spaceship, and aircraft combined

**specific heat:** the amount of heat needed to raise the temperature of 1 g of a substance 1°C

**spectrograph** (SPEK truh graf): a camera that photographs the spectrum of light produced by a source

**spectroscopy** (spek TRAHS kuh pee): method of photography that shows space objects as a spectrum rather than an image

**sperm:** male sex cells

**spinal cord:** connection center between the brain and the nerves that extend throughout the body

**static electricity:** electric charge on the surface of an object produced by the transfer of electrons

**stimulant:** a substance that increases alertness and reduces fatigue

**stimulus:** anything that causes behavior

**sulfides:** compounds formed when sulfur combines with a metal

**sunspots:** dark, cool areas on the sun's surface; the result of magnetic storms in the sun

**supernova:** an exploding star

**suspension** (suh SPEN chun): a mixture in which substances mix but do not dissolve; differs from a colloid in its ability to be separated by settling or filtration

**synapses** (SIHN aps ez): spaces between neurons across which chemical transfers are made

**synthetic elements:** elements with atomic numbers 43, 61, and higher than 92; produced in nuclear reactions

**synthetic fibers:** polymers made from petroleum compounds

**system:** organs that work together to perform one main function

**systemic circulation:** pathway of blood that supplies body tissues with digested food and oxygen

# T

**technology** (tek NAHL uh jee): the application of science for practical purposes

**temperature:** the average kinetic energy of particles of a substance

**tendons:** tough bands of connective tissue that connect striated muscle to bone

**testes:** structures that produce the male sex cells

**thermal pollution:** pollution caused by dumping heated water in rivers and lakes

**thermoplastic:** plastic that may be changed in shape by heating and molding

**thermosetting plastic:** plastic that cannot be reshaped once it has hardened

**thrust:** the force produced by a rocket to overcome its weight

**tissue:** a group of similar cells that perform the same function

**trait:** genetically inherited characteristic

**transition metals:** elements in groups I B through VIII B having one or two electrons in their outer energy levels

**transmutation:** the changing of one element into another as a nucleus emits alpha radiation

# U

**umbra:** the total shadow cast by Earth or the moon into space

# V

**variable stars:** stars whose brightness is not constant

**veins:** vessels that carry blood to the heart

**villi** (VIHL i): small, fingerlike projections that increase the surface area of the small intestine aiding in food absorption

**virtual** (VURCH wal) **image:** image formed without light rays passing through it; cannot be projected onto a screen

**vitamin:** complex compound that aids the body in using proteins, fats, and carbohydrates

**vitamin deficiency disease:** disease resulting from a lack of vitamins in the diet

**volts:** units used to measure the difference in electric potential energy between two points

## W

**watt (W):** unit for measuring electric power

**wavelength:** distance between two corresponding points on consecutive waves

**weightlessness:** the state of zero gravity that exists in space; a weightless object is acted upon by a force that is equal and opposite to gravity

**white blood cells:** blood cells produced in bone marrow and in the spleen; blood cells that fight infection and disease

**white dwarf:** a collapsed star; last stage in the life of many stars

# Index

## C



## D

# E



# F



# G

# N



# O



# P

# Q



# R



# S

# T

# U



# V



# W



# X



# Y



# Z



8 9 10 11 12 13 14 15 – 95 94 93 92 91 90